Making Math Meaningful
to Canadian Students, K–8, Third Edition

Monkey Business Images/Shutterstock

Marian Small

University of New Brunswick

NELSON
EDUCATION

NELSON EDUCATION

Making Math Meaningful to Canadian Students, K–8, Third Edition
by Marian Small

VP, Product and Partnership Solutions:
Anne Williams

Publisher, Digital and Print Content:
Lenore Taylor-Atkins

Marketing Manager:
Terry Fedorkiw

Content Development Manager:
Jackie Williams

Photo and Permissions Researcher:
Rachel Eagen

Senior Production Project Manager:
Natalia Denesiuk Harris

Production Service:
Cenveo Publisher Services

Copy Editor:
Laurel Sparrow

Proofreader:
Pushpa V. Giri

Indexer:
Razorsharp Communications, Inc.

Design Director:
Ken Phipps

Managing Designer:
Franca Amore

Interior Design:
Greg Devitt

Cover Design:
Courtney Hellam

Cover Image:
Artush/Masterfile Royalty Free; RTimages/Shutterstock

Compositor:
Cenveo Publisher Services

Library and Archives Canada Cataloguing in Publication Data

Small, Marian, author
Making math meaningful to Canadian students, K–8 / Marian Small. — Third edition.

Includes bibliographical references and index.
ISBN 978-0-17-658255-5 (paperback)

1. Mathematics—Study and teaching (Elementary)—Canada.
I. Title.

QA135.6.S63 2016   372.7'044
C2015-906760-X

Brief Table of Contents

Preface xx

Acknowledgments xxii

About the Author xxii

Instructor Resources xxiii

Student Ancillaries xxiv

Chapter 1: How Students Learn Math and What Math
We Want Them to Learn 1

Chapter 2: Focusing Instruction on Big Ideas and
Mathematical Processes 15

Chapter 3: Assessment and Evaluation 35

Chapter 4: Planning Instruction 65

Chapter 5: A Focus on Problem Solving 93

Chapter 6: A Focus on Communication 117

Chapter 7: Early Number 137

Chapter 8: Early Operations 157

Chapter 9: Developing Fact Fluency 185

Chapter 10: Representing Larger Whole Numbers 197

Chapter 11: Estimation and Calculation Strategies
with Larger Whole Numbers 219

Chapter 12: Fractions 255

Chapter 13: Decimals 289

Chapter 14: Ratio and Proportion 311

Chapter 15: Extending the Number System to
Negative and Irrational Numbers 335

Chapter 16: Patterns and Algebra 357

Chapter 17: 3-D and 2-D Shapes 393

Chapter 18: Location and Movement 439

Chapter 19: The Nature of Measurement,
with a Focus on Length and Area 465

Chapter 20: Capacity, Volume, Mass, Time, Temperature, and Angles 515

Chapter 21: Data 571

Chapter 22: Probability 627

Index 647

Credits 663

Contents

Preface xx

Acknowledgments xxii

About the Author xxii

Instructor Resources xxiii

Student Ancillaries xxiv

Chapter 1: How Students Learn Math and What Math We Want Them to Learn 1

Chapter Problem 1

In a Nutshell 1

Research on Mathematical Learning 2

    The Importance of Conceptual Understanding 2

    A Constructivist Approach 3

    Using Manipulatives 4

    Mindset 5

What Mathematics We Want Students to Learn 5

    Differing Perspectives on What Mathematics Is 6

    Differing Perspectives on What Mathematics
     Is Valued and at What Grade Levels 7

    Teaching Developmentally 10

Research on Mathematics Teaching 10

    Importance of a Teacher's Pedagogical Content Knowledge 10

Applying What You've Learned 12

Selected References 13

Chapter 2: Focusing Instruction on Big Ideas and Mathematical Processes 15

Chapter Problems 15

In a Nutshell 15

Organizing Content around Big Ideas 16

    Different Approaches to Big Ideas 16

    Big Ideas Applying to Many Strands 18

    Examples of More Strand-Based Big Ideas 21

**Focusing Instruction on Proportional Reasoning, Algebraic
Reasoning, and Spatial Reasoning** 22

    Proportional Reasoning 22

    Algebraic Reasoning 23

    Spatial Reasoning 24

Focusing Instruction on Math Processes 26

    The NCTM Process Standards 26

    Representation 26

    Reasoning 27

Connections 29

Other Processes 30

Assessing Student Understanding 32

Applying What You've Learned 32

Selected References 33

Chapter 3: Assessment and Evaluation 35

Chapter Problem 35

In a Nutshell 36

Introduction 36

Assessment for Learning 36

Assessment as Learning 37

Assessment of Learning 37

How Assessment Has Changed 37

Characteristics of Good Assessment 38

A Good Assessment Plan 38

Framing Assessment Tasks for Specific Purposes 41

Preparing Students for Assessment 41

Evaluation Tools 42

Sources of Assessment Data 43

Portfolios 43

Performance Tasks 45

Observation 46

Interviews 48

Exit Passes 49

Tests and Quizzes 49

Homework 50

Keeping Track 51

Assessing Processes 51

Assessing Problem Solving 51

Assessing Communication 52

Self-Assessment 54

Group Assessment 55

Using Technology in Assessment 55

Interpreting Assessment Results 56

Grading and Reporting 56

Anecdotal versus Letter Grades or Percents 56

Using Discretion 57

Pitfalls of Percent Grades 57

Including Group Evaluations 58

Weighting Schemes 58

Evaluations Based on Observation Assessment Data 58

Large-Scale Assessment 58

Preparing Students for Large-Scale Assessment 60

Applying What You've Learned 62

Selected References 63

Chapter 4: Planning Instruction 65

Chapter Problem 65

In a Nutshell 65

Math Anxiety—A Special Challenge in Teaching Mathematics 66

Causes of Math Anxiety 66

Diminishing Anxiety in Students 67

Diminishing Anxiety in Teachers 67

Unit Planning and Lesson Planning 67

Year Planning 67

Unit Planning 68

Lesson Planning 69

Planning Support 69

Lesson Style 69

The Importance of Varied Lesson Styles 69

Different Lesson Styles 70

Specific Lesson Strategies 71

Planning Grouping 71

Heterogeneous and Homogeneous Grouping 72

Group Size 72

Cooperative Grouping 72

Suitable Tasks for Group Work 73

Limitations of Grouping 73

Balancing Whole Class, Small Group, and Individual Instruction 73

Planning Support 74

How to Use a Textbook 75

Planning Opportunities for Practice 76

Is Practice Important? 76

What Should Be Practised? 77

How Much Practice Is Needed? 77

What Should Practice Look Like? 77

Differentiating Instruction: Supporting Individual Differences 78

Moving from the Concrete to the Symbolic 78

Managing Differentiation 80

Guided Groups 81

Students with Learning Disabilities 82

ESL and Immersion 83

Enrichment for the Mathematically Gifted 87

Home–School Connections 88

Homework 88

Making Contact with Parents 89

Applying What You've Learned 89

Selected References 90

Contents

Chapter 5: A Focus on Problem Solving 93

Chapter Problem 93

In a Nutshell 93

What Is a Problem? 94

Why Is Problem Solving Valued? 94

Teaching through Problem Solving 94

    Why Teach through Problem Solving? 95

    The Problem-Solving Process 95

Characteristics of Good Problems 98

Some Techniques for Creating Good Problems 98

Problem-Solving Strategies 98

    Simpler Problem-Solving Strategies 99

    More Complex Problem-Solving Strategies 104

Suitable Problems 108

    Problems Based on Earlier K–8 Content 108

    Problems Based on Later K–8 Content 111

    Sources for Other Problems 113

Helpful Hints for Problem Solving 114

Assessing Student Problem Solving 114

Applying What You've Learned 115

Selected References 115

Chapter 6: A Focus on Communication 117

Chapter Problem 117

In a Nutshell 117

The Importance of Mathematical Communication 118

Forms of Communication 118

    Oral versus Written Communication 118

    Oral Communication 118

    Written Communication 124

    Symbolic and Graphical Communication 129

    Physical Communication 130

Mathematics Vocabulary and Symbols 131

    The Importance of Vocabulary 131

    Math Terminology and Everyday Language 131

    Strategies for Reinforcing Math Vocabulary 131

    Mnemonics for Math Vocabulary 133

Engaging Students in Communication 134

Assessing Student Communication 135

Applying What You've Learned 135

Selected References 136

Chapter 7: Early Number 137

Chapter Problem 137

In a Nutshell 137

Numbers in the Child's World 138

Counting Principles 138

Zero and One 139

Counting Strategies 139

    Counting On 140

    Counting Back 141

    Skip Counting 141

A Sense of Number 142

    Comparing and Relating Numbers 142

    One-to-One Correspondence 142

    Position in the Counting Sequence 143

    Comparison Language 143

    Spatial Comparison 143

    Numbers to 10 144

    The Teen Numbers 146

Importance of Multiple Representations 146

Reading and Writing Numerals 147

Common Errors and Misconceptions 149

Appropriate Manipulatives 150

Appropriate Children's Books 153

Appropriate Digital Resources 153

Assessing Student Understanding 153

Applying What You've Learned 154

Selected References 155

Chapter 8: Early Operations 157

Chapter Problem 157

In a Nutshell 157

How the Four Operations Are Related 158

Addition and Subtraction 158

    Meanings of Addition 158

    Meanings of Subtraction 159

    Understanding Addition and Subtraction Situations 160

    Solving Addition and Subtraction Number Stories 161

    Relating Addition and Subtraction 161

    Addition and Subtraction Principles 162

Common Errors and Misconceptions 164

Appropriate Manipulatives 165

Multiplication and Division 166

    Meanings of Multiplication 166

    Meanings of Division 169

    Understanding Multiplication and Division Situations 171

    Solving Multiplication and Division Problems 172

    Relating Multiplication and Division 173

    Multiplication and Division Principles 173

Common Errors and Misconceptions 179

Appropriate Manipulatives 180

Appropriate Children's Books 181

Appropriate Digital Resources 181

Assessing Student Understanding 181

Applying What You've Learned 182

Selected References 183

Chapter 9: Developing Fact Fluency 185

Chapter Problem 185

In a Nutshell 185

What Are the Facts? 186

    Why Is It Important to Learn the Facts? 186

    What Does Fact Fluency Mean? 186

Learning Addition and Subtraction Facts 187

    Typical Sequence for Acquiring Addition and Subtraction Facts 189

Learning Multiplication and Division Facts 190

    Typical Sequence for Acquiring Multiplication and Division Facts 193

What Kind of Practice Is Useful? 193

**How Should Facts Be Assessed?
How Should They Not Be Assessed?** 193

Common Errors and Misconceptions 194

Appropriate Manipulatives 194

Appropriate Children's Books 195

Appropriate Digital Resources 195

Assessing Student Understanding 195

Applying What You've Learned 196

Selected References 196

Chapter 10: Representing Larger Whole Numbers 197

Chapter Problem 197

In a Nutshell 197

Larger Numbers in the Student's World 198

Numeration Principles 198

Counting Based on Place Value 204

Estimating Numbers 204

    Rounding 205

    Benchmark Numbers 205

Common Errors and Misconceptions 206

Appropriate Manipulatives 206

Number Theory 208

    Even and Odd Numbers 208

    Multiples 208

    Factors 209

    Prime and Composite Numbers 213

Common Errors and Misconceptions 215

Appropriate Manipulatives 215

Appropriate Children's Books 216

Appropriate Digital Resources 216

Assessing Student Understanding 216

Applying What You've Learned 217

Selected References 218

Chapter 11: Estimation and Calculation Strategies with Larger Whole Numbers 219

Chapter Problem 219

In a Nutshell 219

Addition and Subtraction 220

Estimating Sums and Differences 220

Varied Approaches to Addition and Subtraction 222

Communicating about Adding and Subtracting 231

Common Errors and Misconceptions 232

Appropriate Manipulatives 233

Multiplication and Division 235

Multiplying and Dividing Using Powers of 10 235

Estimating Products and Quotients 237

Algorithms for Multiplication and Division 239

Communicating about Multiplying and Dividing 247

Common Errors and Misconceptions 248

Appropriate Manipulatives 249

Appropriate Children's Books 251

Appropriate Digital Resources 251

Assessing Student Understanding 251

Applying What You've Learned 252

Selected References 253

Chapter 12: Fractions 255

Chapter Problem 255

In a Nutshell 255

Representing and Comparing Fractions 256

Fractions in the Child's World 256

How the Fraction Meanings Are Equivalent 257

Fraction Definitions and Principles 258

Equivalent Fractions 262

Mixed Numbers and Improper Fractions 263

Visualizing with Fractions 264

Principles for Comparing Fractions 264

Relating Fractions to Decimals 268

Common Errors and Misconceptions 268

Appropriate Manipulatives 270

Fraction Operations 272

    Adding and Subtracting Fractions 272

    Multiplying and Dividing Fractions 278

Common Errors and Misconceptions 284

Appropriate Manipulatives 285

Appropriate Children's Books 286

Appropriate Digital Resources 286

Assessing Student Understanding 286

Applying What You've Learned 287

Selected References 288

Chapter 13: Decimals 289

Chapter Problem 289

In a Nutshell 289

Representing Decimals 290

    Decimal Contexts 291

    Decimal Principles 291

    Equivalent Decimals 294

    Equivalent Decimals and Precision 294

    Equivalent Fractions and Decimals 294

    Rounding and Estimating Decimals 296

    Reading and Writing Decimals 297

    Comparing Decimals 297

Decimal Operations 299

    Adding and Subtracting Decimals 299

    Multiplying and Dividing Decimals 301

Common Errors and Misconceptions 304

Appropriate Manipulatives 305

Appropriate Children's Books 308

Appropriate Digital Resources 308

Assessing Student Understanding 308

Applying What You've Learned 309

Selected References 310

Chapter 14: Ratio and Proportion 311

Chapter Problem 311

In a Nutshell 311

Proportional Reasoning 312

Ratio 312

    Equivalent Ratios 313

    Types of Ratio Problems 316

Rates 319

    Using Unit Rates 320

    Fermi Problems 320

    Role of Proportional Reasoning in Other Strands 321

Percent **323**
    Principles for Percent 323

Common Errors and Misconceptions **329**

Appropriate Manipulatives **330**

Appropriate Children's Books **331**

Appropriate Digital Resources **331**

Assessing Student Understanding 332

Applying What You've Learned 332

Selected References 333

Chapter 15: Extending the Number System to Negative and Irrational Numbers **335**

Chapter Problem 335

In a Nutshell 335

Introducing Integers **336**

Integer Contexts **336**

Reading and Writing Integers **336**

Comparing Integers **337**

The Zero Property **337**

Adding Integers **338**

Subtracting Integers **340**

Multiplying Integers **342**

Dividing Integers **345**

Rational Numbers **347**

Exponents **347**
    Using Powers of 10 to Give a Sense of Number Size 348
    Order of Operations Including Exponents 348

Rational versus Irrational Numbers **349**

Common Errors and Misconceptions **351**

Appropriate Manipulatives **352**

Appropriate Children's Books **353**

Appropriate Digital Resources **353**

Assessing Student Understanding 353

Applying What You've Learned 354

Selected References 355

Chapter 16: Patterns and Algebra **357**

Chapter Problem 357

In a Nutshell 357

Patterns **358**
    Types of Patterns 358
    Describing and Extending Patterns 361
    Creating Patterns 364

Mathematical Situations Rich in Patterns 364

Using Patterns to Develop Mathematical Concepts 365

Common Errors and Misconceptions **366**

Appropriate Manipulatives **367**

Algebra **369**

Moving from Pattern to Algebra 369

Algebra as Generalizing Number Relationships 372

Algebraic Notation 372

Describing Functions 376

Using Graphs to Describe Relationships 377

Algebraic Manipulation **381**

Common Errors and Misconceptions **386**

Appropriate Manipulatives **387**

Appropriate Children's Books **388**

Appropriate Digital Resources **389**

Assessing Student Understanding **389**

Applying What You've Learned **389**

Selected References **390**

Chapter 17: 3-D and 2-D Shapes 393

Chapter Problem 393

In a Nutshell 394

Fundamental Aspects of Geometry **394**

Development of Geometric Thinking **395**

Identifying and Classifying Shapes **397**

Identification of 2-D and 3-D Shapes 397

Geometric Attributes and Properties **398**

Comparing Shapes 398

Sorting and Patterning with Shapes 399

Types of 3-D Shapes **401**

Polyhedrons, Spheres, Cones, and Cylinders 401

Components of 3-D Shapes 402

Using Properties to Classify 2-D Shapes **402**

Polygons and Circles 402

Components of 2-D Shapes 402

Planes **406**

Lines, Segments, and Rays **407**

Symmetry **408**

Reflective Symmetry of 2-D and 3-D Shapes 408

Rotational Symmetry of 2-D and 3-D Shapes 410

Representing Shapes **412**

Modelling Shapes 412

Drawing 3-D Shapes 416

Drawing 2-D Shapes 417

Dissecting and Combining Shapes 419
    Combining Shapes 420
    Dissecting Shapes 422

Congruence and Similarity 424
    Congruence of 2-D Shapes 425
    Congruence of 3-D Shapes 427

Similarity of 2-D Shapes 427
    Determining Similarity of 2-D Shapes 428
    Constructing Similar 2-D Shapes 428

Common Errors and Misconceptions 430

Appropriate Manipulatives 433

Appropriate Children's Books 436

Appropriate Digital Resources 436

Assessing Student Understanding 436

Applying What You've Learned 437

Selected References 438

Chapter 18: Location and Movement 439

Chapter Problem 439

In a Nutshell 439

Location and Movement 440

Developing Positional Vocabulary 440
    Using Dance, Song, and Play 440
    Word Walls 440

Maps and Coordinate Grids 442
    Drawing and Interpreting Maps 442
    Working with Grids 443

Transformations 444
    Euclidean Transformations—Slides, Flips, and Turns 445
    Transformations on Simple Grids 445
    Transformations on Coordinate Grids 445
    Slides 446
    Flips 448
    Turns 450
    Non-Euclidean Transformations—Dilatations 452
    Tessellations 454
    Constructions 455

Common Errors and Misconceptions 456

Appropriate Manipulatives 459

Appropriate Children's Books 460

Appropriate Digital Resources 460

Assessing Student Understanding 460

Applying What You've Learned 461

Selected References 462

Chapter 19: The Nature of Measurement, with a Focus on Length and Area 465

Chapter Problem 465

In a Nutshell 465

The Nature of Measurement 466

    Addressing Measurement Principles in the Classroom 467

Stages of Measurement Instruction 468

The Metric System of Measurement 470

    SI Base Units 471

    SI Derived and Customary Units 471

    Metric Prefixes 471

Measuring Length 472

    Introducing Length Concepts 472

    Length: The Definition/Comparison Stage 473

    Length: The Nonstandard Unit Stage 473

    Length: The Standard Unit Stage 477

    Measuring Perimeter 481

Common Errors and Misconceptions 483

Appropriate Manipulatives 486

Measuring Area 488

    Introducing Area Concepts 488

    Area: The Definition/Comparison Stage 488

    Area: The Nonstandard Unit Stage 489

    Area: The Standard Unit Stage 494

    Formulas for Calculating Areas of Shapes 496

    Pythagorean Theorem 504

Common Errors and Misconceptions 505

Appropriate Manipulatives 508

Appropriate Children's Books 510

Appropriate Digital Resources 511

Assessing Student Understanding 511

Applying What You've Learned 512

Selected References 513

Chapter 20: Capacity, Volume, Mass, Time, Temperature, and Angles 515

Chapter Problem 515

In a Nutshell 515

Measuring Capacity, Volume, and Mass 516

Introducing Capacity Concepts 516

    Capacity: The Definition/Comparison Stage 517

    Capacity: The Nonstandard Unit Stage 518

    Capacity: The Standard Unit Stage 520

Introducing Volume Concepts 521

    Volume: The Definition/Comparison Stage 522

    Volume: The Nonstandard Unit Stage 523

    Volume: The Standard Unit Stage 525

Introducing Mass Concepts **530**

    Mass: The Definition/Comparison Stage 530

    Mass: The Nonstandard Unit Stage 532

    Mass: The Standard Unit Stage 534

Common Errors and Misconceptions **535**

Appropriate Manipulatives **538**

Measuring Time and Temperature **540**

Introducing Time Concepts **541**

    Time: The Definition/Comparison Stage 543

    Time: The Nonstandard Unit Stage 543

    Time: The Standard Unit Stage 544

    Measuring and Calculating Elapsed Time 548

Introducing Temperature Concepts **549**

    Interpreting Negative Temperatures 550

    Estimating Temperatures 550

    Measuring and Calculating Temperature Change 550

Common Errors and Misconceptions **550**

Appropriate Manipulatives **553**

Measuring Angles **555**

Introducing Angle Concepts **557**

    Angles: The Definition/Comparison Stage 558

    Angles: The Nonstandard Unit Stage 558

    Angles: The Standard Unit Stage 560

Common Errors and Misconceptions **563**

Appropriate Manipulatives **565**

Appropriate Children's Books **567**

Appropriate Digital Resources **567**

Assessing Student Understanding 567

Applying What You've Learned 568

Selected References 569

Chapter 21: Data **571**

Chapter Problem 571

In a Nutshell 571

Data Organization **572**

    Sorting and Classifying 572

    Recognizing Attributes 572

    Describing a Sorting Rule 573

    Venn Diagrams 574

Common Errors and Misconceptions **576**

Appropriate Manipulatives **577**

Data Collection **578**

    Why People Collect Data 578

    Asking Good Survey Questions 578

Choosing Data Collection Topics 579

Data Sources 580

Factors Influencing Data Collection 580

Common Errors and Misconceptions **581**

Appropriate Manipulatives **582**

Statistics **582**

Measures of Central Tendency 582

Measures of Data Spread 585

Common Errors and Misconceptions **586**

Appropriate Manipulatives **587**

Data Display **587**

Data Display Formats 587

Appropriate Use of Data Display Formats 606

Common Errors and Misconceptions **608**

Appropriate Manipulatives **613**

Data Analysis **615**

Reading Graphs 615

Drawing Inferences from Graphs 617

Misleading Graphs 619

Common Errors and Misconceptions **622**

Appropriate Children's Books **623**

Appropriate Digital Resources **623**

Assessing Student Understanding 623

Applying What You've Learned 623

Selected References 624

Chapter 22: Probability **627**

Chapter Problem 627

In a Nutshell 627

Fundamental Notions about Probability **628**

Probability Misconceptions 628

Early Work with Probability **628**

Using a Probability Line **629**

Outcomes, Events, and Sample Space **630**

Simple and Compound Events 631

Independent and Dependent Compound Events 631

Probabilities as Ratios and Fractions **632**

Experimental Probability **632**

Sample Size 633

Making Predictions Based on Experimental Results 634

Theoretical Probability **635**

Using Logic and Analysis to Make Predictions 635

The Transition from Experimental to Theoretical for Compound Events 635

Reconciling Theoretical and Experimental Probability 637

Determining Theoretical Probability 637

Common Errors and Misconceptions **639**

Appropriate Manipulatives **640**

Appropriate Children's Books **642**

Appropriate Digital Resources **643**

Assessing Student Understanding 643

Applying What You've Learned 643

Selected References 645

Index **647**

Credits **663**

Preface

To the prospective or practising K–8 teacher using this book:

Many teachers who teach at the K–8 level have not had the luxury of specialist training in mathematics, yet they are expected to teach an increasingly sophisticated curriculum to an increasingly diverse student population in a climate where there are heightened public expectations. They deserve help.

This text is designed to provide you with insight into how to make mathematics make sense to students and capture their interest.

This text is designed to support you in teaching mathematics by providing you with insight into how to make mathematics make sense to students and how to capture their interest. Many practising teachers have told me that there were so many ideas in math that they never understood; they just did what they were told. This text provides you with those missing explanations. As a result, you are more likely to gain the confidence to teach mathematics with a student-centred, problem-solving approach. You will be better able to let students explore because you will have a deeper understanding of the mathematics, which will make it easier for you to deal with students' varied ideas.

You will be better able to focus discussion in your classroom because you will be more aware of possible misconceptions and of what aspects of the mathematics are worthy of development. You will also be better able to critically evaluate other people's ideas about how to approach mathematics instruction because you will be starting with a well-founded base of knowledge.

More than that, this text can serve as a resource to which you will return again and again when you are ready to focus on particular content or particular strategies.

Some of the features you will notice include

- chapters dealing with many different aspects of mathematics instruction
  - background chapters dealing with the fundamentals of the kind of mathematics students should and can learn, how to focus instruction on the big ideas and the mathematical processes that span grade levels, assessment and evaluation, and planning instruction
  - chapters dealing with the mathematical processes of problem solving and communication
  - chapters that will make the content clearer and more meaningful to you
- chapter problems to engage you mathematically and that you can later use with students
- the "In a Nutshell" feature to help you focus on the main ideas of each chapter
- highlighted sections that clearly articulate the main principles associated with the content of many chapters
- activities—some of which are open tasks (identified by a blue activity box with an open "top"), and all of which build number sense, algebraic thinking, proportional reasoning, spatial reasoning, critical thinking, or creative thinking—that you can use with students
- teaching tips that reflect the kind of advice an experienced teacher would offer
- student sample responses to show you how students typically respond to certain mathematical tasks
- a focus on Canadian curricula and Canadian approaches to math instruction

- an indication of valuable manipulatives for each content area, with descriptions of how to use them
- charts with common errors and misconceptions described, and strategies to deal with them for each content topic
- some important assessment considerations for each content topic, to supplement the chapter that is dedicated to assessment
- children's literature suggestions to support the various content topics
- suggestions for appropriate digital resources (an online component)
- opportunities to apply what you have learned in the chapter through self-reflection, talking with your classmates, and interacting with students and teachers in schools
- references to allow you to delve more deeply into topics of interest

To the instructor or facilitator:

There are many texts already available for courses for teacher education in mathematics, so what makes this one different?

I think you will find that this text is particularly accessible while also being thorough. Many prospective and practising teachers who have used the text have commented on how readable it is, with many ideas presented visually as well as with words.

I think you will appreciate the Canadian focus. It was written by a Canadian for a Canadian audience. Decisions made about what curriculum should be addressed are based on the various regional curricula in Canada.

I also think you will appreciate the recognition that most of our teacher education programs in Canada do not allow us the instructional hours to introduce our students to as much as we would like. This resource, along with an instructor's manual available on the instructor's website, provides a way to supplement the instruction you offer with the material you would like your students to encounter but do not have time to introduce during class hours. A book study guide is also available on the instructor's website and is designed to help facilitate professional learning activities for practising teachers. The website has other useful resources such as blackline masters, web links, and a glossary. Go to www.nelson.com/instructor.

This resource provides a way to supplement the instruction you offer with the material you would like students to encounter.

What Is New in This Third Edition?

In this third edition, you will find

- increased attention to the issue of mindset
- an enhanced chapter, Chapter 2, on what big ideas in math are and how to teach toward them, including discussion of proportional reasoning, algebraic reasoning, and spatial reasoning, which are spelled out in more detail throughout the resource
- a separate chapter on the acquisition of number facts
- expanded attention to solving proportions, including visual models
- an expanded chapter on integers to encompass order of operations, exponents, and irrational numbers as well
- significant changes in the fraction chapter related to new perspectives on fraction instruction
- very significant changes in the patterns and algebra chapter, with more attention to the link between patterns and algebra and more material on algebra
- streamlining of data chapters
- updates to the reference lists

Acknowledgments

It has been a privilege to be able to take my many years of working in and thinking about mathematics education and translate it into this text. So many people have played a part—my wonderful university colleagues; the thousands of university students with whom I have worked over the years; the many teachers in whose classrooms I have been invited to work; and my many other professional colleagues across the country and internationally, in school board offices, ministries of education, and other universities.

I have certainly appreciated the many positive comments I have received personally on the usefulness of this text to practising teachers, and I have also appreciated the number of faculty members and school district personnel who have chosen this text as a resource for their students and teachers.

I wish to acknowledge the work of the many editors who have shaped my thoughts into text and graphics that make those ideas so much easier to access. Although many editors have contributed, I must single out the enormous contribution of Jackie Williams, an editor who, over the 25 years we have worked together, constantly challenges and impresses me.

For this third edition, I received excellent advice from

- Ralph Connelly, Brock University
- Limin Jao, University of Toronto
- Laura Jones, York University
- Ann Kajander, Lakehead University
- Tim Pelton, University of Victoria
- David Watson, Western University

I must also thank Nelson Education Ltd., both the Higher Education Division and the School Division, for their faith in me and for their support.

Last, but certainly not least, I would like to thank my friends and family, who always support me.

About the Author

Marian Small is the former Dean of Education at the University of New Brunswick. She has been a professor of mathematics education and worked in the field for close to 40 years. Dr. Small is a regular speaker on K–12 mathematics throughout Canada and around the world.

The focus of Dr. Small's professional work has been the development of curriculum and text materials for students of mathematics. She has been an author on eight text series at both elementary and secondary levels in Canada, the United States, Australia, and Bhutan, and a senior author on six of those series. She has produced materials for and been distributed by several ministries of education across the country. She has served on the author team for the National Council of Teachers of Mathematics Navigation series, Pre-K–2; for four years as the NCTM representative on the Mathcounts question writing committee; and on the editorial panel of the 2011 yearbook on motivation and disposition.

Dr. Small has led the research resulting in the creation of maps describing student mathematical development in each of the five mathematical strands for the K–8 level, and has created the associated professional development program, PRIME. She has also written many professional books focusing on differentiated instruction, big ideas in math, and teacher questioning: *Big Ideas from Dr. Small, K–3; Big Ideas from Dr. Small, 4–8;* and *Big Ideas from Dr. Small, 9–12,* published by Nelson Education; *Good Questions: Great Ways to Differentiate Instruction; More Good Questions: Great Ways to Differentiate Instruction; Uncomplicating Fractions to Meet Common Core Standards in Math, K–7;* and *Building Proportional Reasoning Across Grades and Math Strands, K–8,* co-published by Teachers College Press, the National Council of Teachers of Mathematics, and Nelson Education; *Uncomplicating Algebra to Meet Common Core Standards in Math, K–8,* co-published by Teachers College Press and Nelson Education; and *Open Questions for the Three-Part Lesson, K–3* and *4–8,* published by Rubicon Publishing. Recently she has also produced intervention materials for Grade 3–8 students, *Leaps and Bounds toward Math Understanding,* also published by Nelson Education.

Instructor Resources

The **Nelson Education Teaching Advantage** (**NETA**) program delivers research-based instructor resources that promote student engagement and higher-order thinking to enable the success of Canadian students and educators. Visit Nelson Education's **Inspired Instruction** website at http://www.nelson.com/inspired/ to find out more about NETA.

The following instructor resources have been created for *Making Math Meaningful to Canadian Students.* Access these ultimate tools for customizing lectures and presentations at www.nelson.com/instructor.

Image Library

This resource consists of digital copies of figures and art, charts, and student work used in the book. Instructors may use these jpegs to create their own PowerPoint presentations.

Instructor Guide

This resource was written by Marian Small. It is organized according to the textbook chapters and addresses key educational concerns, such as typical stumbling blocks students face and how to address them. Other features include teaching suggestions, assessment tools, and possible projects or demonstrations.

Book Study Guide for Professional Learning

In a number of school districts, this text is purchased for teacher reference. The *Book Study Guide* has been written by Marian Small to be used as a resource for teaching professionals who are taking part in a "book study" of *Making Math Meaningful,* usually set up informally by several teachers within a school, or school-wide, or teachers within a family of schools, or board-wide on a voluntary basis.

Blackline Masters

Blackline masters have been created by Marian Small. The author has provided a set of 35 generic reproducible blackline masters including 10-frames, 100-charts, place value charts, clock faces, tangrams, and many others.

MindTap

MindTap®

Offering personalized paths of dynamic assignments and applications, **MindTap** is a digital learning solution that turns cookie-cutter into cutting-edge, apathy into engagement, and memorizers into higher-level thinkers. MindTap enables students to analyze and apply chapter concepts within relevant assignments, and allows instructors to measure skills and promote better outcomes with ease. A fully online learning solution, MindTap combines all student learning tools—readings, multimedia, activities, and assessments—into a single Learning Path that guides the student through the curriculum. Instructors personalize the experience by customizing the presentation of these learning tools to their students, even seamlessly introducing their own content into the Learning Path.

Student Ancillaries

MindTap

MindTap®

Stay organized and efficient with *MindTap*—a single destination with all the course material and study aids you need to succeed. Built-in apps leverage social media and the latest learning technology. For example,

- ReadSpeaker will read the text to you.
- Flashcards are pre-populated to provide you with a jump start for review—or you can create your own.
- You can highlight text and make notes in your MindTap Reader. Your notes will flow into Evernote, the electronic notebook app that you can access anywhere when it's time to study for the exam.
- Self-quizzing allows you to assess your understanding.

Visit http://www.nelson.com/student to start using **MindTap**. Enter the Online Access Code from the card included with your text. If a code card is *not* provided, you can purchase instant access at NELSONbrain.com.

Chapter 1

How Students Learn Math and What Math We Want Them to Learn

IN A NUTSHELL

The main ideas in this chapter are listed below:

1. There is a strongly held belief in the mathematics education community that mathematics is best learned when students are actively engaged in constructing their own understandings. This is only likely to happen in classrooms that emphasize rich problem solving and the exchange of many approaches to mathematical situations, and that give attention to and value students' mathematical reasoning. Research is increasingly supportive of this approach.

2. There are different perspectives on the discipline of mathematics in terms of what aspects of the content and which processes are valuable and, even when the perspectives are similar, when

(continued)

CHAPTER PROBLEM

A bike is travelling at 35 km/h.
A car is travelling at 80 km/h and begins 180 km behind the bike.
How long will it take the car to catch up to the bike?

Photos.com/Jupiter Images

IN A NUTSHELL (*continued*)

various pieces of content and processes should be encountered. These differences result in varying curricula across the country and affect public responses to mathematics teaching.

3. One of the most influential organizations in mathematics education in North America is the National Council of Teachers of Mathematics (NCTM), in which many Canadian educators take an active role. Many of the central documents produced by this organization have had a profound effect on the mathematics directions taken in Canada and the United States.

4. There continues to be a strong belief that the teacher is key to many students' ability to learn mathematics. Research supports the importance of teachers' development of pedagogical content knowledge, built upon a deep understanding of how students think and develop mathematically, as well as the importance of teachers helping their students to develop a positive mindset in their learning of mathematics.

Research on Mathematical Learning

One of the valuable tools that teachers of mathematics have in the twenty-first century is an increasingly more solid base of research on student learning and mathematics teaching that they can draw upon to inform their instructional strategies. Although research in psychology informed mathematics education in the past—particularly research around optimal ways to teach procedures—research is now much more broadly based, dealing with the acquisition of conceptual understanding as well as skills.

Two particularly valuable and accessible research compendiums are *A Research Companion to Principles and Standards for School Mathematics* (Kilpatrick, Martin, and Schifter, 2003), and *Adding It Up: Helping Children Learn Mathematics* (National Research Council, 2001), which address some of the research cited below, in addition to many other studies.

The Importance of Conceptual Understanding

We all have our own mental pictures of what mathematical understanding looks like.

Carpenter and Lehrer (1999) help us to clarify what we might mean. They speak to the development of understanding not only as the linking of new ideas to existing ones, but as the development of richer and more integrative knowledge structures. These structures allow students to use the new ideas they learn, rather than to only be able to repeat what they have learned.

For example, a student who fully understands what 3×5 means not only realizes that it equals 15, but, at some point, understands all of the following as well:

- It represents the amount in 3 equal groups of 5, no matter what is in the groups.
- It represents the sum of $5 + 5 + 5$.
- It represents the area of a rectangle with dimensions 3 and 5.
- It represents the number of combinations of any 3 of one type of item matched with any 5 of another type of item (e.g., 3 shirts and 5 pairs of pants = 15 outfits).
- It represents the result when a rate of 5 is applied 3 times (e.g., going 5 km/h for 3 hours).
- It describes the final length if a length of 5 units is stretched to triple its size.

Because the student realizes what 3×5 means, he or she can use it to figure out 6×5, 4×5, 3×6, etc., as well as multiply multi-digit numbers like 3×555 and solve a variety of problems involving multiplication of 3 by 5.

Carpenter and Lehrer suggest that understanding is achieved as students engage in these processes:

- constructing relationships
- extending and applying mathematical knowledge
- reflecting about their mathematical experiences
- articulating what they know mathematically
- personalizing mathematical knowledge

They speak to the fact that understanding is most likely to develop in classrooms that focus on problems to be solved, rather than exercises to be completed; classrooms where alternative strategies are discussed and valued; and classrooms where student autonomy is valued.

There have been a number of studies that have examined how students learn mathematics with a deeper understanding. Most of these studies focus on the instructional methods teachers use to facilitate understanding. For example, Ross, Hogaboam-Gray, and McDougall, (2002) report on a variety of studies that show the success of methods based on math reform, that is, classrooms with rich tasks embedded in the real-life experiences of children, and with rich discourse about mathematical ideas. Success was measured on both traditional math tasks and problem-solving tasks.

A Constructivist Approach

The classrooms advocated by Carpenter and Lehrer inevitably value a constructivist approach. Unlike a more traditional approach in which teachers focus on the transmission of mathematical content without considering how their students are perceiving and mentally integrating what is being said, in a constructivist classroom students are recognized as the ones who are actively creating their own knowledge.

For example, in a constructivist classroom, rather than showing students how to add 47 + 38 by grouping the ones, trading, and then grouping the tens, the teacher might provide students with a variety of counting materials and pose a problem such as, "One bus has 47 students in it; another has 38. How many students are on both buses?" and allow students to use their own strategies to solve the problem. There would normally be a discussion where various approaches are shared and additional ideas become available to students to augment their own.

Cobb (1988) explains that the two goals of a constructivist approach to mathematics are students' opportunity to develop richer and deeper cognitive structures related to mathematical ideas, and students' development of a level of mathematical autonomy. In a constructivist classroom, it is through interactions with other students as well as with the teacher, and with the opportunity to articulate their own thoughts, that students are able to construct new mathematical knowledge. These classrooms are ones where varied approaches are expected, shared, and valued. The teacher's role is less about standing at the front talking and more about circulating, engaging in small conversations, facilitating, and gathering information to inform future instruction.

Using Manipulatives

Since the mid-1960s, there has been a belief that the use of manipulative materials—concrete representations of mathematical ideas—is powerful in developing mathematical understanding. Throughout this text, you will see many examples of how manipulatives can be used to make math make sense. For example, the model in the margin embodies place value concepts by showing how the three different digits of 2 in the number 222 represent three different amounts (2 hundreds, 2 tens, and 2 ones).

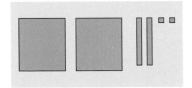

Modelling 222

It is believed that manipulatives help students by providing

- models the student can refer to (i.e., visualize) even when the manipulatives are no longer present
- a reason for students to work cooperatively to solve problems
- a reason for students to discuss mathematical ideas and verbalize their thinking
- a level of autonomy since students could work with the materials without teacher guidance

Research was conducted in the 1960s, 1970s, and 1980s on the value of using manipulatives. Examples are articles by Suydam (1984) and Ball (1988). There is less current research on manipulatives. However, there are a few more recent studies, for example, Puchner, Taylor, O'Donnell, and Fick (2008), and some newer discussions on the use of virtual (computer) manipulatives (Steen, Brooks, and Lyon, 2006). Virtual manipulatives are valued for a number of reasons, but particularly because they are freely available to all students, even at home.

New tools include technological ones. It could be calculators, but it could be tablets with apps that allow students to record their thinking, or digital cameras that allow students to capture their work with concrete materials, or Internet sites that provide access to current data. Clearly, a rich classroom has a mixture of all of these support materials.

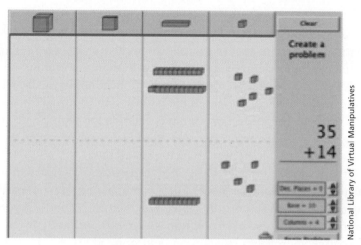

This is an example of the use of virtual manipulatives.

Mindset

There is increasing research about how "a growth mindset" plays a big factor in student success in mathematics (Boaler, 2013). When students embrace challenge rather than shy away from it for fear of failing, when they realize that mistakes are okay and that they improve by having gone through the experience, and when they believe that their ability can grow, they perform better.

A growth mindset can be facilitated by avoiding ability groupings, which seem to suggest that ability is stagnant, as well as by sending the right messages in conversations with students. For example, instead of telling a student that we think a task might be too hard for him or her, we show belief in the student. Instead of classifying students as strong or weak, even if only in our own minds, we start to believe that a student can always improve.

What Mathematics We Want Students to Learn

We have talked about how we teach mathematics, but there is also a question about what mathematics we want students to learn.

The mathematics that teachers teach is based primarily on the outcomes/expectations that their province has decided warrant focus at a particular grade level. Sometimes, teachers supplement this material with other material that they value. But what determines what is valued, either by the provincial or territorial government or by the individual teacher? And what determines the teacher's approach to teaching the mandated curriculum? Often, it is a perspective on what mathematics really is (Mewborn and Cross, 2007).

Differing Perspectives on What Mathematics Is

Some people might wonder how there could be a debate about what mathematics is. But there really are different perspectives.

Mathematics as a Set of Procedures or Not

For many, and certainly for most people in earlier generations, mathematics is viewed as a set of procedures to memorize, whether arithmetic procedures like adding, subtracting, multiplying, and dividing, or high school procedures like factoring or solving trigonometric equations.

For many of these people, there is only one "optimal" procedure for each of these purposes. For example, there is an appropriate way to do "long division," an appropriate way to add a negative integer to a positive one, and an appropriate way to factor quadratics.

Others have a broader view of mathematics. They believe that the learning of mathematics should focus as much, or more, on mathematical concepts and ideas as on the skills. For them, it is not just how to add numbers, but it is also what addition is all about, including when it is used, alternative approaches to addition, and how addition connects to other mathematical ideas.

Mathematics as a Hierarchy of Concepts and Skills

Many view mathematics as a very hierarchical subject. They believe there is a well-defined sequence for learning various concepts and skills. For example, most would suggest that you cannot learn about area until you have learned about length. But even though there are numerous points on which many educators agree, and increased sharing of common learning trajectories, there is no single definitive sequence for the teaching of mathematical concepts and skills.

The lack of agreement becomes apparent simply upon examining how different provinces teach the same topic at different grade levels. Neither do researchers always agree. For example, although some argue that you cannot teach division before multiplication, others say that a child could solve the problem, *How many cookies do each of the 2 children get if they are sharing 8 cookies?*, at the same time as he or she could solve, *How many cookies are on 2 plates if there are 4 cookies on each plate?* Notice that the first is essentially a division problem, and the second is a multiplication problem.

Mathematics as a Study of Pattern

Some suggest that what distinguishes mathematics from other subjects is the central role that pattern plays in its development. Keith Devlin (1996) argues that numbers are based on recognizing patterns in the world; there is no such object as the number 2, but we see a pattern of *twoness* to help us understand what 2 represents. If we see enough things that look like what is shown in the margin, we get the idea of what 2 is supposed to mean.

One strand of mathematics is often called patterns and algebra or patterns and relations. In this strand, students explicitly study repeating, growing, shrinking, and recursive patterns (see Chapter 16). But patterns underlie number, geometry, and measurement as well. For example, not only do we use pattern to define number, as described above, but we use it to understand number. Patterns help us learn to multiply by powers of 10, for example, why $3 \times 10 = 30$, $3 \times 100 = 300$, and $3 \times 1000 = 3000$; they

Representing 2

also help us to understand how our counting system works, for example, counting in a pattern where we say twenty, twenty-**one**, twenty-**two**, etc., to twenty-**nine**, going to thirty, and then starting all over again with thirty-**one**, thirty-**two**, etc.

Patterns in the place value system help us recognize why the first digit to the right of the decimal point must be tenths and the second digit must be hundredths. Patterns even allow us to make sense of a number we have never seen before (e.g., to know that 478 must be between 400 and 500).

Patterns help us understand our measurement system, for example, why a distance of 2 m can be written as 2000 mm, much as a capacity of 2 L can be written as 2000 mL. They also help us interpret geometric situations, for example, the tessellation (or tiling) shown in the margin as a design of hexagons positioned based on geometric transformations.

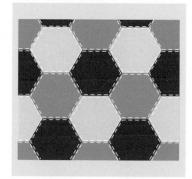

Transformations and tiling

Mathematics as a Way of Thinking

Still others look at mathematics in terms of the processes we use to interpret a situation. Devlin (2000) spoke about mathematics as a way of looking at the world. People who think mathematically look at a phenomenon and see the mathematics in it. For example, on a road trip, people who think mathematically often think about what fraction of the trip they have completed at a certain point, and what their speed would have to be to arrive in a certain amount of time. They may even notice the numerical patterns in licence plates of cars that they pass.

As you learn about the various Canadian provincial and regional curriculum documents, you will see that all of them focus on mathematical processes that should be cultivated to provide the opportunity for students to develop their abilities to think mathematically.

Consider the varying views of mathematics described above. Depending on the perspective taken by the teacher or curriculum writer on what mathematics fundamentally is, different topics might be emphasized or taught in a different way.

Differing Perspectives on What Mathematics Is Valued and at What Grade Levels

Provincial Mathematics Curricula

In Canada, each province or territory has jurisdiction over its curriculum. Each has its own program of studies. However, there are regional agreements wherein provinces and/or territories have agreed to share curriculum frameworks for particular topics, including mathematics.

In the last few years, there have been three major curriculum frameworks in mathematics in Canada. These are the Western and Northern Canadian Protocol (WNCP), applying to the four Western provinces, the four Atlantic provinces, and the three territories; the Ontario curriculum; and the Québec curriculum. The WNCP document was then particularized by the various jurisdictions that use it.

The various curriculum documents differ in the level of detail, the specific topics in each grade level, and the processes that are emphasized. For example, if you examined the 2011 curriculum documents with regards to teaching number in Grade 1, you would notice many commonalities, but also some noticeable differences, for example, whether it is expected that facts be memorized, whether students encounter fractions, whether there is use of ordinal numbers, and whether the emphasis is on numbers 20, 50, or 100.

Currently, both Alberta and British Columbia are revising their curricula to reorganize them around broader competencies. British Columbia is including big ideas around the content strands and focusing learning around the core competencies of communication, thinking, and personal and social. Alberta is looking at the notion of numeracy benchmarks for various ages. It also is considering essence statements. Both provinces are including notions of cross-curricular competencies, which will address numeracy in other subject areas.

It is unlikely that children in the various parts of the country are that different from one another developmentally, so the curriculum differences are clearly an expression of beliefs and/or values.

Moving from one part of the country to another, you may need to alter the content you teach or perhaps even the language you use to emphasize processes, but you will be teaching content that is focused on students gaining and applying a deep understanding of mathematical ideas and processes wherever you teach in Canada.

National Council of Teachers of Mathematics Principles and Standards

The NCTM is a long-standing organization with a very large membership. Math teachers, consultants, and researchers in both the United States and Canada belong to and contribute to the organization.

NCTM produced the *Principles and Standards for School Mathematics* (2000) document to articulate a vision for mathematics. The organization indicated which content and which processes should receive focus, and listed a set of six key principles:

Equity. Excellence in mathematics education requires equity—high expectations and strong support for all students.
Curriculum. A curriculum is more than a collection of activities: it must be coherent, focused on important mathematics, and well articulated across the grades.
Teaching. Effective mathematics teaching requires understanding what students know and need to learn, and then challenging and supporting them to learn it well.
Learning. Students must learn mathematics with understanding, actively building new knowledge from experience and prior knowledge.
Assessment. Assessment should support the learning of important mathematics and furnish useful information to both teachers and students.
Technology. Technology is essential in teaching and learning mathematics; it influences the mathematics that is taught and enhances students' learning.

Important content is identified in each of five mathematical strands (number and operation, algebra, geometry, measurement, and data analysis and probability), and five processes are singled out for consideration:

problem solving, reasoning and proof, communication, connections, and representation. At different grade bands, different strands receive more emphasis, but the processes are critical throughout the grades.

More recently, NCTM (2014) released a document called *Principles to Actions: Ensuring Mathematical Success for All.* This document clarifies the kinds of actions that need to be taken by individual teachers and systems to ensure that the NCTM vision of accessible, engaging math for all is achieved.

The organization produces journals for teachers and researchers in mathematics at all levels, including *Teaching Children Mathematics, Mathematics Teaching in the Middle School, The Mathematics Teacher,* and the *Journal for Research in Mathematics Education,* as well as other electronic resources. These are among the most cited references in mathematics education work.

Public Involvement and Expectations for a Mathematics Curriculum

Increasingly, the public is expressing its opinion about how mathematics should be taught. Many educators find this unsettling; they point out, for example, that the public does not express its opinion in the same way about how medicine or the law should be practised. Yet, because almost every citizen has gone to school, it appears that citizens believe their opinions about educational practice are informed; the notion that there is a body of educational research that is part of the specialized knowledge of educators is not universally accepted.

Similar to the many citizens who expressed concern about a change in philosophy from teaching reading phonetically to what was called a whole language approach (learning to read by reading), many citizens have questioned the advisability of teaching mathematics in a way that does not emphasize standard and uniform approaches to calculations. There has also been concern about less emphasis on memorizing the facts.

It is important for teachers to know how non-teachers feel about these topics, and it is equally important to answer questions that are raised. For example, although it is true that fact memorization is now seen as something that should follow an understanding of what the facts mean, most curricula still speak explicitly to the recall of facts. In other words, we still expect students to recall their facts. Some Ministers of Education have requested revisions in language in provincial curricula to clarify this issue.

The belief that there is only one way to perform an algorithm is mistaken. Although some members of the community may feel that there is a best way to divide, for example, and are not happy that a variety of algorithms are taught to students, in another country a completely different algorithm may be the norm. Neither is better—they are different. In fact, the more tools and approaches that we have, the more likely we are to be successful at a task. And in Canada's increasingly multicultural classrooms, it is important to honour the different approaches used in different countries.

Some believe that there is simply not enough time for students to "discover" math themselves. However, since we know that many adults who grew up with a more traditional mathematics curriculum continue to be math anxious, there is ample evidence that something other than the previous rote approaches to instruction is needed.

Teaching Developmentally

Subsequent chapters speak to other research on how students develop mathematically. However, in this chapter—your initial look at what we know about how students learn mathematics—it is essential also to point out the importance of teachers having a firm understanding of student development in mathematics in order to teach effectively.

Starting with early counting research by Gelman and Gallistel (1978), and later the highly influential Carpenter and Moser (1984) study on children's learning of addition and subtraction, there has been an increasing body of research looking at the sequence with which students make sense of mathematical ideas. As teachers become more familiar with which ideas are more complex for students and why, they are better able to ensure that their instruction is at the appropriate developmental level for students, and that it challenges students' mathematical conceptions in appropriate ways. This minimizes the likelihood of students developing mathematical misconceptions.

This examination of developmental research has led to the creation of important professional development programs, such as Cognitively Guided Instruction (Fennema, Carpenter et al., 1996), mentioned in the section below. More recently, particularly as a result of the adoption of the Common Core curriculum in the United States, there has also been increasing attention to developing learning trajectories for various parts of the mathematics curriculum (Daro, Mosher, and Corcoran, 2011).

Research on Mathematics Teaching

Much of the literature in mathematics education focuses on student achievement, but some of it also looks at the instructional approaches of math teachers. Our intuition and experience tell us of the important role of the teacher in a student's mathematical development. It has been difficult for research to pinpoint which characteristics of a teacher make a difference, given the complexity of the teaching situation. However, we do know a few things about the difference a teacher can make.

There has always been a feeling that teachers need math content background. Most education programs require teachers to have some content courses in mathematics and some methodology. Over the last decade, though, the focus has shifted from how much content to what content.

Importance of a Teacher's Pedagogical Content Knowledge

Since the mid-1980s, there has been a significant push to make sure that teachers understand the mathematics they are teaching from the perspective of the student. Questions teachers might address include

- What might the student be thinking when I present this problem and why?
- How might this subtraction problem look different from that one to a student?

Growing out of a major research study (Carpenter and Moser, 1984) in the mid-1980s was a movement called Cognitively Guided Instruction (CGI). The premise is that if teachers truly understand children's thinking in solving problems related to the topic being addressed, they will be better able to make the mathematics make sense to their students.

In 1996, a long-term, longitudinal study (Fennema, Carpenter et al., 1996) validated that, indeed, student achievement improved significantly in concept knowledge and problem solving in the classrooms of CGI teachers. The researchers witnessed changes in the teachers' behaviour in those classrooms. Teachers were more likely to

- provide time for students to work for significant periods of time with richer problems
- provide opportunities for students to talk to each other about the mathematical ideas with which they were dealing
- adapt instruction to the problem-solving level of the students

A very significant research thread has developed, based in the work of Deborah Ball and her colleagues (Ball, Hill, and Bass, 2005), who have been studying what they call pedagogical content knowledge, that is, teachers' knowledge of the mathematics they are teaching in light of how students might think about the mathematics. This research adds to the work of Liping Ma (1999), who contrasted the deep content knowledge that many Chinese teachers bring to their teaching of mathematics with American teachers' shallower understanding. And more recently, Campbell et. al. (2014) have reinforced the relevance of teacher knowledge on student achievement.

Many of these educators focus on why a student might get something wrong, how to represent a mathematical idea in alternative effective ways, or how to respond when a student performs a task correctly, but in an unexpected way. Ball has spoken widely on how the mathematics that teachers need to know is quite specific and that many teachers do not have the relevant knowledge. Her group has developed instruments that other researchers and education officials are using to assess math teachers' pedagogical content knowledge, so that teachers become aware of their limitations and can work on them.

In the last few years there has been a focus in some provinces on collaborative inquiry in mathematics, with teachers working together, to develop their pedagogical content knowledge in the elementary grades. This direction emphasizes the value of a focus on teacher-initiated issues and the value of collaboration.

The next few chapters delve more deeply into some of the issues raised in this chapter. They look at how to focus instruction on key ideas and mathematical processes, and how problem solving and communication are essential processes to develop at any grade level to ensure that students really do learn mathematics with understanding.

Applying What You've Learned

1. The chapter problem was designed to be solved in a variety of different ways. Show that there are both algebraic and non-algebraic ways to solve the problem.

2. Do a bit of research on the topic of "a constructivist classroom." Describe what you might see that would convince you that a classroom is constructivist in nature.

3. Describe a mathematics topic that you really understand and one that you are uncomfortable with.

   a) What evidence shows that you do understand the topic you selected?

   b) What evidence shows that you do not understand the other topic?

4. Which of the perspectives on mathematics described in this chapter is closest to what you believe? Why?

5. Select a grade level of interest to you in a province of interest to you. Explore the outcomes/expectations that you will be expected to teach.

   a) How is what is on the list different from what you might have expected?

   b) How much support do you feel that you, as a teacher, would be given from the curriculum document for that grade?

6. View the NCTM website (www.nctm.org). Report on some ways that this resource might be useful to you as a teacher of mathematics.

7. Find out about the difference between approaches to teaching math in Japan and North America. What lessons might we learn from the Japanese? What lessons might they learn from us?

8. Investigate the media to locate an argument against a constructivist approach to teaching mathematics. If you, as a teacher, were faced with this argument from a parent, how might you respond?

9. Find out more about pedagogical content knowledge. If possible, have a look at some of the released items that are deemed to measure this knowledge. What surprised you about these items?

Interact with a K–8 Student:

10. Ask a student about a recently explored mathematical topic. Ask the student how he or she knows that he or she really did or did not understand the math learned. Observe whether students focus on their ability to use procedures or their ability to solve problems.

Discuss with a K–8 Teacher:

11. Ask a teacher how the changes in approach to mathematics in the last 10 to 15 years have made it easier (or harder) than expected for him or her to effectively teach mathematics.

Selected References

Alberta Education. (2006). *The common curriculum framework for K–9 mathematics.* Edmonton, AB: Western and Northern Canadian Protocol.

Ball, D.L. (2000). Bridging practices: Intertwining content and pedagogy in teaching and learning to teach. *Journal of Teacher Education, 51,* 241–247.

Ball, D.L., Hill, H.C., and Bass, H. (2005, Fall). Knowing mathematics for teaching: Who knows mathematics well enough to teach third grade, and how can we decide? *American Educator,* 14–17, 20–22, 43–46.

Ball, S. (1988). Computers, concrete materials and teaching fractions. *School, Science, and Mathematics, 88,* 470–475.

Bishop, A.J., Clements, M.A., Keitel, C., Kilpatrick, J., and Leung, F.K.S. (Eds.). (2003). *Second international handbook of mathematics education.* Berlin, Germany: Springer International Books of Education.

Boaler, J. (2013). Ability and mathematics: The mindset revolution that is shaping education. *Forum, 55(1).* Retrieved July 14, 2014, at http://www.ncpdf.org/pdf/steering/2013-09-06/12.0%20Boaler_FORUM_55_1_web.pdf.

Campbell, P.F., Rust, A.H., Nishio, M., DePier, J.N., Smith, T.M., Frank, T.J., Clark, L.M., Griffin, M.J., Contant, D.L., and Choi, Y. (2014). The relationship between teachers' mathematical content and pedagogical content knowledge, teachers' perceptions, and student achievement. *Journal for Research in Mathematic Education, 45(4),* 419–459.

Carpenter, T.P., and Lehrer, R. (1999). Teaching and learning mathematics with understanding. In Fennema, E., and Romberg, T.A. (Eds.). *Mathematics classrooms that promote understanding.* Mahwah, NJ: Lawrence Erlbaum Associates, 19–32.

Carpenter, T.P., and Moser, J.M. (1984). The acquisition of addition and subtraction concepts in grades one through three. *Journal for Research in Mathematics Education, 15,* 179–202.

Cobb, P. (1988). The tension between theories of learning and instruction in mathematics education. *Educational Psychologist, 23,* 87–103.

Daro, P., Mosher, F.A., and Corcoran, T. (2011). *Learning trajectories in mathematics: A foundation for standards, curriculum, assessment, and instruction.* Philadelphia: Consortium for Policy Research in Education. Retrieved on July 14, 2014, at http://files.eric.ed.gov/fulltext/ED519792.pdf.

Devlin, K. (1996). *Mathematics: The science of patterns.* Gordonsville, VA: W.H. Freeman and Company.

Devlin, K. (1998). *The language of mathematics: Making the invisible visible.* New York: W.H. Freeman and Company.

Devlin, K. (2000). *The language of mathematics: Making the invisible visible.* Gordonsville, VA: W.H. Freeman and Company.

Eisenhower Southwest Consortium for the Improvement of Mathematics and Science Teaching. (1997). How can research on the brain inform education? *Classroom Compass, 3,* 14.

English, L.D. (2003). *Handbook of international research in mathematics education.* Mahwah, NJ: Lawrence Erlbaum Associates.

Fennema, E., Carpenter, T.P., Franke, M.L., Levi, L., Jacobs, V.R., and Empson, S.B. (1996). A longitudinal study of learning to use children's thinking in mathematics instruction. *Journal for Research in Mathematics Education, 27,* 403–434.

Gelman, R., and Gallistel, C.R. (1978). *The child's understanding of number.* Cambridge, MA: Harvard University Press.

Hill, H.C. (2010). The nature and predictors of elementary teachers' mathematical knowledge for teaching. *Journal for Research in Mathematics Education, 41,* 513–545.

Kilpatrick, J., Martin, W.G., and Schifter, D. (Eds.). (2003). *A research companion to principles and standards for school mathematics.* Reston, VA: National Council of Teachers of Mathematics.

Lester, F. (2007). *Handbook of research on mathematics education.* Charlotte, NC: Information Age Publishers, Inc.

Ma, L. (1999). *Knowing and teaching elementary mathematics.* Mahwah, NJ: Lawrence Erlbaum Associates.

Mewborn, D.S., and Cross, D.I. (2007). Mathematics teachers' beliefs about mathematics and links to students' learning. In Martin, W.G., Strutchens, M.E., and Elliott, P.C. (Eds.). *The learning of mathematics.* Reston, VA: National Council of Teachers of Mathematics, 259–270.

Ministère de l'Éducation, Gouvernement du Québec. (2001). *Québec education program.* Québec: Ministère de l'Éducation, Province of Québec.

Ministry of Education, Ontario. (2010). *Collaborative teacher inquiry* [Online]. Available from http://www.edu.gov.on.ca/eng/literacynumeracy/inspire/research/CBS_Collborative_Teacher_Inquiry.pdf. Accessed August 13, 2011.

Ministry of Education, Province of Ontario. (2005). *The Ontario curriculum grades 1–8: Mathematics, 2005,* revised. Toronto, ON: Ministry of Education, Province of Ontario.

National Council of Teachers of Mathematics. (2000). *Principles and standards for school mathematics.* Reston, VA: National Council of Teachers of Mathematics.

National Council of Teachers of Mathematics. (2014). *Principles to actions: Ensuring mathematical success* *for all.* Reston, VA: National Council of Teachers of Mathematics.

National Research Council. (2001). *Adding it up: Helping children learn mathematics.* In Kilpatrick, J., Swafford, J., and Findell, B. (Eds.). Mathematics Learning Study Committee, Center for Education, Division of Behavioral and Social Science and Education. Washington, DC: National Academy Press.

Nute, N. (1997). *The impact of engagement activity and manipulatives presentation on intermediate mathematics achievement, time-on-task, learning efficiency, and attitude.* (Doctoral dissertation, University of Memphis, 1997). *Dissertation Abstracts International 58(08),* 2988.

Ontario Education Research Panel. (2010). CIL-M: Collaborative Inquiry and Learning in Mathematics—OERP Partnership Case Studies [Online]. Available from http://www.youtube.com/watch?v=Vo_zkRti5Bw

Puchner, L., Taylor, A., O'Donnell, B., and Fick, K. (2008). Teacher learning and mathematics manipulatives: A collective case study about teacher use of manipulatives in elementary and middle school mathematics lessons. *School, Science, and Mathematics, 108(7),* 313–325.

Roberts, S.K. (2007). Not all manipulatives and models are created equal. *Mathematics Teaching in the Middle School, 13,* 6–9.

Ross, J.A., Hogaboam-Gray, A., and McDougall, D. (2002). Research on reform in mathematics education, 1993–2000. *Alberta Journal of Educational Research, 48,* 122–138.

Steen, K., Brooks, D., and Lyon, T. (2006). The impact of virtual manipulatives on first grade geometry instruction and learning. *Journal of Computers in Mathematics and Science Teaching, 25(4),* 373–391.

Suydam, M. (1984). Research report: Manipulative materials. *The Arithmetic Teacher, 31,* 27.

Chapter 2

Focusing Instruction on Big Ideas and Mathematical Processes

IN A NUTSHELL

The main ideas in this chapter are listed below:

1. By organizing content around big ideas, teachers can teach more efficiently, but, most importantly, students can make connections between seemingly disparate topics that help them learn new mathematical ideas.

2. Proportional reasoning, algebraic reasoning, and spatial reasoning are threads that underlie mathematics curricula at every grade level.

3. There are a number of mathematical processes that can and should be developed no matter what content is being taught. Although the lists of identified processes differ in different jurisdictions, these processes almost always include problem solving, communication, and reasoning.

CHAPTER PROBLEMS

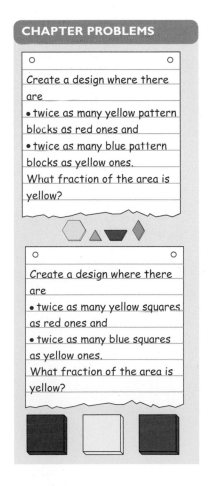

Create a design where there are
• twice as many yellow pattern blocks as red ones and
• twice as many blue pattern blocks as yellow ones.
What fraction of the area is yellow?

Create a design where there are
• twice as many yellow squares as red ones and
• twice as many blue squares as yellow ones.
What fraction of the area is yellow?

Organizing Content around Big Ideas

A significant body of educational research has established the effectiveness of using organizers to present new knowledge to students (Borko and Putnam, 1995; Kennedy, 1997; Schifter, Bastable, and Russell, 1997). These organizers are sometimes called "big ideas," "enduring understandings," "key concepts," or "key ideas." The thinking behind this approach is that, if we can connect a new idea being taught to related ideas that have been previously learned, it is more likely that the new knowledge will be assimilated.

Focusing the learning of each strand in mathematics around a few big ideas makes it easier for students to relate new knowledge to previously learned ideas. In addition, it simplifies the teacher's job of prioritizing what is usually a fairly lengthy list of specific curriculum expectations/outcomes by organizing them around a relatively small number of big ideas. Despite increasing abstraction as students go up the grades, and shifts in focus from grade to grade, big ideas remain relevant.

The big ideas need to be explicit, not implicit. Whether the teacher asks leading questions or states or displays the big ideas, he or she should ensure that the big ideas are overt. The more students hear an idea, the more likely they will be to internalize it and be able to use it to support further learning.

Different Approaches to Big Ideas

Different researchers and curriculum developers look at big ideas in different ways. Some refer to strands or major topics as big ideas. These strands might be more traditional—such as number, measurement, data, etc. Or they might be less traditional, for example, Steen (1990) used the topics of pattern, dimension, quantity, uncertainty, shape, and change as strands to organize mathematical content.

Sometimes the big ideas are statements about the strands. For example, the British Columbia curriculum proposes the big idea: "Number represents and describes quantity. Quantities can be decomposed into smaller parts." for the number strand. They propose the statement "We can describe, measure, and compare spatial relationships: Objects and shapes have attributes." to underlie parts of the shape and space curriculum. The Ontario Guides to Effective Instruction in Mathematics for Kindergarten to Grade 3 (Ministry of Education, 2003, 2005, 2007) and for Grades 4 to 6 (2006, 2008) list sub-topics within each traditional strand as big ideas that vary a bit between grade bands:

- quantity, operational sense, counting, representation, relationships, and proportional reasoning in number
- patterns and relationships, expressions, and equality (or variables, expressions, and equations) in algebra
- attributes, units, and measurement sense as well as measurement relationships in measurement
- properties of two-dimensional shapes and three-dimensional figures, geometric relationships, and location and movement in geometry
- collection and organization of data, data relationships, and probability in data and probability

Within each big idea, they list a set of sub-ideas. For example, for quantity in Grades 4 to 6:

- Having a sense of quantity involves understanding the "how-muchness" of whole numbers, decimal numbers, fractions, and percents.
- Experiences with numbers in meaningful contexts help to develop a sense of quantity.
- An understanding of quantity helps students estimate and reason with numbers.
- Quantity is important in understanding the effects of operations on numbers.

Clements (2004) lists one or two big ideas in each strand that focus on the purpose of the mathematics within the strand. For example, there are two big ideas in number and two in geometry:

- Numbers can be used to tell how many, describe, order, and measure; they involve numerous relationships and can be represented in various ways.
- Operations with numbers can be used to model a variety of real-world situations and to solve problems; they can be carried out in various ways.
- Geometry can be used to understand and to represent the objects, directions, and locations in our world, and the relationships between them.
- Geometric shapes can be described, analyzed, transformed, and composed and decomposed into other shapes.

Other researchers list many big ideas for each subtopic in a strand. Van de Walle et al. (2011), for example, list seven big ideas related to early number and operations and many more big ideas involving later work in number as well as the other strands. As well, their big ideas vary in type. Some describe particular relationships. For example, addition and subtraction are connected. Addition names the whole in terms of parts, and subtraction names a missing part. Some are more like definitions. For example, counting tells how many things are in a set. When counting a set of objects, the last word in the counting sequence names the quantity for that set.

Charles (2004) lists a set of 21 big ideas to cover all mathematical strands for elementary and middle school math. These include statements such as:

- The set of numbers is infinite and each real number can be associated with a unique point on the number line.
- The base ten numeration system is a scheme for recording numbers using digits 0 to 9, groups of ten, and place value.
- Any number, measure, numerical expression, algebraic expression, or equation can be represented in an infinite number of ways that have the same value.
- If two quantities vary proportionally, that relationship can be represented by a linear function.
- Two- and three-dimensional objects with or without curved surfaces can be described, classified, and analyzed by their attributes.

The set of big ideas suggested by Small (2009, 2010) are most similar to those proposed by Charles but tend to be more like Charles's broader statements and not the more specific ones. The intention is that these statements of ideas that students should develop would help teachers focus learning goals on what students will come to know, rather than what they will simply do. Several, but not all, of the big ideas appear in all or most of the strands; others are particular to one strand.

Big Ideas Applying to Many Strands

Small proposes three big ideas that apply to many strands.

- **Comparing mathematical objects/relationships helps us see that there are classes of objects that behave in similar ways.**

For example, students might notice that triangular and rectangular prisms have an even number of vertices and that the number of edges in both cases is a multiple of 3, but that the same is not true for a square pyramid. They could conjecture that it might only be true for prisms and learn that this is indeed true for prisms, although it is true for some pyramids as well.

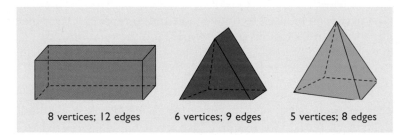

8 vertices; 12 edges   6 vertices; 9 edges   5 vertices; 8 edges

They might compare the fractions $\frac{2}{3}$, $\frac{3}{4}$, $\frac{4}{5}$, and $\frac{5}{6}$ and notice that the one with the greater numerator and greater denominator is greater overall. This might lead students to realize that all fractions of the form $\frac{n-1}{n}$ behave in that way.

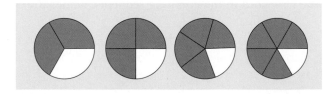

Or, they might compare the patterns:

3, 5, 7, 9, …
2, 4, 6, 8, …
3, 6, 9, 12, …

to decide which two patterns are most alike, why, and what other patterns would behave in similar ways.

- **Limited information about mathematical objects/relationships often, but not always, allows us to determine other information about those objects.**

For example, students could recognize that knowing one measurement of a circle (whether its radius, diameter, circumference, or area) would give you all of the other measurements, although the same would not be true of a general rectangle.

Or, in number, students might realize that if you know that a whole number is less than 20, you know lots more about it: for example, that it is a 1-digit or 2-digit number, that it is less than 25, that it is less than 50, etc.

Or, in geometry, if students know that the two triangles below are similar and the given measurements are true, then side x must be 10 cm long.

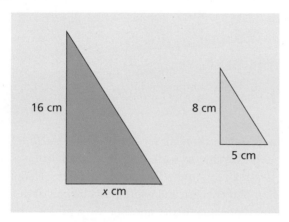

- **Mathematical objects/relationships can often be represented in multiple ways; each of those ways might make something about those objects more obvious.**

For example, when a young student realizes that showing 7 with tally marks emphasizes that $7 = 5 + 2$, but showing it as two 3s and 1 more does not, he or she is using this big idea. When an older student realizes that it might be useful to represent 0.25 as $\frac{1}{4}$ to multiply 0.25×4484, that student is using the same big idea.

Student Response

This student has been asked to choose a fraction and a percent, then tell which is greater and how he knows. He realizes that changing one of the representations makes it easier for him to compare.

① $\frac{2}{5}$　②$34\%$

and $5 \times \square = 100$ and $\square$ must be 20

so when I change 5 by 100 than I get

$\frac{2 \overset{(50)}{\times 10}}{5 \times 20} = \frac{40}{100}$ ← and 40 will be 40% so $(number)$ ✓ ① will be more bigger.

In geometry, younger students are expected to recognize a 3-D shape from its picture. Older students might judge whether one pictorial representation of a 3-D shape is better than another representation of the shape for a particular purpose. The following diagrams show some of the ways to represent a triangle-based prism pictorially.

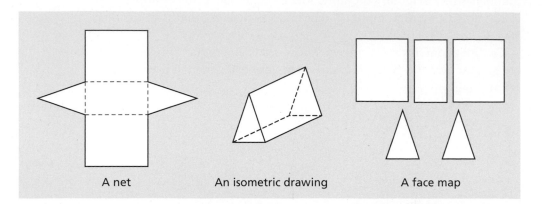

A net   An isometric drawing   A face map

In measurement, when a student recognizes that $P = 2(l + w)$ is as valid as $P = 2l + 2w$ in representing the perimeter of a rectangle, he or she is using a representation that will lead to the realization that if a rectangle has a perimeter of 34, the sum of the length and width must be half of that, or 17.

When students understand that another way of describing the square numbers 1, 4, 9, … is through the set of square shapes (as shown in the margin), they are using this big idea. The same pattern is represented numerically and geometrically; it is the geometric representation that helps the student understand the name of the pattern; it is the numeric representation that helps the student construct subsequent terms in the pattern.

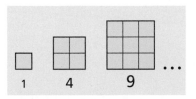

1   4   9   …

This pattern is represented using shapes and numbers.

For example, in data, students might observe that the two displays below show the results of the same spinner experiment. The difference between them, though, is that while the bar graph only shows how many results were in each interval, the stem-and-leaf plot shows each individual result. In this case, the bar graph tells us that 4 students spun red between

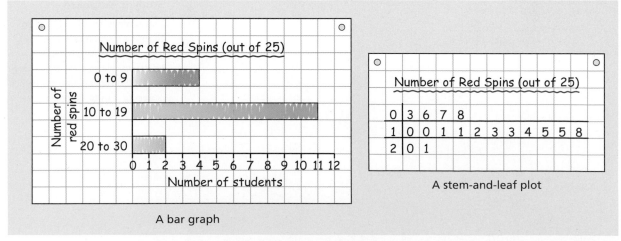

A bar graph   A stem-and-leaf plot

The same data can be displayed in different ways, depending on the purpose.

0 and 9 times in the experiment. The stem-and-leaf plot shows that those students actually spun red 3 times, 6 times, 7 times, and 8 times.

Examples of More Strand-Based Big Ideas

Other big ideas proposed by Small (2009, 2010) are more strand-based. Examples of these are shown below.

> • **Most often, we use numbers to describe how many.**

We want students to realize that numbers like 3, –4, 0.25, and $\frac{2}{3}$ describe "howmuchness," although some numbers, like student IDs, do not.

> • **We can generally use the same algebraic expression to describe different real-world situations and we often use different algebraic expressions to describe the same real-world situation.**

We might ask students for all of the situations to which the expression $2 \times \blacksquare$ might apply. These include situations like the number of ears for $\blacksquare$ people, the number of dollars that $\blacksquare$ toonies are worth, the number of cookies in $\blacksquare$ packages of 2 cookies, etc.

Similarly, we want students to understand that the expressions $3x$, $2x + x$, and $x + x + x$ are all ways to describe tripling a number.

> • **How a shape can be composed and decomposed can help you learn more about the original shape.**

When students put together four linking cubes to build a tower, they are applying this big idea. Sometimes they create new shapes by combining smaller shapes. Other times, they do the opposite—they dissect a large shape into smaller component shapes. For example, using a hexagon to tile a floor involves combining shapes to create a larger shape, but it may

Three 3-D shapes that can be made by combining four congruent cubes

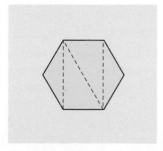

Four 2-D shapes (in this case, all triangles) that can result from dissecting a hexagon

also be viewed as dissecting a larger shape to create smaller component shapes. Students' experience with jigsaw puzzles can also help them see how shapes can be made up of other shapes.

This big idea also leads students to understand how doubling the side lengths of a shape produces a shape with four times the area, and also why a regular polygon can be subdivided into congruent triangles.

Knowing that any shape can be divided into smaller shapes ...

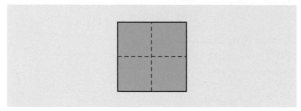

... helps students understand why doubling the side lengths of the square results in a square with four times the area.

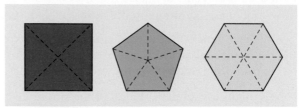

... helps students understand why any regular polygon can be divided into congruent triangles that meet at a central point.

- **Measurement formulas are useful, since you can use simple measurements to figure out more complicated ones.**

For example, we want students to realize that since it is so much easier to measure the radius of a circle directly than to count the squares in the circle's area, a formula for the area of a circle is useful. Similarly, we want students to realize that a formula for the perimeter of a square or rectangle is useful since fewer measurements are required than when actually measuring the entire perimeter.

Teaching to the big ideas within and across strands helps make math much less of a mystery to students; the mathematics starts to feel coherent.

Focusing Instruction on Proportional Reasoning, Algebraic Reasoning, and Spatial Reasoning

Proportional reasoning, algebraic reasoning, and spatial reasoning, much like the big ideas previously articulated, are built around concepts that bind what might seem to be disparate topics in math together, and help students make connections.

Proportional Reasoning

Proportional reasoning is the process students use when they think of one quantity as a number of units of another quantity (Dole, 2010). For example, when the student thinks of 12 as three fours, that student is using proportional thinking. This is in contrast to what is called additive thinking, when the student thinks of the 12 as 10 + 2. Both kinds of thinking have important roles in mathematics, It turns out that proportional reasoning takes somewhat longer for students to develop, but is key to success in upper elementary and secondary math.

Proportional reasoning manifests differently at different grade levels. Even in the primary grades, students use proportional reasoning as they measure lengths with units and think of one length as, for example, 10 of a unit. They also use proportional thinking in early grades when they think about coin conversions (e.g., 1 dime is worth 2 nickels). It is used in upper elementary grades whenever multiplication and division or work with fractions is at play. For example, dividing 12 by 4 is really about thinking of 12 as so many fours. Any fraction is a proportional relationship between numerator and denominator. What makes 4/8 the size it is is the multiplicative relationship between 4 and 8, namely that 4 is half of 8 or 8 is double 4. Proportional reasoning is used further in work with ratio, rate, and percent. For example, when we know that meat costs \$19.29/kg and we want to figure out how much 1.2 kg costs, we use equivalent rates: 19.29/1 = ?/1.2. Proportional reasoning concepts are used in looking at similar triangles, when looking at rates of change when graphing lines or studying linear relationships, and in a variety of other situations.

Encouraging students to think about amounts as fractions of or multiples of other amounts takes a great deal of attention and focus on the part of teachers and has become a goal for many Canadian teachers.

A few of the important general concepts in proportional reasoning are:

- It is often useful to think of one amount as so many units of another amount; for example, 7 days as 1 week, 20 eggs as $1\frac{2}{3}$ dozen eggs, 50 as 2×25, etc.
- If you use a bigger unit, you need fewer of them; for example, it takes more centimetres than metres to measure the same object, or it takes more 5s than 10s to make 100.
- If you use the same number of big units and small units, the total for the big units is greater; for example, 5 kg is heavier than 5 g, or 5 groups of 8 is more than 5 groups of 7.
- If units are related, you can use that relationship to predict how many of one unit if you know how many of the other; for example, since nickels are half as valuable as dimes, something that costs 4 dimes costs 8 nickels. Or, since $\frac{2}{3}$ is double $\frac{1}{3}$, the number of $\frac{2}{3}$ s in 4 is half as many as the number of $\frac{1}{3}$ s in 4.

You will see elements of proportional reasoning emerge in many chapters in this resource, but particularly in the chapters on early operations, fractions, decimals, various measurement chapters, probability, and, of course, the chapter on ratio and proportion. Activities in various chapters linked to developing proportional reasoning are highlighted.

Algebraic Reasoning

Algebraic reasoning is the process students use when they generalize numerical situations, when they model situations using equations and variables, and when they study how quantities are related.

Even in the primary grades, students think algebraically (Kieran, 2004) as they realize that no matter what two numbers you have (and so, a generalization), you can add them in either order without changing the result. In later grades, they think more generally when they realize that no matter what numbers you have, if you add two odds, you get an even, but if you multiply two odds, you get an odd. They use algebra when they write measurement formulas, relating, for example, the length and width of a rectangle to its area. They think algebraically when they create pattern rules that will help them figure out terms very far "down" in a pattern. And they use algebraic reasoning when they use algebraic notation, for example letters or symbols to represent unknowns in order to write expressions or equations to describe situations.

Many students like to focus on specifics. For example, they will conclude that 4×9 is double 2×9 by noticing that 36 is double 18, but, without a push from a teacher, they often won't generalize to the notion that any number can be multiplied by 4 by doubling a double. And then they will often rely on specific cases to "prove" their rule, rather than looking for reasons in the inherent structure of multiplying by 4 that will explain the reasons why doubling a double is, in effect, multiplying by 4. Using algebraic reasoning would encourage them to think more generally, abstracting from specifics but looking at structure.

You will see elements of algebraic reasoning emerge in many chapters in this resource, but particularly in the chapters on number operations and the chapter on pattern and algebra. Activities in various chapters linked to developing algebraic reasoning are highlighted.

Spatial Reasoning

Spatial reasoning is the process students use when they consider the location and movement of objects (Newcombe and Huttenlocher, 2003).

Even in the primary grades, students think spatially as they decide how to move objects around to make them fit together or fit in particular spaces or how they have to position themselves to see an object in a particular way.

Clearly much of the curriculum that deals with location of objects (whether using positional vocabulary in early years or coordinate grids in later years) and that deals with geometric transformations (slides, flips, turns, and dilations) relates very directly to spatial reasoning.

But spatial reasoning is also used when trying to decide why $3 \times 4 = 4 \times 3$. It is when the objects are in one of the two ways shown in the top picture below that we can see both 3 groups/rows of 4 and 4 groups/columns of 3.

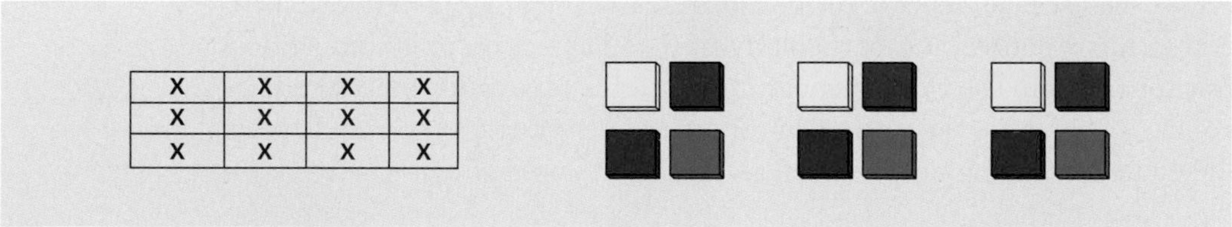

The array arrangement on the top left is obviously both. The arrangement on the top right shows 3 groups of 4, but colour helps the eye see 4 groups of 3 tiles in each of red, yellow, blue, and green.

It is not so obvious with the picture of all yellow squares at the bottom of the previous page.

And spatial reasoning is used to help a student see why the area of a triangle is half the area of a parallelogram with the same base and height.

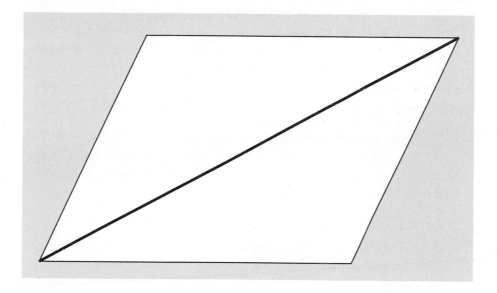

Spatial reasoning has a link to algebraic reasoning, too. For example, this set of pictures below might help a student see why, in general, $(n - 1)(n + 1) = n^2 - 1$, that is, the product of two numbers that are 2 apart is 1 less than the square of the number between them.

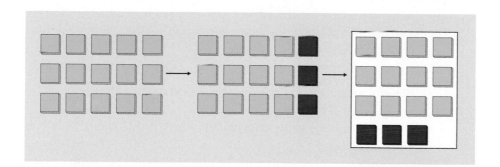

Since there were two fewer rows than columns, moving the last column to become the last row equalizes the number of rows and columns, but one item is missing out of the square since there was one fewer row before than there are columns now.

Spatial reasoning also plays a big role in interpreting and inferring from visual displays like graphs.

You will see elements of spatial reasoning emerge in many chapters in this resource, but particularly in the chapters on measurement, geometry, and data. Activities in various chapters linked to developing spatial reasoning are highlighted.

Focusing Instruction on Math Processes

Thinking about what the big ideas are is certainly one essential element of good mathematics teaching. Another is focusing on the mathematical processes. Just as big ideas are the constant throughout K–12 in terms of content, processes are also a constant.

The NCTM Process Standards

The National Council of Teachers of Mathematics identified five mathematical processes in its *Principles and Standards* document (NCTM, 2000). These are problem solving, communication, representation, reasoning and proving, and connections. These five processes underlie mathematical content through all grades, from early childhood to higher-level mathematics. Just as it is important to develop students' understanding of various mathematical concepts, it is equally and perhaps more important to develop their process skills; these are the tools students use to learn new mathematics.

A detailed discussion of problem solving and communication is found in the next two chapters. This chapter mentions some of the other processes.

Representation

Because mathematics is the study of abstract concepts like numbers and shapes, the way that these ideas are represented is critical to students' understanding. The more flexible students are in recognizing alternative ways to represent mathematical ideas, the more likely they are to be successful in mathematics. This is also noted in the section on big ideas, specifically on page 19.

For example, suppose a child realizes that the number 9 can be represented as $10 - 1$. The child is more likely to be able to calculate $35 + 9$ mentally (as $35 + 10 = 45$, and then $45 - 1 = 44$). If he or she also recognizes that 9 is 3×3, it becomes easier to divide 333 by 9 (as $333 \div 5 \div 3$). The more representations students are comfortable with, the more flexible their calculation skills will be.

Different representations of numbers help clarify ideas. For example,

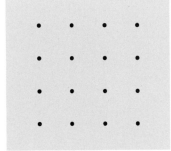

16 is a square number.

- Calling 16 a square number makes more sense when students see it as a square array of dots.
- Realizing that $\frac{5}{5} = 1$ helps students see why $\frac{15}{20}$, which equals $\frac{3}{4} \times \frac{5}{5}$, is another name for $\frac{3}{4}$.
- Representing $(-4) + (+6)$ with counters helps a student see why $(-4) + (+6) = 6 - 4$ since every $+1 + (-1)$ combination is 0.

-4

$+6$

Each pair of white and black counters is 0.

- Representing the difference of $(+5) - (-3)$ as the distance from -3 to $+5$ on a number line helps a student understand why $(+5) - (-3)$ is the same as $(5 + 3)$.

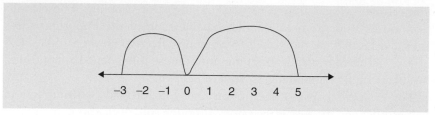

$(+5) - (-3)$ is the distance from -3 to 5, which is 8.

One way to encourage students to use multiple representations is to explicitly ask for them. Ask questions such as

– Can you write the number 5 using only 4s?
– Can you represent a square as a combination of other shapes?
– Can you represent this pictograph as a bar graph?
– In how many ways can you show 10?

$8 + 2 = 10$	$20 - 10 = 10$
$5 + 5 = 10$	$100 - 90 = 10$
$7 + 3 = 10$	$2 + 8 = 10$
	$1 + 9 = 10$
	$15 - 5 = 10$
$20 - 10 = 10$	$3 + 3 + 3 + 1 = 10$
	$5 + 5 = 10$
	$7 + 3 = 10$
	$10 + 0 = 10$
$4010 - 4000 = 10$	$6 + 4 = 10$
	$30 - 20 = 10$

Some of these representations for 10 are symbolic, but not all of them.

Reasoning

Many regard mathematics as being all about logic and reasoning. Indeed, there is a great deal of reasoning that students use to learn new mathematical ideas. Reasoning is about making inferences, generalizing, and verifying. Students infer by deriving implicit information from explicitly stated information. They sometimes attempt to generalize their conclusions through the creation of mathematical conjectures, which they verify using logical reasoning. These skills develop as students mature intellectually. One of the important ideas they learn is that it is dangerous to generalize from too few examples. It is always better to explain something not because it happened a few times, but because, fundamentally, it "had to happen."

For example, consider the notion that you can add two numbers in either order and the sum is the same. Although some students come to this conclusion by observing that $(2 + 3)$ has the same answer as $3 + 2$, $4 + 5$ as $5 + 4$, and $2 + 6$ as $6 + 2$, others recognize that if you put together two items, the sum has to be the same. If you held some items in one hand and some in the other and laid them down, it would not matter which items you let fall first; the total number of items is the same since they are the same items. This sort of generalization is based on proving, which is a very powerful form of reasoning.

One of the ways students develop their reasoning skills is to make conjectures that they then either prove or disprove.

Making and Testing Conjectures

A *conjecture* is a conclusion or opinion that has not yet been verified that students might wonder about. Students use their observations and reasoning about relationships and patterns to develop these conjectures. For example, students might conjecture that the sum of two odd numbers is even. Then they need to develop strategies for testing their ideas.

Conjecture-testing strategies take time to develop. For many students, three or four examples are enough to convince them that something is always true. It is important to note that, although multiple examples are not enough to prove a conjecture true, only one counterexample is required to prove it false.

What might some of these conjectures look like and how can we expect students to prove or disprove them? Two examples are shown below.

Activities to encourage reasoning can begin at the very earliest grades and should be continued through to higher-level mathematics. For some students, reasoning must be modelled by "thinking out loud," so they have an example to follow. Effective questioning is also important. Teachers can use the following list of model questions to prompt and foster reasoning in students:

CONJECTURE	DISPROVING THE CONJECTURE BY COUNTEREXAMPLE
If you combine any group of congruent shapes, you will always be able to make the same type of shape. For example, these four congruent triangles combine to make a larger triangle.	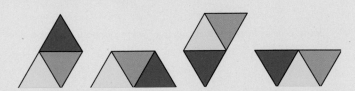 These three congruent triangles cannot be combined to make a triangle of any kind. The only possible shape is a trapezoid. Sometimes a certain number of congruent shapes cannot be combined to make the same type of shape. The conjecture is false.

CONJECTURE	PROVING THE CONJECTURE BY REASONING
Here is a conjecture about sums of 3-digit addends: The sum of two 3-digit numbers has 3 or 4 digits. Students will be able to find multiple examples to support the conjecture and will be unable to find a counterexample to disprove it. But this is not enough to prove the conjecture true; reasoning must be used to prove the conjecture.	The sum of two 3-digit numbers has 3 digits or 4 digits. For example, $123 + 789 = 912$ $234 + 436 = 670$ $274 + 436 = 710$ $598 + 427 = 1025$ $739 + 839 = 1578$ It works for the five examples I tried, but I am not sure it always works. *Teacher:* What is the least possible answer? *Student:* You'd have to add 100 and 100. That's 200 and it has 3 digits. *T:* What is the greatest possible answer? *S:* It's what you get if you add $999 + 999$. That's 1998, which has 4 digits. So, if the least sum has 3 digits and the greatest has 4 digits, all the sums must have 3 or 4 digits.

- Why do you think it happened?
- Does anyone have a different reason? What is it?
- Will this always happen? Why do you think that?
- How are these alike? different?
- What would happen if ...?
- What are some other ways to do this?
- What patterns do you notice?

Connections

The notion of connection is fundamental to all new learning, whether in mathematics or other areas. It may be connections between some mathematical ideas and other ones; it may be connections between mathematical concepts and everyday life experiences; it may be connections between what is learned in math and what is learned in a different subject in school. Any and all connections are helpful for students to make sense of new ideas they encounter. In fact, it is almost impossible for students to solve a set of problems or even complete a set of exercises without making connections. We rarely give students exactly the same numbers to work with twice, so when solving a new question, students must see how it is like a question they have already encountered. Connections to real-life contexts and to literature are particularly important for young learners.

Some possibilities for contexts to help students make connections are

- contexts that are whimsical, fanciful, and even silly, such as superheroes and space monster characters
- contexts in the world of grownups; for example, how much things cost and what adults do with math
- contexts that children suggest in the process of creating their own problems
- cross-curricular situations; for example, symmetry in art or architecture, fractions in music, measurement in science, or mapping in social studies

Student Response

This student made a connection to what he had learned in social studies in this math response to the question "How are 350 and 550 alike?"

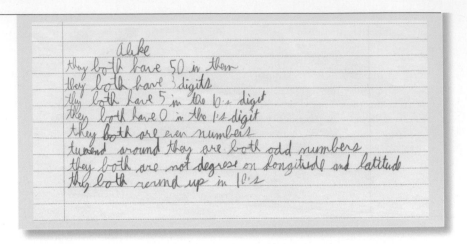

- children's literature that is enjoyable and that also has mathematical value. Note that not only do children like to hear stories, they also like to create them. This is a wonderful way to link math and language arts.
- contexts in the child's world, such as collections, the classroom, friends, and family; for example, How many outfits can you make with 3 T-shirts and 2 pairs of pants?
- cross-cultural contexts; for example, contexts related to students' cultural backgrounds
- other strands of math; for example, number patterns or measurement situations that involve addition or subtraction

Other Processes

Particular educational jurisdictions in Canada have identified other processes that they want to stress for students as well. These include visualization and mental imagery, related to the earlier discussion of spatial reasoning, as well as mental math and estimation in the WNCP curriculum, and selecting tools and computational strategies and reflecting in Ontario.

Visualization

Visualization or *mental imagery* "involves thinking in pictures and images and the ability to perceive, transform, and re-create different aspects of the visual spatial world" (Armstrong, 1999). Visualization, as applied in mathematics, is a process of representing abstract concepts as mental images. These images allow the visualizer to remember and "manipulate" the concepts and to make the concepts meaningful.

There are obvious visualization opportunities for mathematics in geometry, measurement, and data management. Visualization is also important, however, in developing number sense. Although many teachers tend to concentrate on verbalization in their teaching, it is just as important to bring attention to the visual representation of concepts. Students visualize in their minds. At the youngest grades, students become familiar with what

3 (or 4 or 5 ...) looks like. When concrete materials (such as blocks used to represent an addition problem) are no longer present, it is the many previous concrete experiences with such physical aids that enable students to solve the problem, because they have internalized the relevant images. It is essential, therefore, that students receive frequent and varied exposure to manipulatives and other visual representations of mathematical objects and concepts.

Some tools to foster visualization skills are described throughout the chapters of this text.

Mental Math and Estimation

Subsequent chapters in this text present many mental math and estimation strategies. One of the reasons these are highlighted is that solving questions mentally helps to force a student to focus on the relationships between numbers and the effect of number operations, as opposed to simply memorizing rules for performing particular types of computations.

For example, students might solve $49 + 99$ mentally by adding 100 to 49 and subtracting 1, but they might solve $123 + 34$ mentally by adding 30 to 123 and then another 4. Each time they are decomposing one of the addends in a different way.

Mental math and estimation strategies are also useful in everyday life. Sometimes we need to do a quick calculation without benefit of a pencil or a calculator, and often an estimate is sufficient.

Selecting Tools and Computational Strategies

Many secondary school teachers complain that students reach for their calculators for even simple calculations like 20×30. Their concern is real. Calculators are useful tools, but students should be considering when a tool is appropriate to use. The same is true of other technology or physical models like manipulatives. We want students to make reasonable and considered decisions about what tool to use and when.

For example, it is useful to use base ten blocks to model 23×14 (see Chapter 10), but perhaps not to model 236×420. It is useful to use Cuisenaire rods to model $14 + 8$ (see Chapter 8), but not $139 + 52$. It is useful to use a calculator to calculate 389×420, but mental calculation is more appropriate for 30×2. It is useful to use a spreadsheet to perform a large number of calculations, particularly if the values might change, but not to perform a single addition of two numbers. Students learn how to make good choices by being exposed to options. They need to become familiar with possible tools, and then learn which are most efficient and when.

It is also important for students to learn that, for a particular computation, there are many possible approaches. Here, again, students need to know that there are choices and to have experience in making those choices. For example, to multiply 50×84, it is reasonable to use the equivalent computation 100×42. This strategy of doubling and halving would be less useful for multiplying, for example, 39×67. Exposing students to alternative algorithms, particularly mental math algorithms, gives students choices.

Reflecting

Reflecting involves students looking back at their work. It might involve considering why the steps they took were useful ones, which steps were not useful, how the work they did relates to the concept they are trying to explore or the problem they are trying to solve, what made the work easy or difficult, or to which other situations the procedures or strategies they used might apply.

Reflecting can also involve listening to what others think and reflecting on how these alternative ideas relate or do not relate to students' own thinking about a situation.

Students should be encouraged to reflect regularly. This can be accomplished by asking questions such as:

- Why was that a useful step?
- What would you have done differently if the number had been ...?
- Why was it important to include that example?
- Do you agree with ...? Why?

Assessing Student Understanding

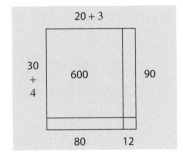

- Make sure that you include items involving a variety of processes when assessing student understanding of a particular topic. For example, after a unit on multiplication, rather than giving a test that only involves computation, make sure to include items that require problem solving, communicating, reasoning, and representation, as well as other processes. For example, you might ask students in Grade 5 to explain why this is a good model to show 23 × 34.
- Help students focus on big ideas by asking about them. For example, to find out if students recognize that any shape can be decomposed into other shapes, you could give Grade 7 students this assignment:

  Show that you can combine two triangles to make any of these shapes: another triangle, a parallelogram, a rectangle, or a hexagon. Would the same be possible with three triangles?

Applying What You've Learned

1. What big ideas do you think contrasting the two parts of the chapter problem on page 15 is most linked to?

2. How could knowing the big ideas in measurement help teachers organize their teaching of measurement?

3. Provide two examples of topics taught in early grades (K–3), and two examples of topics taught in later grades (5–8) for each of the number big ideas listed.

4. Select either the data or geometry strand. Describe an activity which would elicit connections to other mathematical concepts, other subjects, or everyday experiences. Indicate why you think the activity elicits connections. Indicate if the activity is also likely to elicit other processes, which processes, and why.

5. How important do you think it is for primary teachers to be aware of proportional reasoning or algebraic reasoning? Explain.

6. Consider and discuss ways in which multiple representations or visualization play a role in the teaching of fractions.

7. Give three or four examples of how students might use reasoning in working with patterns or algebra.

Interact with a K–8 Student:

8. Use the activity you created for question 4 with a student. Describe evidence you observed that the process you expected was elicited.

Discuss with a K–8 Teacher:

9. Ask a teacher what he or she knows about big ideas, and how, or whether, he or she uses them in planning instruction.

10. Discuss with a teacher how he or she focuses on multiple representations or reasoning.

Selected References

Armstrong, T. (1999). *Seven kinds of smart: Identifying and developing your many intelligences.* New York: Plume.

Borko, H., and Putnam, R. (1995). Expanding a teacher's knowledge base: Cognitive psychological perspective on professional development. In Guskey, T., and Huberman, M. (Eds.). *Professional development in education: New paradigms and practices.* New York: Teacher's College Press, 35–65.

Charles, R. (2004). Big ideas and understandings as the foundation for elementary and middle school mathematics. *Journal of Mathematics Education Leadership, 7,* 9–24.

Clements, D.H. (2004). Major themes and recommendations. In Clements, D.H., and Sarama, J. (Eds.). *Engaging young children in mathematics: Standards for early childhood mathematics education.* Mahwah, NJ: Lawrence Erlbaum Associates, 7–72.

Dole, S. (2010). Making connections to the big ideas in mathematics: Promoting proportional reasoning. Available at http://research.acer.edu.au/research_conference/RC2010/17august/5/. Accessed July 22, 2014.

Kennedy, M. (1997). *Defining optimal knowledge for teaching science and mathematics (Research Monograph 10).* Madison, WI: National Institute for Science Education, University of Wisconsin.

Kieran, C. (2004). Algebraic thinking in the early grades. *The Mathematics Educator,* 8(1), 139–151.

Ministry of Education. (2003). *A guide to effective instruction in mathematics, Kindergarten to Grade 3: Number sense and numeration.* Toronto, ON: Queen's Printer for Ontario.

Ministry of Education. (2006). *A guide to effective instruction in mathematics, Kindergarten to Grade 6: Number sense and numeration, Grades 4 to 6, Vol. 1: The big ideas.* Toronto, ON: Queen's Printer for Ontario.

Ministry of Education (2012). Paying attention to proportional reasoning. Available at http://www.edu.gov.on.ca/eng/teachers/studentsuccess/ProportionReason.pdf. Accessed July 22, 2014.

Ministry of Education (2013). Paying attention to algebraic reasoning. Available at http://www.edugains.ca/resourcesLNS/MathematicsFoundationalPrinciples/PayingAttentiontoAlgebraicReasonin.pdf. Accessed July 22, 2014.

Ministry of Education (2014). Paying attention to spatial reasoning. Available at http://www.edu.gov.on.ca/eng/literacynumeracy/LNSPayingAttention.pdf. Accessed July 22, 2014.

National Council of Teachers of Mathematics (NCTM). (2000). *Principles and standards for school mathematics.* Reston, VA: National Council of Teachers of Mathematics.

Newcombe, N.S., and Huttenlocher, J. (2003). *Making space: The development of spatial representation and reasoning.* Cambridge, MA: The MIT Press.

Schifter, D., Bastable, V., and Russell, S.I. (1997). Attention to mathematical thinking: Teaching to the big ideas. In Friel, S., and Bright, G. (Eds.). *Reflecting on our work: NSF teacher enhancement in mathematics K–6.* Washington, DC: University Press of America, 255–261.

Small, M. (2009). *Big ideas from Dr. Small, Grades 4–8.* Toronto, ON: Nelson Education Ltd.

Small, M. (2010). *Big ideas from Dr. Small, Grades K–3.* Toronto, ON: Nelson Education Ltd.

Steen, L.A. (1990). *On the shoulders of giants: New approaches to numeracy.* Washington, DC: National Academy Press.

Van de Walle, J.A., Folk, S., Karp, K.S., and Bay–Williams, J.M. (2011). *Elementary and middle school mathematics: Teaching developmentally, Third Canadian edition.* Toronto, ON: Pearson Education Canada.

Chapter 3

Assessment and Evaluation

CHAPTER PROBLEM

Marble Mania

Tian will run a marble game at the school's fun fair. His game needs 300 marbles. He finds a store that sells marbles for the prices shown on the three bags.

a) How many marbles do you think are in the large bag? Show your work.

b) What do you think is the best way for Tian to buy the marbles? Give a reason for your answer.

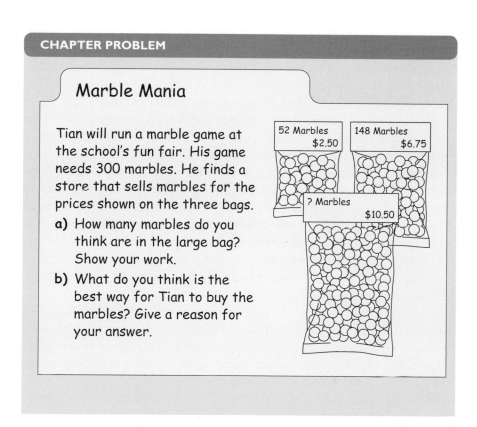

52 Marbles
$2.50

148 Marbles
$6.75

? Marbles
$10.50

IN A NUTSHELL

The main ideas in this chapter are listed below:

1. There are important differences between assessment, evaluation, and grading.

2. Assessment for learning and assessment as learning are a substantial part of the assessment a teacher should plan for.

3. Assessment data should be gathered in many ways and at different times to be reliable and valid. The most recent data is generally most relevant.

4. There are many types of assessment a teacher can use. The type of assessment used should reflect the purpose for gathering the data.

Introduction

In the past two decades, attention to assessment practices has been heightened. A focus has been placed on ensuring that assessments reflect their purpose, that students have a fair opportunity to demonstrate their knowledge, that scoring is appropriate and consistent, and that the results provide an accurate representation of what students know and can do.

Assessment is often defined as the gathering of data about student knowledge and/or skills, either informally or formally. Assessment for learning is designed primarily to help the teacher tailor instruction to the needs of the student. Assessment of learning is designed to inform a variety of stakeholders about what a student's knowledge and skills are at a particular point in time. It forms the basis of what is typically reported to parents and school officials. Assessment as learning focuses on the importance of students thinking about their own performance and learning from it. In the course of building an assessment plan, the teacher must identify strategies for gathering data on assessment for learning and assessment of learning, including the selection or creation of tests, rubrics, interview tools, etc.

Evaluation refers to making judgments about or assigning a "value" to student progress using the assessment data collected. Sometimes evaluation is based on a single task, for example, a summative chapter performance task. Other times, the teacher uses many different pieces of information to make a judgment about a student's progress.

Grading is the specific act of evaluating a set of data to report to students, parents, or education authorities.

Assessment for Learning

Assessment for learning is formative, not summative; the purpose is to identify strengths and weaknesses, not to rank students. Earl (2007) suggests that in assessment for learning, teachers use their knowledge of both the student and the curriculum to identify learning needs; they recognize that different students learn differently and use the information they gather to modify instruction appropriately where needed. In fact, she points out that the value of gathering such data is primarily to provide that corrective instruction.

Assessment for learning is important. A report by Black and Williams (1998) and work by Hattie and Timperley (2007) reveal that studies have consistently indicated that teacher improvement on formative assessment, particularly in the use of descriptive feedback, raises achievement and, in fact, helps low achievers more than others. It is also believed that the best feedback occurs during the performance of a task, rather than later. Hattie (2012) suggests that it is critical that assessment for learning include effective feedback to students, active involvement of students in their learning, and adjustment of instruction based on results of assessment.

Assessment as Learning

Assessment as learning is a particular form of assessment in which students use metacognition to more independently reflect on their own learning.

For students to learn how to do this, teachers might model and teach skills of self-assessment, while providing a safe environment in which students are able to take risks and then assess their successes (WNCP, 2006). Students benefit when teachers provide exemplars so that students can independently compare their work with those exemplars, or teachers provide or assist students in constructing success criteria (Ministry of Education, Ontario, 2010).

Although we can begin with self-assessment tools in which students simply indicate whether they think they have done well or not, we really want students to consider much more specifically what is good about what they have done or where they have weaknesses.

Assessment of Learning

Assessment of learning often has more than one purpose. It might be to provide information to others about whether or to what extent a student has mastered a certain piece of content. It might be to rank order students for some purpose.

Assessment of learning usually takes place at the end of a series of lessons, whereas assessment for learning and assessment as learning should be everyday occurrences.

How Assessment Has Changed

With the push of professional organizations like the National Council of Teachers of Mathematics and ministry and board officials, many teachers are using new ways to look at what is important in mathematics. Views on assessment have also changed. For many teachers, the focus is now on assessing each student's performance relative to the curriculum expectations/outcomes, rather than comparing students to each other. As well, many educators now want to gather information about a broader range of learning—the ability to solve problems, to communicate, to apply concepts, to reason, and to use procedures. Since the range of information needed is greater, a broader range of strategies and tools is required.

The most important change may be in the increased emphasis on assessment for learning and assessment as learning.

Characteristics of Good Assessment

Information about a student's knowledge and abilities needs to be collected from a variety of sources on many occasions to ensure that the information is reliable and valid. Teachers are encouraged to triangulate data, where the data comes from conversations, observations, and products. This might include written work, oral performance in class or in an interview situation, performance tasks, student self-assessment, and tests or quizzes. These are all discussed in greater depth as the chapter progresses. By combining these sources of information, a teacher gains a good sense of what a student knows or can do.

A Good Assessment Plan

A good overall assessment plan

- **balances the measurement of both mathematics content and processes:** The mathematics education community has come to value both the content knowledge and the process abilities that students acquire. For example, a student may be an excellent communicator, but misunderstand a certain piece of content; the reverse can also be true. By finding this out, the teacher knows where to place her or his emphasis.
- **is appropriate for its purpose:** If the teacher's goal is, for example, to collect information about student communication, it is important that the communication task be rich enough to allow for a broad range of performance in communication.
- **includes a variety of assessment formats:** Many students reveal a more accurate picture of their understanding using some assessment formats rather than others. Some show their understanding better in written situations, some by talking, and some by manipulating materials. Some students respond very well to the pressure of formal assessment, but some do not. Using many formats allows each student to show her or his best.
- **is aligned with student needs and expectations:** To have reliable information, it is important that students not be surprised by the task proposed in an assessment situation. The task can, and in assessment of learning situations usually should, be new to students, but it should be consistent with the way they have learned and the kinds of tasks they have met previously. Otherwise, performance may not really reflect the students' true level of understanding.
- **is fair to all students:** This is more likely if the teacher collects information from many types of tasks and allows certain accommodations, where appropriate. Some accommodations would be suggested in a student's individual educational plan. Other times, small adjustments are possible on the spot. For example, a student who was asked to explain something in words may instead be allowed to explain it using a diagram or by speaking into a recording device, such as a smart board recorder or an app on a tablet. A teacher may also offer a second chance at an assessment to acknowledge additional learning that has taken place after the first assessment opportunity and should recognize that there is no need to average both pieces of information—the later information is more current.
- **is useful in assisting students to assess their own learning:** It is important that students understand what is expected. When students complete an assessment task, they should have a sense of how well they have done. Whether it is through examples or descriptions,

students need to know how to look at their own work and assess themselves. This allows them to self-monitor and improve on their performance the next time.

- **measures growth over time:** The educational system is built around helping students grow academically, socially, physically, and emotionally. A teacher should always be focused on whether student understanding has improved, no matter what the level of the initial or final performance.
- **sets high, yet realistic, expectations for students:** Research has shown that students respond to teachers' expectations. Teachers who do not expect a lot do not get a lot, whether from their top students or from their weakest ones. Teachers who set higher, yet realistic, academic expectations are often gratified at how well all students perform.

Sample Assessment Plan

A complete assessment of a topic should involve all of the aspects discussed above. In considering a topic in the number strand, such as subtracting 3-digit numbers, a teacher might gather multiple data.

Initially, a teacher might gather diagnostic information about a student's readiness for the planned unit of instruction. The grain size of this diagnostic information might vary. It might be very global, describing a student's phase of development in mathematics as a whole, informing instruction over a series of units of instruction. It might be specific to a single unit and curriculum focused, assessing whether students bring the previous grade prerequisites for that unit to the instruction. It might be even more specific, looking for particular misconceptions students have that might inform instruction within that unit.

If the student is not ready, the teacher will certainly want to provide bridging activities and might well need to differentiate instruction during the teaching of the unit. If the student is well beyond the topic of instruction, the teacher will want to provide more enrichment activities.

Over the course of the unit of instruction, teachers might gather formative assessment data and, at the end of the unit, summative assessment data about the student's

- performance of the skill, for example, several computations to perform
- interpretation of the symbols, by asking students to describe a situation or display a model for a particular computation
- solution to a straightforward word problem where subtraction is required
- solution to a rich problem that involves subtracting, for example, "The difference between two 3-digit numbers is 472 less than their sum. What could the numbers be?"
- relevant communication and reasoning, for example, a question such as, "How can you use $346 - 125 = 221$ to calculate $345 - 126$?"
- use of estimation, for example, to determine whether a suggested answer is reasonable
- understanding of the "big picture," for example, a question such as, "Some people say that subtraction is the reverse of addition. Explain what they mean and why this might be useful to know."

Sample Assessment Tasks

Sometimes this information can be collected through the assignment of one broadly based task; other times it can be gleaned using a series of discrete questions or tasks.

A Performance Task The following performance task (**On the Move**) could be assigned at the end of a Grade 3 or 4 unit on addition and subtraction (assuming students have already completed a unit on data management). The task requires students to *subtract, relate subtraction to addition, estimate, use relationships,* and *calculate.* It also integrates previous learning about bar graphs. It is assumed that students have access to manipulatives and/or calculators while performing this task.

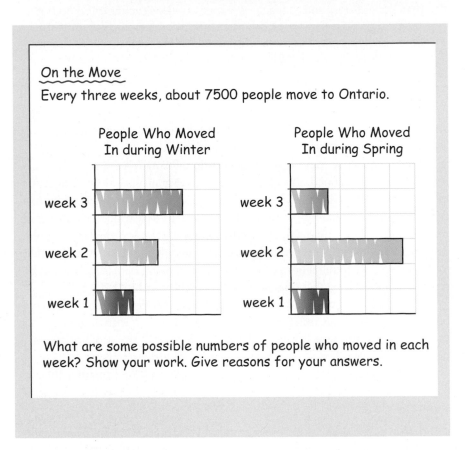

On the Move

Every three weeks, about 7500 people move to Ontario.

People Who Moved
In during Winter

People Who Moved
In during Spring

week 3

week 2

week 1

week 3

week 2

week 1

What are some possible numbers of people who moved in each week? Show your work. Give reasons for your answers.

Discrete Tasks For the topic of subtraction discussed above, a teacher might also choose to use a number of separate small tasks, such as those given below:

Several skills

1. a) 569   b) 312   c) 400   d) 621
   −245   −106   −223   −374

A question requiring the use of addition and subtraction principles

2. Create a new set of four subtraction questions with the same four answers as above.

A question relating to the meaning of the operation

3. Create two word problems, using different meanings of subtraction, where each is solved by one of the computations in Question 1.

A higher-level question involving synthesis or problem solving

4. Sometimes the answer when you subtract is more than what you subtracted. Sometimes it is less. When does each happen?

Framing Assessment Tasks for Specific Purposes

Once a teacher decides on what is to be assessed and in what format, the nature of the task or questions asked can still vary considerably. In each case, the teacher may learn something different about her or his students, and students may get a different impression about what mathematics is all about and what aspects of mathematics the teacher values.

Suppose, for example, that the teacher is interested in assessing students' ability to develop and use pattern rules to extend and describe patterns. The following is a brief list of choices the teacher might make and what information she or he could gather.

Assessment Tasks for Pattern Work

ASSESSMENT TASK	WHY WOULD THE TEACHER USE THIS APPROACH?
The pattern rule is: term value $= 3 \times$ term number $+ 2$. What is the 10th number in the pattern?	To determine students' ability to apply a simple pattern rule.
Model the pattern 3, 7, 11, 15, …. What does the model help you see about the pattern?	To determine students' ability to use various representations of a pattern to gain insight into that pattern.
The pattern is 3, 7, 11, 15, …. What is the pattern rule? Explain how you know.	To determine students' understanding of what a pattern rule is.
The pattern is 3, 7, 11, 15, …. How much greater is the 20th number in the pattern than the 10th number?	To determine students' insight into pattern behaviour. For example, some students will extend the pattern to calculate each term, and then find the difference. Some will develop the pattern rule: term value $= 4 \times$ term number $- 1$ and calculate the values for term number $= 10$ and term number $= 20$. Others will recognize that the difference has to be $10 \times 4 = 40$ because the numbers are 10 terms apart and the difference is always 4.
The pattern rule is: term number $= 4 \times$ term value $- 1$. In which position would you find the number 399?	To determine students' ability to use the pattern rule. This can give some insight into students' algebraic thinking. For example: A student might solve the equation $399 = 4 \times n - 1$ to discover the term number $= 100$.
Create three different patterns where 15 is the fourth term. Provide the pattern rule for each, telling how the term value relates to the term number. Calculate the 10th term in each pattern.	To determine students' ability to solve problems related to pattern.

Preparing Students for Assessment

For assessment to be useful, it is essential that students have a clear understanding of what the desired product looks like. This might involve preparing exemplar responses, might involve co-creating assessment/success criteria with students (Davies, 2007), and certainly involves being explicit with students about the goals of instruction at all times.

Wiggins (2004) discusses the importance of clarifying expectations. He talks about the necessity of providing frequent and "unequivocal" feedback and of relating particular aspects of performance not up to par with appropriate mediation. Guskey (2003) notes that teaching to the test is exactly what we should be doing if tests align to instruction. Keeping tests secret is not the point; the point is knowing whether students can reach a goal when they know that goal.

Evaluation Tools

Scoring of gathered data can be accomplished using a variety of tools—perhaps a scoring guide, a rubric, success criteria, or anecdotal comments, depending on what is appropriate for the task. With current technology, we can access information on paper, but also use clickers where answers are automatically collected or other digital tools.

A **scoring guide** is a document that suggests the assignment of points or marks for various aspects of a piece of work. For example, a question might ask a student to list three factors of 12, and then three multiples. The guide would indicate what performance is required for different numbers of marks.

A **rubric** categorizes responses in usually three, four, or five categories. It assigns a level of performance on a student task that allows for a wide range of performance. Often, the guide is descriptive. A rubric may be used to evaluate work on a rich problem, a portfolio, or a performance task.

If it is possible, rubrics should be shared, if not co-created, with a class prior to their use. Sometimes, the sharing of a rubric for a particular task may actually "give away" the strategies to be assessed; in that case, rubrics for a similar task might be shared. By knowing what is valued, students have the best opportunity to achieve those goals. Students can practise using the rubric to evaluate their own or a peer's work to really understand it.

It is useful if teachers within a school collaborate in the development and interpretation of rubrics. This consistency helps students make better sense of what is important.

Success criteria, which may be co–constructed with students or simply shared and discussed with them, tell the student what is expected for success on a task. Although frequently success criteria speak to how many solutions are needed, details of solutions, etc., they may be more process-oriented, for example, telling a student they must communicate something clearly or must represent something in several ways and discuss why each representation is helpful. For example:

TASK	POSSIBLE SUCCESS CRITERIA
Build a linking cube structure. Then build another structure with a volume 1¼ times as much. What might be the ratio of the surface areas?	• You build two structures with the correct volume relationship. • You correctly calculate the surface areas of both structures and correctly determine the ratio. • You use enough varied examples to draw some general conclusions about the ratios. • You clearly communicate why your findings make sense.

Anecdotal comments, that is, comments without any "score," are another way to evaluate student work. They provide useful feedback for a student, but can also be kept by the teacher to include in her or his bank of assessment information. Other times, the teacher will simply note that work has been done, and provide verbal feedback without keeping a permanent record.

Sources of Assessment Data

Some sources for classroom-based assessment data include the following:

- portfolios (which could include many of the following)
- performance tasks
- projects
- journals
- observations
- interviews
- homework
- exit passes
- tests and quizzes

In each case, the data might be gathered in a group setting or in an individual situation. Students might also assess themselves.

Portfolios

The purpose of an assessment portfolio is to serve as a record of growth related to a student's mathematical thinking. It can serve as the centrepiece of a student-led parent–teacher conference.

Sample Portfolio Items

Suppose the topic is multiplication of fractions. Any of these items might be included in a portfolio:

- a video or photo showing a student modelling a computation with manipulatives, or of a skit that models a certain computation
- a student-narrated video explaining how multiplication of fractions works
- an oral explanation using an app, of the solution to a problem
- a set of word problems showing that students understand different meanings of multiplication involving fractions
- a piece of writing in which students talk about how multiplication with fractions and multiplication with whole numbers are alike and how they are different
- a drawing that incorporates a number of different multiplications
- a problem involving multiplication, with a detailed solution
- a discussion of a mental math strategy involving multiplication of fractions

Evaluating Portfolios

The portfolio can be evaluated over time—each time with the teacher examining a small range of criteria. Some teachers also choose to evaluate attitude using a portfolio (Maxwell and Lassak, 2009). The teacher would likely use a rubric to guide this evaluation. The sample rubric from Cooper (2007), shown on page 44, could be used to evaluate a student-created portfolio. Notice that in this rubric, the strongest performance is shown on the right; in other cases, the strongest performance (usually Level 4) is shown on the left. There are cogent arguments for each approach.

In addition to this overall evaluation, the teacher should also provide feedback about both strengths and areas for growth. The categories used to describe the strengths and areas for growth will likely depend on jurisdictional focus. Individual items could be evaluated with other tools.

Portfolio Product Rubric

Name: _____ Date: _____

- Use this rubric to assess the contents of individual students' portfolios.
- Ideally, assess the portfolio with the student present.
- Do not attempt to assess everything in the portfolio. Remember, you are looking for evidence of the student's learning and growth.
- Each portfolio should be individualized by the student. Avoid looking for sameness or consistency.

CATEGORIES/CRITERIA	LEVEL 1	LEVEL 2	LEVEL 3	LEVEL 4
Contents	• **few** required pieces are included	• **most** required pieces are included	• **all** required pieces are included	
	• **few** student-selected pieces are included	• **some** student-selected pieces are included	• **required number** of student-selected pieces are included	
Thinking/Reflecting	• reflection sheets are **incomplete** and/or attached to **few** selections	• reflection sheets are partially complete and/or attached to **some** selections	• reflection sheets are complete and attached to **all** selections	• reflection sheets are detailed and attached to **all** selections
	• reflection sheets show **limited** evidence of thoughtfulness or insight	• reflections sheets show **some** evidence of thoughtfulness and/or insight	• reflection sheets show **clear** evidence of thoughtfulness and insight	• reflection sheets show **rich** evidence of thoughtfulness and insight
	• selections reflect a **limited** understanding of the portfolio process (i.e., purposeful collecting, selecting, and reflecting on pieces to improve learning)	• selections demonstrate **some** understanding of the portfolio process (i.e., purposeful collecting, selecting, and reflecting on pieces to improve learning)	• selections demonstrate a **solid** understanding of the portfolio process (i.e., purposeful collecting, selecting, and reflecting on pieces to improve learning)	• selections demonstrate a **thorough** understanding of the portfolio process (i.e., purposeful collecting, selecting, and reflecting on pieces to improve learning)
	• selections demonstrate **little** originality or creativity	• selections demonstrate **some** originality and/or creativity (e.g., a creative mind map)	• selections **demonstrate** originality and/or creativity (e.g., a creative mind map)	• selections demonstrate a **high degree** of originality and/or creativity (e.g., a creative mind map)
	• selections demonstrate **little** evidence of growth and learning over time (e.g., initial and revised responses to questions; first and revised written drafts)	• some selections **demonstrate** growth and learning over time (e.g., initial and revised responses to questions; first and revised written drafts)	• **several** selections demonstrate growth and learning over time (e.g., initial and revised responses to questions; first and revised written drafts)	• **many** selections clearly **demonstrate** growth and learning over time (e.g., initial and revised responses to questions; first and revised written drafts)
Organization	• portfolio contents **lack organization** into the required sections and sections are not labelled clearly (e.g., first drafts, personal reflections)	• portfolio contents are **partially organized** into the required sections and sections are labelled to some degree (e.g., first drafts, personal reflections)	• portfolio contents are **appropriately organized** into the required sections and sections are labelled appropriately (e.g., first drafts, personal reflections)	• portfolio contents are **highly organized** into the required sections and sections are clearly labelled for ease of use (e.g., first drafts, personal reflections)

Performance Tasks

Performance tasks, as noted earlier, are rich tasks that allow students to show what they know about a topic. A performance task is designed so that process can be examined as well as product. It should be consistent with curricular goals, ideally representing the "big ideas" of the content being explored. It should be authentic, rich, and engaging, requiring active participation by students, and open ended enough to allow exceptional students to show how far they can go with it. It is, of course, also important that a performance task be achievable in a reasonable amount of time and that it be accessible to all students at some level.

Name Patterns

Nisha uses different-sized square grids to write her name over and over. The grids have fewer than 50 squares.

a) What size grid can she use that will have full copies of her name? Explain your thinking.

b) Use names with different numbers of letters to fill a 6 by 6 grid with full copies of the names. What names did you use? Choose one. Explain why it works.

c) How does the number of letters in the name relate to the size of the grid?

Possible Solution

a) NISHA has 5 letters so the grid has to have a number of squares that can be divided by 5 with no remainder.
5, 10, 15, 20, 25, 30, 35, 40, 45
The grid also has to be a square so the grid must have 25 squares (5 by 5.)

b) I used names with 2 letters, AL, 3 letters, IAN, and 4 letters, LISA. Here's what I did for LISA:

L	I	S	A	L	I
S	A	L	I	S	A
L	I	S	A	L	I
S	A	L	I	S	A
L	I	S	A	L	I
S	A	L	I	S	A

A 6 by 6 grid has 36 squares. LISA has 4 letters. 4 divides evenly into 36 so LISA can be written 9 times in the grid.

c) The number of squares in the grid can be divided by the number of letters with no remainder.

Sample Performance Task

Notice that the **Name Patterns** task has a student-friendly context and is open ended. It could be assigned after a Grade 4 or 5 unit on patterns. In this task, the student must

- solve a problem
- communicate
- apply a pattern rule
- relate patterns to number

Some educators focus on the value of using open-ended assessments to learn more deeply about the student as well as to engage some students who do not respond as fully to closed items (Leatham, Lawrence, and Mewborn, 2005).

This could, at times, lead to a focus on how many responses a student gives, rather than the quality of those responses. Even in a question that asks students to provide many responses, it should still be the quality of those responses that matters most.

Evaluating Performance Tasks

A performance task would generally be assessed using a rubric. Sometimes, the rubric is a combination of various relevant generic process rubrics. Some teachers use a more general performance task rubric, while others create task-specific rubrics.

A specific rubric for a task requiring Grade 8 students to solve problems relating to surface areas of prisms and cylinders is shown on page 47.

Observation

Observational data is collected on an ongoing basis. This is not just a matter of getting a sense of a student's overall progress; it is a deliberate process to provide insight into a particular aspect of a student's performance.

Observing Mathematical Performance

For example, the teacher might be observing any of the following aspects of performance:

- regularity of use of mental math strategies and estimation
- regularity of computational or careless errors
- appropriate, or inappropriate, use of calculators
- a student's understanding of a particular concept
- clarity of a student's oral mathematical communication, and the use of correct math language and terminology
- a student's ability to use manipulative materials to model a concept
- insightfulness of a student's approach
- whether a student relates new ideas to previously learned concepts by making important connections
- problem solving ability
- perseverance in solving problems
- correct use of pencil and paper computation
- originality of a student's responses
- a student's comfort with predicting and the reasonableness of the student's predictions
- regularity with which a student considers the reasonableness of his or her responses
- how likely a student is to consider all possibilities

Surface Area and Volume Rubric

CURRICULUM OUTCOME	EXCELLENT	PROFICIENT	ADEQUATE	LIMITED
Determine the surface area of • right rectangular prisms, • right triangular prisms, and • right cylinders in order to solve problems	Easily recognizes when a problem requires the determination of surface area	Correctly recognizes when a problem requires the determination of surface area	Does not always recognize when a problem requires the determination of surface area	Rarely recognizes when a problem requires the determination of surface area
	Efficiently applies formulas and relationships to determine surface area of prisms or cylinders	Correctly determines surface area of prisms or cylinders	Sometimes correctly determines surface area of prisms or cylinders	Rarely correctly determines surface area of prisms or cylinders
	Correctly solves complex problems involving surface area of prisms or cylinders	Correctly solves reasonably straightforward problems involving surface area of prisms or cylinders	Solves problems involving rectangular prisms, but struggles to solve problems involving other prisms	Struggles to solve problems involving surface area of prisms or cylinders

Teachers might create a chart with a short checklist listing some of the behaviours or performances they are looking for along the top of a sheet of paper, and the students' names along the left side. They could carry a clipboard and check off instances of observing the desired behaviours for various students.

Interviews

With younger students and students who primarily operate in a language other than the one of instruction (Fernandes, Anhalt, and Civil, 2009), interviews are essential for gathering reliable information. An interview differs from observation in that the starting question is more formally planned.

In an interview situation, the teacher can ensure that a student understands the question or task being posed, and can add scaffolding questions where appropriate. Teachers of older elementary students tend not to use interviews as often as primary teachers, but they remain an effective way to gather information.

To create an interview, a teacher would focus on the important curricular goals of a unit of work and develop a few critical questions around those goals. An example of a summary sheet to guide an interview with a young student during a measurement unit is shown below.

Sample Interview Summary Sheet

MATERIALS	WATCH AND LISTEN FOR CHECKLIST
Provide a metre stick, a 30-cm ruler, and some ribbons or strands of yarn in the following lengths and colours: red (10 cm) blue (25 cm) green (50 cm) orange (1 m) brown (4 m)	❑ Uses measurement terms such as "longer" and "shorter" to describe relative lengths ❑ Orders items by length ❑ Chooses an appropriate measuring tool and unit, and justifies the choice ❑ Uses a measuring tool correctly to measure length ❑ Estimates lengths

QUESTIONS/PROMPTS

- Which ribbon is the shortest? the longest?
- How can you put the ribbons in order from shortest to longest?
- Which measuring tool, the ruler or the metre stick, would you use to measure the longest ribbon? Why?
- How long is the shortest ribbon?
- About how many times do you think the blue ribbon would fit along the length of the metre stick?

Managing Interviews

Below are some pointers about interviewing students:

- Use interviews when your intention is to be interactive, and use a student's responses to probe further.
- Forewarn students that when you ask why, it does not mean they are wrong, but that you want to understand their thinking.
- Take notes to be sure that what is said can be recalled. You might use a video, which can be reviewed later. Videos are an excellent medium for showing parents some responses and how they can be interpreted to show understanding.
- Try not to be judgmental during the interview. Absence of criticism should encourage a student to respond comfortably.

- Interview two or three students at one time to be efficient when it is possible. It is critical to plan for what each student will be doing during the interviews. For example, one student might answer a question, and then you ask the other student if she or he agrees, and why.
- Pay attention to the kinds of questions a student asks during the interview. This can provide great insight into a student's level of understanding.
- Ask questions and assign tasks that involve performing or interacting. For example, if the topic were the modelling of algebraic expressions for a Grade 7 or 8 student, the following interview questions might be asked:

Appropriate Interview Questions About Representing Algebraic Expressions

- Choose 4 algebra tiles. What algebraic expressions can you model?
- How would the expressions change if you turned over 2 of your tiles?
- Show how you can model expressions that can be written as one algebraic term using 4 tiles.
- Show how you can model expressions that can be written as the sum of two algebraic terms using 4 tiles.

Criteria for Evaluating Performance in an Interview

A teacher might want to use a standard form to record interview results, such as that shown on page 48 (Sample Interview Summary Sheet). Normally, the results of an interview would then be described as anecdotal comments. Alternatively, a teacher might be prepared to check off a performance level on a rubric describing a student's ability to communicate or a student's problem-solving ability.

Exit Passes

An exit pass is a question or set of questions to which a student responds at the end of a class. Presumably the student must submit the exit pass to actually leave the classroom.

The value of an exit pass is that the teacher gains immediate feedback about the understanding of each student in the class and can use that feedback to tailor instruction in the subsequent lesson.

For example, if a Grade 7 or 8 lesson focused on the formula for the area of a circle, the exit pass might be something like: *Someone says that you can figure out the area of a circle if the only thing you have is a ruler. Do you agree or disagree? Explain.*

Tests and Quizzes

Tests and quizzes are generally time-constrained situations where students' answers show their understanding and knowledge although, increasingly, teachers are realizing that it is not so much about what students know quickly, but what they know; many teachers are now allowing extra time. Quizzes can often be completed fairly quickly. They are particularly useful for very straightforward skill assessment, and the assessment of some conceptual understanding and simple application of knowledge. They are also useful for providing immediate feedback.

Tests can also be used to test skills, application, and simple concepts, but because of their length, it is sometimes also possible to assess some process skills, whether problem solving, communication, reasoning, etc. In addition to this, tests act as preparation for large-scale assessments.

Sample Items for Tests and Quizzes

Suppose the topic is the representation of numbers up to 1000. Some sample items are shown below.

Sample Quiz Items for Representing Numbers to 1000

SKILLS	CONCEPTS	PROBLEM SOLVING

• Write each number:
  a) nine hundred eight
  b) 3 hundreds + 4 tens
  c) 200 + 40 + 3
• What number is 200 less than 436?
  What number is 20 less?
  What number is 2 less?
• Which is greater: 387 or 378?
	• What is the least number of base ten blocks you can use to represent 348? Explain how you know.
	• How could you use 33 base ten blocks to represent 348?
	• Find three ways to make this true and explain your thinking: ▊28 > 3▊4
		• How many 3-digit numbers can you create with the digits 2, 3, and 0? Which is greatest? How do you know?
		• There are three odd numbers with three digits each. The second is 244 greater than the first. The third is 202 greater than the second. The sum of the digits of the first number is 5. What could the three numbers be?

Creating Tests and Quizzes

Many teachers encourage students to contribute items for tests or quizzes. Once students have seen prototypes for the level and types of items that the teacher is seeking, they enjoy becoming question writers. They need to realize that not every question they write will be used, but including a student's question on a quiz is very affirming to that student.

It may be appropriate to allow for some choice when students write a test. For example, if there are several items that would allow a student to show understanding of the concept of prime numbers, it may be appropriate to allow a student to choose one of the two or three items.

Depending on a student's reading comprehension level, it may be necessary to revise test questions for some students by

- allowing students some choice in the way they represent their understanding
- simplifying language by using shorter sentences, defining words, and paraphrasing to exclude extraneous words
- including graphics (such as charts, graphs, pictures, and maps)

Whatever instruments are used to gather data—a test or quiz, an interview, observations, or a task of some sort—it is essential that a teacher attend to what aspects of the curriculum are important so that the instruments reflect this.

Homework

Teachers can discover a great deal about a student's mathematical learning by examining a student's homework. It has potential value as assessment for learning. However, using homework as assessment of learning is problematic for two reasons. The first is that homework is meant to be a learning opportunity, so mistakes should not be penalized. The second is that a teacher cannot really know how much support a student received in completing the homework. Completion of homework may be measured, as it could be part of assessing a student's disposition and learning skills, but making judgments about level of performance is more problematic.

Keeping Track

With the large amount of data that teachers might collect, it is important that they develop tracking tools that are useful.

A summary sheet for a unit of work for each student might include references to the curricular goals being assessed, both content and process; a summary of anecdotal records from observations or homework; and a summary of interview, quiz, test, and task data.

Assessing Processes

Because of the attention to the mathematical processes, it is important that teachers become comfortable assessing them, particularly problem solving and communication.

Assessing Problem Solving

Performance on a rich problem can be evaluated using a rubric. Some teachers teach in jurisdictions where there are common generic rubrics. Some rubrics are designed according to the stages of the problem-solving or inquiry process: Understand the Problem, Make a Plan, Carry Out the Plan and Look Back, and Communicate, whereas others are more holistic.

The following task and the rubric on the next page was used to assess problem solving with respect to the four stages.

Sample Assessment Task: Problem Solving

PROBLEM

Every year the school fair has the same two problems. They run out of some balloon colours and have lots of other colours left over. Also, they run out of hot dogs, but have lots of popcorn left over.

Do a survey to help the school-fair planners solve these problems.

Present your results and recommendations.

SAMPLE SOLUTION

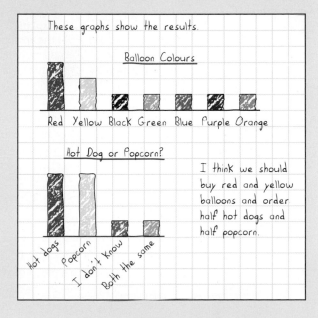

I asked 10 people:
Which colour balloon do you like? Pick one colour.
Do you like popcorn or hot dogs more?

Here is what they picked for favourite balloon colour: red, yellow, yellow, black, red, green, red, blue, purple, orange
Here is what they picked from hot dogs or popcorn: hot dogs, hot dogs, popcorn, popcorn, hot dogs, I don't know, popcorn, hot dogs, popcorn, both the same

These graphs show the results.

Balloon Colours

Red Yellow Black Green Blue Purple Orange

Hot Dog or Popcorn?

Hot dogs Popcorn I don't know Both the same

I think we should buy red and yellow balloons and order half hot dogs and half popcorn.

ASSESSMENT

This is Level 3 problem solving because the student

- did not make it clear that he or she understood the real issue raised in the problem
- modelled the problem correctly by realizing that he or she had to ask questions related to both balloon colours and food and present the results and recommendations
- solved the problem to a reasonable extent by creating somewhat appropriate questions, but the solution has some minor flaws because the first question did not sufficiently limit responses, and neither question included any reference to the school-fair context
- communicated his or her results by creating appropriate and correct graphs to present the data, and making recommendations that reflected the results

Sample Problem-Solving Rubric,

CRITERIA	LEVEL 1	LEVEL 2	LEVEL 3	LEVEL 4
Understand the Problem	Does not seem to understand the problem	Does not make it clear that s/he understands the problem	Appears to understand the problem	Explicitly addresses the issues raised in the problem
Make a Plan	Struggles to model the problem	Models part of the problem	Models the problem correctly	Models the problem in an efficient or creative way
Carry Out the Plan/Look Back	Solution is seriously flawed due to major errors in procedures; student gives up if plan does not work	Solution is faulty due to several errors in procedures; student is hesitant to change plan	Solution is correct, though there may be minor procedural errors; student revises the plan as necessary	Solution is correct and there are few, if any, errors in procedures; student is flexible about the plan and revises it as necessary
Communicate	Provides an incomplete explanation of the results that is unclear and/or imprecise	Provides a partial explanation of the results that is somewhat clear and precise	Provides a complete, clear, and precise explanation of the results	Provides a thorough, clear, and insightful explanation of the results)

Another source for problem-solving rubrics is Cooper (2007), and many others are available on the Internet.

Assessing Communication

Student communication is an important component of mathematics performance. Teachers may set a task that includes a communication component or a task focused primarily on communication. Teachers may evaluate a piece of writing using a generic communication rubric or create a task-specific rubric. As with problem solving, some jurisdictions provide generic communication rubrics that could be applied to any communication task.

It is important to note that an accurate assessment of communication requires that a student be willing to share his or her knowledge and understanding. This can only happen in a climate where risk taking is encouraged and supported.

A good piece of writing should be mathematically correct and can be assessed with respect to any of the following criteria:

- explanation and justification of mathematical concepts, procedures, and problem solving
- organization of material (written, spoken, or drawn)
- use of mathematical vocabulary
- use of mathematical representations (graphs, charts, and diagrams)
- use of mathematical conventions (units, symbols, and labels)

Can you estimate to decide which grade has more students or do you need to find an exact total? Explain.

Number of students in each class			
Grade 3	27	32	31	28
Grade 4	30	22	25	26

you don't need an exact number because grade 3 had a higher number except for one e and that was only by 3.

Student Response

This student's communication is clear, organized, precise, and concise.

Sample Assessment Task

The following task and the rubric on the next page was used to assess communication with respect to understanding of fractions concepts for a student in Grade 4.

This is Level 3 communication because

- some explanations are partial but with some clarity and logic
- organization is sufficient but not effective
- there is clear and precise use of some (but not a broad range of) mathematics vocabulary
- there are representations of two meanings of a fraction. There is a vague reference to another meaning (pattern block), but it is not followed through.
- the diagrams are labelled; the convention for showing a fraction is used correctly

Tell at least 3 things about $\frac{1}{6}$.

$\frac{1}{6}$ is a fraction

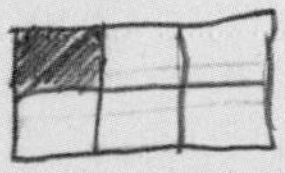

1 is the numerator
6 is the denominator
its not a lot
You need 6 things to use $\frac{1}{6}$

$\frac{1}{6}$ XXXXXX
A pattern block can be $\frac{1}{6}$

Sample Communication Rubric

CRITERIA	LEVEL 1	LEVEL 2	LEVEL 3	LEVEL 4
Explanation and Justification of Mathematical Concepts, Procedures, and Problem Solving	Provides incomplete or inaccurate explanations/justifications that lack clarity or logical thought, using minimal words, pictures, symbols, and/or numbers	Provides partial explanations/justifications that exhibit some clarity and logical thought, using simple words, pictures, symbols, and/or numbers	Provides complete, clear, and logical explanations/justifications, using appropriate words, pictures, symbols, and/or numbers	Provides thorough, clear, and insightful explanations/justifications, using a range of words, pictures, symbols, and/or numbers
Organization of Material (written, spoken, or drawn)	Organization is minimal and seriously impedes communication	Organization is limited but does not seriously impede communication	Organization is sufficient to support communication	Organization is effective and aids communication
Use of Mathematical Vocabulary	Uses very little mathematical vocabulary, and vocabulary used lacks clarity and precision	Uses a limited range of mathematical vocabulary with some degree of clarity and precision	Uses mathematical vocabulary with sufficient clarity and precision to communicate ideas	Uses a broad range of mathematical vocabulary to communicate clearly and precisely
Use of Mathematical Representations (graphs, charts, or diagrams)	Uses representations that exhibit minimal clarity and accuracy, and are ineffective in communicating	Uses representations that lack clarity and accuracy, though not sufficient to impede communication	Uses representations that are sufficiently clear and accurate to communicate	Uses representations that are clear, precise, and effective in communicating
Use of Mathematical Conventions (units, symbols, or labels)	Few conventions are used correctly	Some conventions are used correctly	Most conventions are used correctly	Almost all conventions are used correctly

Another source for communication rubrics is Cooper (2007), and others are available on the Internet.

Self-Assessment

Many teachers recognize the value of having students assess their own work; it is with self-assessment that students become independent learners. Many of the rubrics described previously for communication and problem solving can be used by students to self-evaluate with assessment as learning in mind. Another option is to use a guide like the one on the next page for self-assessment after a unit on graphing.

It is important to cultivate students' objectivity in looking at their own work. Some students find it either too easy or too difficult to criticize themselves. Students need to be helped to attend to details.

Sample Self-Assessment Guide

I CAN ...	HOW OFTEN?		
Draw a bar graph where each square is worth 1.	Not often	Sometimes	Usually
Draw a bar graph with a simple scale where each square is worth 2 or 5.	Not often	Sometimes	Usually
Read a pictograph with a scale.	Not often	Sometimes	Usually
Decide which symbol to use for a pictograph with a scale.	Not often	Sometimes	Usually
Solve simple problems that use information from graphs.	Not often	Sometimes	Usually
Read a circle graph.	Not often	Sometimes	Usually

Some self-assessment may be more "affective." A list of unfinished statements to which students might respond and which would provide valuable information for the teacher could include the following:

- When I got stuck, I ...
- I explained my work best when I ...
- I checked to see if I was right when I ...
- I explained my work in a mathematical way when I ...
- What I understood best was ...
- I need to find out more about ...

Group Assessment

One of the difficulties a teacher in today's classroom faces is dealing with individual evaluations when many activities are performed in a group setting. Many educators believe that group work is critical, not only because it mirrors real-life situations where adults work on teams to accomplish projects, but also because of the belief that the interaction within a group facilitates learning. The issues are varied. One concern is how to or whether to assign individual scores to different members of the group. Another is how to or whether to evaluate performance as a group member. The issue is, of course, ensuring that any evaluation is perceived as—and actually is—fair and equitable.

Sometimes it is perfectly reasonable to treat the group as a whole and use any of the rubrics or schemes previously discussed to describe the group's performance. The difficulty some teachers have is deciding whether to use that same evaluation to describe the work of each group member. (See *Including Group Evaluations* on page 58.)

Using Technology in Assessment

It makes sense, now that we live in an age of technology, that we use technology in formal assessment situations as well as during instruction. Ellemore-Collins and Wright (2008) discuss how they use videotaped interviews. They point out how the videotape allows the teacher to examine and then re-examine, perhaps with other colleagues, student responses to better understand the student's thinking. Similar alternatives are apps like Explain Everything or Show Me or the use of Educreations.

"Clickers" are used in many classrooms to promote instant feedback. A clicker is a personal response device that allows the holder, the student, to register a response that is instantly received by the teacher. One of the advantages of a clicker to a student is that his or her response is private; there is no need to worry about how others might perceive the response. One of the advantages to the teacher is a quick read on whether an idea is or is not understood by most students. A low-tech alternative is the mini white board. Each student has a mini white board and dry erase marker. He or she holds up the board in response to a teacher question. This, too, is relatively private and the teacher can get a quick read on the class's understanding.

These days many students show their learning using tweets, blogs, or other sorts of web pages. The creativity students often demonstrate in these alternative media may give a richer insight into what students know or can do. For example, a student might be asked to use a 140-character tweet as an exit pass.

Technology can also be used to translate questions into another language or provide visual support for assessment tasks.

Interpreting Assessment Results

When a student is successful on an assessment, we usually do not reflect back on whether the assessment was valid, although we probably should. But what if a student does not do well? What should we be thinking?

Perhaps it is important to look at the teacher's role first. It may be that the student really understood the concept, but the wording of the question or task was flawed and the student did not understand what was being asked. Perhaps the lack of success is an indication that the instruction was not appropriate for that student. Only later, after these reasons have been exhausted, should we assume that the student does not understand.

Guskey (2003) suggests that for whatever reason the student is not successful, a second chance is appropriate. We have no problems giving aspiring drivers second chances to pass a driver's test; it is only whether the driver is successful eventually that matters. The same rationale could apply to a classroom assessment; a student's success on a second try should be equally valuable if our goal is not to rank students but to assess understanding. It is important that we model the notion that we learn through our mistakes by allowing for these second chances.

Grading and Reporting

One of a teacher's important tasks is communicating assessment information to students and their parents. There are many opportunities to communicate about particular items of work, and these have been discussed earlier. At some point, though, these assessments must be integrated into an overall grade or mark. The following discussion details some of the issues surrounding this aspect of a teacher's work.

Anecdotal versus Letter Grades or Percents

Some teachers are not required to report a single or small set of measures about a student, but can describe student work in anecdotal ways. These teachers may use a student's portfolio as the centrepiece of a student-led conference with parents. The student is an active participant in talking to his or her parents about his or her mathematical knowledge. Sample items from the portfolio will clarify the comments the parents may have received from the teacher.

Other teachers are expected to find a way to summarize anecdotal data, rubric measures, and numerical scores into a single measure to describe student achievement. Circumstances will vary, so how this summary can be accomplished is affected by local practice, but some principles are fairly universal. These teachers must make some decision about weighting the various pieces of data collected.

The percentages in each case should depend on the amount of data from each source and the reliability and currency of the data from that source. If, for example, in an upper grade class, there had been only one test on a topic, but many pieces of work were submitted for a portfolio and a number of inter-views were held, it might make more sense to weight tests and quizzes less.

Other times, a teacher sorts the assessment information in other ways. A teacher may determine an overall performance level for each of the achievement categories, for example, understanding concepts, applying procedures, communication, and problem solving. Then the performance in the categories is weighted according to jurisdiction-based, school-based, or personal weightings.

Using Discretion

Even once the percentages or weightings are decided, teachers should feel free to exercise some latitude. Suppose a teacher administers a test and a student's performance is significantly lower than all of the other evidence that the teacher has collected for performance on that topic. A teacher should feel free to take this information under advisement, rather than simply feel obligated to factor it in as planned. Alternatively, some teachers reasonably choose to give a lower weight to scores on work collected early in a report-ing period since the work at the end of that period is more likely to be a more accurate demonstration of students' understanding of the relevant material.

Quality of data should always trump quantity. Teachers may provide many opportunities for students to show their understanding and collect a great deal of data. But sometimes less formal data collection, with a focus on data that is more telling, might make more sense.

Pitfalls of Percent Grades

It should be noted that using letter grades or rubric descriptors is generally preferable, where the choice exists, to using percent grades. There are sev-eral reasons for this.

Categorical data is more reliable. A student who earns a B or a score of excellent is likely to earn the same score even if the teacher were to select slightly different tasks to assess this student. It is much less certain that a score of 92% would remain that exact score with slightly different ques-tions. Thus, the categorical score is more reliable.

The use of percent scores seems to focus students on what they get wrong instead of what they get right. This is not as affirming to students as it should be.

The use of percent scores seems to set up some unhealthy competitions. For example, a student who scores 92% cannot realistically be seen as one who knows more than a student who scores 91% on a particular test or quiz.

Including Group Evaluations

Two reasonable positions can be taken on this matter. One is that the purpose of the group work is to learn, but the ultimate goal is individual accountability; for this reason, only scores on individual assessments are used in computing a mark. The other position is that performance within the group should be evaluated. Some teachers assign all members of the group the same mark, with the understanding that it is the group's responsibility to ensure that all participants have earned that evaluation. Many teachers provide the opportunity for students in the group to report on how the work was shared and to compare, usually in advance of the teacher's evaluation, the relative performance of group members.

Weighting Schemes

Teachers of Grades 4 to 8 might use this weighting scheme:

Observations 30%
Portfolio 30%
Performance tasks 15%
Interviews and journal 10%
Tests and quizzes 15%

A primary teacher might use a scheme like this:

Observations 50%
Portfolio 40%
Interviews and journal 10%

Evaluations Based on Observation Assessment Data

Some teachers are still reluctant to use observation data in a formal way when weighting performance measures. They worry that this information is too subjective, but this concern is probably unwarranted. Assuming that the information was collected systematically and that it focused on academic performance and not on other aspects of student behaviour, it is as meaningful as written work.

Ultimately, a teacher's role is to use the information collected in the most meaningful way to communicate to students and their parents what they need to know to maximize a student's mathematical potential.

Large-Scale Assessment

Canada, along with most other developed countries, has embraced a significant amount of testing in mathematics. Some districts, boards, or provinces test in every grade, and others test in selected grades. Some tests are administered to every student, whereas others are administered only to a sampling of students. There are also pan-Canadian and international tests in which many Canadian students participate, including the Pan-Canadian Assessment Program (PCAP), sponsored by the Council of Ministers of Education across the country, and international tests like Third International Math and Science Study (TIMSS). The value of participation in these programs is to provide awareness of where successes have been achieved and where improvement could be useful.

Most provincial and local tests are built around curriculum expectations/outcomes for the jurisdiction, whereas national and international tests, by their very nature, cannot be as specific.

The form of these assessments varies a great deal. Below are some sample assessment items that reflect the types of items that appear on some Canadian provincial tests. Some items are multiple choice, some require explanations, and some require work to be shown, but not explanations.

GRADE 3

Which equation is true when the value of ☐ is 13?

A. $40 - 8 = 17 + ☐$

B. $40 - 8 = 18 + ☐$

C. $40 - 8 = 19 + ☐$

D. $40 - 8 = 20 + ☐$

The shape below has many pairs of angles that are equal. The two angles in one pair have been each marked with an *a*.

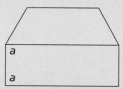

Find other pairs of equal angles.

Mark each pair with a different letter.

Compare each pair to a right angle.

GRADE 4

This chart shows the drink containers collected in one week. Create a bar graph on the grid to show the information in the chart.

Container	Number of Containers
4-L jugs	4
Juice boxes	80
Water bottles	27
Cans	16

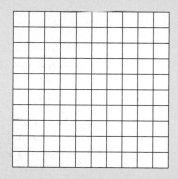

GRADE 6

A certain integer is

• less than –3,

• greater than –10, and

• closer to –10 than to –3.

Which could it be?

A. –2

B. –5

C. –8

D. –11

Cody built a model of a box kite with 5 identical cubes as shown below. The dimensions of each cube are 2 cm × 2 cm × 2 cm.

He wants to paint the outside of the model kite with a special paint that costs $0.75 for each 1 cm².

How much will it cost to paint the model? Show your work.

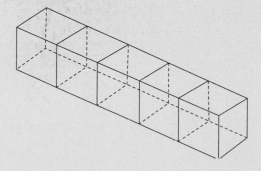

GRADE 6

The area of one face of a cube is 6 cm².
What is the surface area?

A.   12 cm²

B.   18 cm²

C.   24 cm²

D.   36 cm²

GRADE 7

Jennifer and her siblings earn points for chores. They use the points for special treats or events, such as movies. Jennifer earned 65 points. She did **at least one** of each type of chore.

Find all of the different combinations of chores she might have done to earn 65 points. Show ALL your work.

Points for chores:
5 points for small chores,
10 points for bigger chores, or
20 points for very big chores.

Preparing Students for Large-Scale Assessment

Since these large-scale assessments have likely become permanent, it is important to ensure both that the data collected is reliable and that students are as comfortable as possible when taking these tests.

Most importantly, teachers must encourage students to do their best, but not to be overly concerned if there are unfamiliar questions or material on the tests. Students should be made aware that many students take the test, so the items reflect many possible topics, not all of which may be familiar to each and every student. In some jurisdictions, teachers include the score on these tests as a small factor in their evaluation of student progress. This ensures that students take the assessment seriously, but reflects the fact that the situation may not be a completely fair assessment of what a particular student has had the opportunity to learn.

It is important that students are familiar with the formats of the types of questions they might meet on these large-scale assessments, whether it is a question that requires them to explain their thinking or a multiple-choice question. At the same time, it is not a good use of student time to spend excessive numbers of class hours practising previous year items. The goal should not be to do well on the test; the goal should be to understand the curriculum. If that happens, the rest will come.

Many of the earlier parts of this chapter have addressed more open-ended questions, but below is some material to consider about acquainting students with the multiple-choice format.

Multiple-Choice Question Formats

Multiple-choice questions are one of the formats used frequently on large-scale assessments. However, many young students are unfamiliar with them. First of all, students may need practice in using "bubble" or optical scanning papers. They may also need some suggestions for pacing themselves, for example, going through and responding to the questions they are sure of first, and then returning to other items. Students also need practical suggestions for ways to respond to these types of questions, as well as some experience with them. The teacher might create some practice multiple-choice questions or use released samples from various ministries of education or testing agencies.

Distracters Good distracters (the wrong answers on a multiple-choice test) are important. They are not meant to trick students; they are meant to be answers that students with misconceptions will find attractive. In this way, the teacher is able to revise instruction appropriately. Ideas for distracters can be gathered by looking through student work to find typical errors.

Understanding Multiple-Choice Distracters

EXAMPLE	DISCUSSION
Which shape is a triangle-based pyramid? 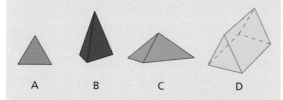	**A.** might "distract" students who are only comfortable with names of 2-D shapes **B.** is the correct response **C.** might "distract" students whose interpretation of pyramid is only the traditional square pyramid **D.** might "distract" students who do not distinguish between prisms and pyramids
Sam described how you can cut a parallelogram into other shapes. Which description is not true? 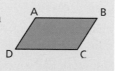 **A.** You can make two congruent triangles. **B.** You can make two congruent parallelograms. **C.** You can make two non-congruent parallelograms. **D.** You can make two non-congruent triangles.	**A.** might "distract" students who believe that, when you cut a shape, you have to end up with the same shape that you started with **B.** might "distract" students who think only about vertical cuts **C.** might "distract" students who think only in terms of cutting into halves **D.** is the correct response

Using Logical Reasoning to Eliminate Answers Students should be encouraged to use logical reasoning to eliminate unreasonable answers. For example, consider the question below:

What number below is the 45th term in the pattern 4, 10, 16, 22, ...?

a) 55

b) 268

c) 49

d) 190

All the numbers in the pattern so far are even, and they have to stay even because you're adding an even number. So it can't be a) 55 or c) 49.

Students can use logical reasoning to eliminate possibilities.

By recognizing that all the numbers in the pattern have to be even (because evens are added to evens), students can immediately eliminate a) and c). As well as realizing that the answer must be even, they also may realize that if you add 6 more than 40 times, the result must be in the 200s, so d) can also be eliminated.

Applying What You've Learned

1. How did you solve the chapter problem? Why might it be a suitable performance task for Grade 3 students?

2. Some teachers count homework and/or participation toward a student's math mark. Why might this be problematic?

3. Sometimes a student who is doing fairly well in math in school performs relatively poorly on a provincial examination.

   a) Why might this happen?

   b) How would you determine which mark best reflects the student's level of performance relative to the provincial expectations/ outcomes when queried by a parent?

4. Create a rubric that could be used to evaluate students' performance in solving this problem:

   > You are buying 100 animals for $100; a horse costs $10, a cow costs $1, and a sheep costs 50¢. How many of each can you buy?

   Keep in mind the curricular expectations/outcomes for your region when creating your rubric.

5. Imagine planning a multiple-choice quiz on the topic of multiplication of 2-digit numbers by 1-digit numbers or a quiz on the topic of multiplication of two integers. Create three items that you think are suitable. For each item, explain how you chose the distracters that you chose.

6. Look at Dr. Douglas Reeve's video on toxic practices in education: https://www.youtube.com/watch?v=jduiAnm-O3w. What is your response to his points?

7. Choose a mathematical topic and grade level of interest. Prepare a potential assessment plan that you could use for that topic and level.

8. Provide an example of how using a tweet or a blog would effectively show students' understanding of a mathematical idea.

Interact with a K–8 Student:

9. Talk to a student about how his or her teacher finds out what he or she knows. Ask the student to elaborate on which form of teacher assessment he or she is most comfortable with, and why.

Interact with a K–8 Teacher:

10. Ask the teacher what large-scale assessment his or her students have taken. Ask the teacher how he or she has prepared students for that assessment, or if not, why not.

Selected References

Barlow, A.T., and Drake, J.M. (2008). Assessing understanding through problem writing. *Teaching Children Mathematics, 14*, 326–332.

Black, P., and Williams, D. (2009). Developing the theory of formative assessment. *Educational Assessment, Evaluation and Accountability, 21(1)*, 5–31.

Bieler, S.K., and Thompson, D.R. (2012). Multidimensional assessment of CCSSM. *Teaching Children Mathematics 19(5)*, 292–300.

Bright, G.W., and Joyner, J.M. (1998). *Classroom assessment in mathematics*. Blue Ridge Summit, PA: University Press of America, Inc.

Britton, K.L., and Johannes, J.I. (2003). Portfolios and a backward approach to assessment. *Mathematics Teaching in the Middle School, 9*, 70-76.

Burrill, J. (Ed.). (2005). *Grades 6-8 mathematics assessment sampler*. Reston, VA: National Council of Teachers of Mathematics.

Bush, W.S. (Ed.). (2001). *Mathematics assessment: Cases and discussion questions for grades K–5*. Reston, VA: National Council of Teachers of Mathematics.

Bush, W.S., and Leinwand, S. (Eds.). (2000). *Mathematics assessment: A practical handbook for grades 6 to 8*. Reston, VA: National Council of Teachers of Mathematics.

Cooper, D. (2007). *Talk about assessment*. Toronto, ON: Thomson Nelson.

Davies, A. (2007). *Making classroom assessment work*. Courtenay, BC: Connections Publishing Inc.

Davies, A., Herbst, S., Reynolds, B.P., and McTighe, J. (2012). *Leading the way to assessment for learning: A practical guide (Canadian Version)*. Courtenay, BC: Connections Publishing.

Diezmann, C. (2008). On-the-spot assessments. *Teaching Children Mathematics, 15*, 290–294.

Earl, L. (2003). *Assessment as learning: Using classroom assessment to maximize student learning*. Thousand Oaks, CA: Corwin Press, Inc.

Earl, L. (2007). Assessment as learning. In Hawley, W.D. (Ed.) *The keys to effective schools*. Thousand Oaks, CA: Corwin Press, Inc., 85.

Ellemore-Collins, D.L., and Wright, R.J. (2008). Assessing student thinking about arithmetic: Videotaped interviews. *Teaching Children Mathematics, 15*, 106–111.

Fernandes, A., Anhalt, C.O., and Civil, M. (2009). Mathematical interviews to assess Latino students. *Teaching Children Mathematics, 16*, 162–169.

Gawronski, J.D. (2005). *Grades 3–5 mathematics assessment sampler*. Reston, VA: National Council of Teachers of Mathematics.

Ginsburg, H.P., Jacobs, S.F., and Lopez, L.S. (1998). *The teacher's guide to flexible interviewing in the classroom: Learning what children know about math*. Boston: Allyn and Bacon.

Glanfield, F., Bush, W.S., and Stenmark, J.K. (Eds.). (2003). *Mathematics assessment: A practical handbook for grades K to 2*. Reston, VA: National Council of Teachers of Mathematics.

Guskey, T. (2003). How classroom assessment improves learning. *Educational Leadership, 60,* 6–11.

Guskey, T.R. (2014). *On your mark: Challenging the convention of grading and reporting.* Bloomington, IN: Solution Tree Press.

Hattie, J. (2012). *Visible learning for teachers: Maximizing impact on learning.* New York: Routledge.

Hattie, J., and Timperley, H. (2007). The power of feedback. *Review of Educational Research 77 (1),* 81–112.

Kulm, G. (Ed.). (1990). *Assessing higher order thinking in mathematics.* Washington, DC: American Association for the Advancement of Science.

Leatham, K.P., Lawrence, K., and Mewborn, D.S. (2005). Getting started with open-ended assessment. Teaching Children Mathematics, *11,* 413–419.

Marzano, R.J., Pickering, D., and McTighe, J. (1993). *Assessing student outcomes: Performance assessment using the dimensions of learning model.* Alexandria, VA: Association for Supervision and Curriculum Development.

Maxwell, V.L., and Lassak, M.B. (2009). An experiment in using portfolios in the middle school. *Mathematics teaching in the middle school, 13,* 404–409.

Ministry of Education, Ontario (2010). *Growing Success. Assessment, evaluation, and reporting in Ontario schools.* Toronto: Queens Printer for Ontario.

National Academy of Sciences. (1993). *Measuring up: Prototypes for mathematics assessment.* Washington, DC: National Academy Press.

Reeves, D. (2010). *Elements of grading A guide to effective practice.* Bloomington, IN: Solution Tree.

Stenmark, J.K. (Ed.). (1991). *Mathematics assessment: Myths, models, good questions, and practical suggestions.* Reston, VA: National Council of Teachers of Mathematics.

Stenmark, J.K., and Bush, W.S. (Eds.). (2001). *Mathematics assessment: A practical handbook for grades 3 to 5.* Reston, VA: National Council of Teachers of Mathematics.

University of Alberta. (1993). *Principles for fair student assessment practices for education in Canada.* Edmonton: University of Alberta.

Westley, J. (1994). *Puddle questions: Assessing mathematical thinking, grade 3.* Mountain View, CA: Creative Publications.

Western and Northern Canadian Protocol for Collaboration in Education (WNCP). (2006). *Rethinking classroom assessment with purpose in mind.* Available from http://www.wncp.ca/media/40539/rethink.pdf. Accessed September 6, 2010.

Wiggins, G. (2004). Assessment as feedback. New Horizons for Learning. Available from http://www.newhorizons.org/strategies/assess/wiggins.htm. Accessed September 6, 2010.

Zorin, B., Hunsader, P.D., and Thompson, D.R. (2013). Assessments: Numbers, context, graphics, and assumptions. *Teaching Children Mathematics 19(8),* 480–488.

Chapter 4

Planning Instruction

IN A NUTSHELL

The main ideas in this chapter are listed below:

1. Planning is key to effective instruction in mathematics. Planning means taking the time to get to know and understand the content to be taught and how it can most effectively be communicated, and also thinking about how to tailor instructional goals to the children who are being taught.

2. Planning should be done at both the micro and macro levels.

3. Many resources, including texts, can be useful to the teacher in her or his planning.

4. Strategies for teaching mathematics may need to be massaged if students have too high a level of math anxiety; usually, anxiety can be dissipated with effective instruction and teaching strategies that are open and inclusive.

CHAPTER PROBLEM

Each letter of the alphabet is assigned a value based on its position. For example, $A = 1$, $B = 2$, $C = 3$, ... , $Z = 26$. Create three different words that are each worth 43.

Math Anxiety—A Special Challenge in Teaching Mathematics

The teaching of mathematics presents some unique challenges for teachers. One of the main challenges in teaching math is the level of anxiety it seems to have historically evoked in many adults and, consequently, in some teachers and some children. Children hear adults saying from early on that math is hard or that they did not like math; this is a big obstacle for some children to overcome.

Causes of Math Anxiety

People who feel math anxious are unable to prevent their stress and worry about doing math from interfering with their ability to perform. Their worry about math so occupies their thoughts, it is hard for them to actually think about the math. What contributes to the creation of math anxiety? and why is it more prevalent in math than in other subject areas?

The emphasis on "black and white" or "right and wrong" answers—no middle ground—is something that has contributed to math anxiety. A teacher asks a student, "What is $23 + 38$?" There is no evading; the student either knows or does not know that the answer is 61. If the student does not know the correct answer, he or she is embarrassed and nervous. Contrast this with a question that might be asked in language arts, for example, a child is asked to retell a story in his or her own words. There are many possible directions in which to go; the chance of success is much greater, and the opinion of the child is relevant.

The emphasis on speed, and the fact that the speed has to be demonstrated in a very public way, has also contributed to math anxiety. Students used to, and sometimes are still asked to, compete against one another, with the winner being the one who could recall most quickly. Those who knew the math but perhaps needed a little thinking time became more anxious.

Recently, the work of Sian Beilock and others has brought to light that it is often the anticipation of the math task and not the task itself that gets in the way for students. They learned, too, that anxiety starts in the early elementary years for many, that anxiety makes it more difficult to actually perform math tasks by robbing the anxious individual of working memory, and that it is often a strong student who is most anxious (Beilock and Willingham, 2014).

Another contributing factor is a view of math as a set of rules. Many students lack confidence that they can figure out a math problem without recalling the relevant memorized rule. When confronted with a real problem, where a rule is not immediately obvious, they do not know how to begin and become even more anxious.

Even in computational situations, math is different from other subjects in that, despite the fact that a rule may have been learned, it must be applied to a new situation each time. For example, you might, for a social studies class, memorize the capitals of the provinces, and all you need to do is repeat them. However, even if you have learned the rules for adding, you must always adapt what you learned to a new set of numbers. This adds to the stress.

There is a widespread belief that you are born either able to do math or not able. Students experiencing difficulty could easily attribute their lack of success to their lack of innate ability. Then, rather than working on improving their performance, they simply assume that they cannot do math—it is not their fault. This perceived inability simply adds to the anxiety.

Diminishing Anxiety in Students

The approaches to math discussed in this book should decrease the level of mathematics anxiety in our schools.

- We now focus on math as making sense, not as an arbitrary set of rules that have to be memorized.
- The use of manipulatives helps ensure that the math makes sense and also provides a starting point for students who may not be sure how to begin. Students who may be less certain of themselves with written work or even oral work feel more comfortable if they can explain themselves using concrete materials.
- We now ask many more questions that have alternative responses. Students have many more opportunities to be right.
- We now use fewer timed tests or very long assignments; this removes some of the anxiety and allows students to perform better.
- We help students to develop a growth mindset where errors are not cause for alarm but are seen as a valuable part of the learning by the teacher, and where students believe they can succeed if they try. This also significantly diminishes anxiety.

Diminishing Anxiety in Teachers

There are many ways that teachers can diminish their own anxiety and, indirectly, help students do the same:

- Teachers must give themselves the same "breaks" that they give students. They, too, should feel comfortable taking their time to find an answer, not being sure right away, or asking another teacher a question.
- Using manipulatives can often help a teacher who is math anxious.
- For many teachers, the active classroom, where they are not at centre stage but just another important player, can diminish anxiety. Working with a small group is often less intimidating than standing up front with 30 pairs of eyes intently watching.
- Preparation effectively diminishes anxiety in any situation. If teachers are uncomfortable with a new topic they are teaching, seeking teaching support in a variety of professional resources can make a significant difference in both the teacher's confidence and the effectiveness of the lesson.

Unit Planning and Lesson Planning

Year Planning

It is critical that teachers plan for both the long term and the short term. To ensure that the curriculum for their jurisdiction is appropriately covered, most teachers develop a long-range plan that maps out the year—what strands, or what topics, will be covered and when. Some teachers like to cover all of a strand together, although most teachers like to revisit a strand several times over the course of a year. In some districts or boards, teachers have collaborated to offer a suggested, although rarely required, sequence that teachers might follow.

One of the considerations in yearly planning is a decision about how much to integrate mathematical strands so that students can see connections between different mathematical topics. As well, teachers might consider whether or how they want to use cross-curricular tasks, so students can see the relationship of mathematics to other subjects, too. Examples of tasks that integrate strands include

- creating patterns that highlight geometric properties of shapes
- measuring to create scale models based on ratios
- exploring the probability that numbers in a certain range have certain properties, for example, the probability that an integer between 1 and 100 is a prime number

Examples of cross-curricular tasks include

- creating artistic tessellations that involve designs
- exploring the effect of mass and string length on the period of a pendulum
- writing math stories
- creating musical compositions based on geometric transformations

Unit Planning

It is equally important that each unit of instruction within that year have some coherence. Thus, most teachers create what they call unit plans. They think about their teaching goals for the unit, they consider what aspects of the curriculum might need to be adapted or modified for a particular group of students, and they organize the materials that they will need to support instruction during that unit.

Like any good story, a unit of instruction needs a beginning, a middle, and an end. The beginning is normally some sort of activity to set the stage for the unit and to provide teachers with important diagnostic information about their students. For example, if teachers are teaching a unit on multiplication, they might want to find out what students already know about the subject, what kinds of problems they can solve, what manipulatives they are comfortable with, any missing prerequisites, etc. Teachers also might want to think about integrating other strands into the delivery of the unit.

There are many ways to introduce a unit. Many teachers use mind maps, concept webs, or organizers like the Frayer model, shown below, that let students show what they know about a topic—in this case, ratio.

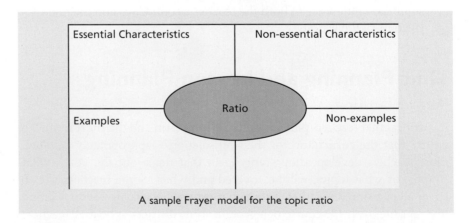

A sample Frayer model for the topic ratio

Some teachers use an anticipation guide—an activity in which students are asked to agree or disagree with statements the teacher proposes about the content that will be addressed. Later, at the end of the unit, these ideas are readdressed and students have an opportunity to reflect on their learning. An anticipation guide about surface area and volume might include a statement such as: A shape with a greater surface area has a greater volume. Students get to agree (or strongly agree) or disagree (or strongly disagree). They discuss with others why they made that choice. Then, after a unit of instruction on, in this case, measurement, they revisit their belief.

The middle of the story is the instruction and formative assessment that are an essential part of good instruction. Teachers base their instruction on the curriculum outcomes/expectations for their jurisdiction, but instruction also needs to be tailored to the particular groups of students they are teaching. This is further discussed in the section on differentiated instruction (see page 78). One valuable strategy that some teachers use to plan their instruction is to consider the assessment tasks they would want students to be successful with at the end of the unit, and then work backwards, thinking carefully about what students would need to experience in the unit to be able to be successful. The backwards design model, which can be applied to lessons as well as units, is advocated by Wiggins and McTighe (2005).

The end of the unit needs to include opportunities for students to consolidate their understanding and connect the new ideas they have learned to mathematical knowledge that they already had. It will often include assessment of learning activities as well.

Lesson Planning

Each individual lesson also needs a plan. By planning, teachers can ensure that they have the appropriate materials ready. More importantly, however, planning makes it more likely that teachers will make good choices about how students spend their instructional time. Classrooms are complex environments. If the teacher has not streamlined the teaching to make sure that the most important ideas are front and centre, it is easy to lose valuable instructional time and make it more difficult for students to attend to the more important ideas. No matter the lesson, it makes sense to first develop an instructional goal, then think about what students would need to demonstrate to show that the goal had been achieved, working backwards to design a task with appropriate reflection questions, and an introduction to lead to the task that would allow for this to happen.

Another important part of that planning is anticipation of student responses to be ready to deal with likely problems or issues.

Planning Support

Although teachers might prefer personal tools to assist them in planning, Ministries of Education across the country support teachers by providing planning tools and templates. For example, the Ontario Ministry of Education, in a variety of locations on its websites, provides lesson plan templates for general or specifically for math use and provides unit planning support. Similarly, the Alberta ministry provides sample templates for long–range, unit, and lesson plans. Many other jurisdictions provide similar support.

Lesson Style
The Importance of Varied Lesson Styles

One decision that teachers can make is about the lesson structures they will use. Different lesson styles appeal to students with different learning styles or work habits. As well, different lesson styles better suit the nature of the different types of mathematics to be learned or whether the lesson is designed to provide practice in previously learned skills or introduce new concepts. For example, getting a sense of the size of larger numbers is better suited to an exploration-style lesson than is learning how to use a ruler. Teachers should take the time to think about the balance of types of lessons, described below, that they will use.

Different Lesson Styles

Exploration

Exploration lessons provide students with an opportunity to have more input into the direction of a lesson. Sometimes it makes sense to set up an exploration at the start of a unit of study. Sometimes an exploration makes a suitable concluding activity, where students explore a reasonably complex situation using what they have learned in the unit. There also may be specific expectations/outcomes within a unit of study for which an exploration would be effective.

In an exploration lesson, students may be using different approaches and may end up with different conclusions. Teachers provide some guidance to get students started, but students have significant latitude in how to proceed.

Explorations can be completed individually or in small groups. Examples of tasks suitable for exploration include a lesson to create as many models and expressions as possible for the number 10, or a lesson to explore the number of possible results using any of the four operations with a set of four numbers (e.g., what the greatest and least possible result is using addition, subtraction, multiplication, or division, and the numbers 10, 11, 12, and 13). Students might make as many different composite shapes as they can using the same five congruent squares, or explore the effect of not having rules for the order of operations.

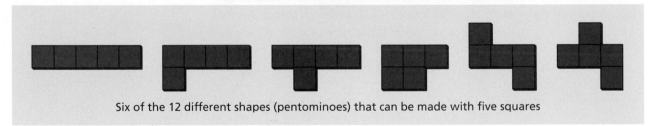

Six of the 12 different shapes (pentominoes) that can be made with five squares

Guided Activity

In a guided activity lesson, students move toward a common goal or set of understandings. However, under the guidance of a teacher, they have a significant participatory role in the development of those understandings. Occasionally, teachers might use a highly guided mini-lesson before or after a more problem-based activity.

Examples of topics that might suit this style of instruction are lessons on different ways to represent a number with base ten blocks, on exploring how multiplication and division of integers are related, or on examining a set of data to choose an appropriate scale for a scale drawing.

Direct Instruction

In a direct instruction lesson, students are led through a mathematical concept or skill under the direction of a teacher. This makes the most sense when students are introduced to rules or approaches that have been externally selected as standards, or conventions. Examples of such topics are learning the rules for reading a clock or for reading a protractor.

Mini-lessons

Mini-lessons are used when the concept being addressed is fairly quick to deal with. They are often teacher directed, but do not need to be. For example, the mini-lesson could be a short open question or a quick task.

Specific Lesson Strategies

Some frequently used strategies have their own names. Here we discuss three that are focused on consolidating a lesson taught through problem solving: a gallery walk, a math congress, and a bansho (Ministry of Education, 2010). In each case, students are presented with a problem to which there may be one solution but for which there are many strategies. They explore the problem, usually with fellow students and without teacher modelling, and the students play a significant role in the debrief of the learning.

Gallery Walk

In this frequently used structure, students are presented with a problem to work on, often in pairs. The teacher observes and supports students as they work. Students post their work so that others can see it, and query or comment on it, in a gallery walk. This is often followed by a full group discussion.

Math Congress

During a math congress (Fosnot, 2001), some students take a leadership role. After students have worked on a problem, the teacher judiciously selects examples so that important ideas come out. The selected students speak to their work, explaining it to the others, and the teacher encourages the others to put those ideas in their own words. Questions raised during the congress are generally answered by students and only when necessary by the teacher.

Bansho

As used in Canada, particularly Ontario, this variation of a Japanese teaching strategy requires pairs or small groups of students to work fairly independently on a problem, recording their thinking (not just their answers) on chart paper. The papers from the various groups are annotated in a classroom discussion; they are organized so that strategies that are different are distinguished from one another and ones that are essentially the same are seen that way. Attention is paid to the sequencing of the strategies being discussed. Often strategies that are conceptual are dealt with first, then those that are more "efficient," and perhaps then those that lead to generalizations. Often students decide which strategy that has been presented most resembles their approach.

The materials created serve as both anchor charts and landscapes of learning. The annotations and organization make the underlying mathematical thinking explicit.

Planning Grouping

Just as there is value in a balance of lesson styles to support different learning styles, different ways of grouping for instruction and, certainly, flexible grouping, also make sense to meet various students' needs. Teachers can develop their own approach to grouping.

Sometimes teachers might group students because they want students to communicate with one another. Sometimes there are practical reasons; for example, it may be easier or necessary to share manipulative materials. Mostly, teachers recognize that students are more comfortable taking the risk of asking or answering questions in a small group of peers than in a teacher–whole class interaction.

Grouping makes sense in situations where a task is complex enough that input from a variety of students with a variety of perspectives is valuable. In situations where students have an opportunity to work on a problem or to develop their own algorithms, group discussion can be very useful.

Heterogeneous and Homogeneous Grouping

Sometimes teachers use heterogeneous groups. In a situation where students of different ability levels could all contribute toward the solution of a problem or completion of a task, this type of grouping makes sense.

Teachers use different techniques to form such groups. Sometimes, they count off students: 1, 2, 3, 4, 1, 2, 3, 4, ... , grouping all the 1s together, all the 2s together, etc., to form four groups. Other times, they provide short computational tasks directing students with the same question to work together, or they allow students to decide with whom they want to work. Still other times, they simply assign groups based on proximity of seating.

Activity 4.1 is a suitable task for a heterogeneous group of varied abilities. One reason this task is suitable for a heterogeneous group is that students can select different items from the flyers, depending on their confidence with particular number values.

On the other hand, there may be times when homogeneous groupings are more appropriate. A teacher may want to pull aside a group of students who are struggling with a particular topic, to work together to deal with the difficulties they are having. Or the teacher may want to provide an enrichment activity for students who are already comfortable with a topic she or he is planning to teach. **Activity 4.2** would be enrichment for students who can already read and represent 2- and 3-digit numbers.

Group Size

There is no ideal group size. Sometimes the size depends on the task, and other times it depends on the interpersonal dynamics in the class or the amount of available material. It is important not to make groups so large that some students end up being left out. Sometimes there is a danger with groups of three that two students might work so well together that the third group member feels left out.

Cooperative Grouping

When students are grouped to work together on a problem or to discuss a concept, it is often referred to as cooperative grouping. Students who are grouped simply to share manipulatives or who are sitting together and helping each other as they work individually are not cooperative groups.

ACTIVITY **4.1**

Provide supermarket flyers to each group. Ask them to create a "shopping" list with a total cost of close to, but not more than, $10.00.

Building Number Sense

ACTIVITY **4.2**

Ask the group to list palindromes (numbers that read the same forward and backward, like 99 or 121) between 10 and 1000.

Building Number Sense

Individual accountability might be fostered by setting out clear expectations for group problem solving and modelling those skills.

Cooperative groups work together on a task, contributing equitably (not necessarily equally) to a single task. For a cooperative group to work effectively, there needs to be individual accountability for the learning. Each student must be held responsible for what is learned. Without that individual accountability, too many students simply opt out, leaving it to other students to complete the work.

Suitable Tasks for Group Work

As mentioned earlier, grouping makes sense in situations where a task is open enough that input from a variety of people with a variety of perspectives is valuable. Here are some sample tasks that are suitable for groups:

- In what situations do you think a map ratio of 1:100 000 makes sense? Explain your thinking.
- Come up with a way to use base ten blocks to show that when you multiply a 2-digit number by a 2-digit number, the answer could be a 3- or a 4-digit number.
- Create a pattern using a set of animal counters.

Limitations of Grouping

It is important to recognize that not all students function best in a group, and some allowances for this should be considered at least some of the time.

Although it may be appropriate to place academically stronger students in groups with weaker students for the purpose of helping those weaker students, it is not appropriate to do this too frequently. The stronger student also needs appropriate learning challenges.

Balancing Whole Class, Small Group, and Individual Instruction

It is important for teachers to provide opportunities for students to work as a large learning community (as a whole class), in small groups, and also sometimes on their own. Within one lesson there will likely be a mix of these approaches, and this will certainly happen over the course of several lessons. Teachers' choices about the appropriate balance reflect not only their own individual styles, but perhaps also the content being explored, instructional needs (e.g., Is there a need for a teacher to work with a small guided group while others work on something else?), and the personalities of students.

Three-Part Lessons

Any lesson would normally have three parts. In Ontario, materials for teachers of Grades 7 and 8, called Targeted Implementation and Planning Supports (TIPS), identify the three parts as

Minds On …

Action!

Consolidate/Debrief

Whether these or other names are used, the lesson still benefits from these parts. The intent of the first part of the lesson is to allow students to connect with the topic. It may involve a warm-up activity, a provocative question for students to consider, or some other device to get students "hooked."

A significant portion of the lesson might involve the solving of a problem that helps students meet the instructional goal of the lesson. Often this problem is completed in pairs or small groups as the teacher scaffolds and probes, as needed.

The last part of the lesson involves consolidation, where students have an oppportunity to share, sort, and discuss their strategies, engage in discussion on the essential understandings the lesson was intended to evoke, as well as apply what has been learned. By closing the lesson with an explicit reflection on the ideas presented in the lesson, whether through oral or written activities, it is much more likely that the lesson goals will be achieved; the communication about the mathematics allows students to "hear" what needs to stay in their heads. Ideally, the lesson provides many opportunities, in all three parts of the lesson, for significant student active involvement and for much student communication. It is when students talk with their colleagues and their teacher that much of the learning takes place.

It is helpful to have notes to teach from. A good lesson plan template reminds teachers of

- what materials they will be using
- what groupings they will use and when
- the amount of time to spend on each activity
- some short notes about each component of the lesson
- what important questions they want to make sure they ask students in the various parts of the lesson

Just as important as planning what to do is planning what to say.

The power of planning with others cannot be overstated. One of the most rewarding forms of professional development is the opportunity for teachers to work with other teachers to discuss their plans for lesson delivery. A professional development approach called Lesson Study, borrowed from the Japanese, is specifically built around teachers jointly planning a lesson, watching its delivery, debriefing, and re-planning. A derivative of this is collaborative inquiry.

Planning Support

When planning a unit of instruction, teachers use a variety of resources. Often these are personal, district, or board-level resources, or, increasingly, digital resources where teachers share lessons, but many teachers continue to use textbooks as a source of teaching ideas. The advantage of a textbook, whether print or digital, is that it has been through a rigorous review and editing process that helps to ensure the mathematics is correct. In addition, the authors, usually experts in the field, have very likely used an appropriate pedagogical sequencing, appropriate contexts for instruction, and appropriate assessment strategies. Most often, these textbooks have been designed around provincial/territorial curricula and include material to help teachers and students prepare for large-scale tests. This leaves teachers free to concentrate on adapting developed lessons to meet the needs of their own students.

Current textbooks are more likely to ask for explanations, expect reasoning, emphasize problem solving and communication, and provide rich contexts in which to learn math. Although there continue to be skill exercises to consolidate learning, they rarely dominate textbooks in Canada anymore.

How to Use a Textbook

Textbooks can be used for introducing topics, extending them, or practising them. Although some teachers use their own teaching/learning activities and only use the textbook for additional practice, the textbook also can provide the rich introductions that teachers can follow up in their own ways.

Teachers should use the teacher's resource that comes with a textbook. Many of the problems that teachers will face have been considered and planned for. The teacher resource often provides

- sample responses for the open-ended questions in the textbook
- additional questions to pose that are not found in the textbook
- insight into how students might handle some of the questions posed in the textbook
- information about situations to avoid
- assessment strategies
- organizational tips
- suggestions for helping struggling students
- suggestions for enriching the instruction for more advanced students

Following the Order of the Textbook

Because authors of textbooks often spend considerable time thinking through an appropriate sequence, it is recommended that the chapters of a textbook be followed in their order of appearance. However, it is often possible to follow an alternative order as long as the teacher is prepared for the odd question in the text that has been designed with the original chapter sequence in mind.

Reading a Textbook

In an attempt to base teaching on real-world situations, and to explain ideas rather than simply demonstrate them, more and more of the presentation of mathematics in texts involves words rather than just symbols. Part of instructional planning should include acquainting students with how to read a math text since the required skills are somewhat unique. Examples of peculiarities of math textbooks include the following:

- rhetorical questions (such as those used as introductions to stimulate discussion)
- some pictures that contain critical information, yet others that are decorative
- worked examples, which are to be read and then referred to and not acted on
- question stems that apply to multiple parts, for example:

Question Stems

USING QUESTION PARTS	CONTINUING THE QUESTION
How many cartons will Peter need for **a)** 50 eggs? **b)** 100 eggs?	How are addition and multiplication the same? different?

• question parts that read in different directions. For example:

Reading Question Parts

READING FROM LEFT TO RIGHT	READING FROM TOP TO BOTTOM
Use 20 + 20 = 40 to calculate each sum. **a)** 19 + 21 **b)** 19 + 19 **c)** 22 + 21	Use mental math to calculate each total cost. **a)** \$17.99 + \$14.99 **b)** \$12.98 + \$3.50 **c)** \$2.50 + \$6.75

READING FROM TOP TO BOTTOM *AND* FROM LEFT TO RIGHT		
Use mental math to calculate.		
a) 73 + 21	**c)** 71 + 29	**e)** 54 + 19
b) 32 + 28	**d)** 49 + 33	**f)** 39 + 49

Some specific strategies for helping students learn to read math textbooks include alerting students to the need for

- recognizing what the title and subheads tell you about what you will do or what will happen in the lesson or section
- deciding if a question is meant to be answered right away, if it is simply an introduction, or if it will be answered later
- recognizing that an illustration to support the text may be positioned above, below, to the right, or to the left of the text
- deciding whether the illustration is "decorative" or essential to the question
- deciding whether the expectation is to write or to say an answer
- looking for math terms and making sure that the terms are familiar; using a glossary to find unfamiliar terms
- understanding how questions are numbered, particularly questions divided up into parts, and whether to look down or right to find the next thing to do (see *Reading Question Parts* above)
- deciding what the various icons mean, for example, a calculator icon denoting that a calculator can be used for a particular question

Planning Opportunities for Practice

Part of the planning process involves thinking about how to ensure that students receive sufficient practice opportunities. The experience of many parents of school-aged students, and certainly of their grandparents, has been that mathematics is about learning rules and then practising them. It is assumed, and it makes sense to many people, that the more a skill is practised, the better the student will be at that skill.

Lately, though, the nature of the work that students bring home in math has changed. To an untrained observer, there does not appear to be much practice.

Is Practice Important?

Of course, skills need to be practised. Ask any athlete or musician whether he or she believes that practice makes him or her a better player, and the universal answer will be "yes." By practising, students "automate" certain aspects of their mathematical work so that they can concentrate on the aspects that require more thought.

As well, many mathematical concepts build on one another. Unless pre-requisites are firmly entrenched, learning new ideas becomes more difficult than it needs to be.

What Should Be Practised?

Initially, you might think that practice may help most in developing specific skills, for example, batting practice for a baseball player, practising scales for a pianist, and practising computation in mathematics. But there also needs to be practice of the following:

- problem solving
- visualization
- communication
- metacognition

How Much Practice Is Needed?

The amount of practice will vary with the complexity of what is being practised. For example, time will be needed to commit basic facts to memory because there are so many of them.

As well, a great deal of practice is needed to become proficient at visualization, problem solving, communication, and metacognition. In each of these cases, not only is there a range of strategies to learn, but there are also nuances, which are not skill-based, in selecting what strategy to call on in a particular set of circumstances.

What Should Practice Look Like?

Ideally, practice should be planned to be engaging and varied, as well as useful. Practice can also be multi-purpose. Take, for example, the possibility of practising 2-digit addition. Rather than preparing a worksheet with 20 multiplication of integer questions, a practice task such as the one shown in **Activity 4.3** could be given to practise both computation and problem solving.

Practising Metacognition, Visualization, and Communication

Metacognition is practised by ensuring that students are regularly asked to explain how they decided to start a problem, what to do next, why they drew a picture, etc.

Visualization is practised by encouraging students to imagine visual configurations of numbers. For example, you could use activities like the ones in **Activity 4.4**.

> ### ACTIVITY **4.3**
>
> You multiply two integers and the result is about 50 less than one of them. What numbers might you have multiplied?
>
> ---
>
> Critical Thinking

ACTIVITY **4.4**

a) Imagine a number that is near the bottom left of a 100-chart. What might it be?

b) Imagine a pile of base ten blocks. There are more ten blocks than one blocks. What number are you seeing?

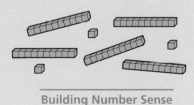

Building Number Sense

Communication is practised by focusing students on the clarity, accuracy, and vocabulary of the language they hear and its use in the context of doing mathematics. For example, you might ask students to record their own explanation for why it is really easy to multiply by 0, and then to look critically at what they wrote. They would ask themselves, for example, if someone else would be able to follow their thinking, if they were clear, and if they showed their knowledge of words such as "multiply" or "product." Some texts even provide communication lessons for students to practise these skills.

Differentiating Instruction: Supporting Individual Differences

Although students in front of a teacher may all be the same age or even have come from the same class last year, they are different. The most critical, and most difficult, part of a teacher's job may be to figure out how to tailor curriculum delivery to the needs of those individual students.

Moving from the Concrete to the Symbolic

Part of instructional planning involves making informed decisions about where students are on the continuum of concrete to symbolic thinking and adapting practice to the needs of those particular students.

The literature has been clear, as has conventional practice, that students move from the concrete to the pictorial to the symbolic, although all three modes of learning have a place throughout the grades. Teachers know that students learn through all of their senses, so the use of concrete materials, or manipulatives, makes sense from that perspective alone. However, what makes the use of manipulatives even more critical in mathematics is that most mathematical ideas are abstractions.

Later chapters in this book provide guidance on which concrete materials are most helpful in teaching various topics.

What follows are some examples of concrete, pictorial, and symbolic models for a few concepts, to show how the same idea can look different at different stages. Teachers could decide where different groups of students are on this continuum for a particular topic and appropriately tailor instruction. There should be no rush to move students away from the concrete if it supports their learning.

Modelling Subtraction Problems

Modelling the Problem: There were 15 ducks and 3 flew away. How many are left?

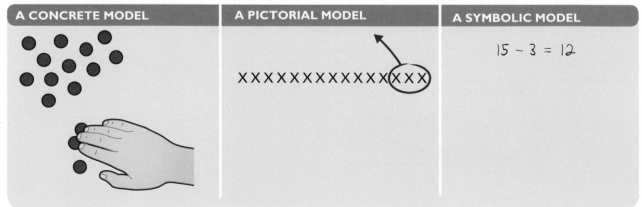

A CONCRETE MODEL	A PICTORIAL MODEL	A SYMBOLIC MODEL
	XXXXXXXXXXXX(XXX)	15 − 3 = 12

Modelling Integers

Modelling the Integer Equation −2 + 3 = 1

A CONCRETE MODEL

Two-sided tiles or counters can be used to represent integers. Each red tile is −1 and each white tile is +1.

Each pair of red and white tiles has a value of 0, so that leaves +1.

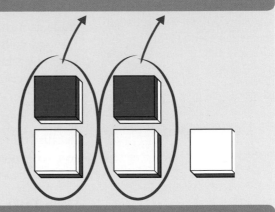

A PICTORIAL MODEL

A number line is a common and very useful pictorial model for integers. Movement right and left on the number line represents adding and subtracting.

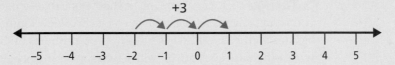

A SYMBOLIC MODEL

−2 + 3 = 1 is a symbolic model.

Modelling the Concept of an Unknown

The same algebra concept can be modelled in a variety of ways. In the following examples, finding an unknown in an equation is shown using three models.

Modelling 2 + ■ = 5 to Find an Unknown

A CONCRETE MODEL

There are 2 cubes and a bag of cubes on the left side of the scale, and 5 cubes on the right side. The sides are balanced. Therefore, there must be 3 cubes in the bag on the left side to balance the 5 cubes on the other side.

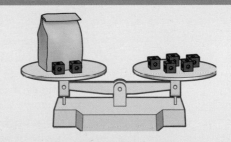

There must be 3 cubes in the bag.

A PICTORIAL MODEL

You have 2 squares and need 5 squares. If you add 3 squares to the 2 you started with, you will have a total of 5 squares.

A SYMBOLIC MODEL

If you add a number to 2, it is equal to 5. Add 3 to 2 to make the sum of 5.

$$2 + \square = 5$$
$$2 + 3 = 5$$

One common misconception made by teachers of mathematics is assuming that, once students reach a certain age, they no longer need the concrete stage. Even with older students, if new concepts and skills are being introduced, a concrete model is always a desirable beginning. How quickly students move to pictorial and then symbolic models to develop straightforward skills will vary. But even later in the learning trajectory, students might be asked to solve problems involving manipulatives to promote creative and critical thinking, for example, the one in **Activity 4.5**.

Managing Differentiation

Because there are usually 20 to 30 different students in a class and only one teacher, it is essential that the teacher use a variety of manageable strategies to meet those students' needs. Some possible strategies are addressed here.

Open Tasks

An open task is a task that can be approached very differently, but meaningfully, by students at different development levels. A key feature of such a task is that there are many possible answers, and many ways to get to the answers.

To create such a task, you might choose one that is centred around a big idea you want students to deal with at any level of development. For example, the big idea for the task shown below is "Some attributes of shapes are quantitative while others are qualitative," with a focus on distinguishing and relating shapes.

Students are provided with the appropriate concrete and/or pictorial models to work with. Less mathematically sophisticated students are likely to relate a rectangle to another polygon, and to relate and distinguish the two shapes based on global properties, for example, whether one has more vertices than the other. More mathematically sophisticated students may relate a rectangle to another quadrilateral or to a 3-D shape with at least one rectangular face. They will distinguish the shapes based on specific properties, such as the number of sides, vertices, and faces, and the relationships among sides and vertices, such as the number of equal sides or the sizes of the angles.

Many examples of open activities (i.e., tasks and questions) are provided in the chapters following this one. More ideas are available in Small (2009).

OPEN TASK	FOLLOW-UP QUESTIONS
A certain 2-D or 3-D shape makes me think of a rectangle, but it's not a rectangle. a) What might the shape be? Name or sketch the shape. b) How is the shape like a rectangle? How is it not like a rectangle? c) Repeat parts a) and b) for a different shape.	• Which shapes did you suggest? • Why did you choose each shape? • In what ways is each shape like a rectangle? • In what ways is each shape different from a rectangle? • What are some other shapes you could have suggested?

Parallel Tasks

Teachers can offer students a choice of two or three tasks that focus on the same big idea(s), but that reflect different developmental levels. The tasks are related closely enough that the same questions can be used to frame a follow-up discussion in which all students look back and communicate about what they did and what they learned.

Parallel tasks allow all students to experience success and learn from peers by seeing responses not only to their own task, but also to a related task completed by others. This ensures that students see the same underlying mathematical concept in different contexts.

For example, both tasks below ask students to describe a situation to match a probability description. Choice A suits students who can match situations to qualitative probability descriptions; choice B suits students who are able to match situations to numerical descriptions of probability. Many more examples of parallel tasks are available in Small (2009).

PARALLEL TASKS	FOLLOW-UP QUESTIONS
You can put 10 square tiles in a draw bag. The tiles can be any combination of red, blue, and yellow. Then, you will draw one tile from the bag. 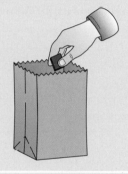	• How did you decide how many red tiles to put in the bag? • How do you know the tiles in your bag match the situation you chose? • Did you think carefully about how many blue or yellow tiles you needed? Why or why not? • Talk to someone who did the other task. What was the same about what you both did? What was different?

Choice A

What tiles will you put in the bag so that drawing a red tile is possible, but not likely? Explain your thinking.

Choice B

What tiles will you put in the bag so that the probability of drawing a red tile is $\frac{2}{5}$? Explain your thinking.

Centres

Teachers can set up activities at different centres/stations to suit students at different levels. The teacher can direct students to the appropriate centres, and then circulate to interact with the various groups. Some teachers build centres students can use fairly independently that derive from the idea of The Daily Five (Boushey and Moser, 2014). Other times teachers circulate and ask important reflecting questions of small groups at the centre.

Guided Groups

Teachers may need to work with small groups of children in a more guided approach for short periods of time, for example 15–20 minutes. This might be to go back to older material to fill in gaps or it might be to slow down newer material. To make this possible, they need to set up activities that other students can do more independently while they work with these small groups. One possibility is to use problems or tasks which are straightforward enough that students can manage them independently but substantial enough to warrant the time spent working on them. Often students would be working in small groups and the teacher would have clarified what is required. Another possibility is to use centres while the teacher works with the small group.

Students with Learning Disabilities

Many forms of learning disability affect math learning; many of them result in difficulties with calculations, with problem solving, and/or with memorizing multi-step procedures. In addition to this, mathematics texts that require a high level of reading ability can create additional challenges for students with learning disabilities.

Students with learning disabilities often have difficulty keeping one piece of information in their minds while processing other information. Thus, it is a question not of being able to do A or B, but of having difficulty doing them together. Many mathematical situations are complex and require multiple subtasks, thereby creating problems for these learners. An example might be dealing with patterns with multiple attributes, where students find it difficult to deal with two or three attributes simultaneously. Information processing difficulties may limit what a teacher can expect these students to handle within one question.

Teaching that focuses on a small number of big ideas to make connections is helpful for students with learning disabilities because it provides a natural structure to new learning.

General Instructional Adaptations Regardless of the specific problem, many general strategies or adaptations can ensure the success of students with learning disabilities. These adaptations may include

- breaking the material into manageable sequential chunks
- providing very explicit instructions
- providing more structure sometimes, even to open-ended activities
- using manipulatives and visuals to support learning as much as possible
- revisiting related material to allow students to make connections
- revisiting vocabulary and concepts with appropriate practice over time
- welcoming unusual approaches
- assigning problems that are related to what is currently of interest or under discussion
- modifying the content to be learned to take into account the developmental level of the student

Organizational Tools and Strategies A number of useful organizational tools and strategies can help students who require more structure. Teachers can

- outline the lesson or activity and post the outline, making sure the goal of the activity is clear
- encourage students to create their own graphic organizers to summarize concepts learned

• prepare study guides or graphic organizer templates, such as concept maps, to help students before and after the lesson or unit of study; for example:

Concept Map before Studying Growing Patterns

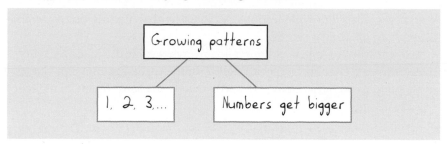

Concept Map after Studying Growing Patterns

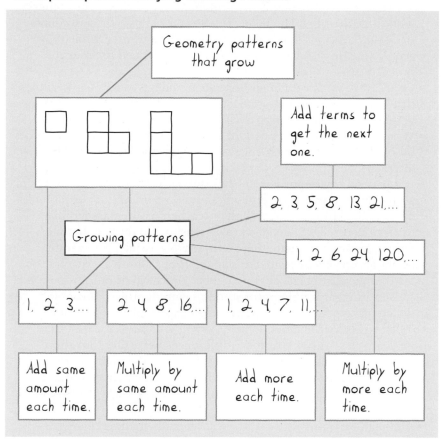

ESL and Immersion

A number of students learn math in their second or third language. It may be because they are immigrants for whom English is a second language (ESL). They may be francophone students learning in English, anglophone students learning in French, or students who have taken "immersion" classes in Ukrainian. The fact that children are learning a fairly abstract subject in an unfamiliar language means that some accommodations will probably be required. This is even more the case now than it used to be in mathematics as a result of the increased focus on problem solving in context and communication.

Students learning in a second language benefit from the more active and child-centred approach that has become fundamental to teaching at the elementary level. Students do not simply have to listen to a speaker whom they may or may not understand; now they have an opportunity to interact with peers, ask their own questions, and work with materials instead of just listening to unfamiliar words.

ESL students are often, although not always, a minority in a class where many students are able to speak English. In the case of immersion classes, most students are functioning at approximately the same level of language "disadvantage."

Considerations for ELL Students

Here are some important considerations for teaching in English language learning (ELL) classrooms in particular:

- There may be value in initially grouping ELL students with others who share their first language. This strategy allows these students to discuss concepts in a familiar and comfortable way while they acquire the English language, which they will need in order to proceed.
- Cooperative work with English-speaking students can also be helpful in that ELL students hear more models of English. They can also develop vocabulary for using English to clarify, justify, explain, compare, etc.
- Working in groups may be more consistent with the cultural practices of some of these students, since many cultures value this kind of interdependence.
- It is particularly important to be sensitive to the use of contexts. Many children who have had different home or cultural experiences are mystified by contexts that their teachers assume are familiar to all students. Teachers need to be sensitive to these potential difficulties and anticipate them as much as possible. An example might be a problem related to shaking hands after a tournament. Furthermore, contexts designed to be whimsical or humorous could cause particular problems for students coming from cultures in which make-believe is not part of their experience, or perceived "silliness" is frowned upon.
- Not only is sensitivity to these differences necessary, but there must be attempts to bridge these differences through a combination of explaining the contexts and finding alternative contexts that are more familiar to the various cultural groups represented in the class.
- Although we normally think of a natural mathematics progression from the concrete to the pictorial and then the symbolic, some slightly older ELL students, who have been schooled in other countries, may be more familiar with a symbolic presentation of mathematical ideas than with their concrete representations. Their experience with manipulatives would be minimal or non-existent, and they may need additional instruction on their use.
- Make sure that communication about homework or other math requirements is straightforward enough for an older sibling to deal with. In many families where the parents do not speak English, older siblings serve as the go-between with the school and often help their younger siblings at home with their homework.

Strategies for ELL and Immersion

The following strategies are important to consider in order to make mathematics instruction comprehensible to ELL students. Some of the strategies are equally applicable to immersion and ELL classrooms.

- Provide visual support, such as graphs, pictures, diagrams, charts, posters, and word cards; for example:

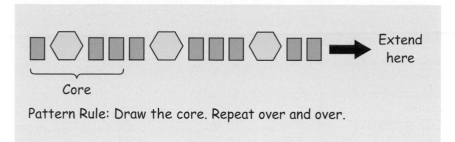

Pattern Rule: Draw the core. Repeat over and over.

- Provide concrete support such as models, manipulatives, and real objects.
- Simplify the language used in teaching rather than the ideas being taught.
- Use as few extra words as possible, and introduce them with manipulative or contextual support.
- Use nonverbal cues such as gestures, facial expressions, and body language to clarify meaning.
- Avoid slang and idioms.
- Allow and encourage students to touch and feel to learn.
- Speak directly to students, emphasizing important words.
- Provide sufficient wait time after asking a question to give these students time to interpret the question, and then think about a possible response.
- Ascertain prior knowledge and vocabulary and build on this.
- Clarify the goals of the activity in advance.
- Write legibly, if handwriting is used.
- Ensure that audio materials are clear and free from unfamiliar accents.
- Be sensitive to alternative symbols used in other cultures, such as a comma instead of a decimal point.
- Encourage students to ask themselves, "What help do I need?" "Who can I ask?" "How should I ask?"
- Repeat, rephrase, or paraphrase big ideas and directions.
- Identify, pre-teach, and expand on key vocabulary required for the development of the concept.
- Encourage students to express themselves orally, focusing on meaning rather than form.
- Spend additional time on the understand-the-problem stage of the inquiry process.
- Have students rewrite problems in their own words.

Assessment As in the case of students with learning disabilities, teachers need to be flexible when assessing second-language students in mathematics. When assessing, the following strategies can be helpful:

- Delay the assignment of marks until the student has sufficient English to be assessed fairly.

- Allow for oral or pictorial, rather than just written, responses.
- Provide scaffolding, such as that shown below, for written tasks. Scaffolding assists students in understanding what it is you are asking for and how much they need to do; for example:

Scaffolding Tasks

ORIGINAL TASK

Show five examples of growing patterns.
Explain how you know they are all growing patterns.

SCAFFOLDED TASK

Here are five examples of growing patterns:

1. _____

2. _____

3. _____

4. _____

5. _____

I know they are all growing patterns because

_____

_____

_____

Modifying Tasks

ORIGINAL TASK

Sketch a pattern with two changing attributes. Make your pattern repeat three times. Tell how the attributes change.

MODIFIED TASK

Use **all** of these shapes:

Make a **pattern**.
Repeat 3 times.
Tell about your pattern.

- Include graphics (such as charts, graphs, pictures, and maps).
- Look at a number of ways for students to represent their understanding (e.g., diagrams, charts, frame sentences, cloze sentences, and graphic organizers).
- Provide examples as part of the structure of the question; for example, "5, 10, 15, ... and 4, 8, 12, ... are both skip counting patterns. What are some other skip counting patterns?"

Enrichment for the Mathematically Gifted

Some students are mathematically gifted; others are average in mathematical ability but are interested and keen to do more. Although society has shown great concern for the needs of students with disadvantages, gifted students have received much less attention. Yet, each of these students, too, deserves appropriate opportunities to grow.

Mathematically gifted students need some special treatment; they need to proceed more quickly than their peers. They usually have deeper levels of understanding, and are prone to losing interest in mathematics if the pace is too slow and if existing interests are not cultivated to a sufficient depth. Some of these students balk at being required to show their work or provide written explanations, especially if they arrive at an answer fairly quickly. Some students who are gifted in understanding concepts and solving problems are less adept at communicating mathematically. Hence, these students benefit from being asked to explain their work.

Gifted mathematics students thrive in a problem-centred classroom culture. Here, the teacher teaches through problem solving, using a problem to motivate and provide a context for the learning. A teacher can have students consider multiple ways to represent numbers by asking them what coins to use to represent 30¢. In the course of this activity, skip counting emerges as nickels or dimes are counted. Or, in a classroom with older elementary students, the teacher might ask students to determine the total number of squares in a 10-by-10 square array. Many students will realize that starting with smaller squares, using a chart or organized list, and looking for a pattern will help to solve the problem. Thus, in the course of solving a problem, they have worked with patterns, square numbers, and graphic organizers.

Problem-Centred Learning

PROBLEM FOR YOUNGER GIFTED STUDENTS

A collection of coins is worth 30¢. What could the coins be?

SOLUTION

Skip counting while solving a simple money problem provides one possible solution.

Coin image © 2015 Royal Canadian Mint. All rights reserved.

PROBLEM FOR OLDER GIFTED STUDENTS

How many squares are in a 10-by-10 grid?

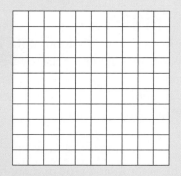

SOLUTION

Size of square	Number of squares
1 by 1	100
2 by 2	81
3 by 3	64
4 by 4	49
5 by 5	36

Working with patterns, square numbers, and graphic organizers while solving a problem

Gifted students also thrive in classrooms where extensions are regularly proposed, for example, by the teacher frequently asking, "What if ...?" questions. For instance, in exploring a pattern involving circles and squares, the teacher might ask, "What if we included triangles in our pattern?"

Strategies for Motivated and Gifted Learners

Some of the ways to meet the needs of both highly motivated learners and gifted students include

- finding a variety of problem, puzzle, and activity sources with mathematics content that suits their interests (logic problems are often of interest to these students)
- letting students create math puzzles for other students to solve
- establishing math clubs for interested students
- providing opportunities for these students to respond frequently to higher-level questions
- encouraging the use of manipulatives in creative ways
- providing alternative but related assignments or tasks. For example, while working on a unit about patterns, if it becomes clear that a particular student has already mastered the ideas to be presented, she or he can learn about more complex patterns, such as the Fibonacci sequence.
- offering alternative projects, problems, or assignments, if the students already know the concepts and skills that are to be taught
- encouraging creativity in assignments and on formal assessments
- differentiating assignments, so that the most able students do not simply do more of the same problems
- allowing students to extend their work beyond the curriculum
- finding ways to ensure public recognition of their talents (unlike artistically, musically, or physically talented students, these students are unlikely to receive external validation for their accomplishments)
- using a teacher-librarian or other external helper like a parent volunteer to work with these students
- providing opportunities for these students to participate in contests or competitions, which can be motivating and which can provide a way to externally validate their abilities. Many math competitions provide rich and challenging questions, which can also be used with students who are not gifted but who enjoy working competitively.

Home–School Connections

Not only does work in the classroom matter. Consideration of the home is also important in providing quality instruction. There are two critical aspects to the home–school connection that could affect student success in the classroom. One is the type and amount of homework assigned; the other is the teacher's or the school's relationship with families.

Homework

There are no agreed-upon ideals for the amount and type of math homework, although certain jurisdictions do set maxima, or minima, for the total amount of homework a student should have.

One of the difficulties with homework is that teachers cannot always be privy to the stress at home that homework might cause. Perhaps the child is scheduled for so many activities after school that homework becomes a negative rather than a positive opportunity for learning. Perhaps family issues are such that there really is no quality time available. On the other hand, we know that time on task makes a difference in learning and additional home time can make a big difference, particularly in skill development.

Homework provides a way to help parents better understand what their children are learning in school, as well as providing that additional practice for students. Teachers might choose one or two interesting problems that help parents see mathematics as a problem-solving venture, rather than send home pages and pages of worksheets to be filled in. For example, a Grade 1 child might be asked to find items in his or her home that are very long and describe how they know the items are long. A Grade 4 child might be asked to look at home for multiplication situations that they see and can describe. A Grade 5 child might be asked to create a number puzzle that uses at least 10 multiplication facts. A Grade 8 child might be asked to create a scale drawing of a room at home or perhaps find some maps around the house or on the Internet and explore what ratios are commonly used.

That said, there may be individual students who benefit from and enjoy worksheets, too. Their wishes should be accommodated at times as well.

Making Contact with Parents

It is valuable to make contact with parents early in the school year to ensure that they understand your approach to teaching math and your reasons for that approach. Communication should be friendly, free of jargon, and informative. Ideally, it is in the parents' language.

Particularly with younger students, teachers might create regular joint math-based parent/child activities that could be completed anytime within a week. An example might be for the parent and child to jointly note and record situations where they used math, or perhaps to solve a set of shape puzzles. Another source for this is the *Figure This! Math Challenges for Families* website.

Other ways to interact with parents include

- holding games nights and inviting parents and students to play math games together
- sending regular e-mails to update parents about what is happening in the math classroom
- inviting parents in both as observers and as helpers to experience, first-hand, what students are learning
- creating short videos for parents to view to help explain what their children have been learning

Applying What You've Learned

1. The chapter problem at the start of this chapter is a "standard" problem in mathematics. How could it be adapted to meet the needs of other groups of students to focus on operations other than addition, or on other types of numbers rather than whole numbers?

2. Choose a mathematical topic of interest to you. Show how you would move from the concrete to the pictorial to the symbolic with that topic. Research to see at what grade levels those stages are expected for that topic.

3. Find an article about lesson study or collaborative inquiry. Why might you find it useful to participate in a lesson study or collaborative inquiry situation? Do you see any "downsides"?

4. Investigate a Canadian math text with a copyright date after 1990. List five to 10 examples of features or approaches in the text that reflect more current views about the teaching of mathematics.

5. This chapter discusses the special care that might be taken to consider how to adapt instruction to meet the needs of learning-disabled, second-language, or gifted learners. Are there other groups of students you think a teacher should be knowledgeable about in terms of delivering math instruction? Explain.

6. Read about the pros and cons of teaching using cooperative grouping strategies. How often would you group students for instruction? for assessment?

7. Find out what you can about math congress or bansho. How does the teacher's role change in these approaches from a more traditional direct instruction approach to math teaching?

8. Find out about lesson plays (see Sinclair and Zazkis (2011)). How could you use lesson plays to co-plan with other teachers?

Interact with a K–8 Student:

9. Ask a student to discuss how much and what kind of math homework they think would be good if there had to be homework.

Discuss with a K–8 Teacher:

10. Ask a teacher to share with you her or his approaches to yearlong unit and lesson planning in mathematics. Discuss with that teacher what aspects of planning have changed as she or he has gained more teaching experience.

Selected References

Beilock, S.L., and Willingham, D.T. (2014). Math anxiety: Can teachers help students reduce it? *American Educator, 38*(2), 28–32.

Boaler, J. (2012). Timed tests and the development of math anxiety. Education Week. Available from http://joboaler.com/timed-tests-and-the-development-of-math-anxiety/. Accessed August 12, 2014.

Boushey, G., and Moser, J. (2014). *The Daily 5*, 2nd Ed. Portland, ME: Stenhouse Publishers.

Bryant, B.R., and Bryant, D.P. (2008). Introduction to the special series: Mathematics and learning disabilities. *Learning Disability Quarterly, 31*, 3–7.

Buxton, L. (1991). *Math panic.* Portsmouth, NH: Heinemann.

Dacey, L., and Bamford Lynch, J. (2007). *Math for all: Differentiating instruction, Grades 3–5.* Sausalito, CA: Math Solutions.

Dacey, L., and Gartland, K. (2009). *Math for all: Differentiating instruction, Grades 6–8.* Sausalito, CA: Math Solutions.

Dacey, L., and Salemi, R.E. (2007). *Math for all: Differentiating instruction, Grades K–2.* Sausalito, CA: Math Solutions.

Fernandez, C., and Yoshida, M. (2004). *Lesson study: A Japanese approach to improving mathematics teaching and learning.* (Studies in Mathematical Thinking and Learning). Hillsdale, NJ: Lawrence Erlbaum Associates.

Fosnot, C.T., and Dolk, M. (2001). *Young mathematicians at work: Constructing multiplication and division.* Portsmouth, NH: Heinemann.

Gregory, G.H., and Chapman, C. (2008). *Activities for the differentiated classroom: Math, Grades 6–8.* Thousand Oaks, CA: Corwin Press.

Huebner, T.A. (2010). Differentiated learning. *Educational Leadership, 67,* 79–81.

Jayanthi, M., Gersten, R., and Baker, S. (2008). Mathematics instruction for students with learning disabilities or difficulty learning mathematics: A guide for teachers. Available from http://www.centeroninstruction.org/resources.cfm?category=math&subcategory=&grade_start=&grade_end=. Accessed September 15, 2010.

Maloney, E.A., Risko, E.F., Ansari, D., and Fugelsand, J. (2009). Mathematics anxiety affects counting but not subitizing during visual enumeration. *Cognition, 114,* 293–297.

Ministry of Education, Ontario (2010). Communication in the mathematics classroom. Available from https://www.edu.gov.on.ca/eng/literacynumeracy/inspire/research/CBS_Communication_Mathematics.pdf.

Parks, A.N. (2009). Can teacher questions be too open? *Teaching Children Mathematics, 15,* 424–430.

Sheffield, L.J. (1999). *Developing mathematically promising students.* Reston, VA: National Council of Teachers of Mathematics.

Sinclair, N., and Zazkis, R. (2011). Lesson plays: Learning how to improvise. *Ontario Mathematics Gazette, 50,* 30–35.

Small, M. (2009). *Good questions: Great ways to differentiate instruction.* New York: Teachers College Press.

Sowell, E.J. (1989). Effects of manipulative materials in mathematics instruction. *Journal for Research in Mathematics Education, 20,* 498–505.

Targeted Implementation and Planning Supports (TIPS). http://www.edu.gov.on.ca/eng/studentsuccess/lms/files/ELLMath4All.pdf.

Thornton, C.A., Langrall, C.W., and Jones, G.A. (1997). Mathematics instruction for elementary students with learning disabilities. *Journal of Learning Disabilities, 30,* 142–150.

Tobias, S. (1993). *Overcoming math anxiety: Revised and expanded.* New York: W.W. Norton and Co.

Wiggins, G., and McTighe, J. (2005). *Understanding by design.* Alexandria, VA: Association for Supervision and Curriculum Development.

Wilburne, J.M., Marinak, B.A., and Strickland, M.J. (2011). Addressing cultural bias. *Mathematics Teaching in the Middle School, 16,* 460–465.

Williams, L. (2008). Tiering and scaffolding: Two strategies for providing access to important mathematics. *Teaching Children Mathematics, 14,* 324–330.

Chapter 5

A Focus on Problem Solving

IN A NUTSHELL

The main ideas in the chapter are listed below:

1. Teaching through problem solving is a natural approach to teaching for those who believe that students learn best by confronting ideas that require them to establish new connections for themselves.

2. There is a set of problem-solving strategies, or approaches, that are often developed independently by children; it can be valuable to introduce or identify these strategies explicitly.

3. Some problem-solving strategies are more natural to younger students than others, but those strategies continue to be valuable throughout those students' mathematical growth.

CHAPTER PROBLEM

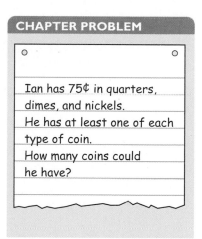

Ian has 75¢ in quarters, dimes, and nickels.
He has at least one of each type of coin.
How many coins could he have?

What Is a Problem?

Mathematics educators regularly talk about the importance of "problem solving," but what is a "problem"? Some might think back to "word problems" they encountered long ago, such as: "Ann had 3 apples. Vanessa had 4 more. How many did they have altogether?" At a very early stage in a student's mathematical development, this is a problem; once the student has learned to translate this situation immediately into writing as 3 + 4, however, it is no longer a problem. Problems require students to have to figure out what to do; the solution is not immediate for them. If they already know what to do (not necessarily what the answer is), it's not a problem.

Why Is Problem Solving Valued?

It is worth considering what it is about problem solving that is valued. One of education's ultimate goals is to equip students to deal effectively with unfamiliar situations, or problems, in life and career. In mathematics, the problems will be those that can be approached using a mathematical lens.

Classroom environment plays a huge role in equipping students to achieve the desired goal. A problem solving environment is one where

- students are encouraged to think independently or with their peers rather than waiting for the teacher to do the modelling
- students enjoy the challenge of thinking on their own and are willing to persevere to solve a problem
- students can use their own judgment to decide if their solution makes sense

It is also an environment where teachers pose questions that prompt thinking rather than telling students how to proceed.

Teaching through Problem Solving

To teach through problem solving, the teacher provides a context or reason for the learning by focusing instruction on a problem to be solved and, within that context and based on student work, drawing out any procedures. This approach contrasts with the more traditional approach of presenting a new procedure and only then offering a few problems to which students can apply that procedure.

Resnick (1987) points out that teaching in this way helps students become adaptable to new situations, for example, new work environments, in their later life. This is likely because students get much more opportunity to *mathematize* real-life situations.

Teaching through problem solving differs from a traditional approach in that

- there is an increased level of mathematical dialogue between students,
- the teacher's role is as a guide or coach more than as a presenter, and
- the teacher uses intervention more judiciously.

A compelling discussion of the importance and efficacy of teaching through problem solving describes Lampert's year-long journey teaching Grade 5 mathematics through problem solving (Lampert, 2001).

Why Teach through Problem Solving?

There are many other reasons for teaching through problem solving:

1. *The math makes more sense.*
   When the problem is a "real-life" one, students have the chance to build essential connections between what the math is, why it is needed, and how it is applied.

2. *A problem-solving approach provides the teacher with better insight into students' mathematical thinking.*
   A problem-solving approach provides the teacher with useful information to improve his or her mathematical interactions with students. The teacher is able to see how effectively students can reach into their "mathematical tool box" to choose the right tools, as well as see how effectively they can use those tools.

3. *Problems are more motivating when they are appropriately challenging.*
   Although some students are comfortable with being told how to do something and then doing it over and over, many do not enjoy this approach. Most students prefer a manageable challenge.

4. *Problem solving builds perseverance.*
   Many students think that if they cannot answer a math question instantly, it is too hard. Through problem-solving experience, they build up a willingness to persevere at solving a problem.

5. *Problem solving builds confidence, maximizes the potential for understanding, and allows for differences in style and approach.*
   Problem solving allows each individual the opportunity to create his or her own path through the mathematics.

6. *Problems can provide practice, both with concepts and with skills.*
   Many good problems have the potential to ensure that students learn concepts and also have the opportunity to practise valuable skills.

7. *A problem-solving approach provides students with better insight into what mathematics is all about.*
   Math requires the same kind of struggle as does creating a new piece of writing or a new work of art. Most rich problems invite many possible solution strategies, and some are even designed to encourage many possible answers. This notion of creativity or choice in mathematics will not make sense to someone who has not struggled on his or her own to try to solve a mathematical problem.

8. *Students need to practise problem solving.*
   If the goal of mathematics education is to enable students to confront new situations involving mathematics, then they must practise doing this. Students need many opportunities to practise problem solving to be able to do so independently.

The Problem-Solving Process

In many jurisdictions, it is expected that a significant part of the science and math curriculums will be taught using problems.

Stages of the Problem-Solving Process

A well-known problem-solving model, developed by George Polya (1957), includes the following four stages:

Stage 1: Understand the problem
Stage 2: Make a plan
Stage 3: Carry out the plan
Stage 4: Look back

The understand-the-problem stage is often a stumbling block for students, as it involves discerning whether all the necessary information is provided and if extraneous information is included. It is important to provide sufficient support to ensure that students understand the problem.

The look-back stage involves checking to see if an answer is reasonable and, where applicable, determining another answer for the problem. It also is an opportunity for students to share strategies and see how different approaches might have been taken.

Although the stages are described as distinct and sequential, there is often a lot of blurring and going back and forth. For some problem solvers, Stages 2 and 3 might happen almost simultaneously. Or a problem solver might get to Stage 3 or 4 and have to go back to Stage 1.

The teacher's role during the process is not to show or model, but to listen, provide constructive feedback, and ask prompting questions to help move students forward. Often these questions will ask students to conjecture, justify, and defend their thinking.

Each stage of the process involves a certain level of communication or reflection about the mathematics that is being used. Students should be sharing their thinking at all stages with their peers.

A Graphic Organizer

An alternative way for students to think about these stages is suggested by Zollman (2009) and is shown below.

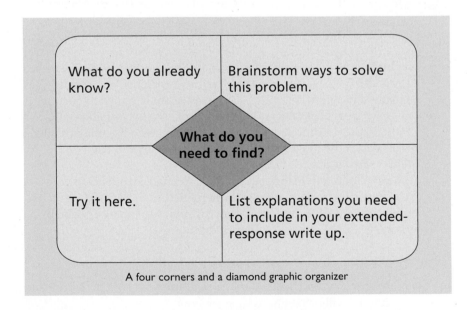

A four corners and a diamond graphic organizer

What the Problem-Solving Process Looks Like

The following section provides an example of what each of these stages of the process might look like using the problem-solving strategy of drawing a picture. The example demonstrates how students can increase their understanding of a problem as they work through the solution.

A Problem and Possible Solution

| STAGE 1: UNDERSTAND THE PROBLEM | STAGE 2: MAKE A PLAN |

A group of children wore boots to school.
Some of them wore mittens.
The teacher counted 12 boots and 8 mittens.
How many children did not wear mittens?

> If we figure out how many more boots there are than mittens, we can figure out how many children that would be.

> There are 12 boots and 8 mittens. Every child is wearing 2 boots. Every child wearing mittens has 2 mittens.

> Let's draw a picture to see how many extra boots there are. Then we can figure out how many children that would be.

Photodisc Blue/Getty Images

| STAGE 3: CARRY OUT THE PLAN | STAGE 4: LOOK BACK |

> There are 4 extra boots, but it's only 2 extra children.

> The answer makes sense because if there were 6 children with boots, that's 6 + 6 = 12 boots altogether. If there were 2 children without mittens, that's 4 + 4 = 8 mittens altogether.

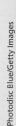

Photodisc Blue/Getty Images

Characteristics of Good Problems

A significant part of a teacher's role is finding or creating good problems. A good problem always requires a student to think about mathematics in a slightly fresh way, but, in addition, it could have any of the following characteristics. The problem might

- require a student to connect new ideas to previously learned ones
- be solved in many ways, often using different problem-solving strategies
- pique curiosity
- have personal meaning or relevance to a student
- have a creative element to it
- require reasoning
- often have many answers to engender good discussion

The problem may have a real-life context, or it may be an interesting mathematical situation. Although problems are richer and more meaningful if contexts are used, the level of reading required must be considered. Many good problems can lead to more general understandings than the particulars of the solution.

Some Techniques for Creating Good Problems

TECHNIQUE	EXAMPLES
The "story book" technique, for which teachers or students create problems based on story books.	The story *Invisible Alligators*, online, by Hayes Roberts (2009), could lead to these problems: • If the castle had 52 steps and toys were on every 4th step, how many steps had no toys? • How big would a bathtub be if it could hold a hippo?
The "use-blanks" technique, for which you create a question with some of the numbers missing	• Put the digits 1, 2, 3, 4, and 5 in the boxes ■ ■ ■ − ■ ■. What are the least and greatest possible answers? [531, 69] • How would you place the digits 6, 7, and 8 in the boxes ■.■ × 0.■ so that the product is as close to 5 as possible? [8.7 × 0.6 = 5.22] • How many pairs of digits can be put in the blanks so that the answer to 6 ■ ÷ ■ is a whole number? [29]
The "what if ..." technique, for which you create a situation that is based on a particular set of assumptions, and then challenge one of the premises by posing a new question	• 35 + 5 × 8 = 75 because of the order-of-operation rules. What if the rule were to add and subtract before you multiplied and divided? What would the expression be worth? [320]
The "turn-it-around" technique, in which you give students the answer and ask them to work backward	• Describe three different pairs of numbers with a common factor of 6. [e.g., 12, 18; 60, 24; 600, 300] • The answer is 45. What's the question? [e.g., 9 × 5 or 135 ÷ 3] • Write three additions with the same sum as 45 + 38. [e.g., 46 + 37, 35 + 48, 25 + 58]

Problem-Solving Strategies

Mathematics educators have identified a list of problem-solving strategies that have proven to be useful in approaching a wide variety of problems. The strategies are described over the next several pages.

It is important to understand that the strategy should be explicitly discussed with students, preferably after it comes up naturally because a student has chosen to use it. There is value in naming the strategies and keeping a strategy list posted, so students can discuss the strategies and use them again and again. The list becomes a menu for students to select from when they face a new problem and are not sure how to proceed.

Students should also be encouraged to combine strategies that suit particular problems when necessary. For example, a student might use a chart or table to look for a number pattern.

Students also need to recognize that different strategies can be used at different stages of the inquiry process. For example, a student might draw a picture to understand a problem, and then use another strategy to carry out the solution.

Below are sample problems that can be used to potentially evoke different problem solving strategies. Because it is important to ask problems that are mathematically significant, suggestions for eliciting some of the big ideas in math with each problem are also included.

Although any of the problem-solving strategies can be used by students of any age, often some strategies are favoured more by younger students. These are described in the group of simpler problem-solving strategies below. Younger students' preference for these strategies does not preclude them being used later, nor does it mean that some of the later strategies might not be used by some younger students.

Problem-Solving Strategy Menu
• Act it out.
• Use a model.
• Draw a picture.
• Guess and test.
• Look for a pattern.
• Use an open sentence.
• Make a chart/table or graph.
• Solve a simpler problem.
• Consider all possibilities.
• Consider extreme cases.
• Make an organized list.
• Work backward.
• Use logical reasoning.
• Change your point of view.

Simpler Problem-Solving Strategies

Everyone benefits from learning through their senses, and this is particularly important for students at a young age. Thus, the act-it-out, use-a-model, and draw-a-picture strategies are particularly suited to young students. The guess-and-test strategy is also suitable. These simple strategies continue to be useful to older students and adults as well.

STRATEGY

Act it out
Students literally "act out" the story of the problem. Sometimes the story is very straightforward, and other times is more complex.

SAMPLE PROBLEM	POSSIBLE SOLUTION
There are 4 students on each of 2 teams. At the end of the tournament, students shake hands with members of the other team. How many handshakes will there be?	Students might act out the problem in a systematic fashion: Two teams of 4 students line up across from each other. Each student shakes hands with each student on the other team, beginning with the first student on one team shaking everyone's hand on the other team in order from left to right. Someone keeps track of the number of handshakes. There are 16 handshakes.

Big Idea Note
By asking, "How does representing the problem by acting it out help you figure out what to do if there are more students?", the teacher is helping the student consider the big idea that different representations of relationships help us gain different insights into those relationships.

STRATEGY

Use a model
This strategy can be very much like the act-it-out strategy, but students model the problem by representing its elements with simple, available materials.

SAMPLE PROBLEM

A company that makes bread sticks has hired you to design their new logo. They want the logo to show 8 bread sticks arranged to make the outline of a polygon. What different polygons can you make with 8 bread sticks?

Big Idea Note
By asking, "What are some ways you can describe each shape?", the teacher is helping students see that some descriptions of shapes are quantitative, but others are qualitative.

POSSIBLE SOLUTION

A student might use toothpicks to represent the breadsticks to model the problem. Notice that this student has also approached the problem in a systematic way.

"I used 8 toothpicks. I know I can make an octagon because it has 8 sides."

"I need at least 3 sides to make a polygon. This is the only triangle I can make."

"Here are some quadrilaterals."

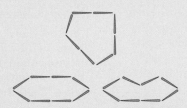

"Here are some with 5, 6, and 7 sides. I already made one with 8 sides and I know 9 sides is impossible."

"I know I can make a triangle, lots of quadrilaterals, a 5-sided shape, a hexagon, a 7-sided shape, and an octagon."

STRATEGY

Draw a picture

This strategy is much like the use-a-model strategy, but students use a pictorial model, rather than a concrete model. Students can draw the actual object or a simple symbol to represent the object.

SAMPLE PROBLEM

It was getting close to the school raffle. Ann's mother knitted 2 mittens on Monday and 2 more than the day before each day after. On what day did she knit 16 mittens?

Big Idea Note

By asking the student how he or she might have predicted that the answer would be "On the 8th day," the teacher is helping students see the relationship between multiplication and repeated addition.

POSSIBLE SOLUTION

A student might use a calendar as a graphic organizer:

On Monday there were 16 mittens.

STRATEGY

Guess and test

For this strategy, a student guesses an answer and then tests it to see if the guess works. If it doesn't, the student revises the "guess" based on what was learned and tries again. This repetitive process continues until the answer is found. Some students are able to think through several guesses at once; others need to go one step at a time. Although we often talk about guessing as bad, this strategy reinforces the value of taking risks and learning from the information that is garnered.

SAMPLE PROBLEM

There are 8 more girls than boys in a room. Altogether, there are 24 people. How many are boys?

Big Idea Note

By asking, "Suppose I had only told you there were 8 more girls than boys; what else could you have been sure of?", the teacher is bringing out the big idea that knowing one piece of information often provides other information.

POSSIBLE SOLUTION

A student might guess and test several times, each time basing the guess on the results of the previous guess:

5 boys and 13 girls is 18 people   not enough people
10 boys and 18 girls is 28 people   too many people
7 boys and 15 girls is 22 people.   not enough people
8 boys and 16 girls is 24 people
There are 8 boys.

STRATEGY

Look for a pattern
Because mathematics is so full of patterns, students soon learn
that using patterns is an effective way to solve problems.

SAMPLE PROBLEM

How many cans do you need to
make the sixth stack in this shape
pattern?

1st   2nd   3rd

Big Idea Note
By asking, "Can you be
sure?", the teacher is
bringing out the big idea
that you can't be sure of a
pattern without a rule.

POSSIBLE SOLUTION

A student could draw a picture (or use a counter model) to figure out
the number of cans in the fourth stack in order to be sure about the
pattern and then use the pattern to figure out the number in the sixth
stack.

1st   2nd   3rd   4th

There's 1 in the 1st stack, 1+2 in the 2nd stack, 1+2+3 in
the 3rd stack, and 1+2+3+4 in the 4th stack. That means
that there would be 1+2+3+4+5+6 in the 6th stack.

1+2+3+4+5+6=21   There are 21 in the 6th stack.

STRATEGY

Use an open sentence
As students become more comfortable with the symbolic forms of
mathematical expressions, they can begin to represent a problem with
an open sentence. Some mathematics educators might argue that this
is simply another form of the use-a-model strategy, but this time the
model is mathematical rather than pictorial or concrete.

SAMPLE PROBLEM

An egg has a mass of about 50 g
and an empty 12-egg carton has
a mass of about 25 g. Jaden is
carrying some cartons of eggs.
The total mass is 5 kg. How many
cartons is he carrying?

Big Idea Note
By asking, "What is it about
each operation you used
that made it useful for this
problem?", the teacher is
bringing out the meanings
of the operations.

POSSIBLE SOLUTION

A student might determine which operation is needed to solve the
problem by writing an open sentence that describes the problem
situation (as shown at the top of the next page).

The eggs in one carton have a mass of
12 × 50g = 600g. The carton is 25g.
So, a full carton is 625g.

I have to find out how many groups of 625g are in 5kg or 5000g. I can write a multiplication sentence to find out

☐ × 625 = 5000

If ☐ × 625 = 5000 then I can divide 5000 by 625 to figure out what ☐ is. I'll use a calculator.

5000 ÷ 625 = ☐

5000 ÷ 625 = 8, so 8 × 625 = 5000

Jaden is carrying 8 cartons of eggs.

STRATEGY

Make a chart/table or graph
Sometimes it is useful to organize data in a chart/table or a graph. This helps students keep track of disparate pieces of information and helps them ensure that they consider many possibilities.

SAMPLE PROBLEM

Suppose you spin each spinner below and add the two numbers you spin. Which is more likely?

• The sum will be less than 9.
• The sum will be greater than 9.

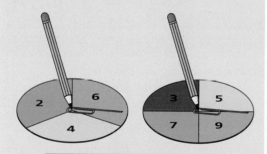

Big Idea Note
By asking, "Why does drawing the graph make it quicker to see the answer than just recording the results of the spins?", the teacher is bringing out the idea that visual displays help us see information more quickly.

POSSIBLE SOLUTION

A student might conduct a spinner experiment and shade a bar graph on grid paper to keep track of and show the results.

I started a graph with the two outcomes. I spun the two spinners 10 times and shaded a square each time for the sum. Sometimes the sum was exactly 9 but I didn't need to keep track of those sums.
A sum >9 is more likely than a sum <9.

STRATEGY

Solve a simpler problem
Sometimes the path through a problem is easier if the numbers are more accessible, or simpler.

SAMPLE PROBLEM

Norah has 3 dimes and 9 nickels. How much money does she have?

Big Idea Note
By asking, "How would you solve the problem differently if the coins were all the same value?", the teacher is helping students recognize that the operations of multiplication and addition are related, but might be used in different situations.

POSSIBLE SOLUTION

A student might begin with a simpler problem:

If it were 3 dimes and 3 nickels, it would be
30¢ + 15¢ = 45¢.
But there are 6 more nickels, which is 3 dimes, or 30¢.
The money is worth 45¢ + 30¢ = 75¢.

More Complex Problem-Solving Strategies

As students develop even more analytic skills, they are able to use organizational strategies more formally to ensure that no case is omitted. These students are also more ready to use logical reasoning and to work either forward or backward.

These strategies may be seen with younger students, but are more likely to be seen with somewhat older elementary students.

STRATEGY

Make an organized list
To use this strategy, a student must realize that there are many "cases," or possible answers. By being systematic in listing the cases, this student is less likely to leave something out and may, in fact, be able to "shortcut" the work. Students must learn to look through the list and eliminate any redundancy.

SAMPLE PROBLEM

How many different products are possible when you multiply the numbers on two dice?

Big Idea Note
By asking, "How is 4 × 3 the same as 2 × 6?", the teacher is emphasizing the value of an alternative representation [4 groups of 3 can be combined to make 2 groups of 6].

POSSIBLE SOLUTION

A student might use an organized list to approach the problem systematically:

Make a list, starting with × 1, then × 2 and × 3, and so on. Check to make sure nothing was missed.

Cross off any products that are the same.

Count the products that are left.

1 × 1 = 1	2×1=2	2×1=3	4×1=4	5×1=5	6×1=6
1 × 2 = 2	2×2=4	2×2=6	4×2=8	5×2=10	6×2=12
1 × 3 = 3	2×3=6	3 × 3 = 9	4×3=12	5×3=15	6×3=18
1 × 4 = 4	2 × 4 = 8	2×4=12	4 × 4 = 16	5×4=20	6×4=24
1 × 5 = 5	2 × 5 = 10	3 × 5 = 15	4 × 5 = 20	5 × 5 = 25	6×5=30
1 × 6 = 6	2 × 6 = 12	3 × 6 = 18	4 × 6 = 24	5 × 6 = 30	6 × 6 = 36
6	3	3	3	2	1

There are 18 different products.

STRATEGY

Consider all possibilities
In many mathematical situations, students must consider a number of different possibilities to ensure that all aspects of the problem are dealt with.

SAMPLE PROBLEM

A set of five data values, all whole numbers up to 10, has a mode of 8, a median of 8, and a mean of 8. There are more than two 8s in the set. What could the data values be? Find as many answers as you can.

Big Idea Note
By asking, "Do you think that all of the data sets are described well by the single number, 8?", the teacher is focusing the student on why we use summary statistics, and their limitations.

POSSIBLE SOLUTION

A student could create and test all the possibilities to see if they follow the clues provided in the problem:

- There are five values.
- There are three, four, or five 8s.
- The mean is 8, so the sum of the values is 40 (5×8).
- The mode and median are both 8.
- The greatest value is 10 or less.

Five 8s: 8, 8, 8, 8, 8. This works.

Four 8s: 8, 8, 8, 8, __ or __ 8, 8, 8, 8.
The missing number has to be 8 for the sum of 40.
Four 8s doesn't work.

Three 8s: 8, 8, 8, __, __ (there's an 8 in the middle for the median to be 8.) The last 2 numbers have to add to 16 for a mean of 8. You can't make 16 with 9s and 10s.

Three 8s another way __, __, 8, 8, 8.
You can't make 16 with 2 numbers less than 8.

Three 8s another way: __, 8, 8, 8, __.
Two ways work: 6, 8, 8, 8, 10 and 7, 8, 8, 8, 9.

There has to be more than two 8s, so there are no more answers.

The numbers are: 8, 8, 8, 8, 8 or 6, 8, 8, 8, 10, or 7, 8, 8, 8, 10.

STRATEGY

Consider extreme cases
Sometimes students can solve problems related to a range of values.
This is a special case of considering all possibilities.

SAMPLE PROBLEM

John has between 100 and 1000 pages to read. He intends to read exactly the same number of pages every day. He hasn't decided if it will be in 1, 2, 3, 4, 5, 6, 7, 8, or 9 days yet.

POSSIBLE SOLUTION

A student might consider the greatest and least possible answers:

Divide the greatest 3-digit dividend by the least 1-digit divisor for the greatest whole number quotient.

Divide the least 3-digit dividend by the greatest 1-digit divisor for the least whole number quotient.

(continued)

What number of pages will he read each day? Predict whether the answer will be

- less than 10
- between 10 and 100
- between 100 and 1000
- between 10 and 1000

> **Big Idea Note**
> By asking, "Why did you only need to do two divisions to solve the problem?", the teacher is bringing out the notion that knowing certain relationships tells you about other ones.

He could read 999 ÷ 1 = 999 pages in 1 day.
He could read 100 ÷ 9 = 11 R1 pages in 9 days.
So it could be between 10 and 1000 pages per day.

STRATEGY

Use logical reasoning

Some people think of logical reasoning not so much as a problem-solving strategy, but as an aspect of mathematics that permeates all mathematical endeavours. However, others think of it as a strategy that is worthwhile to consciously consider when faced with a mathematical problem.

SAMPLE PROBLEM

Jonathan writes his name, one letter per box, in a square 4-by-4 grid.

J	O	N	A
T	H	A	N
J	O	N	A
T	H	A	N

What size square grid is needed for the J to be in the bottom right corner?

> **Big Idea Note**
> By asking, "Why did representing the number of boxes in the grid in different ways (e.g., 25 as $3 \times 8 + 1$) help you solve the problem?", the teacher is helping to highlight the big idea that different representations of numbers are useful to highlight different things about the number.

POSSIBLE SOLUTION

To solve the problem, a student might reason:

The name Jonathan has 8 letters. 16 squares were needed to put the last N in the bottom right corner because 16 is a multiple of 8 and a square number (16 squares can form a square grid).

The number of squares must be a square number. To put the letter J in the bottom right corner, it must also be a multiple of 8 plus 1 more.

A square number that is 1 more than a multiple of 8 is 25 (5 x 5 is 3 x 8 + 1), so the grid could be 5 by 5.

There are other answers too:

49 (7 x 7 is 6 x 8 + 1), so the grid could be 7 by 7.

81 (9 x 9 is 10 x 8 + 1), so the grid could be 9 by 9.

STRATEGY

Work backward
Sometimes, by starting with the result, a student can work backward to determine information about the original situation.

SAMPLE PROBLEM

Aaron cut 0.5 m from a length of wire. Then he cut what was left into four equal pieces. If each of the four pieces was 1.25 m long, what was the length of the wire before Aaron cut it?

Big Idea Note
By asking, "What else did you know once you knew the length of each of the four pieces?", the teacher is focusing on the big idea that if you know some information about a situation, you actually may know other information as well.

POSSIBLE SOLUTION

A student could work backward by determining the sum of the four equal lengths cut from the original piece of wire and then adding the 0.5 m length back on.

> These are 4 pieces that are 1.25m long.
> 4 × 1.25 = 5
>
> Aaron also has the 0.5m piece he cut first.
> 5 + 0.5 = 5.5
>
> Before Aaron cut it, the wire was 5.5m long.

STRATEGY

Change your point of view
Sometimes, students are asked to calculate how many of something there are. In some cases, however, a better approach might be to calculate how many there are not.

SAMPLE PROBLEM

What is the probability that, when you roll two dice, you will get a sum that is the result of adding two different numbers?

Big Idea Note
By asking, "How did knowing the result of adding the same number give you the information you need?", the teacher is focusing on the big idea that if you know some information about a situation, you actually know other information as well.

POSSIBLE SOLUTION

A student might determine the theoretical probability of getting a sum that is the result of doubles, and then use this to determine the probability of getting a sum that is the result of non-doubles (that is, two different numbers).

> There are a lot more ways to get sums from different numbers than from doubles.
> I made an addition table to find the total number of sums and the number of sums from doubles.
>
> Possible Sums for 2 Dice
>
> | + | 1 | 2 | 3 | 4 | 5 | 6 |
> |----|---|---|---|---|---|---|
> | 1 | (2) | 3 | 4 | 5 | 6 | 7 |
> | 2 | 3 | (4) | 5 | 6 | 7 | 8 |
> | 3 | 4 | 5 | (6) | 7 | 8 | 9 |
> | 4 | 5 | 6 | 7 | (8) | 9 | 10 |
> | 5 | 6 | 7 | 8 | 9 | (10) | 11 |
> | 6 | 7 | 8 | 9 | 10 | 11 | (12) |
>
> There is a total of 36 sums. The 6 circled ones are from doubles. So, 30 are not from doubles.
>
> The probability of a sum from 2 different numbers is $\frac{30}{36}$.

Suitable Problems

Below you will find an assortment of problems to explore that are used at a variety of grade levels. Recall that a problem is meant to "stretch" students, so these examples might be just beyond where the students are developmentally.

Many problems can be adjusted to make them more suitable for another level by changing a few specific features. For example, a problem that requires students to put together two concrete triangles to make another shape as shown below can evolve, for more advanced students, into a problem where they must list all possible shapes that can be created, or where they are asked to determine how many congruent triangles can be combined to make a similar triangle.

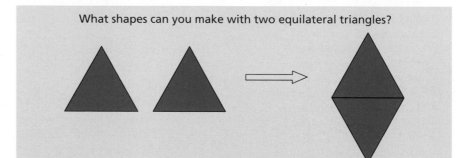

What shapes can you make with two equilateral triangles?

Problems Based on Earlier K–8 Content

PENNY SALE

You have 10¢ to buy school supplies.

An eraser costs 2¢; a pencil costs 3¢; and a paper clip costs 1¢.

a) What items can you buy?

b) Can you buy exactly 6 items and use all of your money?

[**Possible Strategy:** Act it out;

Hint: Students can use 10 play pennies to act out the problem.

For part b), students could start with 6 paper clips and trade up for more expensive items until 10 pennies have been spent.]   [e.g., a) 5 erasers;

3 erasers, a pencil, and a paper clip;

8 paper clips and an eraser;

b) yes, 4 paper clips and 2 pencils]

DRAWING TRIANGLES

The pattern below continues until there are 10 triangles altogether. How many shapes are there in the pattern?

[**Possible Strategy:** Draw a picture.]   [14]

MAKING SNOWMEN

You are making snowmen. Each snowman is made with 2 circles and 4 buttons.

You have 15 circles and 25 buttons. What is the greatest number of complete snowmen you can make?

[**Possible Strategy:** Draw a picture.]   [6]

DO YOU LIKE SPAGHETTI?

I asked students in my class if they like spaghetti. 5 said "no" and 10 more than that said "yes." How many students are in my class?

[**Possible Strategy:** Act it out or Use a model; **Hint:** Students line up 5 red counters to represent the people who said "no," and then add 10 more.]   [20 students]

SHAPE HUNT

A block has some triangle faces and some faces that are not triangles. Find the block in the pile.

[**Possible Strategy:** Guess and test.]   [triangle-based prism]

FILL IT IN

Show three different ways to cover this shape with pattern blocks.

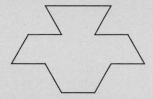

[**Possible Strategy:** Guess and test and Act it out.]

PACKAGES OF PENS

Pens come in packages of 3, 5, and 8.

Mrs. O'Regan bought 26 pens for her class.

How many packages of each type might she have bought?

[**Possible Strategy:** Act it out; **Hint:** Students can use 26 pens, or counters, to represent the pens and try different groupings of 3, 5, and 8.]   [e.g., 2 packages of 5 and 2 packages of 8]

DART ADDITION

Leah must throw at least 4 darts to get a score of 100.

a) What is the least score she can get with 4 darts?

b) How could she get a score of 90 with 4 darts?

[**Possible Strategy:** Make a chart/table; **Hint:** Students can make a chart to show the totals if all of the darts land in the same ring. They notice that a score of 90 occurs between the scores for four darts in the 22 ring and four darts in the 23 ring.]

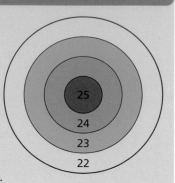

[a) 88; b) e.g., 22, 22, 23, and 23]

WHAT'S THE DATE?

What is the date of the 100th day of a non–leap year?

[**Possible Strategy:** Make a chart; **Hint:** Use a chart to show the number of days in each month in one column, and a running total in a second column. Count the number of days in the first 3 months: $31 + 28 + 31 = 90$. You need 10 more days into the 4th month.]   [April 10]

ADDING NUMBERS

Add the first 100 numbers (starting with 1). What digit is in the ones place of the sum?

[**Possible Strategy:** Solve a simpler problem and Look for a pattern; **Hint:** Try some simpler problems like $1 + 2 + 3 + 4$ and $1 + 2 + 3 + 4 + 5 + 6$ to note the pattern. Then, look for the same pattern in $1 + 2 + 3 + 4 + \cdots + 97 + 98 + 99 + 100$. Match up addends at either end: $100 + 1$, then $99 + 2$, then $98 + 3$, and so on. A pattern emerges of 50 pairs, each with a sum of 101. $50 \times 101 = 5050$.]   [0]

BALANCING ACT

Jenny had some loaves of bread, some cans of soup, and some boxes of cereal. She put one can of soup into the bag, and then added more items. When she was done, the total mass was between 900 g and 1 kg. What could be in the bag? Find as many different answers as you can.

[**Possible Strategy:** Use an open sentence; **Hint:** To find the least and greatest possible combined mass of the other items, students might use open sentences: $105 \text{ g} + \square = 900 \text{ g}$ and $105 \text{ g} + \square = 1000 \text{ g}$.

Once they determine that the other items are between 795 g and 895 g, they can look for combinations with this mass.]   [e.g., 9 soups; 1 loaf of bread and 4 soups; 2 cereals and 1 soup; 1 cereal and 5 soups]

MISSING MEASURES

How long is the red side of this shape? the green side?

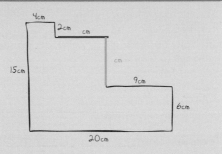

[**Possible Strategies:** Draw a picture (e.g., on grid paper) or Use an open sentence; **Hint:** To solve the problem with an open sentence, students need to recognize that the vertical sides on the right must have a total length of 15 cm, because they cover the same vertical distance as the 15-cm side on the left. The horizontal sides across the top must have a total length of 20 cm to match the bottom side.]   [Both are 7 cm.]

SQUARE CORNER DOTS

These two points are the corners of a square.

Draw two squares with these corners.

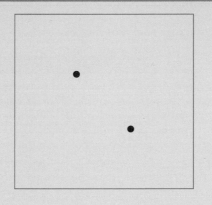

[**Possible Strategy:** Draw a picture;
Hint: Turn the paper and look at the dots from other perspectives.]

[e.g., 2 of these]

Problems Based on Later K–8 Content

Sometimes, a problem like one of those below can be solved by a student younger than expected. The younger student might use a different strategy since his or her content knowledge is different.

MULTIPLYING DOUBLES

A 2-digit number is multiplied by its double. The product is 5618. What is the number?

[**Possible Strategy:** Guess and test;
Hint: Students try a number, and increase or decrease as appropriate.]   [53]

FRUIT AND VEGETABLE

The pictograph shows the number of students who eat different numbers of servings of fruit and vegetables each day. 108 students were surveyed. How many students does each symbol represent?

[**Possible Strategy:** Use an open sentence;
Hint: 12 × ▨ = 108.]   [9]

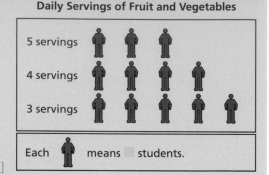

Daily Servings of Fruit and Vegetables

SWITCHING DIGITS

The digits of a 2-digit number are switched around to form a different 2-digit number. The new number is 27 less than the original number. What is the least the original number could be?

[**Possible Strategy:** Use logical reasoning;
Hint: Students reason that if the digits are switched and the difference is 27, the digits are probably 3 apart.]   [e.g., 41]

PERIMETER PAIRS

Two rectangles have the same perimeter, but the area of one is 6 cm² greater than the area of the other. What could their side lengths be, if the side lengths are whole number values?

[**Possible Strategy:** Guess and test or Work backward;
Hint: Students can look for two basic-fact products that are 6 apart, such as 5 × 6 = 30 and 6 × 6 = 36, for the possible areas of the two rectangles, and then use the perimeter formula to see if their perimeters are the same.]   [e.g., 2 × 9 and 3 × 8; 5 × 6 and 3 × 8; 6 × 7 and 9 × 4]

CLOSED DOORS

A set of doors marked from 1 to 100 are all open. 100 students walk by the doors, one at a time, and open and close the doors as described below:

The 1st student closes all the doors. The 2nd student opens every 2nd door.

The 3rd student changes every 3rd door by closing opened ones and opening closed ones.

The 4th student changes every 4th door.

This continues until all 100 students are done. How many doors are closed at the end?

[**Possible Strategies:** Solve a simpler problem, Draw a picture, and Look for a pattern;
Hint: Try 20 doors. Use O to represent an open door and C to represent a closed one. Show each step until a pattern emerges:

Start: OOOOOOOOOOOOOOOOOOOO. ...

After 1st: CCCCCCCCCCCCCCCCCCCC. ...

After 2nd: COCOCOCOCOCOCOCOCOCO. ...

After 3rd: COOOCCCOOOCCCOOOCCCO. ...

The pattern emerges that the closed doors occur at 1, 4, 9, 16, ... , the square numbers.]   [10]

WHAT'S THE FIRST NUMBER?

In a certain pattern, you add two numbers to get the next number. If the 9th number is 212 and the 10th number is 343, what is the first number?

[**Possible Strategy:** Use an open sentence and Work backward;
Hint: 10th term = 9th term + 8th term, so 343 = 212 + ▢ and the 8th term is 131; 9th term = 8th term + 7th term, so 212 = 131 + ▢ and the 7th term is 81; repeat over and over.]   [5]

ROLLING PRODUCTS

Two players each roll a die. Player A wins if the product of the numbers is even. Player B wins if the product is odd. If they roll 20 times, how often is Player A likely to win?

[**Possible Strategy:** Conduct an experiment or Make a chart/table or graph;
Hint: Students make a multiplication table to determine that there are 36 possible products, and that 27 are even. They use the theoretical probability $\frac{27}{36} = \frac{3}{4}$ to calculate the number of even products for 20 rolls.]   [15 times]

NO SQUARES ALLOWED

You can draw lots of different squares by using the dots in this design as vertices. What is the least number of dots you would have to get rid of so that no squares can be made?

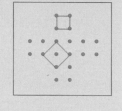

Remove 6 dots.

[**Possible Strategies:** Draw a picture and work backward;
Hint: Draw squares and eliminate some of the points that form their vertices.]   [6]

Sources for Other Problems

A wealth of mathematics problems are available from other sources.

The Internet provides a number of possibilities. One particularly valuable site is the Math Forum's Problems of the Week. Another is a site set up at St. Francis Xavier University in Nova Scotia for Grades 5 to 8 math problems.

Many textbooks designed for elementary-school–aged children are a source of good problems. Many of these problems can be modified to suit different developmental phases and to create other problems.

In addition, a number of print resources offer excellent math problems. Some of these are listed below:

Math League Contest Books
101 Brain-Boosting Math Problems
Awesome Math Problems for Creative Thinking series
www.cemc.uwaterloo.ca
Journals of the National Council of Teachers of Mathematics
Mathcounts handbooks

Student-Created Problems

Another good source of problems is problems created by students. By posing problems, students develop their creativity (although they might model some problems on what they have already seen). Another benefit is that the teacher gains insight into student understanding of concepts and students are still practising problem solving skills since they have to make sure their problem makes sense.

Helpful Hints for Problem Solving

Aside from the strategies already discussed, which are mathematically focused, there are some generic helpful hints, or strategies, that students should consider when working on mathematical problems. These can be posted on a classroom wall.

Helpful Hints for Problem Solving

If you're stuck ...
- Take a deep breath and relax.
- Brainstorm: Write down everything you can think of about the problem.
- Highlight important parts of the question.
- Draw a picture of the problem, if possible.
- Model the problem using any materials you have, if possible.
- Talk yourself through the problem.
- Think about other problems you've solved that are like this one.
- Look at the strategy list. Decide which one to try first.
- Talk about the problem with another student.
- Convince yourself you can do it!

Assessing Student Problem Solving

- It is sometimes difficult to separate out students' problem-solving and communication skills. When you focus on assessing problem solving, try to assist students, if necessary, with the communication aspect, so that you gain better insight into the problem-solving processes they use.
- You may sometimes want to assess the problem-solving process in a global way, but other times you may want to focus on the steps individually; for example, whether students understand the problem may be considered apart from their development of a plan or the plan's execution.
- It is important to share in advance with students the assessment tools you will use. This helps students know what to focus on. Most of the time, a rubric with a set of four categories is used for measuring problem-solving performance.

Applying What You've Learned

1. Which of the problem-solving strategies presented in this chapter would have helped you solve the chapter problem? Explain why these strategies would be useful.

2. Many people argue that problem solving should be a focus for high-ability students, but not for students who are struggling. Make an argument for why problem solving might be even more important for a struggling student.

3. Some teachers are uncomfortable with the guess-and-test strategy. They are concerned that students should not be encouraged to guess. Make an argument for why this is a valid and helpful strategy for solving math problems.

4. Locate and read a journal article that focuses on the notion of teaching through problem solving. List one or two of the most important points made in that article.

5. One of the elements of the inquiry process is the look-back step. Many students skip that step. How might you convince a student of the importance of this aspect of the problem-solving process?

6. Visit an Internet site that includes math contest problems or problems of the week. Create a small resource file of 20 rich problems that you might use with students at a grade level of your choice.

7. Explore several issues of one of the National Council of Teachers of Mathematics journals. What proportion of the journal seems to be devoted to problem solving in the mathematics classroom? Does this proportion seem reasonable to you?

Interact with a K–8 Student:

8. Choose one of your problems from Question 6. Observe how a student of an appropriate grade level for that problem solves it. What do you notice about the approach the student uses?

Discuss with a K–8 Teacher:

9. Ask a teacher how or whether she or he explicitly discusses the common problem-solving strategies with students and why she or he uses the approach they do.

10. Ask the teacher how often she or he assigns problems for student exploration, for example, problems of the day or problems of the week.

Selected References

Bostick, J., and Jacobbe, T. (2010). Promoting problem-solving discourse. *Teaching Children Mathematics, 17,* 3–37.

Buschmann, L. (2004). Teaching problem solving in mathematics. *Teaching Children Mathematics, 10,* 302–309.

Chandler, K. (Ed.). (2004). *2004-2005 Mathcounts school handbook.* Alexandria, VA: Mathcounts Foundation.

Conrad, S.R., and Fleger, D. (1996). *Math contests (grades 4, 5, and 6).* (Vols. 1-4). Tenafly, NJ: Mathematics Leagues.

Egan, L.H. (1999). *101 brain-boosting math problems (grades 4-8).* New York: Scholastic.

Findell, C.R., Cavanagh, M., Dacey, L., Greenes, C.E., Jensen Sheffield, L., and Small, M. (2004). *Navigating through problem solving and reasoning in grade 1.* Reston, VA: National Council of Teachers of Mathematics.

Findell, C., Gavin, K., Greenes, C., and Sheffield, L. (2000). *Awesome math problems for creative thinking, grades 3-8.* Chicago: Creative Publications.

Kalman, R. (2004). The value of multiple solutions. *Mathematics Teaching in the Middle School, 10,* 174-179.

Lampert, M. (2001). *Teaching problems and the problems of teaching.* New Haven, CT: Yale University Press.

Lester, F. (2003). *Teaching mathematics through problem solving: Prekindergarten–grade 6.* Reston, VA: National Council of Teachers of Mathematics.

O'Connell, S. (2000). *Introduction to problem solving: Strategies for the elementary math classroom.* Portsmouth, NH: Heinemann.

Polya, G. (1957). *How to solve it: A new aspect of mathematical method* (2nd ed.). Princeton, NJ: Princeton University Press.

Resnick, L. (1987). Learning in school and out. *Educational Researcher, 16,* 13–20.

Roberts, H. (2009). *Invisible alligators.* Accessed at http://www.magickeys.com/books/invis-allig/index.html#pictop. August 12, 2014.

Schuster, L., and Canavan Anderson, N. (2005). *Good questions for math teaching: Why ask them and what to ask: Grades 5–8.* Sausalito, CA: Math Solutions.

Small, M. (2009). *Good questions: Great ways to differentiate instruction.* New York: Teachers College Press.

Small, M. (2010). *PRIME: Measurement: Background and strategies.* Toronto, ON: Nelson Education Ltd.

Sullivan, P., and Liliburn, P. (2002). *Good questions for math teaching: Why ask them and what to ask, K–6.* Sausalito, CA: Math Solutions.

Walter, M.I., and Brown, S.I. (1993). *Problem posing: Reflections and applications.* Hillsdale, NJ: Lawrence Erlbaum Associates.

Wilburn, J.M. (2011). Venturing into story books: Motivating teachers to promote mathematical problem solving. In Brahier, D. (Ed). *Motivation and disposition: Pathways to learning mathematics.* Reston, VA: National Council of Teachers of Mathematics, 251–264.

Zollman, A. (2009). Mathematical graphic organizers. *Teaching Children Mathematics, 16,* 222–231.

Chapter 6

A Focus on Communication

IN A NUTSHELL

The main ideas in the chapter are listed below:

1. Communication in mathematics, whether silent self-talk or communication with peers or a teacher, is essential to students as they learn; it is also a critical assessment tool for teachers.

2. There are many forms of mathematical communication, including oral, written, physical, and symbolic communication. A variety of types of communication should be encouraged. No one form is more valuable than another.

CHAPTER PROBLEM

10 more families shop at Store E than Store C. How many families shop at Store A? Explain your thinking.

Where We Shop

Store A
Store B
Store C
Store D
Store E

Number of families

The Importance of Mathematical Communication

The National Council of Teachers of Mathematics (NCTM) recognized the importance of mathematical communication in its document *Principles and Standards for School Mathematics* (2000) by creating a communication standard to help shape mathematics programs.

Facilitating effective communication requires time, changes teachers' expectations of students, and changes the nature and variety of assessments used. Therefore, the emphasis on communication in mathematics determines, to some extent, the nature of instructional activities.

THE NCTM COMMUNICATION STANDARD

Instructional programs from Pre-Kindergarten through Grade 12 should enable all students to

- organize and consolidate their mathematical thinking through communication
- communicate their mathematical thinking coherently and clearly to peers, teachers, and others
- analyze and evaluate the mathematical thinking and strategies of others
- use the language of mathematics to express mathematical ideas precisely

(NCTM, 2000)

Forms of Communication

Communication can take various forms in the mathematics classroom:

- oral communication (speaking and listening)
- written communication (reading and writing)
- symbolic, graphical, or pictorial communication
- physical communication through active involvement with manipulative materials

Younger students use mostly oral, pictorial, or physical communication with manipulative materials. Older elementary students probably use a somewhat higher proportion of written and symbolic and graphical communication as well.

The amount of communication that occurs in a math classroom is significantly affected by the nature of teacher questioning. When teachers ask interesting, thought–provoking questions, there is more opportunity for communication than if students simply give short responses to narrow questions.

Oral versus Written Communication

Many people use different language to talk about math than they use to write about it. When you talk, you are much more likely to say, "2 and 3 are 5"; when you write, you are much more likely to record, "$2 + 3 = 5$." Written communication has elements of formality and symbolism that are not present in oral communication, and this causes difficulty for some students.

Oral Communication

There are four main types of oral communication in classrooms:

- teacher with student (or with small group)
- teacher with whole class

- peer talk
- self-talk

Self-talk is a metacognitive activity. Whether they speak silently or out loud, many people talk to themselves to clarify their thinking as they work through difficult problems or situations. This explicit self-talk is then accessible for use in future situations.

Metacognitive behaviour is often learned through teacher modelling and questioning. A teacher should show how she or he thinks through a problem using self-talk. A teacher can also ask questions that promote metacognition, such as, "Do you have a plan?" and "Why do you think this?"

Why Peer Discussion Is Important

Abundant evidence points to the benefits of student discussion about mathematical ideas. We know that students can use "talking time" with peers to

- understand a mathematical situation: "I don't get it. Do you, Megan?"
- work through a problem: "No, I think you should do this next."
- clarify their thinking: "Okay. Let me show you what I mean."
- reflect on their own learning: "Why did I think it was hard? I'll show you what I was thinking."

Communication Patterns

Where a student (S) and teacher (T) or various students and a teacher interchange comments, communication might be of the form T-S-T-S-T, etc. However, it is desirable to have more communication of the form T-S-S-S-S-T, where students are talking among themselves without teacher interruption before they choose to respond to the teacher. Nathan and Knuth (2003) suggest that this is more likely to occur as teachers learn to withhold scaffolding, and allow students to help each other.

Fostering Oral Communication

Communication is fostered when the teacher sets rich tasks, particularly rich open tasks, that allow for many possible responses and for discussion of strategy. Good follow-up questions encourage discourse by asking students to reason, conjecture, justify, and defend their thinking (Bruce, 2007). To encourage more elaborate responses from students, teachers should encourage group discussion, allow more wait time after a question is asked, allow for alternative ways to respond, encourage students to ask questions, and delay reaction to or evaluation of a student response, allowing students to decide what is right or wrong more often.

Grouping Students

Ensuring that students have peers with whom to talk can foster communication. Many teachers regularly seat students in groups, while others form groups for particular purposes. For students whose first language is not English, it may be appropriate to form groups that allow students to communicate about the mathematics in their first language; this makes it easier for them to deal with the mathematical content. On the other hand, to foster the development of their second language, there should also be times when these students work with others in English.

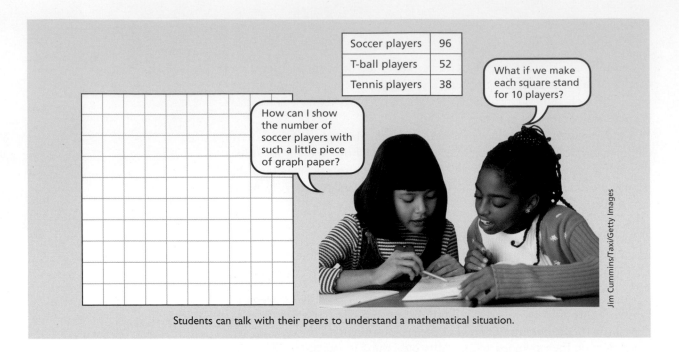

Students can talk with their peers to understand a mathematical situation.

Wait Time

Without time to think about and respond to a question fully, students rarely have the opportunity to show what they really understand. Wait time may be particularly important for ELL students who need additional time to process the question and reformulate it. It is often suggested that teachers wait at least five seconds before saying anything else after asking a question, even though that silence may, at first, feel awkward to both teacher and students.

Teachers must also learn to wait for many volunteers and not to call on the first hand raised every time; some teachers never have students raise their hands but simply call on whomever they choose. Of course students are informed this will occur. There are a number of ways to encourage participation by a broader range of students, including tossing a ball and having whoever catches it respond; choosing names from a hat; or, for students who like to be prepared, using a visible roster for calling on students.

Allowing for Alternative Ways to Respond

Sometimes teachers decrease the anxiety students might feel in responding by making the responses more anonymous. It might be through the use of personal response devices (clickers) on which each student selects an answer which is sent to the teacher electronically, or it might be through asking students to use less visible thumbs-up or -down rather than raising their hands to indicate an opinion about something.

Evaluating and Responding to Student Responses

A teacher can encourage more student independence and better communication, as well as collect more useful assessment for learning information, by withholding judgment on student work. For example, a student asks the teacher if his or her response is correct. Rather than directly answering, the teacher can turn the opportunity around with a response such as, "Do you think it is? Tell me why."

Occasionally, a yes or no reply to a response to a factual question may be appropriate. For example, a teacher asks, "What is 9 + 5?" The student responds, "14," and it may be appropriate to say, "Correct." However, the teacher could still ask someone else if she or he agrees, or could follow up by asking, "How do you know that?"

Suppose a teacher poses the question, "How might you add 427 + 78 in your head?" A student might reply, "I would add the 27 and 78 and then 400." Rather than indicating that this response is acceptable or, perhaps, that it is incomplete, the teacher should ask for more information—for example, "Why did you say that? What would you do next? Do you agree?" (to another student).

How a teacher handles an incorrect response can have an important effect on a student's willingness to continue to describe his or her mathematical thinking. Consider the following response and how the teacher refocuses the student.

Teacher: How many times are you likely to spin green if you spin this spinner 50 times?

Student: I think it will be 4.

Teacher: Why do you say that?

Student: Because $\frac{1}{4}$ of the spinner is green.

REFOCUSING QUESTIONS

What fraction of the spinner is blue $\left(\frac{1}{2}\right)$ Do you think you will spin blue 2 times?

What fraction is red? $\left(\frac{1}{8}\right)$ Do you think you will spin red 8 times?

Try spinning 10 times and see what happens.

The set of refocusing questions above is an example of descriptive feedback. It is much more useful to the student than simply indicating that he or she is incorrect, and it also encourages the student to continue to communicate his or her mathematical thinking.

A teacher should take time to consider the student's response before indicating he or she is wrong. Asking the student to explain himself or herself provides that extra time to think about the student's response, and also allows the teacher to gain a better understanding of what the student is thinking.

Often younger students have greater difficulty communicating, and more prompting is required. However, it is easy to fall into the trap of asking questions that are too narrow and do not allow students to learn to choose the words they are going to use. Finding the right balance is essential, and the balance may be different for different students.

Encouraging Listening

Listening is a very important aspect of oral communication. In fact, Hillen and Smith (2007) argue that sometimes listeners are getting just as much out of the discourse as talkers. To foster a real mathematics community, students need to learn from one another, and this involves listening and learning to analyze and reflect on what others say. This skill must be modelled and cultivated. For example, teachers can provide opportunities for students to explain a concept or how they solved a problem (perhaps by providing a "mathematician's chair"), and then have the listeners describe what they learned from the explanation or ask questions, or, as Kinman (2010) suggests, ask how the listener's method differs from the speaker's.

Prompting Students

In an oral setting, teachers can use probing questions such as these to elicit more mathematical thinking.

- Why do you think that?
- Would it also be true if …?
- Could there be a different answer?
- How did you figure that out?
- What was the easiest part of …? hardest part of …?
- What strategies did you use to …?
- Why did you decide to …?

Anticipation Guides

One particularly valuable way to prompt student discussion, as well as to draw students' attention to the important aspects of a lesson, is to use an anticipation guide at the start of the lesson. An anticipation guide is a set of statements, focused on the main idea(s) of the lesson, with which students can agree or disagree. Students normally complete the guide independently at the very start of the lesson, although the teacher may read the statements to the class. When finished, students share their responses and reasons with a partner or small group, or perhaps with the whole class. Later, after completing the lesson, students respond again to the same questions to see if any viewpoints have been changed.

For example, for a lesson on measuring in centimetres, a student might complete an anticipation guide such as the one shown below. The student has an opportunity to think about these ideas as the lesson proceeds and becomes invested in finding out the answers. Responding again to the same questions after the lesson allows the student to focus on what was learned and provides assessment information to the teacher. Students would normally explain their answer choices at the start of the lesson and the reason for any changes (or not) at the end of the lesson.

Before the Lesson		After the Lesson
Agree Disagree	1. More things in the classroom are shorter than 10 cm than are longer than 10 cm.	Agree Disagree
Agree Disagree	2. You have to use a ruler to measure in centimetres.	Agree Disagree
Agree Disagree	3. A measurement is better if it's in centimetres rather than paper clips.	Agree Disagree

Opposite Sides

Another way to prompt discussion is to use the opposite sides strategy. Using this approach, the teacher makes a statement with which students can agree or disagree. Students who choose each option go to the side of the room assigned to that position. Students on each side work at justifying their position, which is then shared with the rest of the class. Students are allowed to change their minds after the justifications are heard. For example, the teacher might say, "It makes more sense to measure the length of my desk in metres than centimetres. Do you agree or disagree?"

Opportunities for Oral Communication

There are many things students can effectively talk about in the mathematics classroom. These include:

- **recalling past, but relevant, experiences:** Students are asked to recall situations where they have previously seen a graph.
- **determining how they will share a task:** Students can discuss in groups how to solve a particular problem, how they will know when they are satisfied with the solution, and how to share the work.
- **explaining:** Students can test out their explanations on one another before sharing with the whole group.

When 27 people were surveyed about their reading, 4 people said they never read for fun. Estimate the number of people who said they read sometimes or every day. Explain your thinking.

Do you read for fun?

There were 4 out of 27 people who said "never," so 23 said "sometimes" or "every day." The "sometimes" section is bigger, so I estimate that 10 read for fun every day, and 13 do it sometimes. That works because 4 + 10 + 13 = 27.

Chip Henderson/Index Stock

Students can test out their explanations on their classmates.

- **predicting:** Students are asked to predict whether more of the numbers between 10 and 50 have a 3 as one of the digits, or a 6 as one of the digits, and why. Students can predict and then discuss their prediction.
- **comparing approaches or ideas:** Three students in a group offer their ideas about how to find as many ways as they can to continue a pattern beginning with 3, 5, ... They can discuss their ideas, making judgments about which ones to include in the group's final presentation.
- **using manipulatives:** Manipulatives can act like "conversation pieces" in a classroom. They give students something to talk about and, in many cases, suggest appropriate language and vocabulary. For example, if students were asked to tell everything they know about a pyramid, having the pyramid in front of them would help initiate and extend the discussion.

- **discussing relationships they perceive:** Students are asked to comment on how squares are like circles and how they are different. Different students in the group can be asked to suggest possibilities.
- **justifying:** Students can describe how this number trick works. Think of a number. Double it. Double the answer. Subtract 8. Divide by 4. Add 2. The answer is always the number you start with.

Cultural Considerations

Teachers need to be sensitive about cultural issues related to oral communication. Some of the critical issues include being aware and respectful of cultures in which

- students are shy about responding or criticizing
- interrupting is considered acceptable, and setting up classroom practices that allow for children to speak without interruption
- people are reluctant to disagree openly, and ensuring that students feel comfortable about disagreeing with a classmate
- students are not encouraged to talk or ask questions in class, and that an openness to this may take time to develop

Written Communication

Written communication between teachers and students or among students becomes increasingly significant as students get older.

Why Written Communication Is Important

Written, as opposed to oral, communication has many advantages and is used for many purposes including the following:

- It allows for the creation of a more permanent record to enable a student or teacher to look back and see the progress of thought. Some media, such as interactive white boards, allow students to easily amend their thinking, while still providing a permanent record.
- It is deliberate enough that a student can focus on details.
- It provides sensory feedback as the hand is engaged in the writing, fostering better memory of the material.
- It is slow enough to allow for considered reflection and organization. A student can look at his or her own work and actually "debate" with himself or herself about the ideas being recorded.
- It is efficient since everyone in the class can be engaged simultaneously.

A student is shown the following incomplete pattern.

_____, _____, _____, _____, 26, _____, _____, 110, _____, _____

The pattern rule is described as "add 42 each time." The student reasons that the pattern rule is not correct, as shown below.

> If the pattern rule is "add 42 each time" and the 5th term is 26, then
> - the 6th term would be 26 + 42 = 68
> - the 7th term would be 68 + 42 = 110
> - the 8th term would be 110 + 42 = 152
> But the 8th term is 110.
> The pattern rule must be wrong.

- It allows students to feel that they are making progress even if a problem is not completely solved.
- It is a "safer" venue for shy students.
- It provides the teacher with a different sort of insight into student thinking than oral communication does, because the student is forced to stop and think. As well, students are not influenced by, or dependent on, the teacher's visual cues to decide what to say next.
- It can be a vehicle for learning. In the process of completing a written assignment, students might have to ask questions of their peers and teacher to find more information.

That said, teachers need to be aware that written communication can discourage some students who struggle with it. Where they could have felt successful in math, they then feel less successful. It is totally appropriate to use oral communication either live or digitally instead on many occasions.

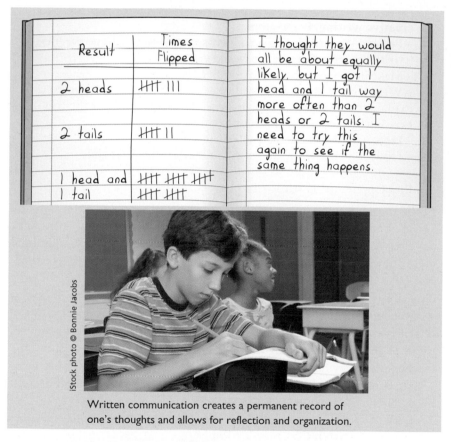

Written communication creates a permanent record of one's thoughts and allows for reflection and organization.

iStock photo © Bonnie Jacobs

Types of Written Communication

There should be opportunities for students to inform, persuade, describe, and evaluate in their writing. Some of the kinds of writing students can use include the following:

- **personal writing**. For example:
  - What do you think we should ask about in our survey?
  - If you could measure any one of your toys and games, which one would you measure?
  - Why that one? What parts of it would you measure?
- **descriptive writing**. For example:
  - What is a geoboard and how can you use it?
  - What does the equation $2n + 5 = 19$ mean?
  - Tell where you have seen patterns around your home.

- **process writing**. For example:
  – What steps did you use to solve that problem?
- **creation of word problems**. For example:

Student Response

This student has created a word problem for two given conditions.

> Make up a word problem where multiplication is involved and the answer is 20.
>
> I have 4 friends. We each have 4 tickets to sell for the raffle. How many tickets do we all have to sell?

- **creative writing**. For example:
  – Pretend you are writing an advertisement to encourage parents to buy tangram kits. What would you say?
  – Make up a poem about the number 100.
  – Write a story in which the number 12 is an important character.
- **explanatory writing** to explain procedures, concepts, or the relationship between concepts. For example:
  – How would you calculate $72 \div 9$ in your head?
  – How do you find the line of symmetry for this triangle?

Finding Opportunities to Write

At the start of a unit of instruction, ask students to write what they already know about a particular topic. They can extend these ideas as the unit develops, or revisit their writing at the end of the unit to include additional ideas they have learned about. Students can be encouraged to summarize ideas discussed in class and record these in a "math journal" or on a blog site.

Teachers might also take the opportunity to encourage writing when the class looks confused. The teacher can stop everything and ask students to write about what is going on. When students read aloud or show the teacher what they have written, the teacher gets a better insight into what was causing the confusion. For many students, the task of writing itself might clarify their thinking.

Criteria for Written Communication

The ability to communicate mathematically is something that needs formal and focused attention. Students might find this checklist of criteria helpful when writing (of course, not all criteria are relevant to all writing):

- Did you show all the steps?
- Did you include reasons for the steps?
- Did you show the right amount of detail?
- Did you explain your thinking?
- Did you use diagrams to help explain?
- Did you use math language and symbols?

The following examples show how communication criteria can be explicitly discussed with students, according to the type of writing.

PROBLEM SOLVING

Problem

How could you arrange these three shapes to make a square?

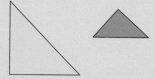

When writing about solving a problem, students could focus on these criteria.

Did you

- show that you understood the problem?
- show all the steps in order?
- include reasons for each step?

Sample Student Solution

I knew I had to use all three shapes to make one square.

I guessed that the shapes that had the square corners were the corners of the square so I tried these arrangements:

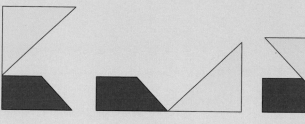

My third way worked because the missing space was the right size for the blue triangle.

This is how the shapes go together.

This student showed that she or he understood the problem and showed the steps in order. She or he also gave reasons for each step.

EXPLAINING A PROCEDURE

Order the numbers 909, 9009, 9909, and 999 from greatest to least. Explain how you ordered them.

When explaining a procedure, students could focus on these criteria:

Did you

- show all the steps in order?
- include reasons for the steps?
- show the right amount of detail?
- use math language and symbols?

I put the numbers with 4 digits first. 4-digit numbers are greater.

9009   9909   909   999

I compared the 100s digit of the 4-digit numbers to see which was greater because the 1000s digit is the same   9909 > 9009

I compared the tens digit of the 3 digit numbers because the 100s digits were the same   999 > 909

The order is 9909, 9009, 999, 909

Student Response

This student explained each step in the procedure, including reasons for the steps. He or she also used an appropriate amount of detail, math language, and symbols.

Student Response

This student explains the relationship between two sets of numbers. He or she uses words, rather than symbols involving variables.

EXPLAINING A CONCEPT

Use words to describe the relationship in this table.

1st Column	2nd Column
1	6
2	7
3	8
4	9
5	10
6	11

When explaining a concept, students can focus on these criteria:
Did you

• explain your thinking?
• use diagrams, patterns, or relationships to other ideas to help explain?
• use math language and symbols?

they relate because $1+5=6$
$2+5=7$ $3+5=8$ $4+5=9$ $5+5=10$
$5+6=11$ in the first column
if you add 5 it equals the
number the second column.

Providing Exemplars and Scaffolding

When an appropriate opportunity arises for teachers to explain something in writing, they should model the process and product for students. Teachers can do this in two ways: by "thinking out loud" and recording as they go, or by providing exemplars of other students' work.

For many students, especially ELL students, it is particularly important to provide some scaffolding, or structured support, for organizing the writing and to provide some of the needed vocabulary.

Fostering Written Communication

The most important consideration when assigning a written task in mathematics is to ensure that the communication is suitable and that the task is as rich as possible. Some of the typical prompts for such tasks are:

• What do you think ... means?
• Tell everything you can about ....
• Tell about a time when ....
• Why is it easy to ...?
• When do you ...?
• How do you know that ...?
• What can you say that is true about all of ...?
• Tell a different way to ....
• ... can mean two different things. Tell about what ... can mean.
• Explain why ....
• What question could you ask to find out about ...?

Tell about a time when you had difficulty trying to figure out a pattern.

it was a number pattern and the numbers got bigger but not by the same amount each time. i asked my partner to help me and we asked the teacher for help. she asked us to look at how much was bettween the numbers then we saw a pattern

Student Response

This student was able to explain, in writing, not only why the number pattern was difficult to figure out but how she or he eventually figured it out.

Many teachers encourage the keeping of a math journal, where students respond to questions such as those above.

Symbolic and Graphical Communication

Young students need to communicate mathematically even before they have all of the formal tools they need. They should be allowed and encouraged to use invented symbolism to describe their mathematical thinking. Sometimes the symbolism may seem unclear, but it is important to ask what students are thinking as this is an effective way to better understand why they chose the symbols they did, and what meaning those symbols hold specifically for them.

One of the symbols used with older students is a letter of the alphabet to describe an unknown quantity (a variable), for example, $n = 5 \times 7$. For younger students, a box or blank is used instead; for example, $\blacksquare = 5 \times 7$.

Many students find it easier to explain their thinking using diagrams rather than words. This should be encouraged, particularly, but not exclusively, for younger students. Leaving a space instead of blank lines for student responses is one way to indicate to students that their response might include a picture or a graphic element of some kind. Older students might need to be prompted to use words to support their diagrams.

a) What is the formula for the perimeter of a rectangle?

$$P = L + L + W + W$$

b) Why does your formula make sense?

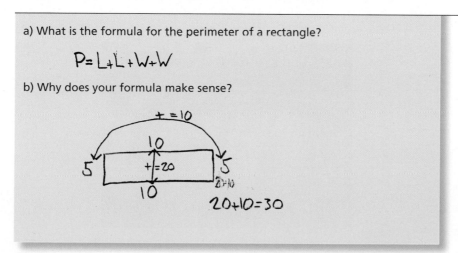

Student Response

This student showed his or her understanding symbolically. You might ask for an oral explanation as well.

Student Response
This student used a picture to show her or his ideas about pattern.

There is a growing pattern and it is growing by ones.

Physical Communication

An important part of communication in the math classroom involves physical actions. Physical actions not only show what students do with manipulative materials, but can also be useful for "explaining" many mathematical concepts. For example, a student who has trouble explaining in words what *area* means might find it easier to describe or explain the concept concretely through demonstration, by covering a surface with square tiles.

Students communicate some of their mathematical thinking by performing actions concretely. For example, one of the meanings of *division* is "sharing." Suppose students are asked to solve the division problem shown below. If students physically share 15 counters among five groups, they are acting out the operation of division and, at the same time, communicating that they understand that this is a division situation.

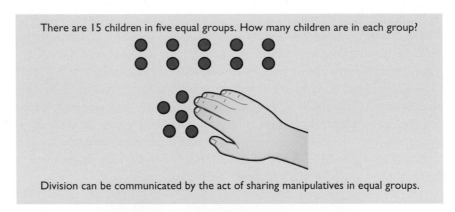

There are 15 children in five equal groups. How many children are in each group?

Division can be communicated by the act of sharing manipulatives in equal groups.

Courtesy Manuel Silva

Many geometric understandings are best shown using physical communication. For example, this student shows her or his understanding of cones.

Mathematics Vocabulary and Symbols

Vocabulary is an issue in both oral and written mathematical communication. Some people even consider mathematics to be a language of its own. No one disputes that students are expected to become comfortable with vocabulary associated with mathematics when reading, speaking, and writing. Some vocabulary terms are content related and others are process related. For example, students are asked to learn mathematical terms like *sum*, *product*, *area*, *pyramid*, and *variable*, but they are also expected to understand what is meant when the words *justify*, *explain*, *estimate*, *extend*, and *solve* are used. These latter terms must be clarified, too.

Another complication in mathematics is the confusion between the symbol and the idea. The terms *number* and *numeral* are used to try to make the distinction, but that distinction is not always clear. For example, this numeral 7 is smaller than this numeral 2, but the number 7 is greater than the number 2. Punctuation marks, such as the colon in a ratio, and grammatical structures, such as saying "8 divided into 2" when we mean 2 ÷ 8 or "8 divided into 2s" when we mean 8 ÷ 2, can also confuse students.

The Importance of Vocabulary

Knowing the right word to use allows students to communicate more effectively and efficiently and, as a result, consolidate their learning. Often, the mathematics cannot really be understood or communicated without reference to appropriate vocabulary.

Math Terminology and Everyday Language

One of the additional complications in mathematics is that some words are used differently in mathematics than in everyday situations. Some examples are shown below:

- *Odd* in everyday language can mean unusual.
- *Unknown*, which in everyday language means something you do not know, but mathematically is something that we temporarily do not know, but then actually do know.
- *Mean* can mean unpleasant (rather than an average).
- *Negative* can mean bad.
- *Right* describes a direction.

Strategies for Reinforcing Math Vocabulary

When introducing new terms, many actions can be taken to help solidify this vocabulary, including the following:

- a **word wall**, where words are posted as reminders for students. Math terms are often grouped by concept or topic; for example, all the words associated with operations might be in one group (e.g., *sum*, *difference*, *product*, and *quotient*), and words associated with geometry would be in another (e.g., *circle* and *triangle*). If the words are on cards, they can be sorted in different ways to show various connections and relationships. They may be illustrated as well.

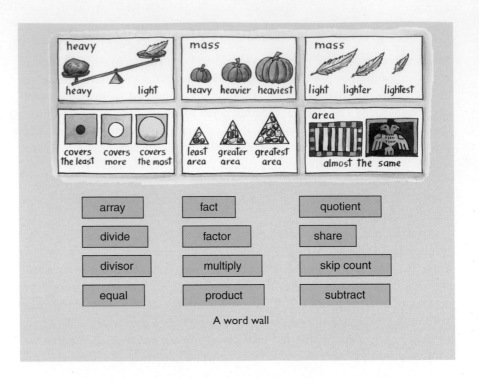

A word wall

- a **glossary**, either posted or in a notebook. The glossary can be created in students' own words, rather than the teacher's, although the teacher will want to ensure that students' definitions are correct. A glossary can use pictures or diagrams, along with words to explain. An example or two with each definition is also helpful.

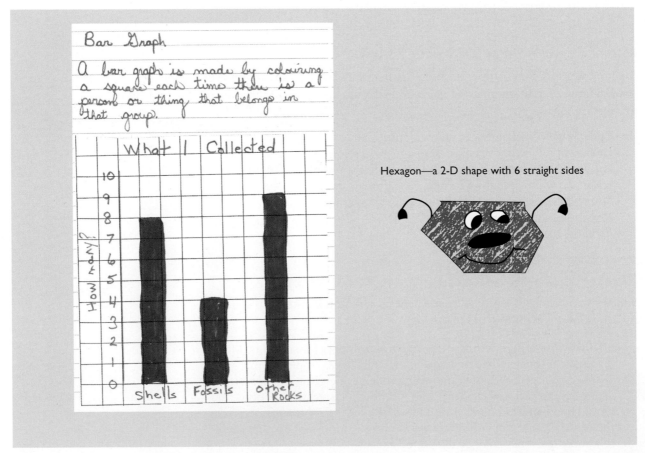

Hexagon—a 2-D shape with 6 straight sides

• **concept maps** like the Frayer model map, for example.

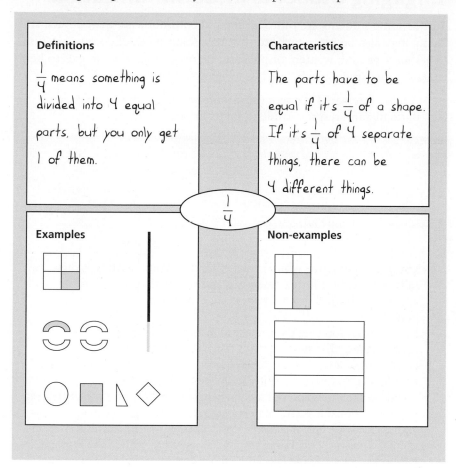

• **sentence completion**. For example, "The _____ of 12 and 8 is 20."
• **sentence creation**. Use the words and numbers *quotient, more, 8,* and *30* in a single sentence.
• **integrating math and language arts**. Some teachers include mathematics vocabulary words in their language arts spelling and comprehension activities.

Mnemonics for Math Vocabulary

In many instances, the formal mathematical meaning of a word can be connected to the everyday meaning, albeit with a bit of imagination and creativity. Making these connections can be a powerful tool to help students remember new vocabulary and also make sense of mathematical language.

Here are some examples:

• When you multiply two numbers, you "produce a product."
• When you pair up students, the expression "the odd one out" could be used to reinforce the fact that, when odd numbers of items are paired, there is always one left over.

As teachers introduce new vocabulary, they should be aware of any potential ambiguity in the meaning of the new term. It is important, though, for teachers to understand the terminology themselves. Teachers should have access to a suitable math dictionary, whether they purchase their own or use the one from the school library. A number of online math dictionaries can be accessed to support both teacher and student understanding.

Engaging Students in Communication

Just as some students are more inclined to communicate than others, students may also be more inclined toward certain types of communication, whether it be oral, written, or physical. Below are some strategies to help engage those students who are less inclined to communicate.

- Adding a personal element to a problem can sometimes make it of particular interest to a student, for example.

PERSONAL ENGAGING MATH TASKS

- Are you older or younger than a million seconds?
- If each letter has a value (A is 1, B is 2, C is 3, etc.), what is your name worth? Is your given name worth more than your family name?
- Describe your family using fractions.

- Using an interactive white board where students' writing is digitally recorded for future reference and where their handwriting actually turns into printed text, is very intriguing for many students.
- Paying attention to what each student says and writes is critical to making that student want to invest in communication. A classroom where students listen to one another respectfully is an essential component to motivate more communication.
- Handling situations appropriately where students say or write something that is questionable is critical to encourage risk taking. The teacher must address the issue but, at the same time, ensure that the learning environment is a positive one. For example, a student has written the **Student Response** below. Some good thinking is demonstrated in recognizing that multiplication is a "short form" for addition, and that should be acknowledged. The teacher needs to probe further, however, to find out what the student means by, "You use it when you cannot add, subtract, or divide." For example, the teacher might say, "You say that multiplication is a shorter way to add and that is true. But you also say that you multiply when you cannot add. How can both of these statements be true?"

Student Response

This student has some good ideas, but further probing is necessary.

Describe what multiplication is all about.

$3 \times 5 = 15$

you use multiplication to shorten your work. You use it to find the answer. You use it when you can not add, subtract or divide. Multiplication iis a shorter way to add.

- Allowing students to use multiple forms of communication might make them more willing to take the risk. For example, if they are told they will have an opportunity to explain what they write orally, they might attempt written communication.
- Encouraging students to use pictures when they write can take the pressure off those students with poor writing skills.
- Allowing students to use manipulatives when explaining themselves orally redirects the focus from a shy student to the manipulatives. The use of manipulatives also allows students to use the language of the manipulatives to make communication easier. For example, a student might struggle with the language necessary to explain place value concepts, such as hundreds, but, when using base ten blocks to explain, he or she might call it the big square block or the flat. The teacher can take this opportunity to model the appropriate language.

Assessing Student Communication

- Make sure to assess communication separately from other processes, content knowledge, or understanding. For example, a student might know the mathematical concept, but not communicate her or his understanding well. On the other hand, a student might communicate quite well, but incorrectly.
- Provide opportunities for students to communicate in different ways, sometimes orally, sometimes in writing, sometimes physically, and sometimes symbolically.
- Share with students the criteria you will be using to assess their communication.

Applying What You've Learned

1. What data skills and what number skills did you use to solve the chapter problem? Did you do a good job of communication? What was good about it or what did it lack?

2. Some teachers who believe in the value of communication expect a student to explain every answer in an exercise. How often would you require explanations? Justify your decision.

3. Find a video of a math classroom. Analyze the discourse. Is it rich or not? Explain your thinking.

4. Choose a grade level and a topic of interest. In what types of situations in the exploration of that topic do you think that written communication is essential? Why?

5. What sorts of questions would you include in an anticipation guide for a lesson in Grade 3 focusing on subtraction?

6. Describe some ways you could infuse creative writing into a mathematics program at a grade of your choice.

7. Create a concept map, for example, a Frayer model (as shown on page 133), to show what you know about adding fractions.

Interact with a K–8 Student:

8. Choose a math term appropriate for the student with whom you are interacting, for example, *add* for Grade 1 or *prime number* for Grade 7. Ask the student to tell you as many things as he or she can about that word. Assess the richness of the communication.

Discuss with a K–8 Teacher:

9. Many teachers are nervous about allowing too many students to explain their thinking on a problem just because other students may get confused with too many approaches. Ask the teacher how she or he handles communication in this sort of situation.

Selected References

Altieri, J.L. (2005). Creating poetry: Reinforcing mathematical concepts. *Teaching Children Mathematics, 12,* 18–23.

Anderson, M., and Little, D.M. (2004). On the write path: Improving communication in an elementary mathematics classroom. *Teaching Children Mathematics, 10,* 468–472.

Barlow, A.T., and McCrory, M.R. (2011). Strategies for promoting math disagreements. *Teaching Children Mathematics, 17,* 530–539.

Bruce, C.D. (2007). *Student interaction in the math classroom: Stealing ideas or building understanding.* Toronto, ON: Literacy and Numeracy Secretariat— What Works? Research into Practice Monograph Series.

Countryman, J. (1992). *Writing to learn mathematics.* Portsmouth, NH: Heinemann.

Griffiths, R., and Clyne, M. (1994). *Language in the mathematics classroom: Talking, representing, recording.* Portsmouth, NH: Heinemann.

Herbel-Eisenmann, B., and Cirillo, M. (Eds.) (2009). *Promoting purposeful discourse: Teacher research in mathematics classrooms.* Reston, VA: National Council of Teachers of Mathematics.

Hillen, A.F., and Smith, M.S. (2007). Is silence golden? What silent participants might be learning in discourse-rich classrooms. *Mathematics Teaching in the Middle School, 13,* 305–311.

Hufferd-Ackles, K., Fuson, K.C., and Sherin, M.G. (2004). Describing levels and components of a math-talk learning community. *Journal for Research in Mathematics Education, 35,* 81–116.

Huinker, D., and Laughlin, C. (1996). Talk your way into writing. In Elliott, P.C., and Kenney, M.J. (Eds.). *Communication in mathematics, K–12 and beyond.* Reston, VA: National Council of Teachers of Mathematics, 81–88.

Kilic, H., Cross, D.I., Ersoz, F.A., Mewborn, D.S., Swanagan, D., and Kim, J. (2010). Techniques for small-group discourse. *Teaching Children Mathematics, 16,* 350–357.

Kinman, R.L. (2010). Communication speaks. *Teaching Children Mathematics, 17,* 22–30.

Lilburn, P., and Rawson, P. (1994). *Let's talk math: Encouraging children to explore ideas.* Portsmouth, NH: Heinemann.

Literacy and Numeracy Secretariat, Ontario (2010). Communication in the mathematics classroom. Accessed at http://www.edu.gov.on.ca/eng/literacynumeracy/inspire/research/CBS_Communication_Mathematics.pdf on August 12, 2014.

Nathan, M.J., and Knuth, E.J. (2003). A study of whole classroom mathematical discourse and teacher change. *Cognition and Instruction, 2,* 175–207.

National Council of Teachers of Mathematics. (2000). *Principles and standards for school mathematics.* Reston, VA: National Council of Teachers of Mathematics.

Novak, J.D. (1990). Concept maps and Vee diagrams: Two metacognitive tools for science and mathematics education. *Instructional Science, 19,* 29–52.

O'Connell, S. (2007a). *Introduction to communication, grades PreK–2.* Portsmouth, NH: Heinemann.

O'Connell, S. (2007b). *Introduction to communication, grades 3–5.* Portsmouth, NH: Heinemann.

Pimm, D. (1996). Diverse communication. In Elliott, P.C., and Kenney, M.J. (Eds.). *Communication in mathematics, K–12 and beyond.* Reston, VA: National Council of Teachers of Mathematics, 11–19.

Reinhart, S.C. (2000). Never say anything a kid can say! *Mathematics Teaching in the Middle School, 5,* 478–483.

Ryve, A. (2011). Discourse research in mathematics education: A critical evaluation of 108 journal articles. *Journal for Research in Mathematics Education, 42,* 167–198.

Shield, M., and Swinson, K. (1996). The link sheet: A communication aid for clarifying and developing mathematical ideas and processes. In Elliott, P.C., and Kenney, M.J. (Eds). *Communication in mathematics, K–12 and beyond.* Reston, VA: National Council of Teachers of Mathematics, 35–39.

Shuard, H., and Rothery, A. (1984). *Children reading mathematics.* London: Alden Press.

Small, M. (2005a). *PRIME: Number and operations: Background and strategies.* Toronto, ON: Thomson Nelson.

Smith, M.S., Hughes, E.K., Engle, R.A., and Stein, M.K. (2008). Orchestrating discussions. *Mathematics Teaching in the Middle School, 14,* 548–556.

Steinbring, H., Bartolino Bussi, M.G., and Sierpinska, A. (Eds.). (1998). *Language and communication in the mathematics classroom.* Reston, VA: National Council of Teachers of Mathematics.

Chapter 7

Early Number

IN A NUTSHELL

The main ideas in the chapter are listed below:

1. There is a difference between rote counting (being able to say the number words 1, 2, 3, etc., in the proper order), and meaningful counting (understanding how counting can be used to describe the size of a set).

2. There are many forms of counting that students need to learn, including counting forward, counting back, counting on, and skip counting. Counting is fundamental to further number work.

3. It is critical that students learn to represent numbers in as many ways as they can. Each of these representations broadens the meaning of the number for the student. Numerals are only one form of representation.

4. Numbers are most meaningful to a student when they are related to anchor or benchmark values that are well understood.

CHAPTER PROBLEM

Describe three ways that 6 and 8 are alike and three ways that they are different.

Numbers in the Child's World

Numbers are a part of even a young child's life. He or she wants to know how many of something there are, whether it is how many cookies he or she can eat, how many fingers someone is holding up, or how many candles are on his or her cake.

According to Baroody (2004), a number has four possible meanings

- a number can tell how many
- a number can describe a measurement
- a number can describe a location (e.g., Platform 4)
- a number can be a name (e.g., Student 24)

All other work with numbers, whether representing quantities or performing operations, is dependent on children learning to count.

In this chapter, the focus will be on numbers that tell how many.

Counting Principles

Before there can be any meaningful counting, students must be able to recite the sequence beginning 1, 2, 3, 4, 5, etc. This is called rote counting. Students need to be able to say those numbers in order, even if they do not know what those amounts actually look like. How high they can meaningfully count depends on how much of the sequence they know. There is interesting research to suggest that the structure of different languages' counting systems affects the ease with which students learn those number words (Sarama and Clements, 2009).

Many, but not all, students can rote count to 10 or even higher, and many can count a small set of objects meaningfully before they begin school. There is disagreement about whether skills precede conceptual development or conceptual development precedes skills in counting, but it is useful for teachers to be aware of the principles below relating to counting that might guide their instructional activities.

COUNTING PRINCIPLES

1. There is one and only one number said for each object (the one-to-one principle).
2. There is a consistent set of counting words that never changes (the stable order principle).
3. The last number spoken tells how many (the cardinal principle).
4. It does not matter what you count; the process for counting remains the same (the abstraction principle).
5. It does not matter in which order you count; the number in the set does not change (the order-irrelevance principle).[*]

Some would argue that the third principle is the most important, since it essentially assigns the number to describe a count, but all of the principles are important to have in place. Some would argue that there should be one more principle indicating that students realize that the number associated with the total count "encompasses" all previous numbers recited within the count.

---

*Gelman and Gallistel, 1978

Zero and One

When students see the sets at the top of the next page, they are likely to think about how many there are.

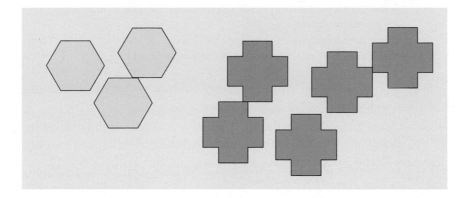

But when they see just one item, for example, the one circle below, they are more likely to think "circle," not "one." Students have to be encouraged to see that the number 1 represents the number of circles.

It is even more difficult for students to visualize zero. How do you visualize nothing? One effective technique is to model several different numbers using paper plates with items on them. For example, seven is modelled as a paper plate with seven circles on it or five as a paper plate with five circles on it. Gradually, take the circles off one at a time and ask, "How many are on the plate now? And now?" Once there is only one circle left on the plate, take it off and ask students how many circles are on the plate now. Many will say "none." Introduce the word *zero* as the word you use to tell the number of circles on the plate and show them how it is written as 0.

TEACHING TIP

It might make more sense to begin counting sets with two, three, or four items, and then go back to sets with one or zero items.

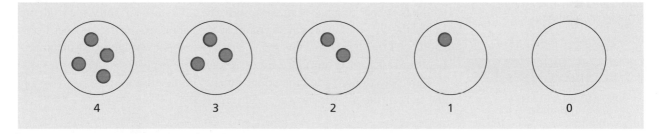

Counting Strategies

Students need to develop a sense of confidence in their counting. For example, if they count out some objects and decide that there are 6 of them, they need to realize immediately that if you rearrange the objects, they do not have to re-count, because the count is still 6. This is often referred to as *conservation of number*.

Students also have to learn physical techniques for counting. For example, children who are good counters usually have strategies for keeping track of what they have counted, such as touching each object and moving an object away once it has been counted. Later, they learn to use visual or other kinesthetic motions, like nodding, to keep track of what has been counted. Students normally learn these techniques by copying others who are efficient counters, whether fellow students or the teacher.

ACTIVITY 7.1

Read a favourite counting book, such as Crews's *Ten Black Dots* (1992). Invite students to predict the number they will hear and see when you turn the page.

Building Number Sense

A number of researchers have elaborated stages of counting. One, the Stages of Early Arithmetical Learning (SEAL) model, based on work by Steffe (1992), lists 6 stages of counting:

Stage 0: Emergent counting (cannot count visible items)
Stage 1: Perceptual counting (can count perceived items, but not concealed ones)
Stage 2: Figurative counting (can count hidden items, but always from one)
Stage 3: Initial number sequence (can count on to add)
Stage 4: Intermediate number sequence (can count back to subtract)
Stage 5: Facile number sequence (many counting strategies, including skip counting)

Once students make the connection between rote counting and cardinality (or how many), they become more flexible in dealing with larger quantities (Stages 3, 4, and 5). At these stages, students use more sophisticated and efficient approaches to counting such as

- counting on (starting at a number other than 1)
- counting back (e.g., counting back from 10 by ones or from 20 by 2s)
- skip counting (e.g., 2, 4, 6, 8, ...)

Counting On

Counting on is a critical prerequisite for success in addition. Students must be able to add $4 + 3$ by starting at 4, and then saying 3 more numbers: 5, 6, 7. If the student has to start back at 1—1, 2, 3, 4, and then 5, 6, 7—his or her progress with addition will be slow. Students become comfortable with counting on through experience. The teacher might have them stand on a walk-on number line or a hopscotch frame, for example, at 5, and ask them to take two more steps, saying the number stepped on each time: "..., 6, 7."

You might also do a lot of counting on as "sponge" activities, activities you can squeeze in when there is a minute or two to spare. For example, while students are packing up for the day, start saying "7, 8, 9, ..." and have students join in the chant. Many teachers emphasize the ability to say the number 1 or 2 more, or 1 or 2 less than a given one. For example, they might call out a number 6 and ask for the number 2 more; students are expected to think, "6, 7, 8."

One way to help students count on is to "hide" the items that make up the start number, as is shown in **Activity 7.3**.

It is essential that students understand that, when they count on, they say the correct number of numbers AFTER the start number. For example, counting on 3 from 5, the child says "6, 7, 8" and not "5, 6, 7." Some children like to say the 5 in a whisper, but say the 6, 7, and 8 out loud.

Counting Back

Counting back is often overlooked by teachers, yet it is an extremely important skill to prepare students for later work in subtraction. Some children's counting books and songs, like *10, 9, 8 Polar Animals* (Davis, 2006) provide counting-back opportunities. But teachers can easily create such opportunities themselves. For example, just before starting a new activity, the teacher might begin "10, 9, 8, ..." and have students join in. It is important to start at different beginning points, for example, sometimes 10, 9, 8, ... , but other times 15, 14, 13, ... , or 6, 5, 4, ... Counting backward usually takes more time for students to learn than counting forward.

Just as with counting on, it is important for students not to include the start number. For example, counting back 2 from 10, the child would say "9, 8" rather than "10, 9." Again, the child might whisper the 10 first if it helps him/her.

Skip Counting

There is an emphasis in early grade curricula on skip counting by 2s, 5s, or 10s, and later 100s, 50s, and 25s. The focus of skip counting in these early years is on helping students see the patterns in our place value system as well as to prepare students for work with money.

Highlighting the numbers that are heard when skip counting on a number line helps the student learn the skip counting patterns. Highlighting can be visual, as shown below, but it can also be physical, for example, by clapping when reaching the number that is to be said. The number line could be pictorial, or it could be a number line students actually walk on.

Over time, students should have experiences skip counting both forward and backward, and not always starting with the obvious start number. For example, we often skip count "2, 4, 6, 8, ... ," but not as often "1, 3, 5, 7, ... ," which would also be helpful to students.

Calculators can be used to reinforce and support counting. For early counting work, students would most likely use the repeat, or constant, function of a calculator to count on or back, or skip count forward or backward. Not all calculators have this function, so a teacher may want to give parents some advice on which calculator to choose for those purchased for home use or for those brought to school.

ACTIVITY 7.4

Ask students: *You are counting some things. The first number you say is 2. What number are you likely to say next?*

You can then see how flexible their counting actually is.

Building Number Sense

1	2	3	4	5	6	7	8	9	10

1	2	3	4	5	6	7	8	9	10

ACTIVITY 7.5

Students can practise skip counting on an animated number line, using software like the Geometer's Sketchpad* sketch below.

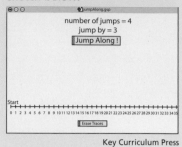

Key Curriculum Press

Proportional Reasoning

ACTIVITY 7.6

Ask students: *A number is a lot more than 2. What do you think it might be?*

Building Number Sense

TEACHING **TIP**

It is useful if students match items that are of similar size initially but later items that are quite different in size.

Matching items of different sizes forces the student to think more explicitly about how to match items.

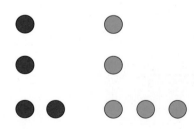

There are more blue than red, since, when the red set is matched with the blue set, there is an extra blue item.

A Sense of Number
Comparing and Relating Numbers

Many everyday situations provide opportunities for students to compare numbers, such as whether there are enough napkins for all of the children at a table, or whether there are 2 too many or 1 too few. Teachers can quickly create many simple comparing opportunities, for example, by asking students to clap 2 times fewer or more than they do.

Students employ two primary strategies for comparing numbers: 1–1 correspondence, and position in the counting sequence.

4 is greater than 3 since each boy matches one of the girls, but there is still an extra girl.

One-to-One Correspondence

One-to-one correspondence is the most basic test for comparison. Both numbers are modelled with elements of the two sets matched up. The set that has items left over is the larger set, and the number representing it is the greater number.

The picture above shows the numbers that are being compared lined up. However, there are other ways to show 1–1 correspondence. For example, it is clear that there is a greater number of blue items than red to the left, since the entire set of red items can be matched with the blue set, but with an extra blue item.

An everyday example of the use of one-to-one correspondence revolves around the interpretation of simple graphs. If, for example, students get to

---

The Geometer's Sketch Pad, Key Curriculum Press, 1150 65th St., Emeryville, CA 94608, 1-800-995-MATH, www.keypress.com/sketchpad.

choose the activity they want to do and they are asked to place a cube on a stack, depending on their choice, they can easily see whether more students are choosing one activity compared to another.

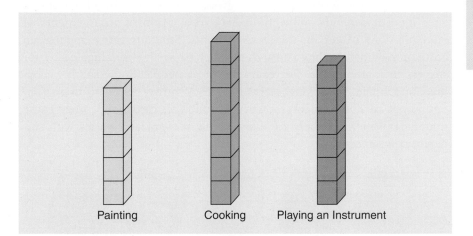

Painting   Cooking   Playing an Instrument

Position in the Counting Sequence

Later, students count the items in both sets separately and compare the position of the two numbers in the number sequence. For example, if one set has 3 items and one has 4, they know that since the number 3 comes before 4 in the counting sequence, 3 is less than 4, and the set of 3 contains fewer items than the set of 4. A focus on the sequence can be facilitated by making a large number line visible to students.

Comparison Language

Many teachers believe that even young children should say "4 is greater than 3" rather than "4 is more than 3" to teach that mathematical language to students. Others believe that when children are young and just starting, this is not necessary. Eventually, students will learn to use the greater-than symbol: $4 > 3$.

Many students have difficulty recognizing that if 4 is greater than 3, 3 is automatically less than 4; they tend to focus on only the "greater than" aspect of the relationship. Make sure that both sides of the relationship are considered.

Spatial Comparison

Graphs are one way to compare numbers spatially; using ordinal numbers is another way. Ordinal numbers describe position, rather than cardinality, but there is a relationship between ordinality and cardinality. For example, if you are 2nd in a race, it is because there is only one person ahead of you, making you person number 2. There are many natural classroom opportunities to use ordinal numbers; for example, "I'd like the third person in line to come to the front."

Many students confuse cardinal and ordinal numbers. Knowing the terms _cardinal_ and _ordinal_ is not that important, but knowing the difference between 2 and 2nd, especially in terms of their use, is important.

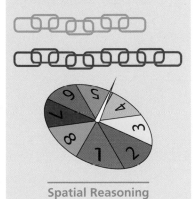

Numbers to 10

Subitizing

A very efficient strategy to tell how many is *subitizing*. Subitizing is a method of determining how many are in a group without specifically counting each item; it depends on an immediate recognition of arrangements or configurations of certain numbers of items. Students can recognize an amount even before they know its number name. It is a valuable skill for success in mathematics. For example, most people immediately recognize, or subitize, the arrangements for 1 to 5 shown below, as these configurations of dots are commonly used on dice, cards, and other game materials. Which numbers are immediately recognizable varies with students' experiences.

Later, they learn to subitize greater amounts using their mathematical knowledge as well as their recognition of smaller amounts. For example, they might see 3 rows of 3 dots and immediately know there is 9 because they easily subitize 3 and know that 3 threes make 9.

Many teachers use paper plates with stickers attached or dots created by bingo dabbers, and play "pattern flash" games. They show a dot pattern very briefly and students are asked if they recognize it. Although some patterns are more commonly used than others, and these can be the ones that are emphasized, some teachers use a variety of representations often enough that students begin to recognize them right away. For example, below are different representations that might be used for 9.

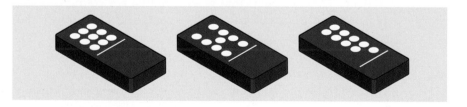

Exploring Numbers

As students explore each of the numbers from 1 to 10, they are automatically engaged in a certain amount of sorting and classifying, distinguishing representations of one number from representations of others.

Although it is reasonable to focus on a single number in a lesson, it is always important to compare and contrast that number with others. For example, a lesson on 3 should draw attention to how the representations for 3 are different from those of, for example, 2.

There are many strategies for helping students to become familiar with specific numbers. Many teachers use counting books. Others ask students to think of items that really come in sets of a given size. For example, students might draw pictures of things that come in twos (such as eyes, arms, etc.) to make sense of 2, or items that come in sixes (such as drinks or hot dogs) to make sense of 6.

5 and 10 as Benchmarks

Many students think of one number in relationship to another; for example, 6 is the number that is 1 more than 5, or 9 is the number that is 1 less than 10. Relating numbers to benchmark numbers can be used as a tool for comparing numbers (as shown below), and should be encouraged. The numbers 5 and 10 often provide the strongest benchmarks for young students.

I know 3 is less than 8 because 3 is less than 5 and 8 is more than 5.

Photodisc/Getty Images

One way to encourage this sort of reference to benchmarks is to use an appropriate visual model. Aside from the obvious model of the fingers on one or both hands, three other models are particularly useful: the 5-frame, the 10-frame, and the beaded number line.

The 5-Frame The 5-frame is a rectangle of 5 squares with each square large enough to hold a counter.

Students learn to *subitize* these representations for 1 to 5, but also think of the numbers 3 and 4 in relation to 5.

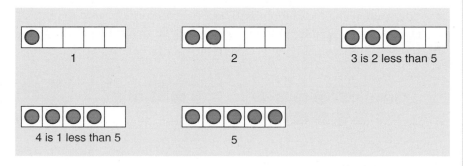

1

2

3 is 2 less than 5

4 is 1 less than 5

5

The 10-Frame The 10-frame is a set of two 5-frames put together in two rows. The frame is filled by beginning at the left, filling the top row, and then starting at the left again to fill the bottom row.

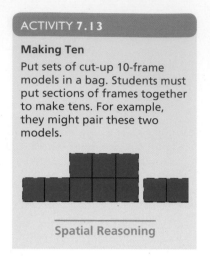
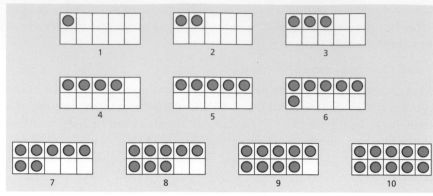

This model focuses students on relationships to 5 and 10, for example, 6 as 1 more than 5, or 8 as 2 fewer than 10.

The Bead Number Line Many teachers use beads to create number lines on strings. They alternate colours every 5 beads.

Initially, they might mark the numbers with stickers on the beads, but later they take the stickers off. This helps students focus on comparisons to a benchmark, for example, 7 as the number 2 past 5.

Once students are familiar with 10-frame arrangements, teachers might want to play a variety of games with them to practise the arrangements for various numbers.

The Teen Numbers

Many students struggle with the teen numbers, the numbers between 10 and 20, particularly the numbers 13 to 19. One of the reasons offered is that we say the numbers in the English language (this is not the case in many other languages) in a different order than we write them, for example, sixteen, with the "six" part last and the "teen" part first—16. The focus for these numbers should always be on the relationship to 10. 16 is sixteen because it is 6 more than 10. Students need a great deal of experience representing and using teen numbers to become comfortable with their use.

The use of a double 10-frame is helpful for the teen numbers. For example, 15 is shown as below, and is clearly 5 more than 10.

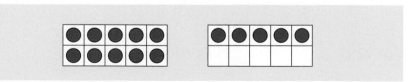

Importance of Multiple Representations

One of the important concepts young students need to learn about number is that there are many ways to represent an amount. For example, the number of arms you have can be represented by the symbol 2, but also by thinking of it as 1 more than 1, or 1 less than 3 or, later, 7 − 5.

The concept of multiple representation can and should be approached in a variety of ways. For example, to model the number 7, the student might draw or show any of the models below:

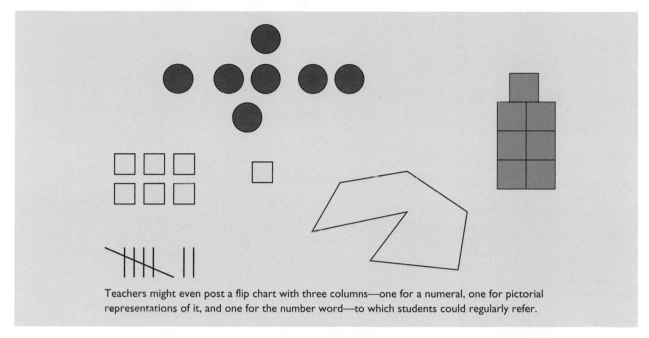

Teachers might even post a flip chart with three columns—one for a numeral, one for pictorial representations of it, and one for the number word—to which students could regularly refer.

The 6 and 1 model using squares above shows what is called a part-part-whole relationship; students view 7, the whole, as being made of two parts, the 6 and the 1. These part-part-whole relationships become the basis for later addition work. As well, if students are shown part of a whole and figure out what the other part is to make the whole, then a foundation for subtraction work is being set.

One particularly important idea to introduce is the meaning of the equals sign as a symbol that tells you that two sets of symbols are representations for the same amount. For example, when you write $3 + 1 = 4$, you are saying that another way to represent 4 is as 3 and 1. Similarly, when you write $3 + 2 = 4 + 1$, you are saying that another way to represent 3 and 2 is as 4 and 1.

Often, this is modelled by using a pan balance. If, for example, 3 green and 2 blue cubes are placed on one pan, they will balance 4 blue and 1 yellow on the other pan.

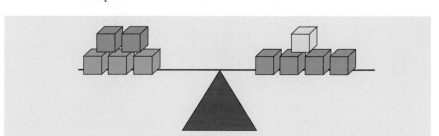

Reading and Writing Numerals

Numerals are one particularly universal way of representing numbers. Children encounter the use of numerals in many everyday situations. For example, a child might receive a birthday party invitation (such as the one shown below) that includes numerals representing different things.

ACTIVITY 7.15

Read the book *10 for Dinner* by J.E. Bogart (1989) to students. The pages require students, in a very interesting setting, to think about combinations for 10. Ask students to act out their own scenarios that would fit the story.

Creative Thinking

ACTIVITY 7.16

Kamii and Rummelsburg (2008) suggest that students arrange a specific number of bowling pins in different ways, trying to knock them down as one would when bowling. Students get a sense of how those representations are alike and different.

Building Number Sense

Encourage students to play games that help them to relate numerals to the amounts they represent. A simple game is Concentration.

Concentration

Have students lay a collection of set cards and small number cards face down. Students take turns turning over cards in search of a matching set, where the set card matches the number card. If they find a match, they can remove the pair of cards from play. When they have uncovered all of the pairs, they can count their cards and the player with the most cards wins the round.

Building Number Sense

Provide a calculator, cards with handwritten numerals on them, and cards with stylized numerals on them. Students press a number button on the calculator, and then find the matching numerals, both handwritten and stylized.

Building Number Sense

Paste large numeral cards onto cardboard and cut each card into three to five parts. Place the pieces for each numeral in an envelope and label the envelope with the corresponding numeral. Using the envelope as a model, students can try to solve the numeral puzzles. You can offer students additional cardboard numeral cards to create their own puzzles.

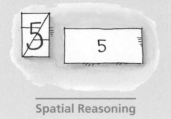

Spatial Reasoning

Numerals can be used to represent age, time, and location, and for identification.

It is important that students recognize numerals and what they represent, and learn to use them. They learn to read them through a variety of opportunities, such as reading storybooks (where they can attend to page numbers and numbers in the story itself). Increasingly, in our digital world, students see "block" form numerals rather than the handwritten forms of numerals that are often taught. It is important that students recognize the variability that is possible. For example, the teacher might show them all of these different versions of the numeral 8 to point out how they are similar and how they are different.

The teacher might follow up with an activity such as **Activity 7.18**.

Students might enjoy a puzzle that helps them focus on what numerals look like as well, such as that shown in **Activity 7.19**.

Students can gain experience in numeral writing by

- completing prepared dot-to-dots to follow a path to construct numerals
- tracing numerals in the air, following teacher instruction
- forming numerals in soft material like sand or salt (to allow mistakes to be erased quickly and to provide additional kinesthetic feedback)
- making modelling clay or edible cookies in the shape of numerals
- tracing numerals on one another's backs, using their index finger, and guessing the numbers

Teachers must be aware that there is no single correct way to write a numeral, although some ways have proven themselves to be simpler for children than others. No matter what style is used, it is important to focus on where the writing begins, the path to follow, and the end point.

One dilemma students have is making the distinction between numerals and numbers. If, for example, a teacher asks a student to show six, the student does not know whether to show the numeral or the number. It might be wise for a teacher to develop some language with students to help them make that distinction. For example, the teacher might say, "Sometimes I am going to ask you to show me what we write when we mean six. Other times, I am going to ask you to show me how much six is. What will you do each time?"

Common Errors and Misconceptions

Many of the common misconceptions and errors related to early number work revolve around not having full comprehension of the counting principles.

Early Number Sense: Common Errors, Misconceptions, and Strategies

COMMON ERROR OR MISCONCEPTION	SUGGESTED STRATEGY
Counting Students do not attend to which objects have been counted and which still need to be counted. They do not keep track of, or they lose track of, the objects they are counting by • skipping some of the objects • counting some of the objects twice • counting one too few when counting on, for example: 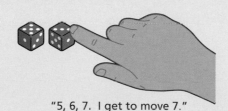 "5, 6, 7. I get to move 7."	• As students count, the teacher should watch to see if they can coordinate their verbal counting with their actions on the objects. • Students should be encouraged to move objects as they count them, one at a time, away from the objects still to be counted. • To minimize the likelihood of incorrect counting on, students should say aloud the number from which they are counting on while pointing to that group, and then count on there, pointing to each item as they count on. For example, to count on to find the sum of a roll of 5 and a roll of 3, students can say "5," while pointing to the die showing 5, and then say "6, 7, 8" as they point to each dot on the other die.
Counting Students who do not conserve number do not recognize the irrelevance of the space occupied by items. For example, they might think that by spreading out 4 counters, there is now a greater number.	Conservation of number is something that comes with experience and maturity. As students mature cognitively, they start to realize that the arrangement of items is irrelevant to the cardinality. Early on, however, it is important for students to have opportunities where they see that when they count, they get the same number both ways.
Counting Some students do not recognize that where you begin to count is irrelevant. For example, in counting the objects below, you could start with the yellow counter, going right and then back to the red and green ones, or you could start with the olive one at the right going left. The count does not change. 	Experience is the best tool in this case. Provide opportunities for students to count a set of objects, starting in several different places, or model how that is done. Ask students whether the total changed each time. Eventually they come to believe that it will not change.

(continued)

Early Number Sense: Common Errors, Misconceptions, and Strategies (Continued)

COMMON ERROR OR MISCONCEPTION	SUGGESTED STRATEGY
Counting Sometimes students struggle counting a part of a set. For example, if they are asked to count only 3 items in a set of 5, they count all 5.	Initially it might be helpful to provide students with a visual or auditory cue to help them stop when they should. For example, the number 3 could be written in large print within their view.
Cardinal and Ordinal Numbers Students misunderstand the difference between cardinal and ordinal numbers; for example, in this situation, the student was asked to show 5 books. 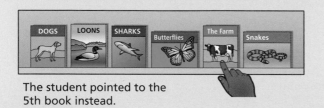 The student pointed to the 5th book instead.	It is through experience that students learn that a number can refer to a group of objects. It may be useful to set up a contradiction that a student will need to deal with. For example, for the situation shown to the left, ask the student to show you a set of 5 books that does not include the book he or she pointed to.

Appropriate Manipulatives

Manipulatives are critical to the development of early number sense.

Early Number Sense: Examples of Manipulatives

COUNTERS

Counters are essential manipulatives in early number work. Many different types of counters are useful:

- counters of different shapes and sizes
- objects of interest to children
- two-sided counters for number activities where random outcomes are desirable. For example, if a child spills ten 2-sided counters, she or he can compare the number of reds and yellows. Each time they are spilled, there could be a different number comparison.

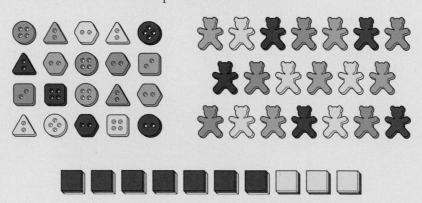

LINKING CUBES

Linking cubes are easy for students to manipulate and group. They are also good for number comparisons, as the attribute of length can help with comparing. If cubes of different colours are used, they can also be used for ordinal work.

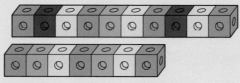

Counting on: "10, 11, 12, 13, 14, 15, 16, 17"
Comparing: "10 is 3 more than 7."
Ordinals: "The 2nd and 8th cubes are red."

DOMINOES AND DICE

Dominoes and dice provide familiar representations for numbers that students can begin to internalize.

"I recognize 6, because it's 2 rows of 3."

5-FRAMES

5-frames are useful for number comparisons and working with the benchmark of 5.

4 is one less than 5.

10-FRAMES

10-frames are useful for number comparisons and working with benchmark numbers (5 and 10).

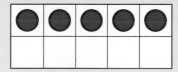 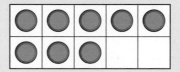

8 is greater than 5 because 8 includes 5.

(continued)

Early Number Sense: Examples of Manipulatives (Continued)

GAME MATERIALS

Game materials such as dice, cards, and dominoes are useful for the development of subitizing configurations that are associated with certain numbers. They are also useful for counting and encouraging the use of efficient counting strategies.

Subitizing with dice: "I rolled a 3 and a 4."

Counting on with dominoes: "6, 7, 8, 9, 10"

Comparing with cards: "9 is more than 3."

A WALK-ON NUMBER LINE

Walk-on number lines are useful for numeral identification, for early counting, both forward and backward, and for number comparisons.

8 is greater than 5 because it's farther along the number line.

REKENREK

Rekenreks come in various forms. This 20-bead rekenrek helps students anchor numbers that are 20 or less to the numbers 5, 10, 15, and 20.

A BEADED NUMBER LINE

Beaded number lines help students anchor numbers to 5 and 10 or even more, depending on the length of the number line.

The number 14 is the next to last blue bead. It is 4 more than 10.

PAN BALANCE

A pan balance reinforces the notion that numbers can be represented in different ways.

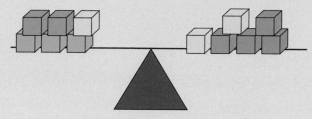

6 is 3 and 2 and 1, or 4 and 2.

Appropriate Children's Books

10 Black Dots (Crews, 1992).

The author uses graphic designs based on different numbers of dots. The focus is on the numbers from 1 to 10. For example, the page for 2 talks about how two dots can make the eyes of a fox, and the two dots are visually represented to show this. A teacher might have students then construct their own pictures using different numbers of dots and might, if appropriate, focus on the combinations of dots that make up the total.

Eggs and Legs: Counting by Twos (Dahl, 2005).

This story about a mother hen looking for her eggs focuses on counting by twos from zero to 20; she finds her eggs by counting pairs of legs emerging from the eggs. Each page designed to focus on one number includes the eggs and legs, but also includes dots showing that number and hides the numeral in the illustration.

Zero (Otoshi, 2010).

This is a humorous book about how the number zero, who is worth nothing, looks and feels. It is often hard for students to really believe that zero is a number, so a book that delves into this is valuable.

The Right Number of Elephants (Sheppard, 1992).

Original drawings and an unusual story line focus the reader on the sequence of numbers you hear as you count backward. The story line involves a girl deciding how many elephants are needed to help her accomplish various silly tasks.

Appropriate Digital Resources

See the MindTap site for a selection of appropriate digital resources.

Assessing Student Understanding

- Observe whether students stumble as they count, whether they count groups of objects efficiently, for example, by counting on, and whether they recognize certain configurations immediately and do not actually need to count them.
- Observe whether students can represent quantities in more than one way. For example, if asked to show 6 items, do they realize that the 6 can be arranged spatially in many ways?
- Some students can compare numbers more easily if they are very different than if they are close in size. Make sure to assess students' ability to compare in both situations.

• There should be little, if any, paper and pencil assessment at this level. Observation is the best tool to get a sense of what students at this age understand.
• Examine this student's response to a question about examples of the number 5 in the real world. Ask yourself, "What does it show that the student understands about numbers less than 10? the number 5? What would be a good follow-up question and why?"

Student Response

This student lists examples of when the number 5 is used in her classroom.

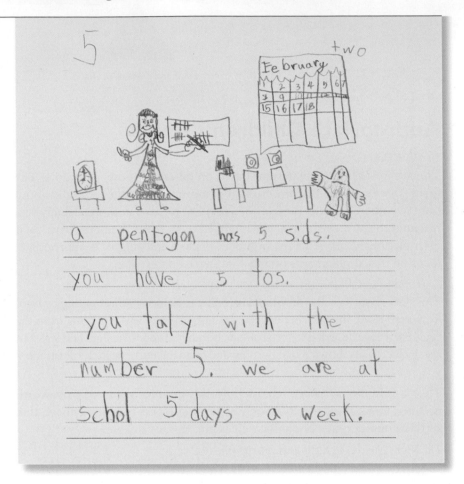

a pentogon has 5 sids.

you have 5 tos.

you taly with the number 5. we are at schol 5 days a week.

Applying What You've Learned

1. To solve the chapter problem, you listed some ways that 6 and 8 are alike and different. How frequently might you use an activity like this involving different pairs of numbers? Explain your decision.

2. Read one or two articles on developing a strong sense of five and/or ten. Explain why developing an understanding of those two numbers is particularly fundamental.

3. One of the main differences between a walk-on number line (e.g., see page 152) and a standard number line, such as that shown below, is that instead of using numbers to mark points on the number line, the numbers in the walk-on line occupy spaces. What are the advantages of a number line where spaces are marked? What are the disadvantages?

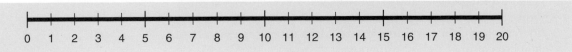

4. Locate five counting books that have particular mathematical merit. What makes each one valuable?

5. Develop a lesson plan around comparing numbers that are 10 or less. Include in the plan what assessment you will use to determine the success of the lesson.

6. a) Describe two or three interesting approaches to numeral writing that you could use with students.

   b) Do you think that numerals should be written as they appear on digital displays? (For example, the loops in 8 would be square rather than round.)

7. Examine several texts at the Kindergarten and Grade 1 levels. Do these texts emphasize the relationship of other numbers up to 20 to the anchor numbers of 5 and 10? Choose one or two lessons in the text to talk about how that relationship could be strengthened.

Interact with a K–8 Student:

8. Observe a fairly young child counting a set of five or six objects. What does the child do to keep track of objects to make sure that they are not counted twice? Is this strategy effective or not?

Discuss with a K–8 Teacher:

9. Ask a Kindergarten or Grade 1 teacher to share his or her knowledge of typical students' comfort with counting when they enter that grade level. Ask how the teacher adapts instruction for those students whose counting is significantly more advanced than that norm.

Selected References

Barker, L. (2009). Ten is the magic number! *Teaching Children Mathematics, 15,* 337–346.

Baroody, A.J. (1992). Remedying common counting difficulties. In Bideaud, J., Meljac, C., and Fischer, J.P. (Eds.). *Pathways to number: Children's developing numerical abilities,* Hillsdale, NJ: Erlbaum, 307–324.

Baroody, A.J. (2004). The developmental bases for early childhood number and operations standards. In Clements, D.H., and Sarama, J. (Eds.). *Engaging young children in mathematics.* Mahwah, NJ: Lawrence Erlbaum Associates, 173–220.

Baroody, A.J., and Benson, A. (2001). Early number instruction. *Teaching Children Mathematic, 8,* 154–158.

Bogart, J.E. (1989). *10 for dinner.* Richmond Hill, ON: Scholastic Tab.

Brizuela, B.M. (2004). *Mathematical development in young children: Exploring notations.* New York: Teachers College Press.

Brown, C.S., Sarama, J., and Clements, D.H. (2007). Thinking about learning trajectories in preschool. *Teaching Children Mathematics, 14,* 178–181.

Cavanagh, M., Dacey, L., Findell, C.R., Greenes, C.E., Sheffield, L.J., and Small, M. (2004). *Navigating through number and operations in prekindergarten–grade 2.* Reston, VA: National Council of Teachers of Mathematics.

Clements, D.H. (1999). Subitizing: What is it? Why teach it? *Teaching Children Mathematics, 5,* 400-405.

Clements, D.H., and Sarama, J. (2008). Focal points—Pre-K to kindergarten. *Teaching Children Mathematics, 14,* 361–365.

Clements, D.H., and Sarama, J. (2009). *Learning and teaching early math: The learning trajectories approach.* New York: Routledge.

Cooper, C.H. (1997). *Counting your way through 1–2–3: Books and activities.* Lanham, MD: Scarecrow Press.

Copley, J. (2010). *The young child and mathematics,* 2nd edition. Reston, VA: National Council of Teachers of Mathematics and National Association for the Education of Young Children.

Crews. D. (1992). *Ten black dots.* Toronto, ON: Scholastic.

Dahl, M. (2006). *Eggs and legs: Counting by twos.* Mankato, MN: Picture Window Books.

Davis, R.F. (2006). *10, 9, 8 polar animals! A counting backward book.* London, ON: A+ Books.

Fuson, K.C., Grandau, L., and Sugiyama, P.A. (2001). Achievable numerical understandings for all young children. *Teaching Children Mathematics, 7*(9), 522–526.

Gelman, R., and Gallistel, C.R. (1978). *The child's understanding of number.* Cambridge, MA: Harvard University Press.

Kamii, C., and Rummelsburg, J. (2008). Arithmetic for first graders lacking number concepts. *Teaching Children Mathematics, 14,* 389–394.

Merriam, E. (1996). *Twelve ways to get to 11.* New York: Aladdin.

Novakowski, J. (2007). Developing "five-ness" in kindergarten. *Teaching Children Mathematics, 14,* 226–231.

Otoshi, K. (2010). *Zero.* Mill Valley, CA: Ko Kids Books.

Sarama, J., and Clements, D.H. (2009). *Early childhood mathematics education research: Learning trajectories for young children.* New York: Routledge.

Sheppard, J. (1992). *The right number of elephants.* New York: HarperTrophy.

Steffe, L.P. (1992). Learning stages in the construction of the number sequence. In Bideaud, J., Meljac, C., and Fischer, J.P. (Eds.). *Pathways to number: Children's developing numerical abilities.* Hillsdale, NJ: Lawrence Erlbaum, 83–98.

Weiland, L. (2007). Experiences to help children learn to count on. *Teaching Children Mathematics, 14,* 188–192.

Wilburne, J.M., Napoli, M., Keat, J.B., Dile, K., Trout, M., and Decker, S. (2007). Mathematics through storybooks: A kindergarten story. *Teaching Children Mathematics, 14,* 231–237.

Wright, R.J., Martland, J., and Stafford, A.K. (2006). *Early numeracy: Assessment for teaching and intervention.* London: Paul Chapman Publishing.

Chapter 8

Early Operations

IN A NUTSHELL

The main ideas in this chapter are listed below:

1. The four operations—addition, subtraction, multiplication, and division—are related.

2. There are multiple meanings for each operation. Students need exposure, over time, to each of these meanings.

3. Different models should be employed to model the operations since some ideas about the operations are better explained with one model than another.

CHAPTER PROBLEM

A division problem includes these words:
- bananas
- most
- 24
- less

What could the problem be? How could you solve it using addition instead of division?

How the Four Operations Are Related

The four operations that are the focus of K–8 mathematics are addition, subtraction, multiplication, and division. The picture below shows how they are related.

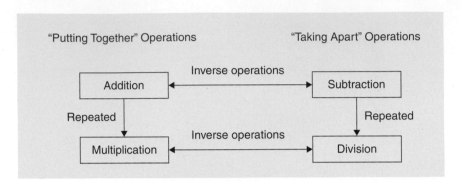

"Putting Together" Operations   "Taking Apart" Operations

Addition ← Inverse operations → Subtraction

Repeated ↓   ↓ Repeated

Multiplication ← Inverse operations → Division

TEACHING TIP

Students might be asked to solve subtraction, multiplication, or division questions using more than one operation to reinforce the relationship between the operations

Frequently, the same problem can be viewed using any of the four operations. For example, consider this problem:

Rafi had 12 cookies on a plate. If he ate them 3 at a time, how many times could he go back for cookies?

- Using addition: I'll add 3s until I get to 12: $3 + 3 + 3 + 3 = 12$. Solution: 4 times.
- Using subtraction: I'll subtract 3s until there are 0 cookies left: $12 - 3 - 3 - 3 - 3 = 0$. Solution: 4 times.
- Using multiplication: I'll figure out what to multiply by 3 to get 12. $4 \times 3 = 12$. Solution: 4 times.
- Using division: I'll divide 12 by 3: $12 \div 3 = 4$. Solution: 4 times.

Addition and Subtraction

In Canadian schools, teachers generally introduce addition and subtraction formally before multiplication and division. Work in all four operations requires facility with counting.

Meanings of Addition

Although addition always relates to the situation of combining things, students find it easier to first consider active situations, where a joining actually occurs, and later more static situations, where a whole is made up of two parts. Sometimes the part that is added is based on a comparison. For example, Ben had 3 more books than Andrea. Andrea had 6 books. How many did Ben have? In this case, the two parts are what Andrea had and

MEANING	EXAMPLE
Joining is an active addition situation.	A child has 5 marbles. His mom then brings him 3 new ones. 5 marbles + 3 new marbles = 8 marbles
Part-part-whole is a static addition situation where no action takes place.	A child has 8 marbles; 5 of them are blue and 3 are red. No action occurs, but it is still an addition situation. 5 blue marbles + 3 red marbles = 8 marbles

the extra that Ben had. In all of these situations, the numbers you add are called *addends* and the result is called a *sum*.

Meanings of Subtraction

Subtraction is a more complex operation than addition. Most simply, it is the opposite of addition, but there are many nuances.

MEANING	EXAMPLE
Taking away is an active separating situation.	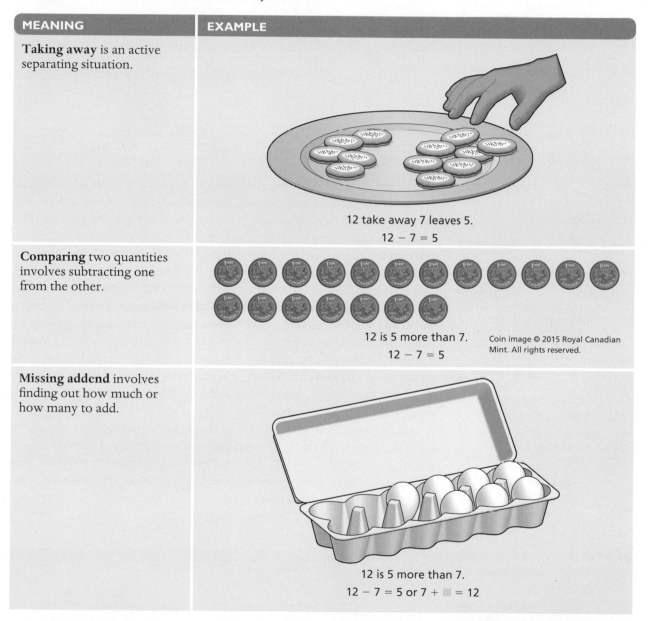 12 take away 7 leaves 5. $12 - 7 = 5$
Comparing two quantities involves subtracting one from the other.	12 is 5 more than 7. $12 - 7 = 5$ Coin image © 2015 Royal Canadian Mint. All rights reserved.
Missing addend involves finding out how much or how many to add.	12 is 5 more than 7. $12 - 7 = 5$ or $7 + \blacksquare = 12$

It is important for students to realize that these varying meanings for subtraction are related; in other words, it makes sense to apply the same operation in each situation. Therefore, a teacher must ensure that the connections are explored. One example is described below.

How Is Taking Away Like Comparing?

Consider the situation modelled and described below. To compare the number in the top row (*the minuend*) with the number in the bottom row (*the subtrahend*), you are finding how many more are in the top row than in the bottom row. You can take away the 3 counters that match in each row and what is left (*the difference*) is how many more were in the top row. So to compare to find how many more, you can take away.

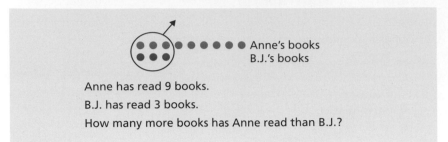

Anne has read 9 books.

B.J. has read 3 books.

How many more books has Anne read than B.J.?

Understanding Addition and Subtraction Situations

The chart that follows summarizes the many different addition and subtraction situations students will encounter. Some involve actions, like joining or taking away (separating), some involve recognizing the parts that make up a whole, and some involve comparing. Sometimes the whole and one part are known and the other part must be determined; other times the two parts are known and the whole must be determined.

Each situation can be represented by either an addition or a subtraction number sentence, or equation, with one number missing, and each is solved either by adding or by subtracting the two known quantities. When equations are introduced can vary. It is important that students have an understanding of what the equal sign represents before these equations are used. What is interesting is that sometimes an addition sentence can be solved by subtracting and sometimes by adding; the same is true of subtraction sentences.

It is important to ensure that students encounter a wide variety of these structures to help them construct a more complete understanding of addition and subtraction. The different meanings for the operations can be distinguished only through appropriate contexts. Note that the term *separating* is used to mean *take away*.

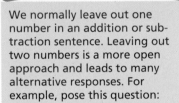

ACTIVITY 8.1

We normally leave out one number in an addition or subtraction sentence. Leaving out two numbers is a more open approach and leads to many alternative responses. For example, pose this question:

I have some books to start with. I get some more. Now I have 8. How many did I start with, and how many did I get?

Critical Thinking

ADDITION AND SUBTRACTION SITUATIONS			
Joining situations	1	2	3
	Result (sum) is unknown	Change (addend) is unknown	Start (addend) is unknown
	I have 3 books to start with. I get 1 more. How many do I have now?	*I have 5 books to start with. I get some more. Now I have 10. How many more did I get?*	*I had some books to start with. I got 3 more. Now I have 8. How many did I start with?*
	$3 + 1 = \blacksquare$	$5 + \blacksquare = 10$	$\blacksquare + 3 = 8$
	$a + b = \blacksquare$	$a + \blacksquare = c$	$\blacksquare + b = c$
	To solve, you can add $3 + 1$.	To solve, you can subtract $10 - 5$.	To solve, you can subtract $8 - 3$.

ADDITION AND SUBTRACTION SITUATIONS (Continued)

Separating situations	4	5	6
	Result (difference) is unknown	Change (subtrahend) is unknown	Start (minuend) is unknown
	I had 6 books. I gave away 3. How many do I have left?	I had 6 books. I gave away some. I have 2 left. How many did I give away?	I had some books. I gave away 4. I have 6 left. How many did I start with?
	$6 - 3 = \blacksquare$	$6 - \blacksquare = 2$	$\blacksquare - 4 = 6$
	$c - a = \blacksquare$	$c - \blacksquare = b$	
	To solve, you can subtract $6 - 3$.	To solve, you can subtract $6 - 2$.	To solve, you can add $6 + 4$.
Part-part-whole situations	7	8	
	Whole (sum) is unknown	Part (addend) is unknown	
	I have 3 small books and 4 big ones. How many books do I have altogether?	I have 7 books altogether. 3 of them are small books. How many are big books?	
		$3 + \blacksquare = 7$	
	$3 + 4 = \blacksquare$	$a + \blacksquare = c$	
	$a + b = \blacksquare$	To solve, you can subtract $7 - 3$.	
	To solve, you can add $3 + 4$.		
Comparing situations	9	10	11
	Difference is unknown	Comparing quantity (subtrahend) is unknown	Referent quantity (minuend) is unknown
	I have 7 big books and 2 small ones. How many more big books than small ones do I have?	I have 7 big books and some small ones. I have 2 more big books than small ones. How many small books do I have?	I have some big books. I have 3 small books. I have 2 fewer small books than big books. How many big books do I have?
	$7 - 2 = \blacksquare$	$7 - \blacksquare = 2$	$\blacksquare - 3 - 2$
	$c - a = \blacksquare$	$c - \blacksquare = b$	$\blacksquare - a = b$
	To solve, you can subtract $7 - 2$.	To solve, you can subtract $7 - 2$.	To solve, you can add $2 + 3$.

Solving Addition and Subtraction Number Stories

Students must decode and interpret number stories and not just rely on looking for "clue words" to decide what operation to perform. Notice that the word "more" appears both in Situation 1 in the Addition and Subtraction Situations chart, which involves adding the two given numbers, as well as in Situation 2, which involves subtracting the two given numbers.

Generally, but not always, students find joining and separating (take-away) situations easiest to deal with compared to other addition and subtraction situations. If students are encouraged to model number stories as they are presented, however, even young children can deal with part-part-whole and comparing situations. Students should always be encouraged to check to see if their answers seem reasonable.

Relating Addition and Subtraction

Notice that any addition situation can also be viewed as a subtraction one, and vice versa. In fact, what we call a fact family is a set of number sentences, or equations, that can be used to describe the same situation.

ACTIVITY 8.2

Provide students with a "script," for example, an expression like $4 + 6$ or an equation like $12 - 5 = 7$, and ask them, with a partner, to act out a "play" to show that script. They should be encouraged to use a variety of situations that are meaningful to their own experiences, rather than merely copying a familiar form over and over.

Creative Thinking

ACTIVITY 8.3

You might provide triangle cards like this one and ask students to describe the four facts in the fact family that go with them. Then ask why sometimes there are only 2 facts (e.g., with 10, 5, and 5).

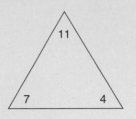

Building Number Sense

Fact Family for 2, 3, and 5

3 + 2 = 5	3 blue + 2 red = 5 altogether
2 + 3 = 5	2 red + 3 blue = 5 altogether
5 − 2 = 3	5 altogether; 2 are red, so 3 must be blue
5 − 3 = 2	5 altogether; 3 are blue, so 2 must be red

Addition and Subtraction Principles

There are a number of principles about addition and subtraction that students need to learn and discuss. Some of them are restatements of what mathematicians call properties inherent in our number system; others are built from those properties.

The idea is not to memorize the principles by name, but to be so familiar with our number system, that they are used naturally and informally. These principles are meant to become intuitive and second nature.

TEACHING TIP

Using the formal terms "commutative property" and "associative property" is not essential. Sometimes students make up names that are more meaningful to them. For example, some students call the commutative property the "turn-around property."

ADDITION AND SUBTRACTION PRINCIPLES

1. Addition and subtraction "undo" each other. They are related inverse operations. For example, if $4 + 8 = 12$, then $12 - 8 = 4$.

2. You can add numbers in any order (the commutative property). With subtraction, the order in which you subtract the numbers matters.

3. To add three numbers, you can add the first two and then the last one, or the sum of the last two to the first one (the associative property). For example, to add $5 + 4 + 3$, you can add $5 + 4$ to get 9 and then add 3, or you can add $4 + 3$ to get 7 and then calculate $5 + 7$. This property exists since addition is actually defined in terms of how to combine two numbers, so rules for three numbers had to be created.

4. You can add or subtract in parts. For example, $2 + 5 = 2 + 4 + 1$; $8 - 5 = 8 - 3 - 2$.

5. To subtract two numbers, you can add or subtract the same amount to or from both numbers without changing the difference. For example, $12 - 7 = (12 + 1) - (7 + 1)$.

6. When you add or subtract 0 to or from a number, the answer is the number you started with.

7. When you add 1 to a number, the sum is the next counting number. When you subtract 1 from a number, the difference is the counting number that comes before.

ACTIVITY 8.4

Students might have visuals of a variety of items with price tags with amounts 10¢ or lower. They are told that they started with 10¢, they bought one of the items, and how much is left. They have to decide what was purchased. For example, if 6¢ was left, they have to realize they bought a 4¢ item since $4 + 6 = 10$.

Building Number Sense

Principle 1: Addition and subtraction "undo" each other. They are related, but inverse, operations.

Mathematicians define subtraction as the inverse operation to addition, that is, it undoes what addition accomplishes. Suppose you start with 4 items, and you add 8 more and end up with 12. How do you get back to where you started at 4? You subtract the 8 you added. Similarly, if you start with 12 items and take away 4, you get back to the starting number, 12, by adding the 4 you took away.

This relationship allows students to use an addition table to solve a subtraction problem. They look inside the table in the row for 4 for the number 12 to determine $12 - 4$ (by looking up at the column header where 12 is found).

Principle 2: You can add numbers in any order (the commutative property). With subtraction, the order in which you subtract the numbers matters.

The commutative property, or order property, can be modelled and explained using counters. Show a group of 3 counters and a group of 4 counters on a piece of paper, and then turn the paper 180 degrees. It is clear that you have exactly the same counters, so $3 + 4 = 4 + 3$.

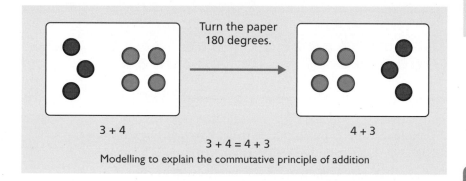

3 + 4   4 + 3
3 + 4 = 4 + 3
Modelling to explain the commutative principle of addition

This also shows up in the addition table by noticing that any row is equivalent to a matching column.

However, order does matter when you subtract. For example, if you take 3 cookies away from 7, you have 4 left. You cannot take 7 cookies away from 3, although later students will learn that you can calculate $3 - 7$, using integers.

Principle 3: To add three numbers, you can add the first two and then the last one, or the sum of the last two to the first one (the associative property).

As a consequence of this property, you can take away from one number and add what you took away to the other number without changing the sum. Suppose you are adding 4 counters and 6 counters as shown below; you can move any number of counters from one pile to the other without changing the total. Moving 2 counters from the left pile to the right changes the calculation to $2 + 8$, but does not change the sum. In fact, you have renamed $(2 + 2) + 6$ as $2 + (2 + 6)$.

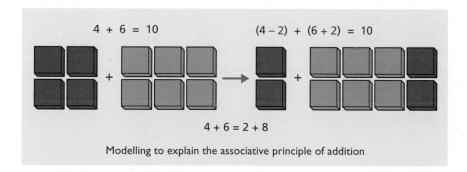

4 + 6 = 10   (4 − 2) + (6 + 2) = 10

4 + 6 = 2 + 8
Modelling to explain the associative principle of addition

Principle 4: You can add or subtract in parts.

Suppose you want to add 5 objects to a group of objects. It really does not matter if you add all 5 objects at once or if you do it in stages. For example, you can add 3 and then add 2; you are still adding 5 ($2 + 5 = 2 + 3 + 2$). The same is true for subtraction. For example, to subtract 5 objects from a group, you can take away 3 and then take away 2 more ($8 - 5 = 8 - 3 - 2$).

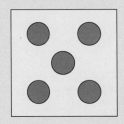

ACTIVITY 8.7

Pose the following question.

• *Choose an amount of cookies on a plate. Choose an amount of cookies that you want to eat. Tell how many would be left.*

• *Now imagine a plate with 2 more cookies. How many cookies would you need to eat this time to have the same number left? Why is that?*

Building Number Sense

Principle 5: To subtract two numbers, you can add or subtract the same amount to or from both numbers without changing the difference.

If a boy is 12 years old and his brother is 7, the older brother is 5 years older than the younger one. What about next year and the year after that? How much older will he be then? He will always be 5 years older. Because the same amount is added to each age each year, the difference remains unchanged. You could model the situation as shown.

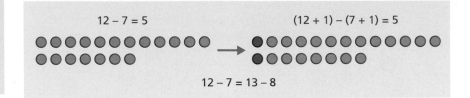

$$12 - 7 = 5 \qquad (12 + 1) - (7 + 1) = 5$$

$$12 - 7 = 13 - 8$$

Principle 6: When you add or subtract 0 to or from a number, the answer is the number you started with.

One useful model to show this principle is a walk-on number line:

3 + 2 means start at 3 and step 2 spaces forward, ending up on 5.
3 + 0 means start at 3 and step 0 spaces forward, staying at 3.

Principle 7: When you add 1 to a number, the sum is the next counting number. When you subtract 1 from a number, the difference is the counting number that comes before.

Again, a walk-on number line is helpful for demonstrating this principle since adding 1 means to move 1 space forward, for example, $3 + 1 = 4$, and subtracting 1 means to move 1 space back, for example, $3 - 1 = 2$.

ACTIVITY 8.8

To make sure that all students have success, play a game with a small group of students where you roll a great big die that is easy for all students to see. Then say "And [ ] more is?" Vary the amount [ ] to add. For struggling students, say "And 0 more is?" or "and 1 more is?"

Building Number Sense

Common Errors and Misconceptions

Addition and Subtraction: Common Errors, Misconceptions, and Strategies

COMMON ERROR OR MISCONCEPTION	SUGGESTED STRATEGY
Understanding Open Sentences Students are confused by open sentences with missing addends, and missing subtrahends and minuends. For example, they might interpret $3 + \blacksquare = 8$ as $8 + 3 = \blacksquare$.	Have students explain what the sentence actually says; for example, "A number is added to 3 and you end up with 8." Then ask how they know the missing number has to be less than 8.
Interpreting Walk-On Number Lines Students have difficulty using walk-on number lines to add or subtract. For example, to show $8 - 3$, some students will start at 8 but include 8 as they count back 3, landing on 6 instead of 5.	Encourage students to stand with both feet on the start number of the number step before taking their first step. This will force their first step onto the next square.

Appropriate Manipulatives

Manipulatives can be used to model both the joining (or active addition) and part-part-whole (or static addition) meanings of addition.

Addition: Examples of Manipulatives

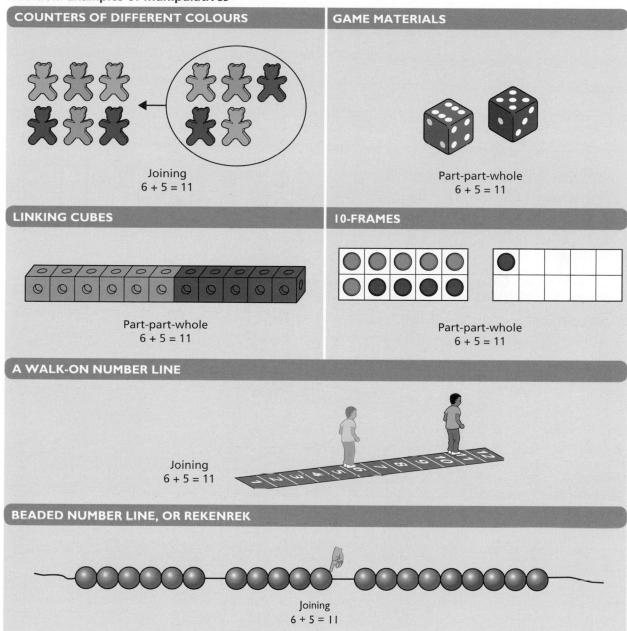

COUNTERS OF DIFFERENT COLOURS

Joining
6 + 5 = 11

GAME MATERIALS

Part-part-whole
6 + 5 = 11

LINKING CUBES

Part-part-whole
6 + 5 = 11

10-FRAMES

Part-part-whole
6 + 5 = 11

A WALK-ON NUMBER LINE

Joining
6 + 5 = 11

BEADED NUMBER LINE, OR REKENREK

Joining
6 + 5 = 11

Manipulatives can be used to model take-away, comparison, missing addend, and part-part-whole meanings of subtraction. Sometimes the meaning of subtraction is tied to the physical representation, but other times it depends on the words that are said when looking at the model. Counters of different colours are more useful for missing addend and, particularly, for comparison than single-coloured counters.

Subtraction: Examples of Manipulatives

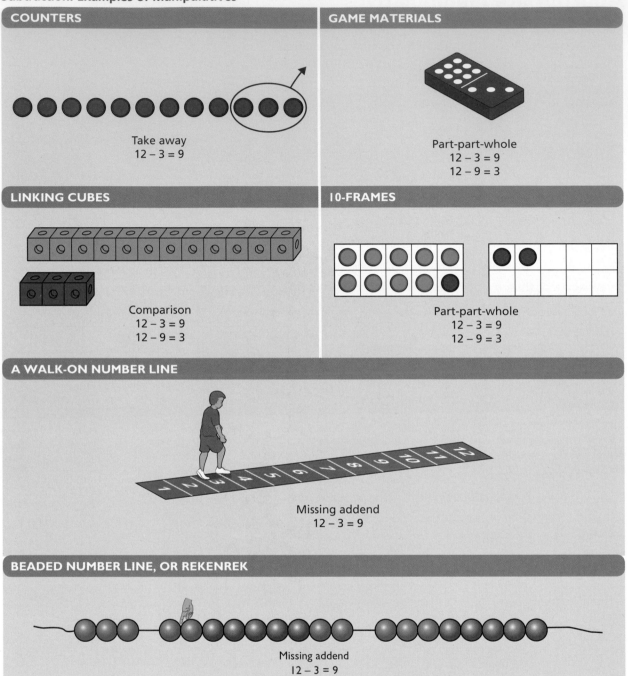

COUNTERS

Take away
12 – 3 = 9

GAME MATERIALS

Part-part-whole
12 – 3 = 9
12 – 9 = 3

LINKING CUBES

Comparison
12 – 3 = 9
12 – 9 = 3

10-FRAMES

Part-part-whole
12 – 3 = 9
12 – 9 = 3

A WALK-ON NUMBER LINE

Missing addend
12 – 3 = 9

BEADED NUMBER LINE, OR REKENREK

Missing addend
12 – 3 = 9

Multiplication and Division

The other two important operations in the elementary grades are multiplication and division.

Meanings of Multiplication

The operation of multiplication is used in many situations. The two numbers multiplied are called *factors* and the result is called the *product*.

MEANING	EXAMPLE
Repeated Addition	The first factor, in this case 3, tells how many times to add the second factor, 4. $3 \times 4 = 4 + 4 + 4$ Note that some teachers define 3×4 as adding 3 four times, but the convention shown here is more typical in Canada.
Equal Groups or Sets	3×4 is the total number of objects in 3 sets of 4.  $4 + 4 + 4 = 12$ $3 \times 4 = 12$ This model shows both equal groups and repeated addition. Note that some teachers define 3×4 as the total number of objects in 4 sets of 3, but the convention shown here is more typical in Canada.
An Array (An array is not different from an equal group situation; it is simply one that is arranged in a rectangular fashion.)	3×4 is the total number of items in a 3-by-4 array.  $3 \times 4 = 12$ An array of 3 rows with 4 counters in each has 12 counters altogether.
Area of a Rectangle	3×4 is the area of a 3-by-4 rectangle. 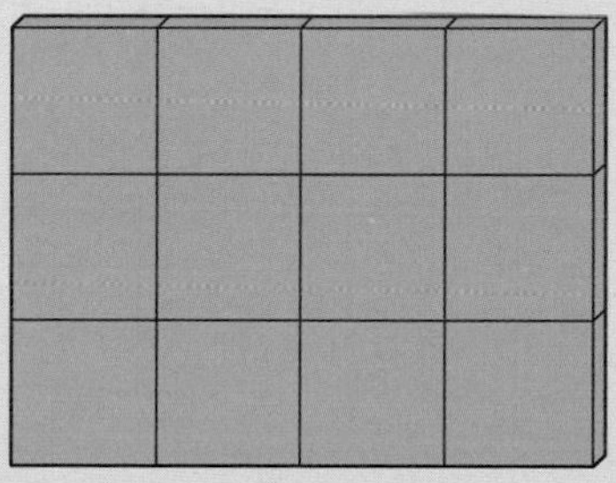 $3 \times 4 = 12$ A rectangle that is 3 units wide by 4 units long has an area of 12 square units.

MEANING	EXAMPLE
A Rate/Comparison	A rate describes how a quantity is "stretched," whether a continuous measure, like a length, or a discrete quantity, like a set of pencils. 3×4 represents the final amount when a 4-unit measure is increased to 3 times its original value. The result, 12, is compared to the original 4, by thinking of it as 3 times as much.

$3 \times 4 = 12$

A 4-unit long line stretched to 3 times its length is 12 units long

3×4 describes how many pencils Poli has if Mia has 4 pencils and Poli has 3 times as many.

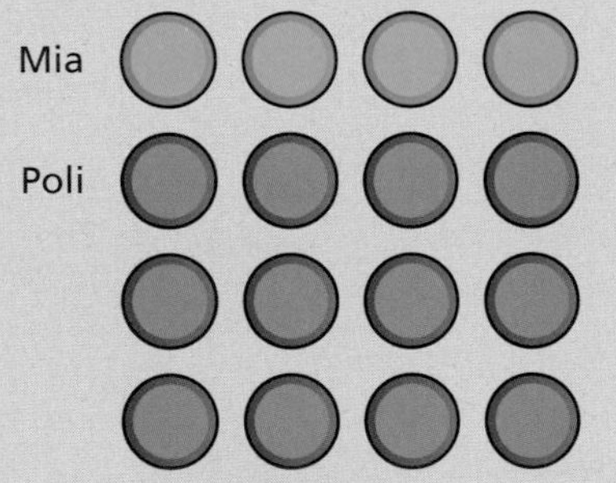

Mia

Poli

$3 \times 4 = 12$

At a rate of 3 times as many, Poli has 12,
if Mia has 4.

Combinations

3×4 is the number of paper–envelope combinations possible, if there are 3 kinds of envelopes and 4 colours of paper.

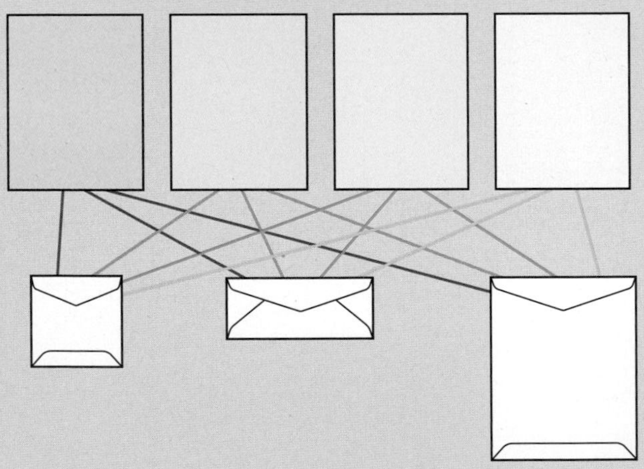

$3 \times 4 = 12$

3 envelopes and 4 colours of paper makes
12 different paper–envelope combinations.

Limitations of Meanings

Although all these meanings make sense when whole numbers are involved, some need to be adjusted when decimal, fraction, or integer numbers are involved. For example, $1\frac{1}{2} \times 3$ can mean to repeatedly add 3, but the second addend is only half of 3. The same adjustment needs to be made for equal sets or arrays.

The combinations meaning is difficult to make sense of unless both numbers are whole numbers. This meaning is usually introduced later than some of the others.

Even the rate and area meanings, which make sense for whole numbers, fractions, and decimals, must be adjusted for integers. A definition of a negative rate or a negative dimension is required. This is further discussed in Chapter 15.

How the Meanings of Multiplication Are Equivalent

Simply knowing the meanings will not help students develop a well-rounded understanding of the operation. It is important for students to understand why these various meanings are equivalent and are, therefore, all related to multiplication. One such relationship is shown below.

How Is a Rate the Same as Repeated Addition or an Array? If Mia has 4 items and Poli has 3 times as many items as Mia, then Poli has 12 items (3 items for each 1 item that Mia has). This can be modelled in an array as shown (Poli's array) and can be represented by adding the number in each row using repeated addition: $4 + 4 + 4$.

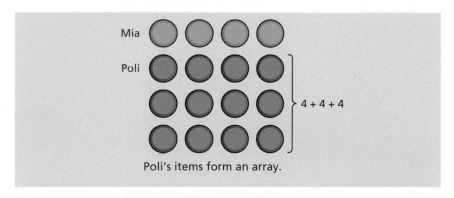

Poli's items form an array.

ACTIVITY 8.9

Draw arrays on cards and cut off a corner so that some dots are missing, but the numbers of rows and columns are clear. Present a card, suggesting that a dog bit off the missing corner. Ask how many dots were originally on the card, given that the array was originally complete.

Building Number Sense

Meanings of Division

When one number is divided by another, the number being divided is called the *dividend*, the other number is called the *divisor*, and the result is called the *quotient*.

MEANING	EXAMPLE
Equal Sharing (Partitive)	12 ÷ 4 = 3 is the amount each person gets if 12 items are shared equally among 4 people. 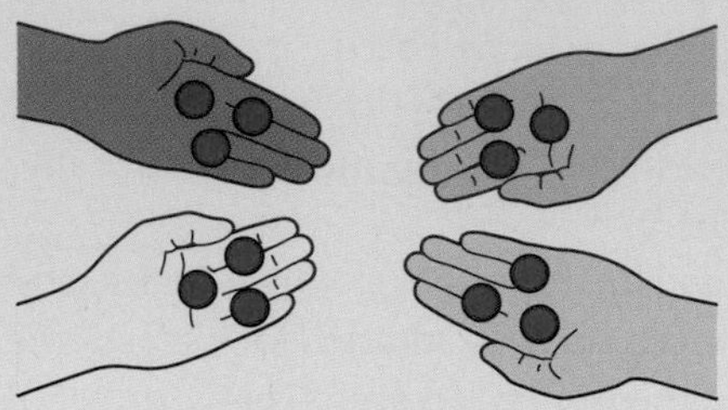 12 ÷ 4 = 3
Equal Grouping (Quotative)	12 ÷ 4 = 3 is the number of equal groups of 4 you can make with 12 items. 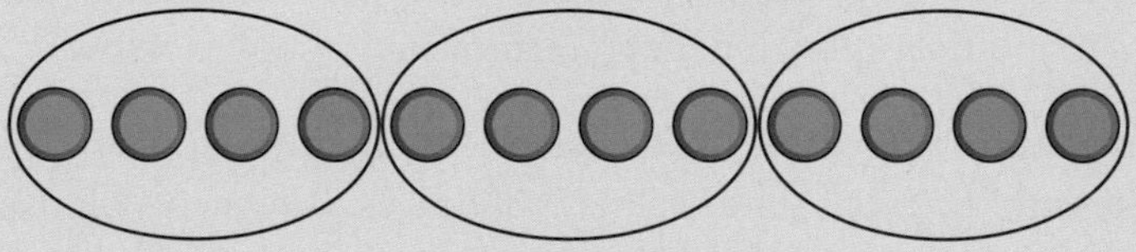 12 ÷ 4 = 3
Repeated Subtraction	12 ÷ 4 = 3 is the number of times you can subtract 4 from 12 before you get to 0. 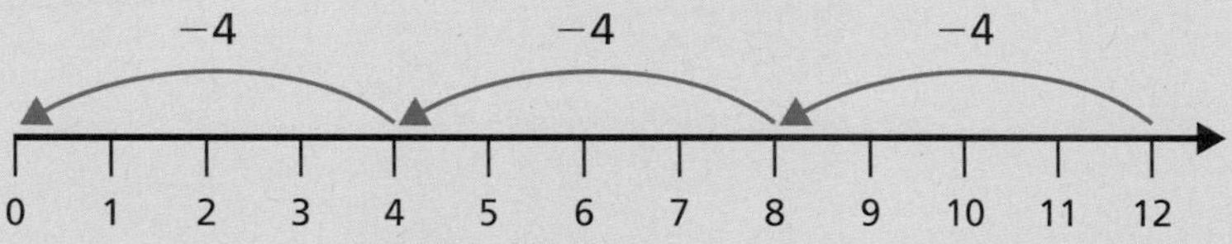 -4 -4 -4 0 1 2 3 4 5 6 7 8 9 10 11 12 12 − 4 − 4 − 4 = 0 12 ÷ 4 = 3
Width or Length of a Rectangle	12 ÷ 4 = 3 is the width of a rectangle with an area of 12 square units and a length of 4 units. Area is 12 square units 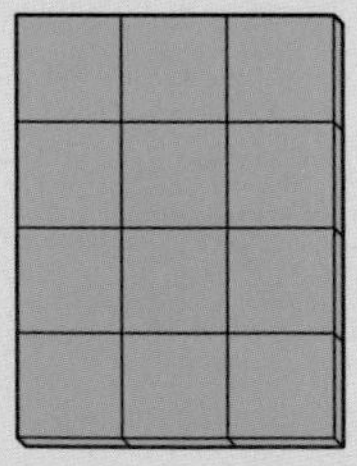 4 units long 12 ÷ 4 = 3 units wide
Rate	12 ÷ 4 = 3 is the unit rate if 4 units make 12.  4 toy cars for $12 If 4 toy cars cost $12, then 1 toy car costs $3.

How the Meanings of Division Are Equivalent

It is important for students to understand why these various meanings are equivalent and, therefore, all relate to division. One such relationship is shown below.

How Is Equal Sharing Like Equal Grouping? Suppose you want to share 12 items among 4 people. One of the most natural ways to do this is to give each of the 4 people one item, then give each of them a second item, and then a third item, until all the items are gone. After you have given each of the 4 people his or her first item, you have created a group of 4. After you have given each of the 4 people a second item, you have created another group of 4, and so on. So, even though you are sharing, you are also creating equal groups of 4 for each round of sharing.

TEACHING TIP

Although the rate meaning of division is more likely to be used in higher grades, even young students can be asked what one item costs if the total price of several is known.

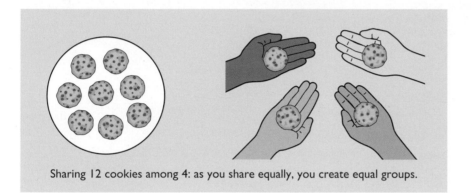

Sharing 12 cookies among 4: as you share equally, you create equal groups.

Understanding Multiplication and Division Situations

As with addition and subtraction, there are many types of multiplication and division situations. Each situation can be represented by either a multiplication or a division number sentence with one number missing, and each is solved by either multiplying or dividing the two known quantities. Sometimes a multiplication sentence can be solved by dividing and sometimes by multiplying; the same is true of division sentences. It is also possible to be more open-ended and use these same sorts of multiplication/division situations when two quantities are unknown, for example, $\Box \div \triangle = 3$.

As with addition and subtraction, it is very important to ensure that students encounter a wide variety of these structures to help them construct a more complete understanding of multiplication and division. The different meanings of multiplication and division can only be distinguished through appropriate contexts.

MULTIPLICATION AND DIVISION SITUATIONS

Equal group situations (including equal groups and arrays)	1	2	3
	Whole (product) is unknown *I have 3 boxes with 4 tomatoes in each. How many tomatoes do I have?* $3 \times 4 = \blacksquare$ $a \times b = \blacksquare$ Multiply to solve.	Size of group (quotient) is unknown *I have 12 tomatoes packed equally in 3 boxes. How many tomatoes are in each box?* $12 \div 3 = \blacksquare$ $c \div a = \blacksquare$ You can divide to solve.	Number of groups (divisor) is unknown *I have some boxes of tomatoes. I have 12 tomatoes altogether, and there are 4 in each box. How many boxes do I have?* $12 \div \blacksquare = 4$ $c \div \blacksquare = b$ You can divide to solve.

Area situations	4	5	
	Area (product) is unknown *A rectangle has a length of 4 units and a width of 2 units. What is its area in square units?* $4 \times 2 = \blacksquare$ $a \times b = \blacksquare$ Multiply to solve.	One dimension (length or width) is unknown *A rectangle has an area of 15 square units. One dimension is 3 units. What is the other dimension?* $15 \div 3 = \blacksquare$ $c \div a = \blacksquare$ You can divide to solve.	

Rate situations (comparison)	6	7	8
	Result of comparison (product) is unknown *Meg has 5 pennies and I have 3 times as many as she does. How many do I have?* $3 \times 5 = \blacksquare$ $a \times b = \blacksquare$ Multiply to solve.	Size of original group (factor) is unknown *I have 15 pennies. I have 3 times as many pennies as Meg. How many does Meg have?* $3 \times \blacksquare = 15$ $a \times \blacksquare = c$ You can divide to solve.	Size of comparison ratio (factor) is unknown *Meg has 5 pennies and I have 15. How many pennies do I have for each of Meg's?* $\blacksquare \times 5 = 15$ $\blacksquare \times b = c$ You can divide to solve.

Combination situations	9	10	
	Total (product) is unknown *I have 3 shirts and 2 pairs of pants. How many shirt–pant outfits do I have?* $3 \times 2 = \blacksquare$ $a \times b = \blacksquare$ Multiply to solve.	Size of one set (factor) is unknown *I have 8 shirt–pant outfits and 4 shirts. How many pairs of pants do I have?* $4 \times \blacksquare = 8$ $a \times \blacksquare = c$ You can divide to solve.	

Notice that the sentence $\blacksquare \div 4 = 3$ is not shown in the chart. It is equivalent, though, to Situation 1. For example, the problem might be worded as, "I have some tomatoes. I was able to make 3 boxes of 4 tomatoes. How many tomatoes did I have?" and could be solved by multiplying 3×4.

Solving Multiplication and Division Problems

As with addition and subtraction, students should work with a wide variety of structures to help them construct a more complete understanding of multiplication and division situations. Because students find equal group situations easier to understand, combinations and comparison situations are usually encountered after equal group situations have been explored. As with addition and subtraction, the most difficult situations for students are those represented by $\blacksquare \times b = c$ and $\blacksquare \div a = b$, where the first term is unknown.

Once students are comfortable solving simple multiplication and division number stories, they may want to create their own number stories.

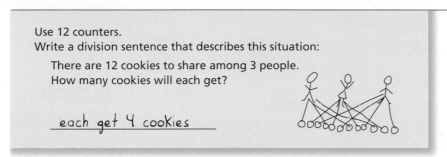

Use 12 counters.
Write a division sentence that describes this situation:

There are 12 cookies to share among 3 people. How many cookies will each get?

each get 4 cookies

Student Response

This student solves a division problem using a diagram to explain his or her thinking rather than representing it symbolically. You might follow up by asking how he or she would write this using a sentence of the form [ ] ÷ [ ] = [ ].

Even early on, students should meet and create division problems where there are remainders. For example, a student might encounter a problem where 19 books are being shared equally by 4 students. They have to figure out what it makes sense to do with the remainder.

Relating Multiplication and Division

Notice that any multiplication situation can also be viewed as a division situation, and vice versa. In fact, what teachers call a fact family is a set of number sentences, or equations, that can be used to describe the same situation.

Fact Family for 3, 4, and 12

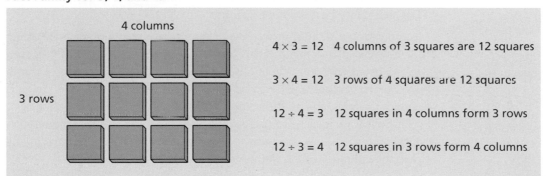

4 columns

3 rows

$4 \times 3 = 12$ 4 columns of 3 squares are 12 squares

$3 \times 4 = 12$ 3 rows of 4 squares are 12 squares

$12 \div 4 = 3$ 12 squares in 4 columns form 3 rows

$12 \div 3 = 4$ 12 squares in 3 rows form 4 columns

Multiplication and Division Principles

Students need to become familiar with and use a number of principles about multiplication and division. As with the addition and subtraction principles, these principles are meant to become intuitive and not memorized; they are simply used so often they become second nature. In the explanations of the principles on the following pages, different meanings of multiplication and different models are used each time. Often, one meaning of an operation is much more helpful than another in explaining a particular idea.

As with addition, some properties of multiplication have been named by mathematicians, in particular, the commutative, associative, and distributive properties. These are identified in the chart.

MULTIPLICATION AND DIVISION PRINCIPLES

1. Multiplication and division "undo" each other. They are related inverse operations. For example, if $12 \div 3 = 4$, then $3 \times 4 = 12$.

2. You can multiply numbers in any order (the commutative property). With division, the order in which you divide the numbers matters.

3. To multiply two numbers, you can divide one factor and multiply the other by the same amount without changing the product (a variation of the associative property). For example, $8 \times 3 = 4 \times 6$, $(8 \div 2) \times (3 \times 2)$.

4. To divide two numbers, you can multiply both numbers by the same amount without changing the quotient. For example, $15 \div 3 = 30 \div 6$, $(15 \times 2) \div (3 \times 2)$.

5. You can multiply in parts (the distributive property). For example, $5 \times 4 = 3 \times 4 + 2 \times 4$.

6. You can multiply in parts by breaking up the multiplier as a product (a variation of the associative property). For example, $6 \times 5 = 2 \times 3 \times 5$.

7. You can divide in parts by splitting the dividend into parts (the distributive property), but not the divisor. For example, $48 \div 8 = 32 \div 8 + 16 \div 8$. It is not equal to $48 \div 4 + 48 \div 4$.

8. You can divide by breaking up the divisor as a product. For example, $36 \div 6 = 36 \div 3 \div 2$.

9. When you multiply by 0, the product is 0.

10. When you divide 0 by any number but 0, the quotient is 0.

11. You cannot divide by 0.

12. When you multiply or divide a number by 1, the answer is the number you started with.

TEACHING TIP

Encourage students to always think about what a calculation means rather than simply memorizing principles or properties.

ACTIVITY 8.10

Tell students that they can use more than 20 but fewer than 30 items, and that you want them to make equal groups. If it's available, have students model the groups using an interactive white board, moving items around.

Ask them to write both multiplication and division sentences that describe the equal groups they can make.

Building Number Sense

Principle 1: Multiplication and division "undo" each other. They are related inverse operations.

Multiplication and division are inverse operations; one "undoes" the other. In fact, division is defined as the "opposite" of multiplication. If you start with 12 items and share them among 3 people, each person gets 4 items. How do you get back to where you started (to 12)? You think of the 3 people, each with 4 items, as a multiplication situation, or 3 groups of 4, which is 12.

This allows a student to use a multiplication table to determine a quotient. He or she solves $12 \div 4$ by looking for 12 in the 4 row and reading up to see the column header, in this case, 3.

Principle 2: You can multiply numbers in any order (the commutative property). With division, the order in which you divide the numbers matters.

If you model 3 groups of 4 as shown below, it is not clear why it is the same as 4 groups of 3.

But, if you rearrange the same 12 items in an array as shown at the top of the next page, it is obvious why $3 \times 4 = 4 \times 3$. The same model shows both 3 sets of 4 and 4 sets of 3.

This shows up in the multiplication table by noticing that the row for any number matches the column for that number.

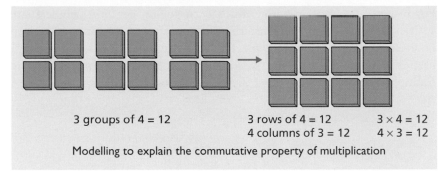

3 groups of 4 = 12

3 rows of 4 = 12   3 × 4 = 12
4 columns of 3 = 12   4 × 3 = 12

Modelling to explain the commutative property of multiplication

Note that the order does matter when you divide. For example, if you were to divide 12 items into groups of 3, you would have 4 groups of 3. If you were to try to divide 3 items into groups of 12, you would not have even 1 full group.

Principle 3: To multiply two numbers, you can divide one factor and multiply the other by the same amount without changing the product.

The associative property of multiplication suggests that to multiply $a \times b \times c$, you can multiply $a \times b$ first and then multiply by c, or calculate $b \times c$ first and then multiply that product by a. For example, $4 \times 2 \times 3 = 8 \times 3$ or 4×6. The property exists since multiplication is only defined for two numbers, and rules had to be created to allow you to deal with more numbers than that.

Consider the 8 groups of 3 (8×3) shown below. If you pair up groups of 3, you will have 6 in each group or twice as many in each group but only 4 groups, that is, half as many groups (4×6).

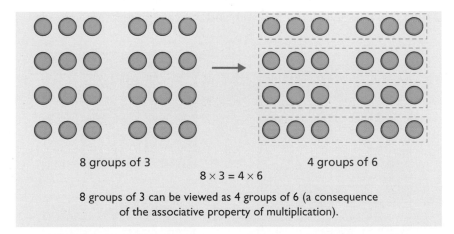

8 groups of 3   4 groups of 6

$8 \times 3 = 4 \times 6$

8 groups of 3 can be viewed as 4 groups of 6 (a consequence of the associative property of multiplication).

To multiply 12 × 5, Chris thinks "6 × 10." Explain his thinking.

Its easier to myltiply by 10 in your head and the answer doesn't change anyway because its half of 12 but twice 5.

Student Response

This student demonstrates an understanding of the value of using an equivalent form of a product with numbers that are easier to multiply mentally.

Principle 4: To divide two numbers, you can multiply both numbers by the same amount without changing the quotient.

For instance, $15 \div 3$ asks how much each person gets if 3 people share 15 items equally. It makes sense that if there are twice as many items to be shared by twice as many people, the share size stays the same. It does not matter what the dividend and divisor are multiplied by. As long as they are multiplied by the same amount, the quotient does not change.

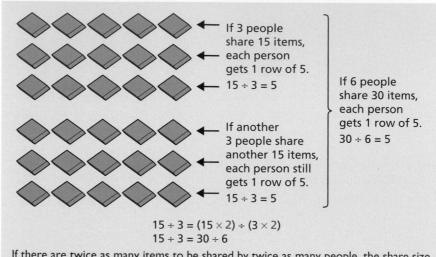

If 3 people share 15 items, each person gets 1 row of 5.
$15 \div 3 = 5$

If another 3 people share another 15 items, each person still gets 1 row of 5.
$15 \div 3 = 5$

If 6 people share 30 items, each person gets 1 row of 5.
$30 \div 6 = 5$

$$15 \div 3 = (15 \times 2) \div (3 \times 2)$$
$$15 \div 3 = 30 \div 6$$

If there are twice as many items to be shared by twice as many people, the share size stays the same.

Principle 5: You can multiply in parts (the distributive property).

For instance, you can separate 5 rows of 4 squares into 3 rows of 4 and 2 rows of 4 ($5 \times 4 = 3 \times 4 + 2 \times 4$) without changing the total number.

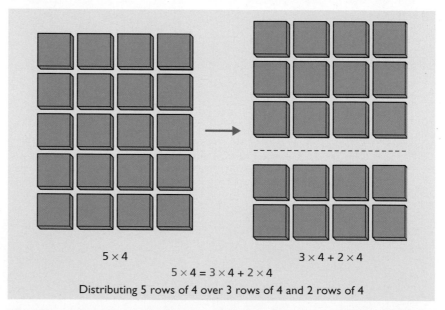

5×4 $3 \times 4 + 2 \times 4$

$$5 \times 4 = 3 \times 4 + 2 \times 4$$

Distributing 5 rows of 4 over 3 rows of 4 and 2 rows of 4

This shows up in the multiplication table by noticing that if you add matching elements in two rows in the table, you often get another row in the table. For example, if you add any number in the 2 row to the number in the 5 row below it, you get the number in the 7 row below them. The same idea works with columns.

Principle 6: You can multiply in parts by breaking up the multiplier as a product (a variation of the associative property).

An array is a good way to show this principle. For example, you can easily separate 6 rows of 5 squares into 2 groups, each with 3 rows of 5, without changing the total number of squares, as shown at the top of the next page.

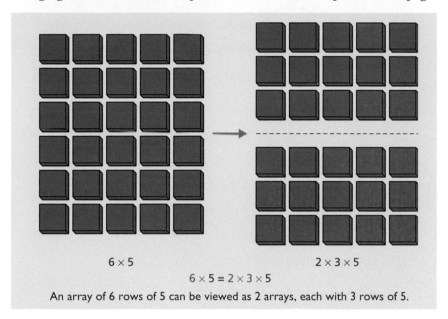

6 × 5

2 × 3 × 5

6 × 5 = 2 × 3 × 5

An array of 6 rows of 5 can be viewed as 2 arrays, each with 3 rows of 5.

Principle 7: You can divide in parts by splitting the dividend into parts (the distributive property), but not the divisor.

For example, 48 ÷ 8 asks how many items each person gets when 48 items are shared equally among 8 people. It is possible to "distribute" the first 24 among the 8 people, and then "distribute" the other 24 among the same 8 people.

Notice that 48 ÷ 8 does NOT equal 48 ÷ 6 + 48 ÷ 2. This is because 48 ÷ 8 tells how many groups of 8 are in 48. 48 ÷ 2 tells how many groups of 2 are in 48; that is already a lot more than 48 ÷ 8, even before you add the 48 ÷ 6.

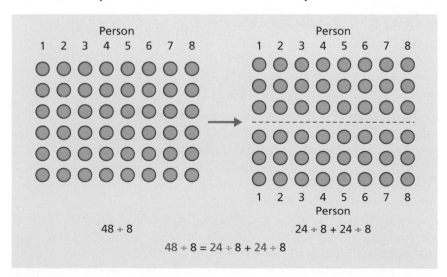

48 ÷ 8

24 ÷ 8 + 24 ÷ 8

48 ÷ 8 = 24 ÷ 8 + 24 ÷ 8

Principle 8: You can divide by breaking up the divisor as a product.

The expression 36 ÷ 6 tells how many items there are in each group if 36 items are shared equally among 6 groups. You could share the 36 items among

6 groups (36 ÷ 6), or you could split the 36 items into 2 groups of 18 and then share within each of the 18s, each into 3 smaller groups of 6 (that is, 36 ÷ 2 ÷ 3).

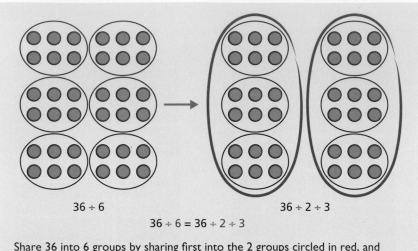

36 ÷ 6   36 ÷ 2 ÷ 3

36 ÷ 6 = 36 ÷ 2 ÷ 3

Share 36 into 6 groups by sharing first into the 2 groups circled in red, and then sharing within each red group into 3 groups.

Principle 9: When you multiply by 0, the product is 0.

To show, say, 5 sets of 0, you might use 5 empty plates. Since there is nothing on any of the plates, the total number of items is 0.

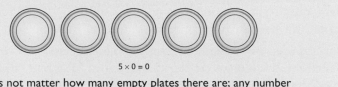

5 × 0 = 0

It does not matter how many empty plates there are; any number of plates with 0 items on them results in 0 items altogether.

Principle 10: When you divide 0 by a number other than 0, the quotient is 0.

For example, 0 ÷ 5 asks the share size if 5 people share nothing. The amount is clearly nothing.

Principle 11: You cannot divide by 0.

It is more difficult to explain 5 ÷ 0 than 0 ÷ 5. How can 5 items be shared among 0 groups? Here a repeated subtraction meaning for division might make more sense to explain the principle. To divide, for example, 15 ÷ 5, you can subtract 5 three times from 15, until you get to 0, so 15 ÷ 5 = 3. So, to divide 5 ÷ 0, you must determine how many times you can subtract 0 from 5 before getting down to 0. There is no answer; you will simply never get to 0. Therefore, 5 ÷ 0 is undefined.

As for 0 ÷ 0, you can subtract 0 any number of times from 0 to get to 0, so the answer could be 1, 2, 3, or any number. Since there are too many answers, 0 ÷ 0 is indeterminate.

Another way to describe this principle is to appeal to the relationship between multiplication and division. If the answer were ■, that is, 5 ÷ 0 = ■, then 0 × ■ = 5. Since 0 × anything is 0, there are no answers. If 0 ÷ 0 = ■, then 0 × ■ = 0. Here there are an infinite number of answers (any number works). In either case, it makes no mathematical sense to divide by 0.

Principle 12: When you multiply or divide a number by 1, the answer is the number you started with.

The following models explain this principle for multiplication and for division.

1 × 6 is 1 group of 6,
or 6 items altogether.

6 ÷ 1 is 6 items in 1 group,
or 6 items in each (of 1) group.

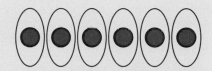

6 × 1 is 6 groups of 1,
or 6 items altogether.

6 ÷ 1 is 6 items in groups of 1,
or 6 groups altogether.

It is interesting that, for some students, multiplication by 1 is less comfortable than multiplying by other numbers where they actually see several groups of the same size.

Common Errors and Misconceptions

Multiplication and Division: Common Errors, Misconceptions, and Strategies

COMMON ERROR OR MISCONCEPTION	SUGGESTED STRATEGY
Generalizing about Products Students incorrectly generalize that the product of two numbers is always greater than the sum of the same two numbers. These students are stymied by expressions like 5 × 1, 5 × 0, and 2 × 2.	More often than not, this misconception arises because it is inadvertently promoted. Teachers tell their students that multiplication makes things "bigger," and they forget about the contradictions to this rule. This can be avoided if teachers are aware of the contradictions, and are careful with their generalizations.
Reversing Dividend and Divisor Students reverse the dividend and divisor when recording a division sentence (and may or may not calculate correctly). For example, to represent the number of groups of 3 in 15, they record 3 ÷ 15 instead of 15 ÷ 3. This common error should not be surprising, though, as one of the ways students are taught to record this division is as $3\overline{)15}$ for 15 ÷ 3.	The connection between words and symbols must be carefully crafted. When writing 15 ÷ 3, you should be saying aloud, "How many 3s are in 15?" and writing both forms of the symbolic expression at the same time, as shown: $3\overline{)15}$ for 15 ÷ 3
Remainders Students struggle with division problems that have remainders. For example: • They might think an expression like 17 ÷ 4 is impossible since you cannot make perfect groups of 4. • They think that 17 ÷ 4 is 4 since you can make 4 groups of 4, or that 17 ÷ 4 is 5 since there are 4 groups of 4 and 1 group of 1 for a total of 5 groups.	Students should meet situations involving remainders early on in their work with division. They need to understand that the result need not always be a whole number. Note that these misconceptions about remainders actually lead to correct answers in certain contexts. For example: • 17 marbles shared equally among 4 children: The answer is 4 because you cannot share the leftover marble. • 17 children transported in cars that hold 4 children each: The answer is 5 because you need a fifth car to transport the "leftover" child.

Appropriate Manipulatives

Manipulatives can be used to model many multiplication meanings. (See *Meanings of Multiplication* on page 166 for other examples of ways to use manipulatives to model different meanings of multiplication.)

Multiplication: Examples of Manipulatives

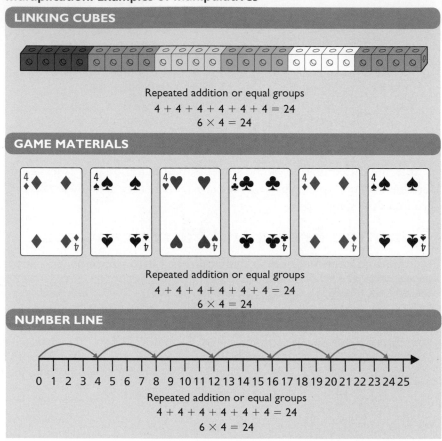

LINKING CUBES

Repeated addition or equal groups

$4 + 4 + 4 + 4 + 4 + 4 = 24$

$6 \times 4 = 24$

GAME MATERIALS

Repeated addition or equal groups

$4 + 4 + 4 + 4 + 4 + 4 = 24$

$6 \times 4 = 24$

NUMBER LINE

0 1 2 3 4 5 6 7 8 9 10 11 12 13 14 15 16 17 18 19 20 21 22 23 24 25

Repeated addition or equal groups

$4 + 4 + 4 + 4 + 4 + 4 = 24$

$6 \times 4 = 24$

Manipulatives can be used to model many division meanings. Some examples are shown below. (See *Meanings of Division* on page 169 for other examples of ways to use manipulatives to model different meanings of division.)

Division: Examples of Manipulatives

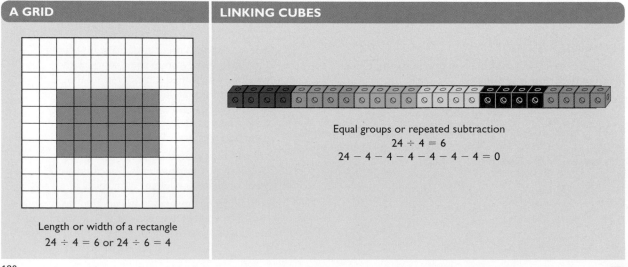

A GRID

Length or width of a rectangle

$24 \div 4 = 6$ or $24 \div 6 = 4$

LINKING CUBES

Equal groups or repeated subtraction

$24 \div 4 = 6$

$24 - 4 - 4 - 4 - 4 - 4 - 4 = 0$

Appropriate Children's Books

Two of Everything: A Chinese Folktale (Hong, 1993).
A magic pot doubles whatever is put into it. The context of the story can be continued to practise doubling. The teacher puts items into a "pot" and students predict how many items will emerge if the pot doubles its contents.

Counting by Kangaroos (Hulme, 1995).
Australian animals populate this story. Different elements of the story allow the reader to skip count by different amounts. Because skip counting is the basis for multiplication, this will support familiarity with simple products.

Sea Squares (Hulme, 1991).
Students see visual representations of the special products 1×1, 2×2, 3×3, etc., on the attractive pages of this book. They observe that the product of a number and itself can always be modelled as a square.

Sea Sums (Hulme, 1996).
Ocean animals are the "actors" in addition and subtraction stories in this book.

A Remainder of One (Pinczes, 1995).
Twenty-five bugs march in different-sized groups, where there is usually a remainder of 1. This book suits early division work with remainders.

Appropriate Digital Resources

See the MindTap site for a selection of appropriate digital resources.

Assessing Student Understanding

- Ask questions that focus on the meanings of the operations. For example, "What does 4×6 mean?" instead of, "How much is 4×6?"
- Examine this response. What does it tell you about the student's understanding?

How is multiplication like addition? How is it different?

Multiplication is like addition becaus both of them go up. Just like this 2x2=4 2+2=4. It is diffrent because you have to cont by 2's 3's or 4's. for additon you can cont by 1 each time.

Student Response

This student has answered a question about comparing the operations of addition and multiplication.

- Make sure that students recognize how to apply each operation in situations that represent different meanings; for example, ask how these two situations are alike:

  I have $4 and need $10 to buy a gift. How much more do I need?

  I am 10 years old and my sister is 4. How much older am I?

- Ask students to create problems to match different calculations, for example, 10 − 3 or 16 ÷ 4.

Applying What You've Learned

1. What was your solution to the chapter problem? What is it about your problem that led you to think of the situation as division?

2. How would you help students recognize the relationship between addition and subtraction? Why do you think that your approach might be effective?

3. Teachers often read a subtraction sign saying the words *take away*, for example, 8 − 2 as *eight take away 2*. Would you? Why or why not?

4. Which of the principles for addition and subtraction could be explained effectively using 10-frames? Why?

5. To calculate 14 − 8, a student says, "14, 13, 12, 11, 10, 9, 8, 7" as she holds up 8 fingers, one at a time. How would you respond to this approach to the calculation?

6. Which of the principles for multiplication and division do you think are most critical for students to understand? Why?

7. Develop an engaging task that would involve students in exploring some aspect of multiplication. What idea about multiplication would they learn? Why do you think your task would be engaging?

8. How would you help students distinguish between the sharing (partitive) and how-many-groups (quotative) meanings of division?

Interact with a K–8 Student:

9. Ask a student to show what each of these means (not what the answer is) with models (if they are not yet in Grade 3, only use parts a) and b)). What meanings of each operation did they choose to use?

   a) 6 + 7   b) 13 − 5

   c) 5 × 8   d) 16 ÷ 2

Discuss with a K–8 Teacher:

10. Ask a teacher whether she or he teaches addition and subtraction at the same time or separately. Ask why she or he takes that approach.

Selected References

Baroody, A.J., and Dowker, A. (2003). *The development of arithmetic concepts and skills.* Mahwah, NJ: Lawrence Erlbaum Associates.

Battista, M.T. (2012). *Cognition-based assessment and teaching of addition and subtraction.* Portsmouth, NH: Heinemann.

Battista, M.T. (2012). *Cognition-based assessment and teaching of multiplication and division.* Portsmouth, NH: Heinemann.

Betts, P., and Crampton, A. (2011). Informally multiplying the world of Jillian Jiggs. *Australian Primary Mathematics Classroom, 16(1).*

Carpenter, T.P., Fennema, E., Franke, M.L., Levi, L., and Empson, S. (1999). *Children's mathematics: Cognitively guided instruction.* Portsmouth, NH: Heinemann.

Cavanagh, M., Dacey, L., Findell, C.R., Greenes, C.F., Sheffield, L.J., and Small, M. (2004). *Navigating through number and operations in prekindergarten–grade 2.* Reston, VA: National Council of Teachers of Mathematics.

Champagne, Z.M., Schoen, R., and Riddell, C.M. (2014). Variations in both-addends-unknown problems. *Teaching Children Mathematics, 21(2),* 114–121.

Drake, J.M., and Barlow, A.T. (2008). Assessing students' levels of understanding multiplication through problem writing. *Teaching Children Mathematics, 14,* 272–277.

Fosnot, C.T., et al. (2007). *Investigating number sense, addition and subtraction.* Portsmouth, NH: Heinemann.

Fosnot, C.T., and Dolk, M. (2001). *Young mathematicians at work: Constructing number sense, addition, and subtraction.* Portsmouth, NH: Heinemann.

Fuson, K.C., and Fuson, A.M. (1992). Instruction supporting children's counting on for addition and counting up for subtraction. *Journal for Research in Mathematics Education, 23,* 72–78.

Hagen, P.A., Hooyberg, T., Marsden, P., Simonski, J., and Yuen, G. (2007). To share or not to share—How is the question! *Teaching Children Mathematics, 14,* 88–95.

Hong, L.T. (1993). *Two of everything: A Chinese folktale.* Morton Grove, IL: Albert Whitman and Company.

Hulme, J.N. (1995). *Counting by kangaroos: A multiplication concept book.* New York: W.H. Freeman & Co.

Hulme, J.N. (1999). *Sea squares.* New York: Hyperion Books for Children.

Hulme, J.N. (1996). *Sea sums.* New York: Hyperion Books for Children.

Marshall, A.M., Superfine, A.C., and Canty, R.S. (2010). Star students make connections. *Teaching Children Mathematics, 17,* 38–47.

Murphy, S. (2002). *Double the ducks.* New York: Harper Collins.

Murphy, S. (2005). *Leaping lizards.* New York: Harper Collins.

Pinczes, E.J. (1995). *A remainder of one.* Boston: Houghton Mifflin.

Polly, D., and Ruble, L. (2009). Learning to share equally. *Teaching Children Mathematics, 15,* 557–563.

Roberts, S.K. (2003). Snack math: Young children explore division. *Teaching Children Mathematics, 9,* 258–261.

Sullivan, A.D., and McDuffie, A.R. (2009). Connecting multiplication to contexts and language. *Teaching Children Mathematics, 15,* 502–511.

Whitin, P., and Whitin, D.J. (2008). Learning to solve problems in primary grades. *Teaching Children Mathematics, 14,* 426–432.

Thinkstock/Getty Images

Chapter 9
Developing Fact Fluency

IN A NUTSHELL

The main ideas in this chapter are listed below:

1. It is important that students develop fact fluency.

2. An instantaneous response is not as much the goal, as a reasonably quick, but well under-stood, response to a math fact question.

3. Students need opportunities to use principles of the four operations and mental strategies to relate facts to one another. They must not be rushed into memorizing facts before they are ready.

4. It is often through practice activities, such as games and problem-solving experiences, that students develop quicker recall.

CHAPTER PROBLEM

Addition facts describe the results of adding two single-digit numbers. They are often shown in a table like this one:

+	0	1	2	3	4	5	6	7	8	9
0										
1										
2										
3										
4										
5										
6										
7										
8										
9										

Which number appears most often in the table? Why?

What Are the Facts?

The term *fact* is used to describe the result of a computation, generally of two single-digit numbers, resulting in a single-digit or double-digit result. For example, $3 + 6 = 9$ or $4 \times 8 = 32$ are an addition and a multiplication fact, respectively. Two of the associated subtraction and division facts are $9 - 3 = 6$ and $32 \div 4 = 8$.

Many people recognize the facts as the computations typically shown in addition or multiplication tables.

+	0	1	2	3	4	5	6	7	8	9
0	0	1	2	3	4	5	6	7	8	9
1	1	2	3	4	5	6	7	8	9	10
2	2	3	4	5	6	7	8	9	10	11
3	3	4	5	6	7	8	9	10	11	12
4	4	5	6	7	8	9	10	11	12	13
5	5	6	7	8	9	10	11	12	13	14
6	6	7	8	9	10	11	12	13	14	15
7	7	8	9	10	11	12	13	14	15	16
8	8	9	10	11	12	13	14	15	16	17
9	9	10	11	12	13	14	15	16	17	18

×	0	1	2	3	4	5	6	7	8	9
0	0	0	0	0	0	0	0	0	0	0
1	0	1	2	3	4	5	6	7	8	9
2	0	2	4	6	8	10	12	14	16	18
3	0	3	6	9	12	15	18	21	24	27
4	0	4	8	12	16	20	24	28	32	36
5	0	5	10	15	20	25	30	35	40	45
6	0	6	12	18	24	30	36	42	48	54
7	0	7	14	21	28	35	42	49	56	63
8	0	8	16	24	32	40	48	56	64	72
9	0	9	18	27	36	45	54	63	72	81

The Facts

One of the distinctions between facts and "algorithms" or "procedures" is that it is intended that students automatically describe the result of a fact computation rather than going through a procedure to arrive at it; this, of course, is after they have had many experiences to commit those facts to memory. Some people include "facts" up to $10 + 10$ or 12×12, intending for students to memorize these amounts, but others only go up to $9 + 9$ and 9×9.

Why Is It Important to Learn the Facts?

One of the reasons that it is important for students to commit facts to memory is to ease the load on the brain when performing more complex calculations. If a student has to struggle over each piece of a more calculated computation, it will be difficult to get through it.

Another reason that facts are important is that they are an essential piece of knowledge for estimation. For example, it is not possible to estimate 22×31 without realizing that $2 \times 3 = 6$. Even as society moves to a situation where digital tools are regularly used for computational purposes, users still need to estimate to see if the answers the tools provide make sense. This cannot be done without facts.

Students need to keep seeing how important it is for them to learn the facts for their success in number work in math.

What Does Fact Fluency Mean?

Fact fluency requires students both to know facts and to understand them. Students are expected to be flexible, accurate, efficient, and appropriate using facts. Just memorizing sets of number combinations without being able to make sense of them is not particularly effective and is not what fluency demands. Eventually, except for students with memory disabilities, students should commit facts to memory and be able to retrieve those facts in a reasonable amount of time.

Flexibility requires that students have strategies for retrieving facts if they were forgotten. The strategies should make sense for the situation. For example, different strategies might be used to add 7 + 9 (perhaps rearranging to the double 8 + 8) than 8 + 3 (perhaps making 10 with 8 + 2 and then adding 1 more).

Initially, students determine sums by counting all or counting on (initially from whatever is the first number and later from the greater number) and determine differences by removing and counting all or counting back or counting up. Eventually students use reasoning with mental strategies and later commit these facts to memory. They often determine products and quotients, initially using skip counting or addition and subtraction, and then later use reasoning with mental strategies, and later still commit multiplication and division facts to memory.

Learning Addition and Subtraction Facts

Students learn addition and subtraction facts in the primary grades. After using counting strategies, they move to reasoning strategies.

Using Addition and Subtraction Principles

There are 100 addition facts, from 0 + 0 to 9 + 9, as well as the related subtraction facts. The principles that students learn about addition and subtraction (see Chapter 8, pages 162–164) can substantially reduce the number of separate facts they need to learn. For example:

Principle	Example
Principle 1 Subtraction and addition are related The subtraction facts do not have to be learned as separate facts. The student can always think of the related addition fact.	8 + 3 = 11, so 11 − 3 = 8 and 11 − 8 = 3
Principle 2 Numbers can be added in any order 45 of the addition facts can be related to 45 reverse facts, eliminating the need to memorize them separately.	4 + 3 = 7, so 3 + 4 = 7

Students who become comfortable with the principles above will recognize which strategies might be useful in which situations to relate an unknown fact to a known one. Typical strategies include:

Strategy	Relevant Principle	Example
Counting on to add 1 or 2	Principle 7	5 + 1 Count: (5), 6
Counting back to subtract 1 or 2	Principle 7	9 − 2 Count back: (9), 8, 7 A number line is useful for counting on or back since students can see all the numbers in order. 0 1 2 3 4 5 6 7 8 9
Adding or subtracting 0	Principle 6	4 + 0 = 4 There is no more. 3 − 0 = 3 There is no less.

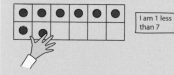

Counting on or back to add or subtract 1 or 2 describes 36 of the 100 addition facts students need to learn. Adding or subtracting 0 deals with an additional 15 of those facts.

Using Addition and Subtraction Principles Indirectly

Many facts can be related so closely to known facts that it is sometimes almost as quick or efficient to reconstruct them as it is to memorize them.

Building on Doubles Students seem to learn the ten double facts easily, for example, $3 + 3 = 6$, $7 + 7 = 14$, etc. Other facts can be related to these. This will help students learn 24 more addition facts.

STRATEGY		PRINCIPLE ADDRESSED
$6 + 8 = (6 + 1) + (8 - 1)$ $\quad = 7 + 7$	Move 1 from the 8 to the 6. Now add doubles.	Principle 3 (the associative property)
$7 + 8 = 7 + (7 + 1)$ $\quad = (7 + 7) + 1$ $\quad = 14 + 1$, or 15	Recognize that 8 is 7 and 1. First add 7 to make a double. Then add 1.	Principle 3 (the associative property) Principle 7 (the adding 1 property)

Making Tens Once students learn the combinations for 10 (e.g., $4 + 6$, $7 + 3$), they can relate other calculations to these. This is efficient, since to determine $10 + \blacksquare$, if $\blacksquare$ is less than 10, does not require addition; it is simply a representation of the number $1\blacksquare$.

STRATEGY		PRINCIPLE ADDRESSED
$9 + 5 = (9 + 1) + (5 - 1)$ $\quad = 10 + 4$	Move 1 from the 5 to the 9.	Principle 3 (the associative property)
$8 + 6 = (8 + 2) + (6 - 2)$ $\quad = 10 + 43$	Move 2 from the 6 to the 8.	Principle 3 (the associative property)

Subtraction facts can also be related to 10. Again, $1\blacksquare - 10$ does not require use of facts.

STRATEGY		PRINCIPLE ADDRESSED
$15 - 9 = (15 + 1) - (9 + 1)$ $\quad = 16 - 10$	Add 1 to both to keep the difference the same.	Principle 5 (maintaining a difference)

Getting to 10 along the way is also useful.

STRATEGY		PRINCIPLE ADDRESSED
$7 + 6 = (7 + 3) + 3$ $\quad\quad = 10 + 3$	Add 6 in two stages; add 3 and then 3.	Principle 4 (add in parts)
$13 - 4 = (13 - 3) - 1$ $\quad\quad = 10 - 1$	Subtract 4 in two stages; first 3 and then 1.	Principle 4 (subtract in parts)
$13 - 9$ Think: $9 + 1 = 10$ $\quad\quad 10 + 3 = 13$ So I've added $1 + 3 = 4$. So, $13 - 9 = 4$.	Think of subtraction as the opposite of addition. Add enough to get to 10. Then add the rest.	Principle 1 (addition undoes subtraction) Principle 4 (add in parts)

The listed strategies account for almost all of the addition and subtraction facts students must learn.

ACTIVITY 9.3

It is important for students to associate each number less than 10 with a partner to add to it to make 10. Create sets of squares with numbers less than 10 on each side. Sides with a sum of 10 can be put together to make a design.

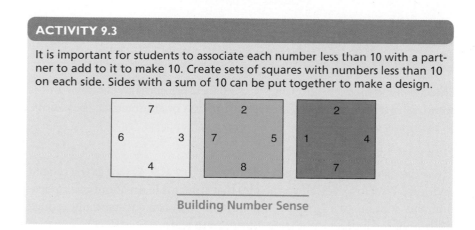

Building Number Sense

Typical Sequence for Acquiring Addition and Subtraction Facts

Research has suggested a sequence in which students typically acquire addition and subtraction facts (Sarama and Clements, 2009). Generally, students learn smaller facts first, often the facts up to 10. Adding 1 or 0 is easier than adding other numbers. Certain combinations come earlier just because they are more familiar, for example, $5 + 5$. In general, doubles come earlier than other combinations.

Students' strategies become more diverse and complex with time and experience, especially when they are encouraged to reason.

It takes time to develop and nurture the thinking strategies that help students learn their facts. Initially, the emphasis should be on the development of the many relations among the facts, rather than speed of recall.

One of the best ways to explore facts is in rich problem-solving situations.

ACTIVITY 9.4

Provide students with small circles with numbers from 0 to 10 on them. Ask them to arrange six of the circles on the triangle so that each side sums to 10.

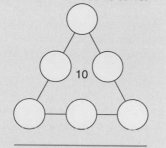

Building Number Sense

ACTIVITY 9.6

Set up a grid of 2 rows of 9 seats and gather students around them. Sing the song "The Wheels on the Bus" with students. Pause at various points and indicate how many people are to get on and off the "bus." Some students act the situation out while the other students predict how many will be left on the bus after each situation is acted out.

Building Number Sense

ACTIVITY 9.5

The activity not only promotes mathematical thinking, but also provides an opportunity to practise facts.

Show 3 ways to spend exactly 10¢.

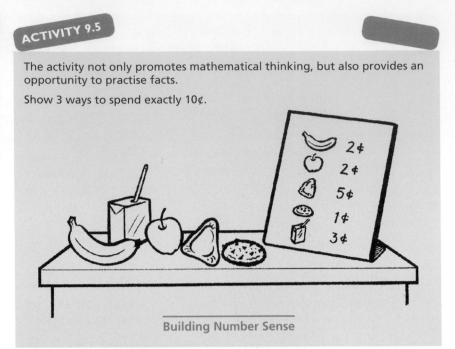

Building Number Sense

ACTIVITY 9.7

Have students roll 3 dice. They multiply 2 of the numbers and then add the 3rd value to explore what results are possible.

$4 \times 3 + 5 = 17; 5 \times 4 + 3 = 23$

Building Number Sense

Learning Multiplication and Division Facts

Students learn multiplication and division facts primarily in Grades 3 and 4. After using skip counting and repeated addition or subtraction, they move to reasoning strategies.

How Many Facts Are There?

There are 100 multiplication facts, from 0×0 to 9×9, as well as the related division facts. However, the principles that students learn about multiplication and division (see Chapter 8, pages 173–179) can substantially reduce the number of independent facts they need to learn.

PRINCIPLE	EXAMPLE
By knowing Principle 2 (the commutative property for multiplication), students need only learn half of the multiplication facts involving different factors.	If students know $6 \times 5 = 30$, then they know $5 \times 6 = 30$.
By knowing Principle 1 (division and multiplication undo each other), students realize they do not need to separately learn the division facts, but can use a related multiplication fact instead.	Since $4 \times 6 = 24$, $24 \div 4 = 6$ and $24 \div 6 = 4$
By knowing Principle 12 (multiplying by 1 does not change the value of the other factor), students do not need to separately memorize facts involving multiplication or division by 1. This accounts for nine more of the 55 facts students need to learn.	$\blacksquare \times 1 = \blacksquare$ $1 \times \blacksquare = \blacksquare$ $\blacksquare \div 1 = \blacksquare$ $\blacksquare \div \blacksquare = 1$ no matter what number (except 0) is used for $\blacksquare$.
By knowing Principle 9 (multiplying by 0 results in 0), students do not need to separately memorize facts involving multiplication or division with 0. This accounts for nine additional multiplication facts students must learn.	$0 \div \blacksquare = 0$ $0 \times \blacksquare = 0$ $\blacksquare \times 0 = 0$ no matter what number is used for $\blacksquare$.

Using Other Principles of Multiplication and Division to Develop Fact Strategies

Students who become comfortable with the principles will recognize which strategies might be useful in which situations to relate an unknown fact to a known one.

Building on Doubles Students seem to learn the double facts easily, for example, $2 \times 4 = 8$; $2 \times 7 = 14$, etc. Other facts can be related to these.

STRATEGY		PRINCIPLE
$4 \times 7 = 2 \times (2 \times 7)$ $= 2 \times 14$ $= 14 + 14$	Double 7 first Double the double, perhaps by adding.	Principle 6 (a variation of the associative property)
Every $4 \times$ fact can be calculated by doubling a $2 \times$ fact; every $8 \times$ fact can be calculated by doubling a $4 \times$ fact.		

ACTIVITY 9.9

To explore doubles, allow students to use a transparent mirror to see the double of what they put on one side of the mirror.

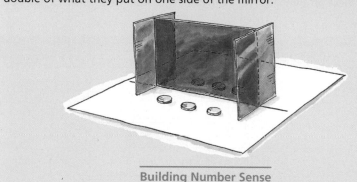

Building Number Sense

Half/Double If students are multiplying by a number like 6 or 8, they might use a half/double strategy.

STRATEGY		PRINCIPLE
$4 \times 6 = (4 \times 2) \times (6 \div 2)$ $= 8 \times 3$	Double one factor and halve the other.	Principle 3 (a variation of the associative property)
The student could have used $(4 \div 2) \times (6 \times 2)$ to get the right answer, although 2×12 might not be as familiar as 8×3.		

ACTIVITY 9.10

Show students how to multiply by 9 on their fingers.

Number the fingers from 1 to 10 starting at the left.

To multiply 9 by, for example, 7, fold in finger 7. Count the fingers at the left for the tens digit and at the right for the ones digit.

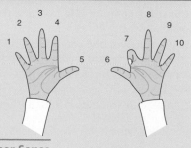

Building Number Sense

ACTIVITY 9.8

Students can make space creatures using blobs of clay. They roll a die to determine the number of eyes and again to determine the number of toothpick legs. They roll once more to tell how many creatures to make. But before they make them, they predict the total number of eyes and legs.

Building Number Sense

TEACHING TIP

Some teachers encourage students to name the strategies they are using to facilitate communication. This also allows for a posted reference list of strategies that can be very useful to students. Some students, however, will prefer using more natural language to describe the strategies, for example, "If there are twice as many groups, each has half has many."

ACTIVITY 9.11

Encourage students to play the game Metre Race.

- Each player chooses a coloured counter and then picks 2 number cards, labelled from 1 to 6.
- The first card tells how many jumps to make, and the second card tells how far to jump each time along the metre stick.
- The first player to get to 100 cm wins.

Building Number Sense

Add Parts Students can break up a multiplication or division into simpler components.

STRATEGY		PRINCIPLE
$8 \times 6 = (5 \times 6) + (3 \times 6)$ $\quad = 30 + 18$	Treat 8 groups as 5 groups and 3 groups.	Principle 5 (the distributive property)
$21 \div 3 = (15 \div 3) + (6 \div 3)$ $\quad = 5 + 2$	Share 21 by sharing 15 and then 6.	Principle 7 (the distributive property)

Easier Tables Besides the 2 × table, 1 × table, and 0 × table, two other tables that students find particularly easy to learn are the 5 × table and the 9 × table. They skip count by fives, sometimes using a clock: 5, 10, 15, 20, ..., to calculate a multiple of 5. To determine a multiple of 9, they observe the pattern where the tens digit goes up by 1 and the ones go down by 1, with the digits totalling 9:

$$9 \quad 18 \quad 27 \quad 36 \quad 45 \quad 54 \quad 63 \quad 72 \quad 81$$

These five easier tables constitute a large portion of facts students have to learn. Using these known facts, they can calculate other products. For example, $8 \times 7 = 5 \times 7 + 2 \times 7 + 1 \times 7$, or $8 \times 7 = 9 \times 7 - 1 \times 7$.

ACTIVITY 9.12

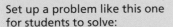

Set up a problem like this one for students to solve:

Julia's school is having a read-a-thon. Julia's goal is to read 100 pages. If she starts on April 1 and reads 5 pages every night, will she get to her goal by the end of the month or before that? Show how you know.

Building Number Sense

ACTIVITY 9.13

Ask students to choose any number of marbles. Then they have to show different ways that children could share those marbles so each gets the same number.

Building Number Sense

ACTIVITY 9.14

Have students play a multiplication fact board game like the one below.

The Product Game

1	2	3	4	5	6
7	8	9	10	12	14
15	16	18	20	21	24
25	27	28	30	32	35
36	40	42	45	48	49
54	56	63	64	72	81

1	2	3	4	5	6	7	8	9

The first player puts his colour of counter on one of the numbers on the strip below the board.

The second player puts his counter on the same or a different number on the strip, multiplies the two, and then puts a counter of his colour on that product on the board.

Player 1 moves one counter on the strip, multiplies the two covered numbers from the strip, and puts his counter on the board on that product.

Play continues until a player gets four of his coloured counters in a row on the board.

It takes time to develop and nurture the thinking strategies that help students learn their facts. Developing the many relations among the facts is the initial emphasis when facts are first being explored, rather than speed of recall.

Building Number Sense

Typical Sequence for Acquiring Multiplication and Division Facts

Often students learn the multiplication facts for 2 × and 5 × first because of their ability to skip count. Learning the 0 × and 1 × facts tends to be easy as well. Students can learn the 3 × facts as doubles and one group more. They then learn the 4 × facts as double the doubles and 6 × facts as double the triples. They then learn the 9 × facts, often using the idea that the tens digit is one less than what is being multiplied and the ones digit is 9 – the tens digit. They finally learn the 8 × facts and 7 × facts.

What Kind of Practice Is Useful?

Facts can be practised in the course of solving problems and by playing games as well as through direct practice. Some of this practice is appropriate for home activity and some for school activity. This practice should be repeated throughout the year as needed.

Many problems could be set that involve the practice of facts. For example, a few problems to practise addition facts might be:

- Two sums on the addition table are 5 apart. What could the numbers that were added be?
- You calculate an addition fact by adding 1 to a double. What addition fact might you be trying to calculate?
- You had some blue marbles, but fewer than 10. You had some yellow marbles, but fewer than 10. Altogether you had more than 8 marbles. How many of each colour might you have had?

Many games can be created to allow students to practise multiplication facts. For example:

- Roll two dice. Multiply the values. The person with the greater ones digit wins a point. The first person with 10 points wins the game.
- Use the 2 to 9 cards from a deck of cards. Pick four cards. Arrange them into two pairs. Multiply the values in the pairs and then add the two products. The person closest to 50 wins a point. The first person with 10 points wins the game.

There are many computer games and tablet games that allow students to practise addition, subtraction, multiplication, and division facts after facts have been committed to memory. Programs such as Mathletics©, Prodigy©, and Reflex© are used in many schools in Canada for fact practice. One of their advantages is that they monitor student responses and alter the questions offered to students based on their needs.

No matter how fact learning and practice is approached, as with any other learning situation, the tasks assigned to students should be appropriate to the level of the student and should build confidence and success.

How Should Facts Be Assessed?
How Should They Not Be Assessed?

Many researchers are now discouraging the use of timed tests to improve fact retention. Research now shows (Boaler, 2014) that the anxiety produced by timed tests actually gets in the way of many students' ability to show their knowledge of math facts; students who actually might know the facts might be unable to show this knowledge because of their anxiety.

Another reason timed tests are discouraged as the primary means for assessing fact knowledge is that these tests often do not address flexibility, which is part of fact fluency. If "quizzes" are used, students should be asked not only for answers but also for how they knew the answer. They should compare their performance to previous performance rather than to other students' performance.

In order to assess fluency, teachers should include interviews and observations as well as paper and pencil opportunities. But in all of these situations, teachers should be looking not only at what the answers are, but also at what flexibility is demonstrated, what strategies are used, etc. Speed does not mean being instantaneous; it means reasonable efficiency. Keeping records of what facts students know and which they do not is helpful.

When recall is being assessed, it makes sense to mix up the facts and not use all of one type together.

Common Errors and Misconceptions

Mastering Facts: Common Errors, Misconceptions, and Strategies

COMMON ERROR OR MISCONCEPTION	SUGGESTED STRATEGY
Facts for 7 and 8 Students struggle, in particular, with the facts for $+ 7$ and $+ 8$ and for $\times 7$ and $\times 8$.	These might well be the last facts students learn but students can and should use strategies to relate these facts to simpler ones. For example, instead of adding 7, add 5 and then 2; instead of multiplying by 8, double three times.
Compensating Too Much or Not Enough Students might assume that $16 - 9 = 5$ since they think $16 - 10 = 6$ and then subtract another 1.	When students subtract a different amount than they should, they need to think carefully about whether they subtracted too much and have to add back, or did not subtract enough. In this case, they subtracted too much and so must think of $16 - 9$ as 1 more than $16 - 10$, which is 7. Another approach avoids this problem; students recognize that the space between 16 and 9 on a number line is the same as the space between 17 and 10 and simply subtract 10 from 17; this way they don't have to compensate.

Appropriate Manipulatives

Working on facts implies primarily mental strategies, but there are tools that are useful for, for example, games that students can use to practise facts.

Mastering Facts: Examples of Manipulatives

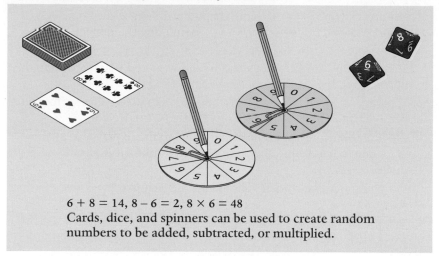

$6 + 8 = 14$, $8 - 6 = 2$, $8 \times 6 = 48$
Cards, dice, and spinners can be used to create random numbers to be added, subtracted, or multiplied.

Appropriate Children's Books

2 × 2 = Boo! (Leedy, 1996).
This book shares a set of "spooky" multiplication stories that focus on Halloween themes. Various multiplication facts involving smaller numbers are illustrated with witches, ghosts, etc.

12 Ways to Get to 11 (Merriam, 1993).
Each spread shows different combinations of items for a total of 11 items. For example, it could be 9 pinecones and 2 acorns in a forest, or it could be 6 peanut shells and 5 pieces of popcorn at the circus. The pictures are very attractive.

Now ... for My Next Number (Park, 2007).
This book provides rhymes students can use to recall multiplication facts. For example, "Do you see those shoes? Do you hear their beat? Two by two ... walking down the street: 2, 4, 6, 8, 10, and 12, ..."

The Best of Times (Tang, 2002).
Students explore multiplication by different amounts on colourful spreads. For example, they learn that multiplying by 1 does not change a number and that multiplying by 2 is about adding a number to itself.

Appropriate Digital Resources

See the MindTap site for a selection of appropriate digital resources.

Assessing Student Understanding

- Ask students what other facts knowing 3×4 would help them with.
- Ask students how they could use addition to figure out these facts: $12 - 9$ or $15 - 8$.
- Focus assessment of fact recall on understanding and not speed in the early stages. Even later, although you want students to commit facts to memory, the student can still take a few seconds to use a strategy to recall a particular sum, difference, product, or quotient.
- Encourage students to tell you why a particular strategy is useful to recall a fact. For example, if you want to remember what 7×4 is, what other facts could you use to help you? Why?

Applying What You've Learned

1. What was your solution to the chapter problem? How could you have predicted the answer without completing the table?

2. To calculate $14 - 8$, a student says, "14, 13, 12, 11, 10, 9, 8, 7" as she holds up 8 fingers, one at a time. How would you respond to this approach to the calculation?

3. A parent asks you whether it is a good idea to use flashcards for fact recall for her Grade 2 son. What would your advice be?

4. Do you think it is important for students to name the strategy they are using to determine an addition, subtraction, multiplication, or division answer?

5. Do you think that students should recall a fact like $11 - 4 = 7$ in that way or as $4 + ? = 11$?

6. What do you see as the difficulty in allowing students to use calculators to calculate facts?

7. Examine a current text for Grade 3 students. Which multiplication fact strategies do they emphasize? Which is introduced first? Why might that make sense?

Interact with a K–8 Student:

8. Ask a student which facts he or she finds most difficult to remember and what s/he does to help.

9. Ask a student which facts they find easiest to remember and why. It could be addition facts with younger students or multiplication facts with older ones.

Discuss with a K–8 Teacher:

10. Ask a teacher how she or he develops games to provide fact practice.

Selected References

Baroody, A.J. (2006). Why children have difficulties mastering the basic fact combinations and how to help them. *Teaching Children Mathematics 13(1)*, 22–33.

Bay-Williams, J.M., and Kling, G. (2014). Enriching addition and subtraction fact mastery through games. *Teaching Children Mathematics, 21*, 238–247.

Boaler, J. (2014). Research suggests that timed tests cause math anxiety. *Teaching Children Mathematics, 20(8)*, 469–473.

Buchholz, L. (2004). Learning strategies for addition and subtraction facts: The road to fluency and the license to think. *Teaching Children Mathematics, 10*, 362–367.

Crespo, S., Kyrkiakides, A.O., and McGee, S. (2005). Nothing "basic" about basic facts: Exploring addition facts with fourth graders. *Teaching Children Mathematics, 12*, 60–67.

Flowers, J.M., and Rubenstein, R.N. (2010). Multiplication fact fluency using doubles. *Mathematics Teaching in the Middle School, 16*, 296–303.

Forbinger, L., and Fahsl, A.J. (2010). Differentiating practice to help students master basic facts. In White, D.Y., and Spitzer, J.S. (Eds.) *Responding to Diversity: Pre K–Grade 5*. Reston, VA: National Council of Teachers of Mathematics, 7–22.

Hopkins, S., and Egeberg, H. (2009). Retrieval of simple addition facts: Complexities involved in addressing commonly identified mathematical learning difficulty. *Journal of Learning Disabilities, 42(3)*, 215–229.

Kling, G and Bay-Williams, J. M. (2014). Assessing basic fact fluency. *Teaching Children Mathematics 20(8)*, 488–497.

Leedy, L. (1996). *2 × 2 = Boo: A Set of Spooky Multiplication Stories*. Markham, ON: Holiday House.

Merriam, E. (1993). *12 Ways to Get to 11*. New York: Simon and Schuster.

Park, M. (2007). *Now … for My Next Number*. Salt Lake City: Great River Books.

Postlewait, K.B., Adams, M.R., and Shih, J.C. (2003). Promoting meaningful mastery of addition and subtraction. *Teaching Children Mathematics, 9*, 354–357.

Sarama, J., and Clements, D.H. (2009). *Early childhood mathematics education research: Learning trajectories for young children*. New York: Routledge.

Sun, W., and Zhang, J.Y. (2001). Teaching addition and subtraction facts: A Chinese perspective. *Teaching Children Mathematics, 8*, 28–31.

Tang, G. (2002). *The Best of Times*. New York: Scholastic.

Chapter 10

Representing Larger Whole Numbers

IN A NUTSHELL

The main ideas in this chapter are listed below:

1. Students gain a sense of the size of numbers by representing them in many ways and comparing them to meaningful benchmarks.

2. The place value system we used is built on patterns to make our work with numbers efficient.

3. To gain an understanding of the place value system, students should initially use proportional materials, ideally materials they can group themselves.

4. Thinking of numbers as factors and/or multiples of other numbers enriches a student's number sense while providing alternative representations for those numbers.

CHAPTER PROBLEM

What is the least whole number that is divisible by 2, 3, 4, 5, 6, 7, 8, 9, and 10?

How do you know?

Larger Numbers in the Student's World

As students get older, the numbers they deal with in their everyday lives become more complex. Students need strategies for representing and making sense of these greater numbers. Although it is possible to count, say, 87 items individually, it is not practical. When items are grouped, counting is made easier and probably more accurate.

This becomes very clear when a teacher puts, for instance, 35 items in a disorganized fashion on an overhead projector, allows students to look for a few seconds, and then turns off the projector. Very few students can tell how many items there were. In contrast, if 35 items are shown in 3 groups of 10 and 5 more (as shown below), students find it easier to identify the amount. Grouping is a real help.

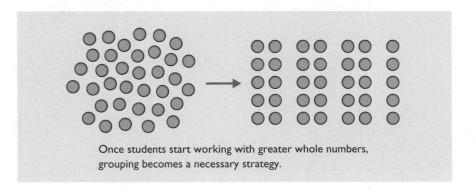

Once students start working with greater whole numbers, grouping becomes a necessary strategy.

Numeration Principles

The most basic principles that students need to learn in order to work with our number system relate to the base ten trading rules and the concept of place value. Base ten is a trading system in which you trade groups of 10 ones for 1 ten, 10 tens for 1 hundred, and so on. Place value is a system in which the position that a symbol (a digit 0 to 9 in the case of our numeration system) occupies in a number has a bearing on the value of that symbol. For example, the 2 in 23 means 20, but the 2 in 42 means 2.

A number of researchers, including Kamii (1986), have expressed caution about moving into place value too quickly. Kamii points out how a number of students read the number 16 and really have no sense of what the 1 really means; they often treat it as 1 rather than 10. She suggests teaching numbers more holistically for longer, for example, thinking of 23 as twenty three, not as 2 tens and 3 ones, until students are ready for the transition, which may be later than some teachers think.

Even when students eventually do get an understanding of the system, there is often a significant period of time between when they are comfortable with numbers in the 100s or even 1000s, and when they have gained a full understanding of the structure of the system going farther to the left or to the right (to decimal values).

One of the difficulties is that a place value system requires students to deal with a multi-unit conceptual structure (Fuson, 1990). Many students are very focused on single unitary structures.

The base ten place value system is defined by conventions; these conventions are not implicit in what number is all about. Because they are conventions, they must be explicitly taught. Some of the principles that students need to learn are listed below.

NUMERATION PRINCIPLES

1. You group in tens for convenience so that you need only 10 digits (0 to 9) to represent all numbers.
2. Patterns are inherent in our numeration system because each place value is 10 times the value of the place to the right.
3. A number has many different "forms." For example, 123 is 1 hundred, 2 tens, 3 ones, and also 12 tens, 3 ones.
4. A place value system requires a symbol for a placeholder. For example, the 0 in 304 is a placeholder; it pushes the digit 3 over to show that it represents 300 instead of 30.
5. Numbers might be more easily compared when written in standard, or symbolic, form (Fuson, 1990).

Principle 1: You group in tens for convenience so that you need only 10 digits (0 to 9) to represent all numbers.

Students quickly realize how convenient the base ten system is if they are asked to memorize separate symbols for, say, the first 25 different numbers instead of just recognizing 10 digits. But they require a considerable time to internalize the structure of the system.

Many young students have difficulty thinking about the one item that represents a 10 as being worth more than the one item representing 1. For that reason, models that are "proportional," that is, where the 10 looks 10 times as big as the 1, the 100 looks 10 times as big as the 10, etc., are important. Some of these models, showing 23, are

- the 10-frame

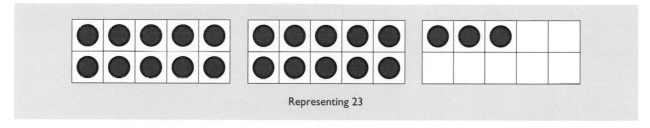

Representing 23

- unifix cube stacks, or linking cube trains

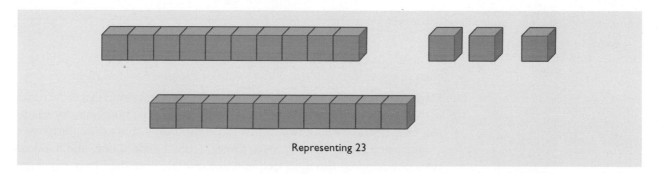

Representing 23

ACTIVITY 10.2

ACTIVITY 10.2

Put out a jar with 10 counters and indicate to students that it has 10 counters in it. Then provide other containers, initially of the same size as the jar holding 10, each filled with 20 to 60 counters. Have students estimate how many counters they think are in each of the other containers, then count, and write the appropriate numerals.

Proportional Reasoning

ACTIVITY 10.3

An engaging context for young students to think about grouping items in tens is a roller coaster with cars that hold 10 people. Students could be asked to fill empty roller coaster cars to show various numbers of people, or could describe how many people are in cars that the teacher models.

Roller Coaster

Building Number Sense

• craft stick bundles

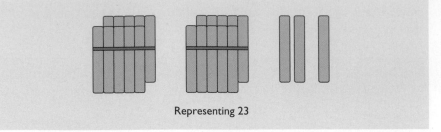

Representing 23

• base ten blocks

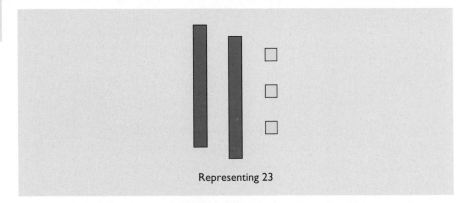

Representing 23

Although all of the models presented above can be extended to numbers greater than 100, usually only the base ten block model is extended.

Pre-grouped models like base ten blocks are certainly more convenient to use, but some students do not realize that the value of, say, 2 ten rods and 3 ones is the same as the value of 23 ones. If students group the materials themselves, as would be the case with craft sticks, unifix trains, or 10-frames, it is easier for them to recognize this.

Later, students can use non-proportional materials, such as counters on a place value mat. The place value model below shows the number 21 324, but it is not obvious that, for example, that each red counter is worth 100 times more than each blue one.

Thousands		Ones		
Ten Thousands	Thousands	Hundreds	Tens	Ones
●●	○	●● ●	● ●	●● ●●

Representing 21 324

Principle 2: Patterns are inherent in our numeration system because each place value is 10 times the value of the place to the right.

Many students easily take to the rhythm of the number system that is the result of the base ten relationships (once they get past the teen numbers), for example, twenty-**one**, twenty-**two**, ..., twenty-**nine**, thirty, thirty-**one**, thirty-**two**, ..., thirty-**nine**, forty. Or **one, two, three**, ..., one hundred **one**, one hundred **two**, one hundred **three**, ..., two hundred **one**, two hundred **two**, two hundred **three**, ... Later, it might be twenty-one thousand, twenty-two thousand, twenty-three thousand, ...

The hundreds chart is a useful tool for helping younger students recognize patterns for numbers up to 100, including patterns in the digits of the numerals and patterns in the number words.

0	1	2	3	4	5	6	7	(8)	9
10	11	12	13	14	15	16	17	(18)	19
20	21	22	23	24	25	26	27	(28)	29
30	31	32	33	34	35	36	37	(38)	39
40	41	42	43	44	45	46	47	(48)	49
50	51	52	53	54	55	56	57	(58)	59
60	61	62	63	64	65	66	67	(68)	69
70	71	72	73	74	75	76	77	(78)	79
80	81	82	83	84	85	86	87	(88)	89
90	91	92	93	94	95	96	97	(98)	99

The circled numbers are read eight, eighteen, twenty-eight, thirty-eight, forty-eight, ...

Another important pattern in our system allows us to interpret unfamiliar numerals. Each place value is 10 times the value of the unit to its right. To understand the place values to the right of the decimal point, students learn to think in reverse; that is, each new place value is $\frac{1}{10}$ of the unit to its left.

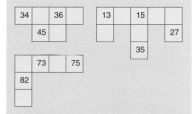
Millions	Thousands			Ones			Thousandths		
Millions	Hundred Thousands	Ten Thousands	Thousands	Hundreds	Tens	Ones	Tenths	Hundredths	Thousandths
10×100 000	10×10 000	10 × 1000	10 × 100	10 × 10	10×1	1	$\frac{1}{10}$ of 1	$\frac{1}{10}$ of $\frac{1}{10}$	$\frac{1}{10}$ of $\frac{1}{100}$

The base ten block models typically used to represent whole numbers are designed to show the 10 times relationship. Below, 10 cubes make 1 rod, 10 rods make 1 flat, and 10 flats make 1 thousand cube. And, when they are arranged in the following order, show how the place value system relates to the base ten system.

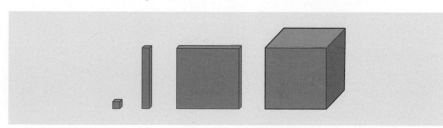

Very large numbers can also be modelled with base ten blocks. A model for 10 000 is a "rod" made of 10 thousand cubes. Similarly, a model for 100 000 is a flat made of 100 thousand cubes, although usually there are not enough cubes in a classroom to make the complete model.

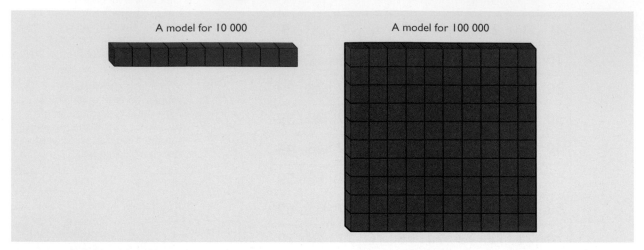

A model for 10 000   A model for 100 000

ACTIVITY 10.6

To bring out patterns in the place value system, ask students to write down the digits of a number which would require them to include these words (in any order) when it is read: forty, thousand, million, two, five, sixty, hundred

Student responses will show you whether they realize that it is the word *million* that tells you that there are at least 7 digits and that the digits 4 and 6 must be in the middle of place value periods (the tens place, the ten thousands place, and the ten millions place).

Building Number Sense

Another pattern in the system pertains to larger numbers. Numbers are written in pattern groups called periods. For example, 235 235 235 is read as, "two hundred thirty-five million, two hundred thirty-five thousand, two hundred thirty-five" since the digits 235 appear in the millions, the thousands, and the ones periods. Within each period, there are hundreds, tens, and ones. For example, 234 123 345 is 234 millions, 123 thousands, 345 (ones). Students need to learn the grouping names in order to read numbers, but then can use the similarity within the groupings to help them deal with numbers they had not previously encountered.

Principle 3: A number has many different "forms."

The ability to rename numbers is fundamental to many of the algorithms involving addition, subtraction, multiplication, and division that students will learn. For example, regrouping 3 hundreds, 1 ten, and 2 ones as 2 hundreds, 10 tens, and 12 ones makes the traditional subtraction algorithm possible for a calculation such as 312 − 178 (see Algorithm 1 on page 228).

When calculating with greater numbers, there are times when students want to rename 1 000 000 as 1000 thousands or as 10 hundred thousands or as 100 ten thousands, for example, to divide 1 000 000 by 1000 or 100 000 or 10 000. Similarly, there are times when it is convenient to write 3 600 000 as 3.6 million, for example, to write a newspaper headline.

Student Response

This student has used Principle 3, the notion of alternative representations, to create a "creature" with a value of 321 using 32 tens and 1 one.

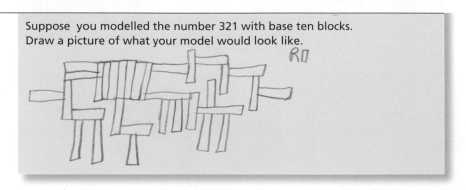

Suppose you modelled the number 321 with base ten blocks. Draw a picture of what your model would look like.

RO

It is valuable for students to be flexible with the relationships between powers of ten in order to rename numbers. For example, a student should realize that any whole number of the form ██00 can be written as ██ hundreds, or as ██0 tens. For example, 2400 can be written as 24 hundreds or as 240 tens. Similarly, the number ██ 000 000 can be written as ██ millions, or as ██ 000 thousands, or as ██0 000 hundreds, or as ██00 000 tens.

To show that she or he has a good understanding of a quantity, the student should be able to apply Principle 3 to rename a number in many ways. This sort of flexibility helps students relate one number to other numbers. For example, the number 32 462 could be renamed as

- 32 thousands + 4 hundreds + 62 ones, or
- 3 ten thousands + 2 thousands + 46 tens + 2 ones, or
- 324 hundreds + 6 tens + 2 ones, or ….

Principle 4: A place value system needs a symbol for a placeholder.

When you write a number in its symbolic form using digits, for example, 304, you call the digit 0 a placeholder. But many people cannot really explain what this means. The idea is that, if you did not have the digit 0, the number would be recorded as 34, and you would mistakenly think that the 3 represented 30 instead of 300.

If you always recorded the digits on a place value mat or worked with base ten blocks, as shown below, the digit 0 would not be necessary. In symbolic recordings, however, you need a placeholder.

A place value mat to show 304.

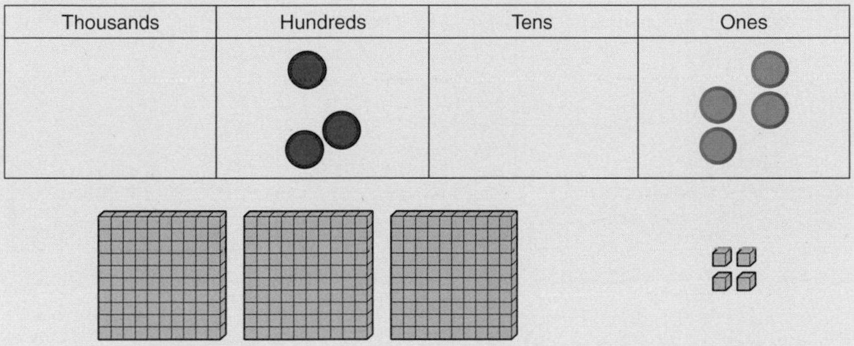

Thousands	Hundreds	Tens	Ones

A place holder is not necessary when representing 304 on a place value mat or with base ten blocks.

Principle 5: Numbers might be more easily compared when written in standard, or symbolic, form.

To learn to write numbers in standard form, students must realize that the order in which digits appear matters. That is, 53 and 35 mean two very different things. For some students, this takes more time than for others. One thing that teachers can do to help is to continue to work on place value mats as long as students benefit from them, and to take the time to make sure that the greater place values always appear to the left from the students' point of view.

Once whole numbers are represented in their standard, or symbolic, form, students can use the number of digits to get a sense of their size in order to compare them. For example, any 3-digit whole number is 100 or

ACTIVITY 10.9

You could pose a question such as:

How do you know that 3[ ]32 > 3025 no matter what value is missing?

Building Number Sense

ACTIVITY 10.10

Present problems of interest that involve numbers close to multiples of 100, 1000, or 10000. For example,

The population of a town is 15197. A new family moves to town. What might the population be now?

Building Number Sense

greater. Similarly, any 2-digit whole number is less than 100. Therefore, any 3-digit whole number is greater than any 2-digit whole number. This can be modelled on a number line, for example:

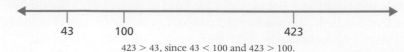

43 100 423

423 > 43, since 43 < 100 and 423 > 100.

When two whole numbers have the same number of digits, the leftmost digits matter most when ascertaining the size of the numbers, because that place tells the most about the value of the number.

489 500 523

489 < 523, since 489 < 500 and 523 > 500.

Another way for students to think about the role of the various digits in a numeral is to realize that there are digits that are more and less important in the numeral. For example, in 3021, the 3 is quite important; it really gives a sense of the size of the number. The 1 is important, perhaps, in clarifying that the number is odd, but not in terms of the size of the number.

Student Response

This student's clues narrow down the number, but don't close in on one specific number. It might have been better to use a different three clues.

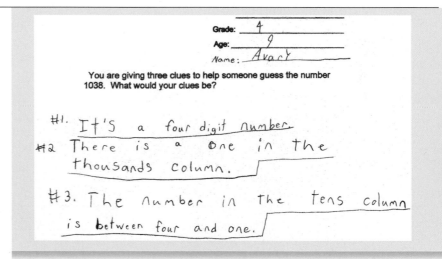

Grade: 4

Age: 9

Name: Avary

You are giving three clues to help someone guess the number 1038. What would your clues be?

#1. It's a four digit number.

#2 There is a One in the thousands column.

#3. The number in the tens column is between four and one.

Counting Based on Place Value

Place value work depends on students' ability to count using more than one grouping in the same situation. When you count by ones, twos, fives, or even hundreds, you are counting in a consistent way. But when you count to, for example, 223 by saying 100, 200, 210, 220, 221, 222, 223, this is more complicated. Students must realize that they can start counting by 100s, and then continue counting differently, that is, by 10s and then by 1s.

Another stumbling block for students in counting is the transition from numbers like $x99$ to $x00$. You can support students in this by presenting problems like those in **Activity 10.10**.

Estimating Numbers

Often you do not require an exact amount to represent a number, but only an estimate. Students should be comfortable with a variety of ways to estimate numbers, depending on the context and the numbers involved. Estimating is used

- in computation; for example, to estimate 35 1 27, you could estimate 35 as 30 and 27 as 30 to estimate 30 1 30 5 60
- to get a sense of the size of numbers in order to compare them; for example, 389 is about 400 and 315 is about 300, so 389 > 315
- to report numbers; for example, about 400 people came to the event

As students share their estimates, you gain insight into their number sense.

> Tell about an estimated number you heard or read about. It could be on the radio, on TV, on the Internet, or in a magazine or newspaper.
>
> _how many people in the world_

Student Response

This student knows that the population of the world is an estimate. It would be interesting to ask the student to explain her or his thinking.

Rounding

One approach to estimating is to round a number to the nearest multiple of 10, 100, 1000, ... This is a type of estimating that follows prescribed rules or conventions. To round a number, students can think of a number line as a highway with "gas stations" at the multiples to which the number could be rounded. The rounded number is the location of the closest "gas station." For example, when rounding to the nearest ten, the gas stations appear at multiples of 10. The nearest gas station to 133 is at 130, so 133 rounds to 130.

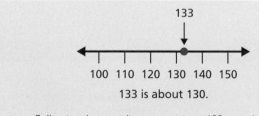

133 is about 130.

Following the rounding conventions, 133 rounds to 130 because 33 is closer to 30 than 40.

If, instead, numbers were rounded to the nearest 100, the gas stations would be at 0, 100, 200, 300, etc., and 133 would round to 100. Keep in mind that rounding to the nearest multiple of 10, 100, 1000, ... is only one way to estimate and is neither better nor worse than other approaches.

Benchmark Numbers

Other benchmark, anchor, or "comfortable" numbers can also be used to estimate. For example, many people are comfortable with the 25s, likely because of the monetary system. For example, a principal might estimate a class with between 23 and 28 students as having about 25 students instead of estimating it as 20 or 30.

To become comfortable with greater benchmark numbers, students might enjoy exploring numbers like 1 million or 1 billion in contextually interesting ways, as described in **Activity 10.12**.

You might want to use some of the David Schwartz books about a million to introduce some of these activities.

TEACHING TIP

- It is important not to over-emphasize rounding to the nearest multiple of a power of ten. Rounding is just one way to estimate.

- Be flexible about rounding numbers "in the middle." Even if there are conventions, it makes as much sense to round 135 to 130 as to 140 and may make even more sense in particular situations.

ACTIVITY 10.11

Pose the following question:

A newspaper reports that 150 people attended an event. Exactly how many people might there have been?

Building Number Sense

ACTIVITY 10.12

Think about 1 million pennies.

- How many loonies is that? How many toonies? How many $100 bills?

- If you lined up 1 million pennies against a wall, how long would the line be?

- If you made a square of 1 million pennies, how long would the side of the square be?

- How long would it take you to roll 1 million pennies?

- How high a stack would 1 million pennies make?

Proportional Reasoning

Common Errors and Misconceptions

Larger Whole Numbers: Common Errors, Misconceptions, and Strategies

COMMON ERROR OR MISCONCEPTION	SUGGESTED STRATEGY
Interpreting 0 Digits Students do not effectively distinguish between numbers like 304 and 3004. In fact, some students think that, since 0 is nothing, there is no difference between the numbers.	One of the ways to deal with this is to model both numbers and ask students if the amounts are the same. Students will likely observe the difference. Then ask students to record the numeral for each. If they record the same numeral, ask which of the two models would better represent that value and why.
Interpreting Teen Numbers Students have trouble with the teen numbers. When hearing "seventeen," they write 71.	Encourage students not to write a number down until they have heard the entire number. For example, when saying "seventeen," ask students to listen without writing anything down, and then say the number again as they record it. As well, ask students to interpret numbers they record or read in terms of tens and ones; for instance, 17 means 1 ten and 7 ones, but 71 means 7 tens and 1 one.
Space Placement Students have difficulty knowing where to locate the space for whole numbers greater than 9999.	The conventional practice in English Canada for whole numbers is to write the digits in groups of 3, starting from the right with spaces between those groups, except for 4-digit numerals (e.g., 3 123 103, 10 325, and 4123). Note that students will learn this convention through exposure and practice, but it should also be explicitly taught. It is sometimes helpful to allow students to write numerals by using commas (the previous convention and one still used by many financial institutions) to show where the spaces should be. Students can then rewrite the numerals with the spaces.

Appropriate Manipulatives

Larger Whole Numbers: Examples of Manipulatives

100 CHART	STUDENT-MADE BASE TEN MATERIALS

A 100 chart is one of the most valuable tools you can use in developing early numeration ideas. In a very simple way, it shows how numbers are grouped and the patterns inherent in the system. It also displays all the numbers 0–99 (or 1–100) at a glance.

0	1	2	3	4	5	6	7	8	9
10	11	12	13	14	15	16	17	18	19
20	21	22	23	24	25	26	27	28	29
30	31	32	33	34	35	36	37	38	39
40	41	42	43	44	45	46	47	48	49
50	51	52	53	54	55	56	57	58	59
60	61	62	63	64	65	66	67	68	69
70	71	72	73	74	75	76	77	78	79
80	81	82	83	84	85	86	87	88	89
90	91	92	93	94	95	96	97	98	99

The 100 chart makes place value patterns clearer.

Students can create their own models using

- craft sticks in bunches of 10 (with elastics around each bunch), each representing 10, and bags with 10 bunches of 10 in them, each representing 100
- buttons in small bags of 10, each representing 10, and larger bags with 10 small bags of 10 in them, each representing 100

1 hundred, 3 tens, 6 ones
136

Student-made numeration models are excellent for early numeration work and for developing an understanding of the need for a numeration system.

LINKING CUBES

Linking cubes can be grouped in trains of tens; for example, 27 would be modelled with 2 trains and 7 loose cubes. (To introduce the number 100, 10 trains of 10 can be bound together by an elastic into a large bundle.)

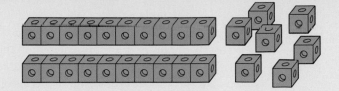

2 tens, 7 ones is 27

A linking cube model is most effective for modelling 2-digit numbers.

BASE TEN BLOCKS

Base ten blocks are an efficient and valuable model. As with the other models described here (buttons, craft sticks, and cubes), base ten blocks are proportional (e.g., the ten block is 10 times as big as the one block, and the hundred block is 100 times as big as the one block). This helps with developing number sense, as a number like 250 is 10 times as big as the number 25.

It is preferable to use blocks that can be physically linked or connected; for example, 10 one blocks can be connected to create 1 ten block, and 10 ten blocks can be connected to form 1 hundred block. This allows students to see that 10 ones is the same as 1 ten and they can more literally perform the trade when instructed to.

Base ten blocks can be used with or without place value mats (the blocks below would represent 1235 no matter what order they were in). However, place value mats allow for a transition from the blocks, which inherently do not require any thought of place value, to numerals, which consist of digits that have place value.

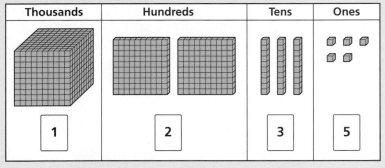

Thousands	Hundreds	Tens	Ones
1	2	3	5

1235

Thousands blocks can be put together to show ten thousands or perhaps hundred thousands, if there are enough in the school.

Students can move from modelling with just blocks, to modelling with blocks on a place value mat, to working with blocks and digit cards on a place value mat, to working with just digit cards on the place value mat, to finally working with just digit cards.

MONEY

A money model uses dollars (hundreds), dimes (tens), and pennies (ones) or $100 bills, $10 bills, and loonies to model 3-digit numbers. Note that this is not a proportional model (e.g., the dime is not 10 times as "big" as the penny, nor are the bills different sizes). It is a value model because the dime has a value that is 10 times that of the penny or the $10 bill has a value worth 10 times the loonie's value. Note that play pennies can be used. The money model could be used in conjunction with a place value mat to reinforce the place value concepts underlying the symbolic representation (the numeral) of numbers.

Some students find this model easy to work with as they have internalized money concepts. Others need to work with a proportional model, such as base ten blocks.

437

Number Theory

Number theory is a study of integers, but often just counting numbers, that focuses on multiplicative and divisive properties of numbers, as opposed to a number's representation in the place value system. Multiplicative thinking, the foundation of proportional reasoning, is thinking that focuses on how one number is made up of groups of another "unit," as opposed to additive thinking where that is not the case. For example, thinking of 20 as 4 fives is thinking of the 20 being made up of units of 5. Thinking of 20 as 11 + 9 is valid, but is additive, not multiplicative, thinking. As students work with multiplication and division, they deal with the concepts of divisibility, multiples, and factors.

Even and Odd Numbers

Even before students work with multiplication and division, they learn that the 0, 2, 4, 6, 8, 10, ... pattern represents the even numbers. In fact, many older students will define even numbers as those that end in 0, 2, 4, 6, and 8. The concept of "evenness," however, is a multiplicative idea.

Each even number represents an amount that is a multiple of 2; it can be modelled using groups of 2 or two equal groups with nothing left over. Odd numbers are defined by what they are not; they are the non-even numbers. Students can also represent odd numbers by relating them to even numbers, as either 1 more or 1 less than even numbers.

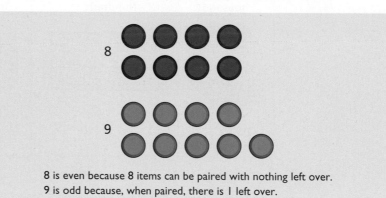

8 is even because 8 items can be paired with nothing left over.
9 is odd because, when paired, there is 1 left over.

Many students wonder whether 0 is an even number. There are two reasons why 0 is considered even: one is that it is part of the pattern of even numbers (2, 4, 6, 8, 10, ...), and the other is that it is a multiple of 2 (because $2 \times 0 = 0$), and all multiples of 2 are even numbers.

Multiples

A multiple of a number is the product of that number with an **integer** multiplier. For example, 8 is a multiple of 4 since $8 = 2 \times 4$. −8 is also a multiple of 4: −2 × 4). But even though 9 can also be expressed as the product of 4 and another number ($9 = 2.25 \times 4$), it is not a multiple of 4; the multiplier is not an integer.

Common Multiples

Sometimes you need to determine the multiples that two numbers have in common. Common multiples come in handy for solving problems like the one in **Activity 10.13** and for later work with fractions to determine the least common denominator (which is the least common multiple of the numbers in the denominators).

To determine the common multiples of, for instance, 12 and 15, you might list the multiples for each, and then look for multiples common to both lists:

Multiples of 12: 12, 24, 36, 48, 60, 72, 84, 96, 108, 120, 132, ...

Multiples of 15: 15, 30, 45, 60, 75, 90, 105, 120, 135, ...

The common multiples of 12 and 15 are 60, 120, and so on.

There is an infinite list of common multiples of 12 and 15. The least common multiple is 60, but every multiple of 60 is also a common multiple of 12 and 15.

To write the fractions $\frac{2}{3}$ and $\frac{3}{4}$ with the same denominator, you might determine the least common denominator (LCD) of thirds and fourths, that is, the least common multiple (LCM) of 3 and 4:

Multiples of 3: 3, 6, 9, 12, 15, 18, 21, ...

Multiples of 4: 4, 8, 12, 16, ...

The LCM of 3 and 4 is 12, which means the LCD is twelfths:

$\frac{3}{4} = \frac{9}{12}$ and $\frac{2}{3} = \frac{8}{12}$.

Another tool for determining least common multiples, particularly for numbers less than 10 or 20, is a set of counting rods (i.e., Cuisenaire rods). For example, to show the least common multiple of 4 and 6, trains of 4 rods are matched to trains of 6 rods in length. For example, the model below shows that 12 is a common multiple of 3 and 4.

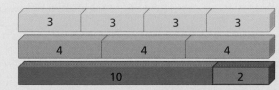

12 is a common multiple of 3 and 4.

Factors

Whenever there is a multiple, there are factors. The number 18 is a multiple of 6 because $3 \times 6 = 18$, which means 18 is also a multiple of 3; 3 and 6 are, therefore, factors of 18. Students will discover that some numbers have many factors, some have a few, and some have only 1 or 2. For example:

Factors of 24		Factors of 6		Factors of 97	
(8 factors)		(4 factors)		(2 factors)	
1	24	1	6	1	97
2	12	2	3		
3	8				
4	6				

As shown in the chart above, factors come in pairs, although some numbers have an odd number of different factors (square numbers), and the number 1 has only 1 factor (it is the only such counting number). For example:

Factors of 16		Factors of 1	
(5 factors)		(1 factor)	
1	16	1	1
2	8		
4	4		

Determining Factors

Organized lists, like those on page 209, are a way of determining factors in a systematic fashion, beginning with 1 and the number itself, and then 2 or the next possible factor and its factor partner, etc. Another way to organize and display the factors of a number is using a factor rainbow. For example:

If students attempt to construct a factor rainbow for a number like 100, they will discover that there is a repeated factor.

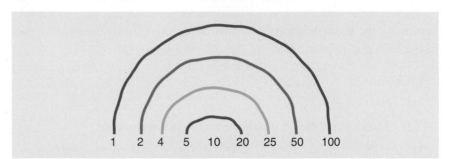

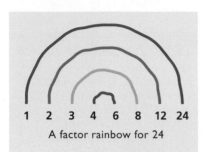

A factor rainbow for 24

Concrete models and other pictorial models can also be used. For example, to determine the factors of 12, take 12 square tiles and try to arrange them into a rectangle. Record the length and width of each rectangle you can make; these are the factor pairs. This can also be done pictorially by drawing rectangles on grid paper (as shown below). You can approach this systematically, beginning with a width of 1 unit, and then 2 units or the next possible width that is a factor.

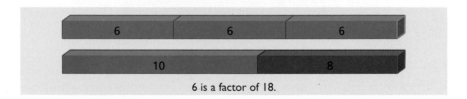

6 is a factor of 18.

As shown before, Cuisenaire rods can also be used. For example, the fact that a train of 6 rods can be used to create 18 shows that 6 is a factor of 18.

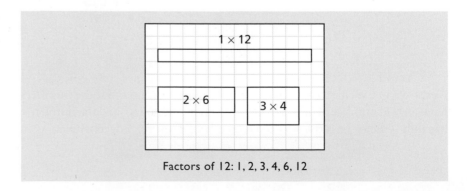

Factors of 12: 1, 2, 3, 4, 6, 12

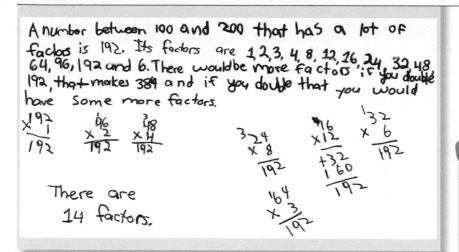

A number between 100 and 200 that has a lot of factors is 192. Its factors are 1, 2, 3, 4, 8, 12, 16, 24, 32, 48, 64, 96, 192 and 6. There would be more factors if you double 192, that makes 384 and if you double that you would have some more factors.

$$\begin{array}{cc} \times \frac{192}{1} \\ \overline{192} \end{array}$$

There are 14 factors.

Sample Response

This student realizes that multiplying by 2 creates more factors. She is good at determining factors, even though there is no indication of how it was done.

ACTIVITY 10.15

Pose a problem such as this:

One number has a lot more factors than another. What could the two numbers be?

———————————
Critical Thinking

Common Factors

Sometimes you need to determine the factors that two numbers have in common. Common factors can be used to solve problems such as the one in **Activity 10.16** and for expressing fractions in lowest or simplest terms. To determine the common factors of, for example, 18 and 30, you list the factors for each and then look for factors common to both lists.

> Factors of 18: 1, 2, 3, 6, 9, 18
>
> Factors of 30: 1, 2, 3, 5, 6, 10, 15, 30
>
> The common factors of 18 and 30 are 1, 2, 3, and 6.

To write the fraction $\frac{12}{18}$ in lowest terms, you need to divide the numerator, 12, and denominator, 18, by the greatest common factor (GCF). To determine the GCF, you can list the factors for each, and then look for the greatest common factor:

> Factors of 18: 1, 2, 3, 6, 9, 18
>
> Factors of 12: 1, 2, 3, 4, 6, 12
>
> The GCF of 12 and 18 is 6. So $\frac{12}{1} = \frac{12 \div 6}{18 \div 6} = \frac{2}{3}$.

Factors and Divisibility

If a number is divisible by another number, it means that the first number is a multiple of the second number (the second number being a factor). There are a number of tests for determining if a number is a multiple of certain factors. Some of the tests are described below.

ACTIVITY 10.16

Present this problem involving common factors:

Peter's dad put cookies in bags with the same number in each. Peter has 30 cookies altogether in his bags and his brother has 18 cookies altogether. How many cookies could his dad have put in each bag?

———————————
Building Number Sense

ACTIVITY 10.17

Let students explore a graph like $y = $ GCF $(4, x)$. Have them interpret what the peaks mean and where they will occur.

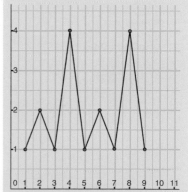

Have them predict what the graph of $y = $ GCF $(6, x)$ looks like and test their prediction.

———————————
Algebraic Reasoning

Divisibility Tests

RULE	EXPLANATION
Divisibility by 2 A number is divisible by 2 if the ones digit is 0, 2, 4, 6, or 8.	This works because of the pattern of the number system. The number 2 is automatically divisible by itself. Then every 2nd number follows the pattern 2, 4, 6, 8, $x0$, $x2$, $x4$, $x6$, $x8$, $x0$, with only the digits 0, 2, 4, 6, and 8 appearing in the ones place.
Divisibility by 3 A number is divisible by 3 if the sum of the digits is a multiple of 3.	Consider the number 414 (4 hundreds, 1 ten, and 4 ones): • If 1 hundred block is divided into groups of 3, there will be 1 one block left over. So, if the 4 hundred blocks are grouped into 3s, there will be 4 one blocks left over. • If the 1 ten block is grouped into 3s, there will be 1 one block left over. And there are already 4 one blocks. • After grouping the 4 hundreds and 1 ten into as many 3s as possible, there are 9 one blocks left over (since $4 + 1 + 4 = 9$), and 9 can be grouped into 3s because it is a multiple of 3. That makes 414 a multiple of 3. This explanation holds true for any number for which the sum of the digits is a multiple of 3.
Divisibility by 4 A number is divisible by 4 if the sum of twice the tens digit and the ones digit is a multiple of 4.	Every 100, 1000, 10 000, etc., can be divided by 4. So only the tens and ones digits have to be considered. If each 10 is broken up into $8 + 2$, the 8 part is divisible by 4, so only the 2 part needs to be considered. For example, $352 = 100 \times 3 + 5 \times 8 + 5 \times 2 + 2$ 100×3 is a multiple of 4 and so is 5×8. Since $2 \times 5 + 2$ is also a multiple of 4, 352 is a multiple of 4.
Divisibility by 5 A number is divisible by 5 if the ones digit is 5 or 0.	This works because $5 \times 1 = 5$. Further multiples are determined by adding 5. When you add 5 to any number that has 5 as the ones digit, the ones digit is 0. When you add 5 to any number that has 0 as the ones digit, the ones digit is 5.
Divisibility by 6 A number is divisible by 6 if it is even and divisible by 3.	The multiples of 3 are 3, 6, 9, 12, 15, 18, ... Every second multiple of 3 is even (6, 12, 18, ...); these are the multiples of 6.
Divisibility by 8 A number is divisible by 8 if $4 \times$ hundreds digit + $2 \times$ tens digit + the one digit is a multiple of 8.	Every 1000, 10 000, etc., can be divided by 8 since $1000 \div 8 = 125$. So only the hundreds, tens, and ones digits have to be considered. If each 100 is broken up into $96 + 4$, the 96 part is divisible by 8, so only the 4 part needs to be considered. If each 10 is broken up into $8 + 2$, the 8 part is divisible by 8, so only the 2 part needs to be considered. For example, $352 = 3 \times 96 + 3 \times 4 + 5 \times 8 + 5 \times 2 + 2$ Note that 3×96 and 5×8 are already multiplies of 8. $4 \times 3 + 5 \times 2 + 2 = 24$ Since 24 is divisible by 8, the entire number is divisible by 8.
Divisibility by 9 A number is divisible by 9 if the sum of the digits is a multiple of 9.	The same explanation used for divisibility by 3 pertains here.

(continued)

Divisibility Tests (Continued)

RULE	EXPLANATION
Divisibility by 10 A number is divisible by 10 if its ones digit is 0.	If a number is divisible by 10, it can be grouped into 10s with 0 ones left over. That means that the tens place or any places to its left can be anything, but the ones place must be 0.
Divisibility by 11 A number is divisible by 11 if the sums of alternate digits are equal, or a multiple of 11.	The powers of 10 alternate between being 1 greater and 1 less than a multiple of 11. $1 = 0 + 1$　　　　$10 = 11 - 1$ $100 = 99 + 1$　　　$1000 = 1001 - 1$ $10\,000 = 9999 + 1$　$100\,000 = 100\,001 - 1$ Because of this, if you add the digits in the 1s, 100s, 10 000s, ... places, and then subtract the sum of the digits in the 10s, 1000s, 100 000s, ... places, the values should be equal or else a multiple of 11 (including 0) if the number is a multiple of 11. For example, 5412 is divisible by 11 since $2 + 4 - (1 + 5) = 0$.

ACTIVITY 10.18

Provide practice in working with divisibility using games like this.

Each player chooses three cards from a deck of cards and tries to arrange them into a number that is divisible by as many of the numbers 2, 3, 4, 5, 6, 8, 9, and 10 as possible. The score is the number of those divisors the number has.

_____

Building Number Sense

Prime and Composite Numbers

Numbers with exactly 2 factors have a special name; they are called prime numbers, or primes. There are very small prime numbers such as 2, 3, and 5, but there are also very large ones, for example, 6299. In fact, mathematicians continue to identify greater and greater prime numbers. Note that 2 is the only even prime number. Composite numbers have 3 or more factors. Every whole number other than 1 that is not a prime is called a composite number. The number 1 is generally, although not always, regarded as neither prime nor composite (mathematicians call it a unit).

Determining Whether a Number Is Prime

There are many ways to decide whether a number is prime. One way, which is very tedious, is to try to divide the number by every possible smaller number to see how many factors it has. This would take a long time, even if done systematically. Another more interesting way is to use a technique called the Sieve of Eratosthenes, as described below.

> **TEACHING TIP**
>
> Make sure students recognize that we only use *prime* and *composite* to talk about counting numbers, not fractions or decimals.

There are many famous conjectures about prime numbers. Ask students whether they think this one (called Goldbach's conjecture) is true:

Every even number can be written as the sum of two primes, for example,

6 = 3 + 3   8 = 5 + 3   10 = 7 + 3

Ask students to explore these other conjectures about prime numbers, as well:

- Every odd number is the sum of a prime and a power of 2, for example,

  $15 = 2^3 + 7$ $101 = 2^6 + 37$.

- There is always at least one prime between consecutive square numbers, for example, 7 between 2^2 and 3^2 and 101 between 10^2 and 11^2.

Critical Thinking

Use a 100 chart to determine the primes from 1 to 100:

Step 1 Place a blue counter on 1.

Step 2 Place red counters on every multiple of 2 but not 2 itself.

Step 3 Place yellow counters on every uncovered multiple of 3 but not 3 itself.

Step 4 Place blue counters on uncovered multiples of 5 but not 5 itself.

Step 5 Place green counters on uncovered multiples of 7 but not 7 itself.

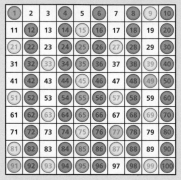

The Sieve of Eratosthenes "catches" the prime numbers.

The remaining uncovered numbers are prime numbers: 2, 3, 5, 7, 11, 13, 17, 19, 23, 29, 31, 37, 41, 43, 47, 53, 59, 61, 67, 71, 73, 79, 83, 89, and 97.

Some students will observe that the only possible final digits for primes greater than 2 and 5 are 1, 3, 7, and 9. This occurs because no other multiple of 2 can be prime (since it has a minimum of 3 factors: 1, 2, and itself), eliminating ones digits of 0, 2, 4, 6, or 8, and no multiple of 5 other than 5 itself can be prime (since it has a minimum of 3 factors: 1, 5, and the number itself), eliminating a ones digit of 5.

At some point, students will learn that the primes are the "building blocks" of our whole numbers in the sense that each whole number can be broken down into prime factors in one unique way. This is called prime factorization. For example, $36 = 2 \times 2 \times 3 \times 3$. Students often use factor trees to determine these prime factors; what is interesting is that the trees end up with the same factors even if they start differently.

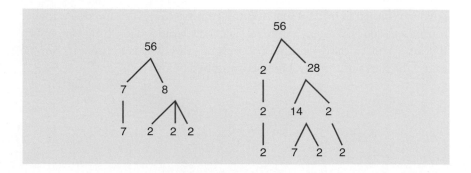

Common Errors and Misconceptions

Number Theory: Common Errors, Misconceptions, and Strategies

COMMON ERROR OR MISCONCEPTION	STRATEGY
Confusing "Factor" and "Multiple" Students confuse the terms "factor" and "multiple."	To help students remember, you might write a definition and example on a word wall: factor × factor = multiple For example, 3 × 2 = 6.
Mistaking 1 for Prime Students identify the number 1 as a prime number. The number 1 is not a prime since it has only 1 factor.	Perhaps if 1 had a name, students would be less inclined to call it a prime. It is called a "unit."
0 as a Multiple Students struggle with the notion that 0 can be a multiple of other numbers.	There are two ways to approach this. One is to observe that, for example, 0 = 0 × 3, so 0 is a multiple of 3. The other is to use patterns. The multiples of 4 are 4 apart, so going down from 4, you get to 0: 24, 20, 16, 12, 8, 4, 0.
Mistaking Odd Composites for Prime Numbers Students mistake many odd composite numbers for prime numbers, particularly numbers such as 33, 39, and 51, because they do not immediately see how to factor the number.	If students have lots of experience working with hundred charts and calculating multiples, particularly multiples of 3, 7, and 9, they will see that many numbers ending in the digits 1, 3, 7, and 9 are, in fact, composite numbers.
Basing "Primeness" on Individual Digits Students think that if each digit of a number is prime, the number is prime.	Present an example, such as the numbers 25 and 35, which students know are composite but have two prime digits.

Appropriate Manipulatives

Number Theory: Examples of Manipulatives

COUNTERS	100 CHARTS
Counters can be used to show the concept of "evenness." If the counters can be paired up, the number is even; if they cannot, it is odd (see *Even and Odd Numbers* on page 208). Counters can also be used to form rectangular arrays for working with multiples and factors, if square tiles or grid paper are not available.	100 charts are useful for working with number patterns (even and odd numbers), multiples, and prime numbers (see page 214).

SQUARE TILES AND GRID PAPER	GEOBOARDS AND SQUARE DOT PAPER
Square tiles and grid paper can be used to form or draw rectangles for working with multiples and factors (see *Determining Factors* on page 210). Tiles are concrete models while grid paper is pictorial. Both have their advantages. Tiles can be manipulated and allow students the opportunity to explore and try different arrangements. Grid paper offers a permanent record. Ideally, the two can be used together, with students using tiles to manipulate, and then drawing what they have done on grid paper. Some interactive white boards allow for a combination of manipulation and a permanent record.	Geoboards or square dot paper can be used to form rectangles in order to work with even and odd numbers, multiples, factors, and prime and composite numbers. 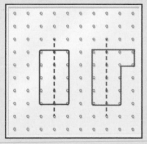 A geoboard for exploring evenness: 8 squares is even; 9 squares is odd.

Appropriate Children's Books

A Million Dots (Clements, 2006).
This book includes a million dots. Its purpose is to give students a sense of the size of 1 million. The groups of dots on individual spreads are also given meaning, for example, a page representing the 525 600 minutes from one birthday to the next.

How Much Is a Million? (Schwartz, 1985).
This beautifully illustrated book (illustrator Steven Kellogg) encourages students to think about a million, billion, and trillion in a number of different contexts, including, for example, the height of a "tower" of 1 million, billion, or trillion children.

The King's Commissioners (Friedman, 1995).
This story is designed, through humour, to show that there are a number of ways to count in groups, including by tens. The concepts developed in the book lead naturally into a discussion of the place value system.

Sir Cumference and All the King's Tens: A Math Adventure (Neuschwander, 2009).
This book sets up a situation, a surprise birthday party, where grouping guests in tens, hundreds, and thousands is useful.

Appropriate Digital Resources

See the MindTap site for a selection of appropriate digital resources.

Assessing Student Understanding

- Frequently, teachers use items like this to test place value understanding:
  234 = __ hundreds __ tens __ ones.
  Even if a student has no idea what the question means, he or she is likely to put the numbers 2, 3, 4 in the blanks in order since it is the only information available. In other words, the item may not tell the teacher what the student really does or does not know. Instead, ask a question like: What digit is in the tens place? or Why might someone say there are 3 tens in 234 and someone else say there are 23 tens?

- A good question to determine whether students recognize that a number can be represented in many ways using place value ideas is to ask them to list as many numbers as they can that can be represented with 15 base ten blocks (e.g., 591, 492, ..., but also 15 or 150).

- Students should have assessment opportunities where a model is provided and the number associated with it must be determined as well as asking them to model a given number.

- It is important to encourage flexibility in estimating numbers. If, for example, a student estimates 339 as 300 rather than 340, this should be considered appropriate.

- How would you assess this student's response? What would you say next to find out more?

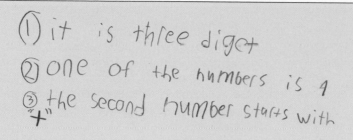

① it is three diget
② one of the numbers is 1
③ the second number starts with
④ "

Student Response

This student was asked to write three clues for the number 123. How would you assess this student's response?

Applying What You've Learned

1. Describe your process for solving the chapter problem. Which concept in the chapter does it relate to? How?

2. a) Why is the term *place value* appropriate for our number system?

   b) Why is a place value system an efficient one?

3. Explain why proportional materials that require students to create groups of 10 themselves (rather than having the 10s pre-made for them) are important when students are first exploring place value ideas.

4. Look at the hundreds chart shown on page 206. Describe four or five number patterns related to place value that could emerge as students become familiar with the chart.

5. Read one of the suggested appropriate children's books described on page 216. Build a lesson plan around that book that engages students in thinking about the related math concept.

6. Many students struggle with an understanding of very large numbers, for example, numbers in the hundred thousands or millions. What suggestions do you have to make these numbers more meaningful to students?

7. Create a set of two or three problems that you think would be good to assess student understanding of the place value system for numbers beyond the thousands. Describe what aspects of place value are being assessed.

8. Some people would argue that knowing about prime numbers is an unnecessary aspect of the math curriculum. How would you respond? Explain your reasoning.

Interact with a K–8 Student:

9. Ask a student to show you how to model a number with base ten blocks. Then ask them to model the same number a different way. Observe:

   a) Do they start with the digit at the left or the digit at the right?

   b) Do they have difficulty thinking about another way to model or do they fairly immediately replace either a large block with 10 small ones or 10 small ones with a large one? How might your observations influence how you approach the teaching of place value?

Discuss with a K–8 Teacher:

10. Ask a teacher what aspects of place value he or she finds most difficult to teach. Do some research. What ideas do you have that might create more success in teaching that topic?

Selected References

Burkhart, J. (2009). Building numbers from primes. *Mathematics Teaching in the Middle School, 15,* 157–167.

Burris, J.T. (2013). Virtual place value. *Teaching Children Mathematics, 20,* 228–236.

Clements, A. (2006). *A million dots.* New York: Simon & Schuster Publishing.

Cotter, J. (2000). Using language and visualization to teach place value. *Teaching Children Mathematics, 7,* 108–114.

Davis, B. (2008). Is 1 a prime number? Developing teacher knowledge through concept study. *Mathematics Teaching in the Middle School, 14,* 86–91.

Friedman, A. (1995). *The king's commissioners.* New York: Scholastic.

Fuson, K.C. (1990). Conceptual structures for multiunit numbers: Implications for learning and teaching multidigit addition, subtraction, and place value. *Cognition and Instruction, 7,* 343–403.

Harrell, M.E., and Slavens, D.R. (2009). Using base-ten block diagrams for divisibility tests. *Teaching Children Mathematics, 17,* 256–262.

Kalb, K.S. and Gravett, J.M. (2012). Out of this world calculations. *Teaching Children Mathematics, 18,* 410–417.

Kamii, C.K. (1986). Place value: An explanation of its difficulty and educational implications for the primary grades. *Journal of Research in Childhood Education, 1,* 75–86.

Kari, A.R., and Anderson, C.B. (2003). Opportunities to develop place value through student dialogue. *Teaching Children Mathematics, 10,* 78–82.

Kurz, T., and Garcia, J. (2010). Prime decomposition using tools. *Teaching Children Mathematics, 15,* 370–378.

Neuschwander, C. (2009). *Sir Cumference and all the king's tens: A math adventure.* Watertown, MA: Charlesbridge Publishing.

Ross, S. (2002). Place value: Problem solving and written assessment. *Teaching Children Mathematics, 9,* 419–423.

Schwartz, D. (1985). *How much is a million?* New York: HarperCollins.

Taylor, A.R., Breck, S.E., and Aljets, C.M. (2004). What Nathan teaches us about transitional thinking. *Teaching Children Mathematics, 11,* 138–142.

Yolles, A. (2001). Making connections with prime numbers. *Mathematics Teaching in the Middle School, 7,* 84–86.

Chapter 11

Estimation and Calculation Strategies with Larger Whole Numbers

IN A NUTSHELL

The main ideas in the chapter are listed below:

1. There are many procedures, or algorithms, for adding, subtracting, multiplying, and dividing. The traditional ones are simply some of these and not necessarily better than the others.

2. It is valuable for students to have opportunities to invent their own procedures, including mental math strategies.

3. Procedures for estimating and calculating should always be taught with meaning, referring to the meaning of the operation, principles of the operation, and concrete manipulations that describe the procedure.

CHAPTER PROBLEM

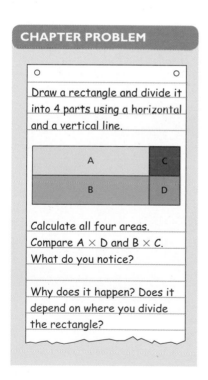

Draw a rectangle and divide it into 4 parts using a horizontal and a vertical line.

Calculate all four areas. Compare $A \times D$ and $B \times C$. What do you notice?

Why does it happen? Does it depend on where you divide the rectangle?

Addition and Subtraction

Estimating Sums and Differences

Estimating sums and differences is valuable as it helps in checking calculations, and predicting answers, and sometimes estimating is all that is required.

Estimating Rather Than Rounding

TEACHING TIP

When confronted with a mathematical situation, students should always first decide if an estimate or an exact calculation is required.

In many parts of Canada, curriculum has changed so that students are encouraged to use many different forms of estimating, not just rounding. Rounding is based on rules, whereas a request to estimate, not necessarily round, allows for more flexibility. For example, a child adding 43 + 53 might choose to estimate 43 as 40, but 53 as 55 in order to be closer to the correct values while still being able to calculate mentally. If the child had rounded, both numbers would be rounded down (as would be the case if rounding to the nearest ten), which would lead to an underestimate.

Factors Influencing Estimation

A number of factors come into play when making decisions about estimating, such as the context and the numbers and operations involved.

Context The context will determine

ACTIVITY **11.1**

Ask students to think of two or three different situations where they might want to estimate 58 – 17.

Building Number Sense

- if an estimate or an exact answer is more appropriate. For example, when a customer wants to know if she or he can afford two items, an estimate might be appropriate. When the clerk is giving the customer change, however, an exact difference is required.
- how close the estimate should be to the exact value. For example, estimating the total number of people at a sports event for a news report would not require as close an estimate as would estimating the total cost of two items if your budget was tight.
- whether a high or low estimate is more appropriate. For example, to estimate the total cost of two items, a high estimate is safer than a low estimate. A low estimate is probably better when someone is estimating how many of something he or she can afford to buy.

The Numbers and Operations Involved

- The individual numbers involved matter. For example:
  836 + 94 is about 836 + 100 = 936, estimating 94 as 100 because 100 is close and easy to work with
  672 − 69 is about 675 − 75 = 600, estimating both numbers so that they are compatible
- Whether you are adding or subtracting: Increasing one number and decreasing the other is usually appropriate for adding, but not necessarily for subtracting; increasing or decreasing both numbers is usually appropriate when subtracting, but not necessarily when adding. For example:
  46 + 36 is about 50 + 30 (closer than 50 + 40)
  84 − 36 is about 90 − 40 (closer than 80 − 40)

ACTIVITY 11.2

Ask students to estimate which animals with certain masses can safely cross a set of bridges with particular load limits.

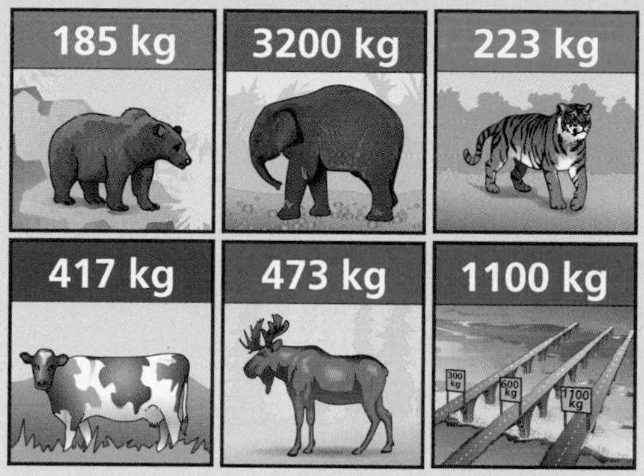

| 185 kg | 3200 kg | 223 kg |
| 417 kg | 473 kg | 1100 kg |

Building Number Sense

Estimating Strategies

To estimate sums and differences, students might use strategies such as these:

STRATEGY	EXAMPLE
Estimate each number as a nearby multiple of 10, 100, 1000, etc.	693 + 458 is about 700 + 500 = 1200 693 − 458 is about 690 − 460 = 230
Estimate one number but not the other.	693 + 458 is about 700 + 458 = 1158
When adding, estimate both numbers, increasing one and decreasing the other.	693 + 458 is about 700 + 450 = 1150
When subtracting, increase or decrease both numbers.	693 − 458 is about 700 − 500 = 200 693 − 458 is about 650 − 450 = 200
Estimate within a range.	428 + 397 is between 700 (400 + 300) and 900 (500 + 400) 516 − 147 is between 300 (500 − 200) and 500 (600 − 100)
Estimate in terms of money.	385 + 245 is about 3 loonies, 3 quarters + 2 loonies, 2 quarters, which is 6 loonies, 1 quarter, or 625
Estimate by using compatible numbers, which are often not "round" at all.	867 − 471 is about 867 − 467 = 400

There is neither one right strategy nor one right answer when estimating. Notice that one approach shown in the chart above was to estimate within a range. Onslow et al. (2005) suggest that students might estimate the sum of 323 and 428 as a number in the 700s, rather than as a particular single value. Or, estimates can be qualified, for example, as to whether they are "almost" or "a bit more than" a certain value. This can often require more sophistication in both number and operation sense than simply saying that an estimate is "about" a certain value.

As is evident in many of the estimating examples described above, it is essential that students know the addition and subtraction facts and how to add and subtract multiples of 10, 100, 1000, etc., in order to estimate.

Student Response

This student recognizes that some estimating situations require no calculations at all.

Here is what two friends spent each day.

	Tuesday	Wednesday	Thursday	Friday
Jane	$5.96	$12.48	$37.26	$18.95
Ricki	$7.10	$12.50	$37.50	$18.74

To find out who spent more, do you need to calculate an exact answer? _____No_____

Explain.

No, because there's only one time when Jane spends more than Ricki and it's not by very much.

Student Reluctance to Estimate

Many students are reluctant to estimate. Most likely, this is insecurity about what estimate is actually desired by the teacher. There are several ways to work around this.

One strategy is for the teacher to show students that he or she believes that a lot of estimates are valid by both offering and accepting many estimates for a given calculation. Once students see that this is okay, they will probably be more likely to believe it.

Another strategy is to ask questions such as: Which do you think is a good estimate for 252 – 143: 100, 150, or 200? Why?

A third strategy involves making it impossible for a student to calculate by using missing digits. You might, for example, ask students to estimate the value of 4■3 – 291.

Varied Approaches to Addition and Subtraction

Students, even as early as in Grade 2, are expected to apply what they know about adding and subtracting single-digit numbers ("the facts") and the meanings of those operations for adding and subtracting greater numbers.

When faced with a mathematical situation requiring an exact answer, there is always a choice between technology, paper-and-pencil algorithms or procedures, or mental math. Students should realize that the choice may depend on the exact numbers involved (e.g., 40 + 30 makes more sense using mental math than 459 + 1382) or personal preference.

We teach paper-and-pencil algorithms so that students gain greater insight into how operations work, even if later they use calculators for many of those same calculations.

As with estimating sums and differences, before students can work efficiently and flexibly with algorithms, they must

- know their addition and subtraction facts
- understand the basic principles underlying the place value system
- know how to add and subtract multiples of 10, 100, 1000, etc.
- understand the basic addition and subtraction principles, as many algorithms are built on those principles

Invented Algorithms

Students should be encouraged to develop their own algorithms. These are sometimes referred to as invented algorithms, student-generated algorithms, or personal strategies. Research has shown that students can have much greater success if they have opportunities early on to develop their own algorithms, generally using concrete models (Hiebert, 1984; Kamii, Lewis, and Livingston, 1993). The transition to more conventional algorithms, if ever made, is best done when a student is ready and not necessarily according to a teacher's timetable.

Mental Math

Some of the algorithms presented here are more appropriate for pencil-and-paper work. Others are mental algorithms. There is great value in using mental algorithms as they are often quicker and easier to use.

Most mental algorithms require students to compose and decompose numbers; for instance, think of $99 + 36$ as $100 + 35$, or think of $111 - 89$ as $100 - 90 + 11 + 1$. Mental computation is about considering which form or representation of a number is most useful for a particular calculation. Students who do mental calculations exercise and further develop their number sense. One of the ways that teachers can encourage students to calculate mentally is to present computations in horizontal, rather than vertical, form. In this way, students do not immediately think in columns, and, for example, are more likely to think of the 2 in 324 as 20 and not 2.

Explain the steps you would follow to add $48 + 17$.

> I would round 48 to 50
> then Add 17 on which is 67
> Then subtract 2 which is 65

Student Response

This student has performed a mental math algorithm that involves adding "convenient" numbers, and then compensating.

Alternative Algorithms

Many people find it surprising that there is considerable flexibility in calculating sums and differences, just as there is with estimating. Teachers should be aware of this and be prepared to expose students to multiple algorithms.

Why Encourage Alternative Algorithms?

- One algorithm might make more sense to a particular student than another.
- One algorithm might be more convenient for a particular set of numbers.
- Some algorithms lend themselves to mental computation.
- A student may get help at home from a parent who uses a very different algorithm than what has been taught at school. It is helpful if students are open to both.
- Students who have come from different countries will often bring with them very different approaches. It is important to provide an open and accepting atmosphere.

- Students who have a repertoire of algorithms to choose from can use one algorithm to perform a calculation, and a different one to check it.
- Something a student creates himself or herself is almost always more meaningful to him or her.

Although the algorithms shown below look "formal," they may well be invented by students in the given or a similar form. It is the intention that the teacher be aware of, and open to, these alternatives, rather than present them all.

"TRADITIONAL" ALGORITHM	AN ALTERNATIVE ALGORITHM
The "traditional" algorithm focuses on single digits and is recorded:	This alternative algorithm uses number sense and addition principles and lends itself to mental math:

$$\begin{array}{r} {}^{9}\ {}^{13}\ {}^{12} \\ \cancel{1}\ \cancel{0}\ \cancel{4}\ \cancel{2} \\ -\ 9\ 8\ 5 \\ \hline 5\ 7 \end{array}$$

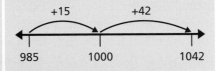

+15 ... +42

985 ... 1000 ... 1042

ACTIVITY 11.3

Encourage students to use alternative algorithms by making them realize how knowing one piece of information makes another one easy to figure out.

For example, have students solve each string of calculations to bring out how later items in each string relate to earlier ones.

35 + 8 =	35 + 18 =
45 + 8 =	25 + 28 =
55 + 8 = _____	15 + 38 =

Building Number Sense

Alternative Addition Algorithms For the traditional algorithm (Algorithm 1 as described on the next page) and many others, it is appropriate, initially, to model the algorithm with manipulatives or drawings. A written record is not necessary in the early stages of algorithm use, but is useful later on, with each step of the algorithm matching a physical action with the manipulatives. No matter what algorithm is used, it is important that students understand and are able to explain why they do what they do. Algorithms suitable for mental calculation will be noted as they are described.

Algorithm 1 Using the traditional algorithm, the digits are combined, beginning at the ones place and working left. An example is shown.

Step 1 Model both numbers with blocks, on a place value mat, if available.

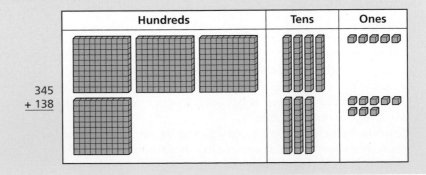

345
+ 138

Hundreds	Tens	Ones

Step 2 Add the ones. Trade 10 ones for 1 ten. Record the ones that are left.

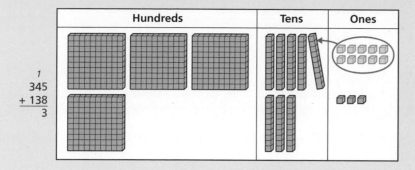

1
345
+ 138
___
3

Step 3 Add the tens. Record the tens.

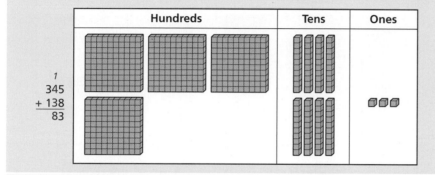

1
345
+ 138
___
83

Step 4 Add the hundreds. Record the hundreds.

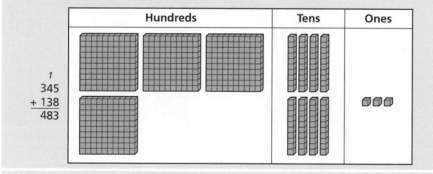

1
345
+ 138
___
483

Step 5 Check the answer.

The sum 483 makes sense since 345 + 138 is about 350 + 130, which is 480.

ACTIVITY 11.4

Ask students to record an addition equation where the digits 4, 8, and 2 appear on the left and the digit 9 appears on the right. For example, 489 + 320 = 809. Other digits can also be used.

Building Number Sense

ACTIVITY 11.5

Pose problems that require students to use addition, but in more mathematically rich ways. For example, two problems might be:

- Imagine tossing a pair of dice again and again to create two 2-digit numbers, which are then added. What is the least number of tosses needed for a sum greater than 200? How do you know?

- A triangle has a perimeter of 44 cm. What could the lengths of the sides be, if each side is a whole number of centimetres?

Critical Thinking

Algorithm 2 This algorithm involves finding partial sums and then totalling them. For Algorithm 2A (front-end addition), the adding begins at the left (the greatest place value), while, for Algorithm 2B, it begins at the right, or the ones. Each step in the addition is shown as a partial sum. This algorithm lends itself to **mental calculation**.

Algorithm 2 is based on the commutative and associative principles described on page 163.

ALGORITHM 2A	**ALGORITHM 2B**
345 + 138 400 (Add the hundreds.) 70 (Add the tens.) + 13 (Add the ones.) 483 (Add the partial sums.)	345 + 138 13 (Add the ones.) 70 (Add the tens.) + 400 (Add the hundreds.) 483 (Add the partial sums.)

Algorithm 2 can be modelled with base ten blocks. Algorithm 2A is shown below.

Step 1 The student models both numbers with blocks. (Note that a place value mat is optional.)

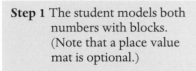

345
+ 138

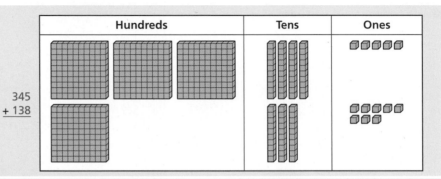

Step 2 Add the hundreds. Record the partial sum.

345
138
400

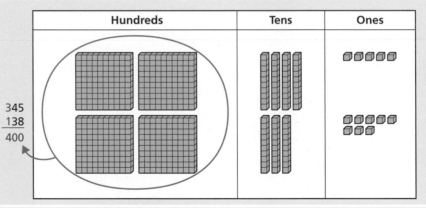

Step 3 Add the tens. Record the partial sum.

345
+ 138
400
70

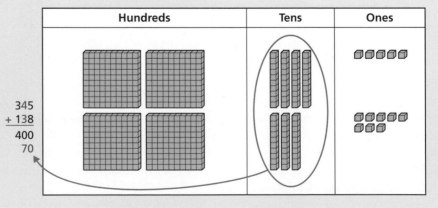

Step 4 Add the ones. Record the
partial sum.

$$
\begin{array}{r}
345 \\
+\ 138 \\
\hline
400 \\
70 \\
13 \\
\end{array}
$$

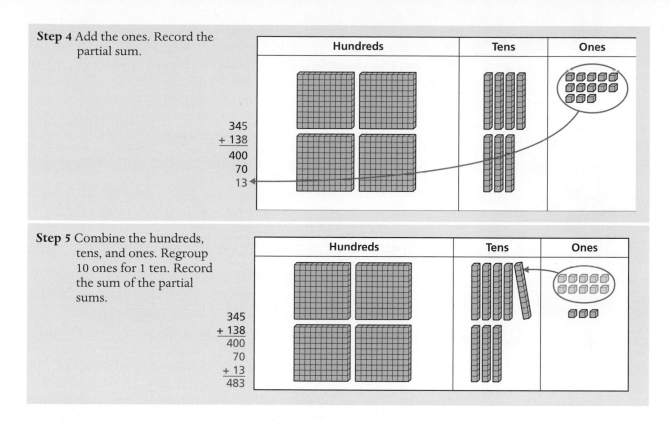

Hundreds	Tens	Ones

Step 5 Combine the hundreds,
tens, and ones. Regroup
10 ones for 1 ten. Record
the sum of the partial
sums.

$$
\begin{array}{r}
345 \\
+\ 138 \\
\hline
400 \\
70 \\
+\ 13 \\
\hline
483 \\
\end{array}
$$

Hundreds	Tens	Ones

Algorithm 3 This algorithm is based on the principle that addition and subtraction "undo" each other. In this case, you add too much in order to get
an easier addend to work with, often mentally, and then "undo" what you
did by taking away:

$$357 + 597 \rightarrow 357 + (597 + 3) \quad \text{(Add 3 too many.)}$$
$$= 357 + 600$$
$$= 957 \rightarrow 957 - 3 \quad \text{(Take away the extra 3.)}$$
$$= 954$$

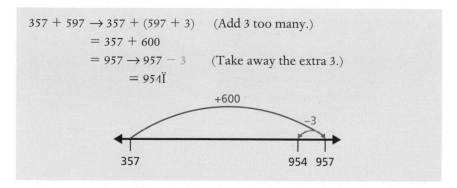

Algorithm 4 This algorithm is based on the principle that you can take away
from one addend and add what you took away to the other addend without
changing the sum. This allows for the creation of addends that are easier to
calculate with, often mentally.

$$389 + 197 = (389 - 3) + (197 + 3) \quad \text{(Move 3 from 389 to 197.)}$$
$$= 386 + 200$$
$$= 586$$

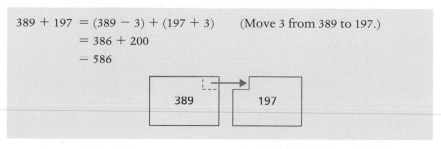

ACTIVITY 11.6

Ask students to choose three different 2-digit numbers for the three parts of the dart board. Then have them calculate all the possible sums if the board is hit three times.

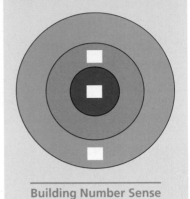

Building Number Sense

Algorithm 5 This algorithm is based on one of the principles of addition, that is, adding can be completed in parts, a variation of the associative property. This algorithm is easiest to use when the adding of subsequent amounts does not affect previous additions as shown below. Note that for a calculation such as 345 + 178, adding the 70 (in 178) requires more than a straightforward adding of the tens digits; regrouping is required to add 70 to 40. This algorithm can often be performed **mentally**.

345 + 138
Start with 345 and add 138 in parts:
First add 100: 345 + 100 = 445
Then add 30: 445 + 30 = 475
Then add 8: 475 + 8 = 483
345 + 138 = 483

Alternative Subtraction Algorithms Just as with addition, there is a broad range of possible subtraction algorithms. These algorithms would usually be invented by students and not necessarily taught. A number of these are described here. Algorithms suitable for mental calculation will be noted.

Algorithm 1 The traditional North American algorithm is not always the easiest for students. One of the reasons is that it proceeds in a left-to-right direction to regroup but in a right-to-left direction to subtract. The algorithm is built around focusing on one place value position at a time and, therefore, often involves several stages of regrouping. At each place value, students have to first decide whether to regroup, and then actually perform the regrouping. This requires students to go back and forth between thinking about regrouping and performing the subtraction.

TEACHING **TIP**

Notice, by the language used, that Algorithm 1 is built on a take-away meaning for subtraction. If a problem involves the comparison meaning, models for both numbers (the minuend and subtrahend) need to be shown (not just the minuend, as in the case of the take-way meaning) and the language changes. For example, "How many more ones does the greater number have?" and so on.

Step 1 Model the minuend, on a place value mat, if available. (Notice that the subtrahend is not modelled since it is to be taken away from the minuend.)

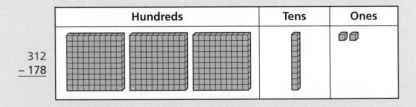

Step 2 Recognize that there are not enough ones to be able to take away 8 ones. Trade 1 ten for 10 ones so you can take away 8 ones.

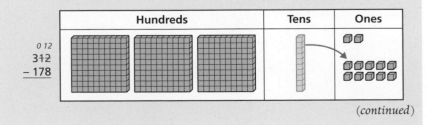

(continued)

Record the ones that are left.

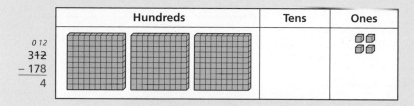

Step 3 Recognize that there are not enough tens to be able to take away 7 tens. Trade 1 hundred for 10 tens so you can take away 7 tens.

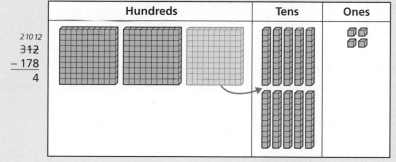

Record the tens that are left.

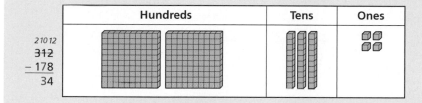

Step 4 Take away 1 hundred. Record the hundreds that are left.

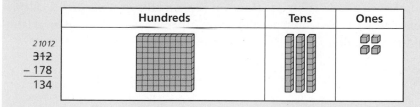

Step 5 Check the answer.

312 − 178 is going to be a bit more than 300 − 200 or 100, so 312 − 178 = 134 makes sense.

A variation of this algorithm involves doing all trading at once to make sure there are enough tens and ones to take away from.

In this case, 3 flats, 1 rod, and 2 ones are exchanged for 2 flats, 10 rods, and 12 ones right at the start, and then the subtraction proceeds.

Algorithm 2 Because addition and subtraction "undo" each other, if you subtract too much in order to use a number that makes the calculation easier, you need to "undo" what you did by adding back the amount you subtracted. This algorithm can be performed **mentally**.

ACTIVITY 11.7

Encourage students to use alternative algorithms by helping them see how knowing how to do one calculation makes another one easy to figure out.

For example, have students solve each string of calculations to bring out how later items in each string relate to earlier ones.

37 − 8 =	132 − 33 =
47 − 8 =	132 − 43 =
57 − 8 =	132 − 53 =
67 − 8 =	132 − 63 =

Therefore, if faced with a question like 132 − 63, they might relate back to 132 − 33 and then adjust the answer.

Building Number Sense

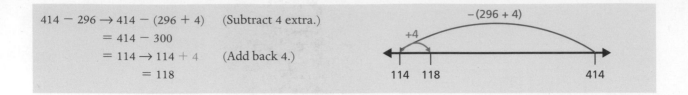

$414 - 296 \rightarrow 414 - (296 + 4)$ (Subtract 4 extra.)

$\qquad = 414 - 300$

$\qquad = 114 \rightarrow 114 + 4$ (Add back 4.)

$\qquad\qquad = 118$

Student Response

This student has subtracted too much and then compensated (Subtraction Algorithm 2).

Explain the steps you would follow to subtract 50 − 37.

You would round 37 to 40, then subtract 40 from 50, then add 3.

TEACHING TIP

The method of recording shown here for each algorithm (Subtraction Algorithms 2 to 5) is just one possibility. Students should be encouraged to record in whatever way is most meaningful to them, but that is understandable by someone who reads it.

Note that many of these are potential mental math strategies, which require little to no recording. If students are asked to show what they did mentally, they might use some of the methods of recordings shown here.

Algorithm 3 This algorithm is based on the principle that you can subtract in parts. You subtract in parts because the parts are easier to subtract **mentally**.

$414 - 302 = 414 - 300 - 2$ (Subtract 300. Then subtract 2.)

$\qquad\qquad = 114 - 2$

$\qquad\qquad = 112$

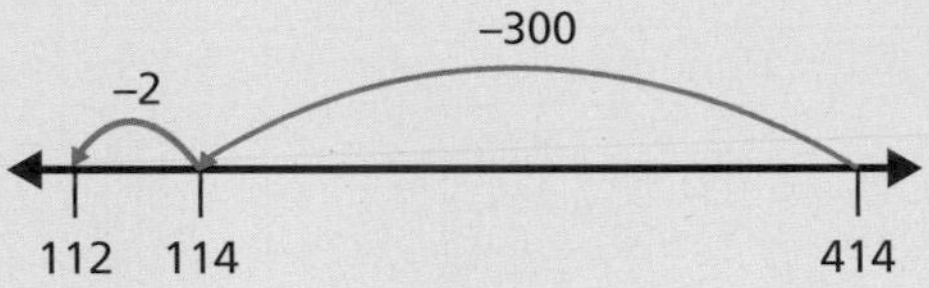

Algorithm 4 This subtraction algorithm is built on the principle that, to subtract two numbers, you can add or subtract the same amount to or from both numbers without changing the difference. By selecting appropriate amounts to add or subtract, a student is often able to transform a calculation that she or he would need to do on paper into one that can be accomplished **mentally**.

$414 - 296 = (414 + 4) - (296 + 4)$ (Add 4 to each number.)

$\qquad\qquad = 418 - 300$

$\qquad\qquad = 118$

Algorithm 5 The relationship between addition and subtraction underlies what is sometimes called the "making change" algorithm. When you make change in money situations, you count from the price (the subtrahend) up to the money paid (the minuend) to find the difference. Although the counting up can be done mentally, the "change" must still be added; some students would need to jot down these amounts in order not to forget them.

Step 1 Think of the subtraction as a missing addend number sentence:

$$327 - 158 = \blacksquare \rightarrow 158 + \blacksquare = 327$$

Step 2 Count up:

Add 2 to get to a multiple of 10: $158 + 2 = 160$

Add 40 to get to a multiple of 100: $160 + 40 = 200$

Add enough to get to the minuend, or total: $200 + 127 = 327$

Add up the "change": $+ 2 \quad + 40 \quad + 127 = 169$

Since $158 + 169 = 327$, then $327 - 158 = 169$.

Communicating about Adding and Subtracting

Notice that in many of the examples on the previous pages, the terms "regroup," "trade," and "exchange" are used rather than "carry" or "borrow." This is because carrying and borrowing have no real meaning with respect to the operation being performed, but the term "regroup" suitably describes the action the student must take.

Students sometimes use poor or inaccurate math language when they perform algorithms that focus on one place value or digit at a time. For example, in the addition below using Addition Algorithm 1 (the "traditional" algorithm), in Step 2, you are not adding 2 and 3; you are adding 2 tens and 3 tens, or 20 and 30. It is important for teachers to model the appropriate place value language and expect students to use it. Modelling the appropriate place value language will help students think more holistically about the numbers they are working with instead of the individual digits in those numbers. Note that if students are introduced to these algorithms using base ten materials, they are more likely to use the appropriate language.

Step 1 Add the ones:

$$\begin{array}{r} 325 \\ + 134 \\ \hline 9 \end{array}$$ "5 + 4 = 9"

Step 2 Add the tens:

$$\begin{array}{r} 325 \\ + 134 \\ \hline 59 \end{array}$$ "2 tens + 3 tens = 5 tens"

Step 3 Add the hundreds:

$$\begin{array}{r} 325 \\ + 134 \\ \hline 459 \end{array}$$ "3 hundreds + 1 hundred = 4 hundreds"

ACTIVITY 11.8

This is called a magic square because the rows, columns, and diagonals all add to the same amount. Ask students to determine which numbers are missing.

	17	22
19		23
20	25	

To create additional magic squares, you can always begin with one that you have, like the one above, and add, subtract, multiply, or divide all entries using the same value. You can also rotate or reflect the square.

Building Number Sense

ACTIVITY 11.9

Set up a problem-solving centre where students use tiles with the digits 0 to 9 on them, each once, to complete calculations begun for them.

```
   ▨ 3          58
+ ▨ 7        − ▨▨
  6 ▨          42
```

```
  6 ▨          ▨ 3
+ ▨▨        − ▨ 4
 149           19
```

Building Number Sense

ACTIVITY 11.10

Students can solve interesting problems involving addition and subtraction.

Examples include:

• Five numbers add to 100. The difference between the least one and greatest one is 12. How do you know that none is greater than 50? What could the numbers be?

• Which numbers between 50 and 100 can be expressed as the sum of four consecutive numbers?

Critical Thinking

Use of Calculators

Although students might use calculators to solve problems where the computation itself is not the focus, if calculation is the focus it makes more sense to take these actions:

• Provide many situations where computations can be performed mentally, if desired.

• Provide some opportunities for students to perform calculations on paper, limiting the size of the numbers to what is appropriate for the student's grade level and encouraging students to vary strategies depending on the numbers being used and the student's preferences.

Common Errors and Misconceptions

Many of the common errors in performing addition and subtraction algorithms stem from a lack of understanding of the underlying principles (numeration, addition, and subtraction principles). If students continue to make these kinds of errors and do not seem to understand what they are doing wrong, they should be using concrete models or number lines to work through the algorithms, while at the same time recording the written algorithms.

Addition and Subtraction Algorithms: Common Errors, Misconceptions, and Strategies

COMMON ERROR OR MISCONCEPTION	SUGGESTED STRATEGY
Regrouping Students forget to regroup when adding, and write a 2-digit number where there should be only one digit. $\quad\quad 1\,4\,5$ $+\ 2\,4\,7$ $\quad 3\,8\,1\,2$	Students should be encouraged to estimate to check their answers. In this case, if students overestimate 145 + 247 as 200 + 300 = 500, they would realize that an answer such as 3812 is much too high.

(continued)

Addition and Subtraction Algorithms: Common Errors, Misconceptions, and Strategies (Continued)

COMMON ERROR OR MISCONCEPTION	SUGGESTED STRATEGY
Regrouping Students remember to regroup, but reverse which digit is recorded in the sum and which is recorded in the regrouping area above; for example, $\overset{2}{1}45$ instead of $\overset{1}{1}45$ $+237$ $+237$ $\,391$ $\,382$	If the actual sum and the incorrect sum are close, w westimating may not be helpful. Another strategy is to have students use place value mats for recording calculations. This way, when they record or place the number below and above the addition, they are placing it in an identified place value position.
Misunderstanding the Algorithm Students subtract the lesser digit from the greater digit within each column, regardless of whether it is in the minuend or the subtrahend; for example, $\,325$ instead of $\overset{2\,11\,1}{\cancel{3}\cancel{2}5}$ -189 -189 $\,264$ $\,136$	Estimating may or may not be helpful, depending on how close the actual and incorrect differences are. Students who estimate $300 - 200 = 100$ to check their answer will suspect there is an error. Students who estimate $300 - 100 = 200$ may not. Another strategy is to appeal to a simpler problem where the error is more obvious. For example, if students subtract incorrectly within columns for a question such as $15 - 9$, they are more apt to notice the error.
Misalignment of Digits Students misalign digits when recording calculations and end up computing incorrectly.	Students can use grid paper or lined paper turned sideways to align digits. 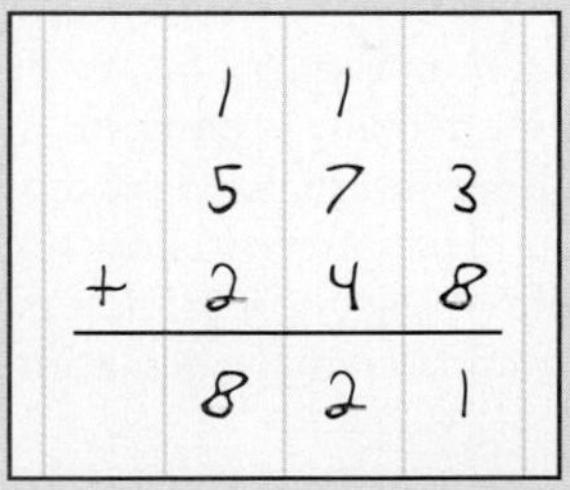 $$\begin{array}{c|c|c|c} & 1 & 1 & \\ \hline & 5 & 7 & 3 \\ \hline + & 2 & 4 & 8 \\ \hline & 8 & 2 & 1 \end{array}$$

Appropriate Manipulatives

Any of the algorithms described on the previous pages can be initially modelled with manipulatives, such as those described on the next page, so that students understand the procedure and why it works.

Addition and Subtraction Algorithms: Examples of Manipulatives

BASE TEN MATERIALS

Base ten materials come in many forms. However, commercial base ten materials are particularly useful because they are sturdy, easy to manipulate, and present a proportional model.

All of the algorithms shown on the previous pages can be modelled using base ten materials.

This model shows Algorithm 4 for addition on page 227 using base ten blocks.

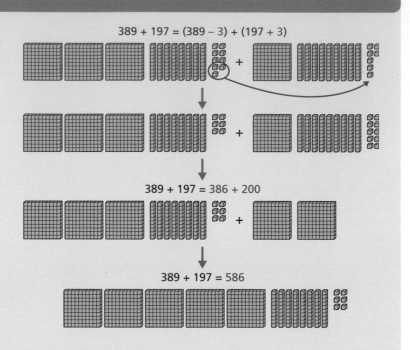

$$389 + 197 = (389 - 3) + (197 + 3)$$

$$389 + 197 = 386 + 200$$

$$389 + 197 = 586$$

PLAY MONEY

Play money is a nonproportional model (sometimes called a value model) and is particularly useful for students who have internalized place value money concepts. (Note that some teachers reserve money for modelling decimal calculations; others use it for both whole number and decimal calculations.)

In a money model, only the loonie, dime, and penny are used: the loonie represents 100, the dime represents 10, and the penny represents 1. Even though students do not see real pennies in everyday money transactions, they can still use play pennies. All of the algorithms shown on the previous pages can be modelled using the money model in the same way as base ten blocks, with the loonie substituting for the hundred block, the dime for the ten block, and the penny for the one block.

$$\begin{array}{r} 345 \\ + 138 \end{array}$$

PLACE VALUE MATS

Place value mats are optional when working with base ten materials or the money model, but they do help reinforce the place value concepts underlying the algorithms. The model at right uses a place value mat for Algorithm 1 for subtraction shown on page 228, using coins instead of blocks.

$$\begin{array}{r} 312 \\ - 178 \end{array}$$

Hundreds	Tens	Ones

Multiplication and Division

Multiplying and Dividing Using Powers of 10

Both estimation and calculation of multi-digit products and quotients are based on students knowing multiplication and division facts, and knowing how to multiply and divide with multiples of 10, 100, 1000, etc. The following models can be used to teach and explain multiplication by tens, hundreds, etc. Students might record their work pictorially using sticks to represent rods (ten blocks) and squares to represent flats (hundred blocks).

Multiplying by 10, 100, and 1000 Using Place Value Concepts

Example 1 This model shows 5 × 30. It can be extended to 5 × 300 using base ten hundred blocks for hundreds, and to 5 × 3000 using base ten thousand blocks for thousands.

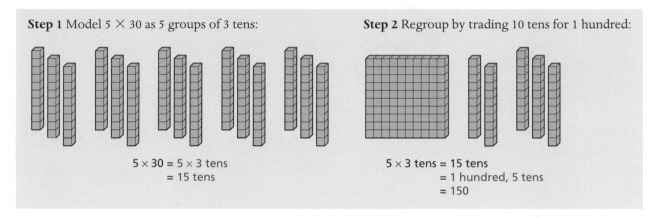

Step 1 Model 5 × 30 as 5 groups of 3 tens:

$$5 \times 30 = 5 \times 3 \text{ tens}$$
$$= 15 \text{ tens}$$

Step 2 Regroup by trading 10 tens for 1 hundred:

$$5 \times 3 \text{ tens} = 15 \text{ tens}$$
$$= 1 \text{ hundred, } 5 \text{ tens}$$
$$= 150$$

Example 2 This model shows 20 × 30. (Note that students usually find calculations like this, in which both factors are multiples of 10, more difficult than when only one factor is a multiple of 10, for example, 2 × 30.)

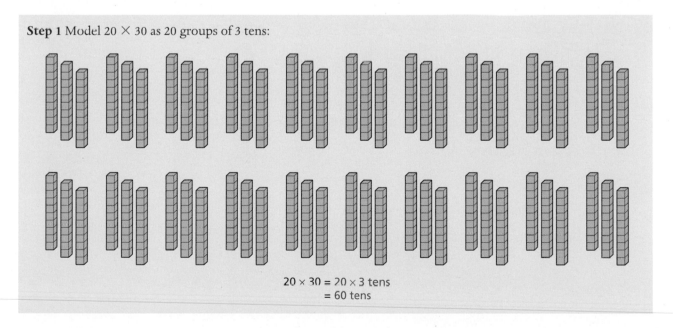

Step 1 Model 20 × 30 as 20 groups of 3 tens:

$$20 \times 30 = 20 \times 3 \text{ tens}$$
$$= 60 \text{ tens}$$

Step 2 Regroup by trading groups of 10 tens for hundreds, creating a rectangle with length 30 and width 20:

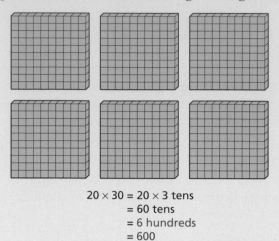

20 × 30 = 20 × 3 tens
= 60 tens
= 6 hundreds
= 600

Multiplying by 10, 100, and 1000 Using Patterns

Example This model uses patterning to multiply.

2 × 3 = 6	
20 × 3 = 60	(One factor is 10 times as much, so the product is 10 times as much.)
20 × 30 = 600	(One factor is 10 times as much, so the product is 10 times as much again.)
200 × 30 = 6000	(One factor is 10 times as much, so the product is 10 times as much again.)
200 × 300 = 60 000	(One factor is 10 times as much, so the product is 10 times as much again.)
2000 × 300 = 600 000	(One factor is 10 times as much, so the product is 10 times as much again.)
2000 × 3000 = 6 000 000	(One factor is 10 times as much, so the product is 10 times as much again.)

Dividing with 10, 100, and 1000 Using Place Value Concepts

Example 1 This model shows 320 ÷ 8. It can be extended to 3200 ÷ 8, using hundred blocks, and to 32 000 ÷ 8, using thousand blocks.

Step 1 Model 320 as 32 tens:

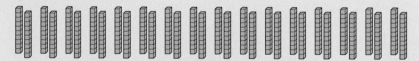

320 is 32 tens.

Step 2 Divide the 32 tens into 8 groups. There are 4 tens, or 40 in each group:

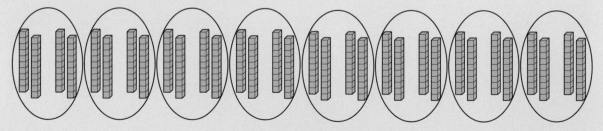

320 ÷ 8 = 32 tens ÷ 8
= 4 tens
= 40

Make up a problem to go with this number sentence:

200 ÷ 10 = 20

Katy has 200 cookies that she is going to share with 9 other friends equaly. How many will each friend get?

Answer-20

Example 2 This model shows 400 ÷ 80 and uses place value language instead of concrete models (e.g., the word "tens" is used instead of a base ten block).

$$400 \div 80 = 40 \text{ tens} \div 8 \text{ tens}$$
$$= 5$$

Dividing with 10, 100, and 1000 Using Patterns

Example This model uses patterning to divide.

40 ÷ 8	= 5	
400 ÷ 8	= 50	(The dividend is 10 times as much so the quotient is 10 times as much.)
4000 ÷ 8	= 500	(The dividend is 10 times as much so the quotient is 10 times as much again.)
4000 ÷ 80	= 50	(The divisor is 10 times as much so the quotient is $\frac{1}{10}$ as much.)
4000 ÷ 800	= 5	(The divisor is 10 times as much so the quotient is $\frac{1}{10}$ as much again.)

Estimating Products and Quotients

The factors influencing estimation for addition and subtraction also influence estimation for multiplication and division. However, when it comes to considering the operations involved, it is important to note that estimates involving multiplication and division often tend to be further from the actual values than is the case for addition and subtraction, simply because of the nature of the operations. Students should pay particular attention to whether the estimated product or quotient might be too low or too high (see *Overestimating and Underestimating* below).

Estimating Strategies

To estimate products and quotients, students might use strategies such as the following:

> **TEACHING TIP**
>
> Be aware that estimating for division is less likely to involve rounding to multiples of powers of ten. For example, to estimate 853 ÷ 9, it makes more sense to estimate using 810 ÷ 9, not 850 ÷ 9. Notice that just like with other operations, it is about using convenient values.

STRATEGY	EXAMPLE
Estimate one or both numbers using nearby multiples of 10, 100, 1000, etc.	25 × 52 is about 25 × 50 = 1250 39 × 31 is about 40 × 30 = 1200 642 ÷ 32 is about 600 ÷ 30 = 20
Estimate one or both numbers so that familiar multiplication and division facts can be used.	574 ÷ 9 is about 560 ÷ 8 = 70 574 ÷ 9 is about 540 ÷ 9 = 60
When multiplying, increase one factor and decrease the other.	65 × 15 is about 60 × 20 = 1200
When dividing, increase or decrease both numbers.	337 ÷ 8 is about 360 ÷ 9 = 40 337 ÷ 8 is about 280 ÷ 7 = 40

Overestimating and Underestimating

Students should keep in mind the effect that the operations of multiplication and division have on numbers. They need to consider this when deciding on what strategy to use to ensure that the estimate is reasonable.

When multiplying, changing one factor has a different effect than changing the other

In the following example of multiplying 68×8, rounding the 8 to 10 has a greater effect on the estimated product than rounding the 68 to 70, even though it is an increase of 2 in each case. This is because two extra 68s in 68×10 is more significant than two extra 8s in 70×8.

Multiply exactly:
$68 \times 8 = 544$
Round the second factor up:
$68 \times 10 = 680$
680 is 136 greater than 544.
Round the first factor up:
$70 \times 8 = 560$
560 is 16 greater than 544.

When dividing, changing the dividend has a different effect than changing the divisor

The following example of dividing 450 by 7 uses the sharing model of division to explain why increasing the dividend increases the estimated quotient, but increasing the divisor decreases the estimated quotient.

Divide exactly:
$450 \div 7$ is about 64.3
450 items shared among 7 people is 64 items each with a few left over.
Increase the dividend:
$450 \div 7$ is about $490 \div 7 = 70$
70 is greater than the exact quotient since there are more items to share among the same number of people.
Increase the divisor:
$450 \div 7$ is about $450 \div 9 = 50$
50 is less than the exact quotient, since there are more people sharing the same number of items.

Student Response

This student uses a clue word to help her decide whether to estimate. It would be preferable, instead, if she realized that an estimate is likely all that is needed anyway.

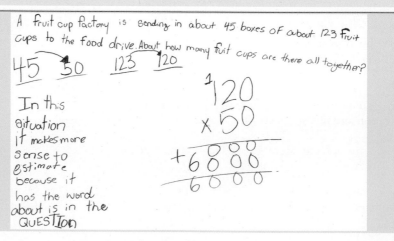

Algorithms for Multiplication and Division

Students usually begin working with multiplication and division algorithms in about Grade 4, after they become more proficient with the multiplication facts. For most multiplication and division algorithms, students must

- know their multiplication and division facts
- know how to multiply and divide with multiples of 10, 100, and 1000
- know how to add and subtract
- understand the basic principles underlying the place value system (see *Numeration Principles* on page 199)
- understand the basic multiplication and division principles, as many algorithms are generally built on those principles (see *Multiplication and Division Principles* on page 174)

Alternative and Invented Algorithms

There are many good reasons why students should be exposed to multiple algorithms for multiplication and division and be allowed to invent their own algorithms (see *Alternative Algorithms* on page 223).

Find the product of 36 × 14. ___509___

Explain the steps you followed to multiply.

I went 40 x 15 = 600 then subtracted 4 groups. of 15 and then subtracted 36 and got 504

Student Response

This nontraditional approach by a student reveals considerable number sense.

ACTIVITY 11.12

Students enjoy "broken calculator key" activities. For example, they might be asked to come up with a way to multiply 7 × 59 if the 9 key on the calculator is not working. This requires students to use their number sense.

Critical Thinking

Alternative Multiplication Algorithms For the "traditional" algorithm (Algorithm 1) and many others, it is appropriate to initially model the algorithm with manipulatives. Normally, a written record is not necessary in the early stages of algorithm use, but might be useful later on, with each step of the algorithm matching a physical action with the manipulatives. No matter what algorithm is used, it is important that students understand and be able to explain why they do what they do.

A number of the algorithms that follow translate well into mental algorithms and will be noted as they are described. Students should be manipulating the models, rather than watching the teacher do it.

Algorithm 1 The "traditional" multiplication algorithm is built on the principle that you can multiply in parts, the distributive property, introduced in Chapter 8 on page 176. To multiply 5 × 423, the number 423 is broken up into 400 + 20 + 3, and each part is multiplied by 5. In the version of the "traditional" algorithm modelled on the next page, the parts are calculated starting with the smaller values.

Step 1 Model 5 groups of 4 hundreds, 2 tens, and 3 ones. (Note that a place value mat is optional.)

$$\begin{array}{r} 423 \\ \times\, 5 \\ \hline \end{array}$$

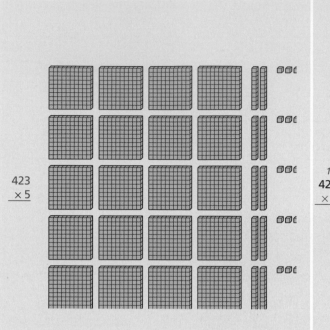

Step 2 Combine the ones. Trade 10 ones for 1 ten. Record the ones that are left.

$$\begin{array}{r} ^1 \\ 423 \\ \times\, 5 \\ \hline 5 \end{array}$$

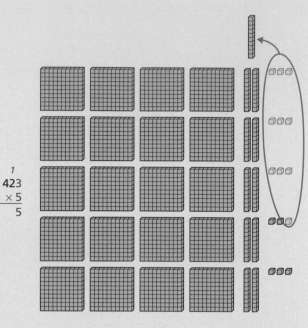

Step 3 Combine the tens. Trade 10 tens for 1 hundred. Record the tens that are left.

Step 4 Record the hundreds.

$$\begin{array}{r} ^{11} \\ 423 \\ \times\, 5 \\ \hline 15 \end{array}$$

$$\begin{array}{r} ^{11} \\ 423 \\ \times\, 5 \\ \hline 2115 \end{array}$$

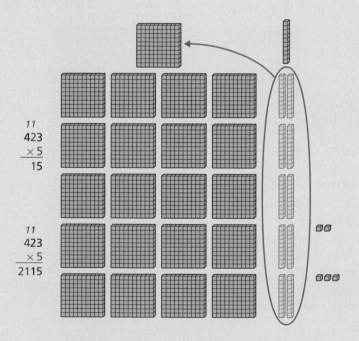

Step 5 Check the answer.

5 × 423 is a bit more than 5 × 4 hundreds = 20 hundreds, or 2000, so 5 × 423 = 2115 makes sense.

Algorithm 2 This algorithm is sometimes called the partial product algorithm because all partial products are recorded, and then they are added up at the end (as opposed to Algorithm 1, for which partial products are not recorded because students regroup as they go). The multiplying can be done beginning with either the greater values (Algorithm 2A) or the lower values (Algorithm 2B).

ALGORITHM 2A	ALGORITHM 2B
423	423
× 5	× 5
2000 (5 × 400)	15 (5 × 3)
100 (5 × 20)	100 (5 × 20)
+ 15 (5 × 3)	+ 2000 (5 × 400)
2115 (Add the partial products.)	2115 (Add the partial products.)

Algorithm 2 for 5 × 423 can be modelled using base ten blocks beginning with 5 groups of blocks, each with 4 hundred blocks, 2 ten blocks, and 3 one blocks (as modelled in Step 1 of Algorithm 1):

- For Algorithm 2A, the next step is to combine first the hundred blocks, then the ten blocks, and finally the one blocks (forming the three partial products in the recorded algorithm). Then, the last step is any final regrouping.
- For Algorithm 2B, the next step is to combine first the one blocks, then the ten blocks, and finally the hundred blocks (forming the three partial products). Then, the last step is any final regrouping.

Algorithm 2 can also be modelled using what is called an area model. This model is based on the area meaning of multiplication; that is, the area of a rectangle is the product of its length and width. Below is a pictorial model of the multiplication.

ACTIVITY 11.13

Ask students to determine which digits should replace each letter. The same digit is used each time the letter appears.

A × BCB = DAEB

Building Number Sense

A PICTORIAL AREA MODEL FOR 5 × 423

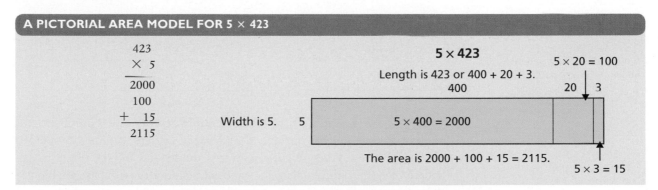

423
× 5
2000
100
+ 15
2115

5 × 423

Length is 423 or 400 + 20 + 3.
400

Width is 5.   5   5 × 400 = 2000

5 × 20 = 100
20 3

The area is 2000 + 100 + 15 = 2115.

5 × 3 = 15

Explain how to use mental math to multiply 3 × 35.

> I would take the 5 off of 35 to make it 30. So I would multiply 30 by 3 and get 90. Then I would take the 5 multiply that by 3 and get 15. Then I would add 90 and 15 to get 105.

Student Response

This student has described a mental math strategy based on Algorithm 2 (the partial product algorithm).

Algorithms for Multiplying with 5, 25, and 15

The algorithms below are useful, not to deliver to students, but to emerge from their consideration about how they might simplify multiplying by 5, 25, or 15.

ALGORITHM	EXAMPLE	
Multiplying by 5 To multiply a number by 5, you can multiply by 10 **mentally**, and then divide by 2, or vice versa because $5 = 10 \div 2$. This is based on the principle that you can halve one factor and double the other without changing the product, a variation of the associative property introduced in Chapter 8.	$34 \times 5 \rightarrow 34 \div 2 = 17$ $ 17 \times 10 = 170$ $34 \times 5 \rightarrow 34 \times 10 = 340$ $ 340 \div 2 = 170$	(Divide by 2.) (Multiply by 10.) (Multiply by 10.) (Divide by 2.)
Multiplying by 25 To multiply a number by 25, you can multiply by 100 **mentally**, and then divide by 4, or vice versa because $25 = 100 \div 4$. This is based on the principle that you can take one fourth of one factor and quadruple the other without changing the product, another variation of the associative property. Many students will think of this as similar to finding the value of 480 quarters. Note that to divide by 4, it is often easier to divide by 2 twice.	$48 \times 25 \rightarrow 48 \times 100 = 4800$ $ 4800 \div 4 = 1200$ $48 \times 25 \rightarrow 48 \div 4 = 12$ $ 12 \times 100 = 1200$ $48 \times 25 \rightarrow 48 \times 100 = 4800$ $ 4800 \div 2 = 2400$ $ 2400 \div 2 = 1200$ $48 \times 25 \rightarrow 48 \div 2 = 24$ $ 24 \div 2 = 12$ $ 12 \times 100 = 1200$	(Multiply by 100.) (Divide by 4.) (Divide by 4.) (Multiply by 100.) (Multiply by 100.) (Divide by 2.) (Divide by 2 again.) (Divide by 2.) (Divide by 2 again.) (Multiply by 100.)
Multiplying by 15 To multiply a number by 15, you can multiply the number by 10 **mentally**, and then add on half of the product. The product is essentially found in parts, first by multiplying by 10, and then by 5.	$36 \times 15 = 36 \times 10 + 36 \times 5$ $ = 360 + \text{half of } 360$ $ = 360 + 180$ $ = 540$	

Student Response

Many children invent algorithms that are based on money concepts. This student may have calculated 5×4 dollars $= \$20$, then 5 quarters $= \$1.25$, and then added the partial products.

Explain how you would use mental math to solve this problem:

425×5

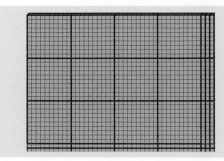

I would think in money. $4.25 \times 5 = $21.25 then take away the decimal and there is your answer.

Multiplying Two 2-Digit Numbers When multiplying two 2-digit numbers, students put together the various ideas already presented. For example, to multiply 32×43, they might use an area model and add the pieces to calculate the total. This duplicates what can be modelled with base ten blocks. It is important that students see that there are actually 32 rows of 43 as well as 43 columns of 32 when the models are arranged as shown.

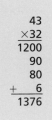

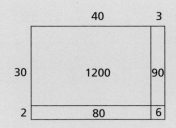

Alternative Division Algorithms Algorithms suitable for mental calculation will be noted as they are described.

Algorithm 1 This algorithm is built on the numeration principle that a number has many different "forms" and on the division principle that you can divide in parts. This traditional algorithm is best explained using the sharing meaning of division and a concrete base ten model, as shown below. Two alternative written forms of the algorithm are presented.

If 3 people shared 346 items, how many would each get?

$$346 \div 3$$

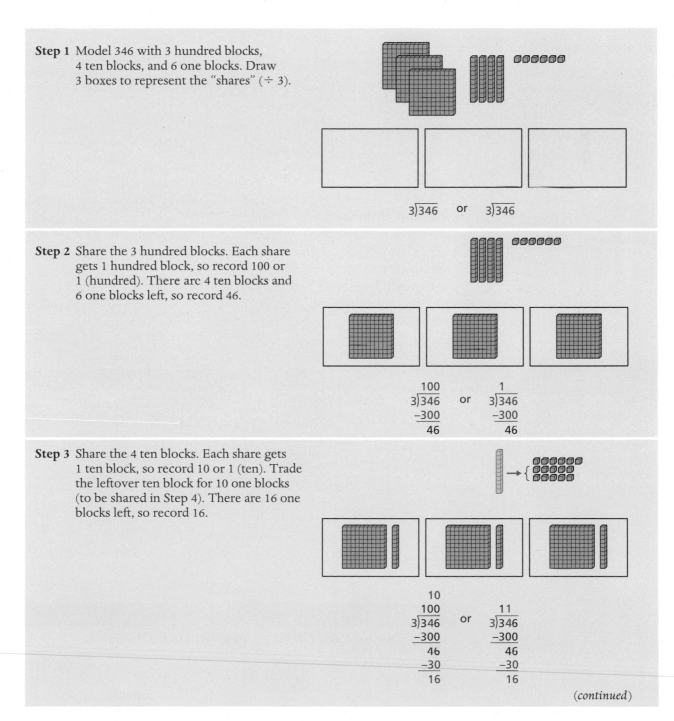

Step 1 Model 346 with 3 hundred blocks, 4 ten blocks, and 6 one blocks. Draw 3 boxes to represent the "shares" (÷ 3).

3)346   or   3)346

Step 2 Share the 3 hundred blocks. Each share gets 1 hundred block, so record 100 or 1 (hundred). There arc 4 ten blocks and 6 one blocks left, so record 46.

$$\begin{array}{r} 100 \\ 3{\overline{)346}} \\ -300 \\ \hline 46 \end{array} \quad \text{or} \quad \begin{array}{r} 1 \\ 3{\overline{)346}} \\ -300 \\ \hline 46 \end{array}$$

Step 3 Share the 4 ten blocks. Each share gets 1 ten block, so record 10 or 1 (ten). Trade the leftover ten block for 10 one blocks (to be shared in Step 4). There are 16 one blocks left, so record 16.

$$\begin{array}{r} 10 \\ 100 \\ 3{\overline{)346}} \\ -300 \\ \hline 46 \\ -30 \\ \hline 16 \end{array} \quad \text{or} \quad \begin{array}{r} 11 \\ 3{\overline{)346}} \\ -300 \\ \hline 46 \\ -30 \\ \hline 16 \end{array}$$

(*continued*)

Step 4 Share the 16 one blocks. Each share gets 5 one blocks, so record 5. One block is left over as a remainder.

R 1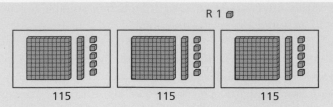

115   115   115

Each share is 115 and there is a remainder of 1.

```
    115
      5
     10
    100           115
  3)346    or   3)346
  −300          −300
    46            46
   −30           −30
    16            16
   −15           −15
     1             1
```

Step 5 Check the answer.

346 ÷ 3 should be a bit more than 300 ÷ 3 or 100, so 346 ÷ 3 = 115 R1 makes sense.

Algorithm 2 As with Algorithm 1, this algorithm is based on the principle that you can divide in parts by splitting the dividend into parts. This algorithm makes most sense to model using the equal group meaning of division, as shown. You count the total number of groups by building groups out of one part of the number at a time.

Algorithm 2B shows how you can underestimate the number of groups and still successfully complete the algorithm, although you might end up taking more steps to do it. (This is not the case with Algorithm 1.)

How many groups of 3 are in 346?

TEACHING **TIP**	**ALGORITHM 2A**	**ALGORITHM 2B**
Notice that the language for Algorithm 2 would have to change for a sharing situation. For example, it might begin with, "Can they each get 100? How many hundreds were used? What is left?"	``` 3)346 −300 100 (100 groups of 3) 46 −30 10 (10 groups of 3) 16 −15 5 (5 groups of 3) 1 115 ```	``` 3)346 −150 50 (50 groups of 3) 196 −60 20 (20 groups of 3) 136 −90 30 (30 groups of 3) 46 −30 10 (10 groups of 3) 16 −15 5 (5 groups of 3) 1 115 ```

ACTIVITY 11.14

To encourage invented algorithms, ask students how they might use a number line to figure out the number of 3-packs of juice that can be made with 426 juice boxes.

—————

Building Number Sense

Algorithm 3 This algorithm is based on breaking up the dividend into comfortable parts, that is, into parts, or numbers, that are easy to divide. The underlying principle is that you can divide in parts by splitting the dividend into parts. This makes sense if you visualize the sharing model of division for the first example shown below: to share 400 among 3 people, you could first share 300 among the 3 people, then 90 among the 3 people, and then the last 10 among the 3 people. (See *Appropriate Manipulatives* on page 249 for a base ten block model of this algorithm.)

$$\begin{array}{c} 133 \quad \text{R } 1 \\ \overline{100 \; + \; 30 \; + \; 3} \\ 3)\,\overline{400} \; = \; 3)\,\overline{300 \; + \; 90 \; + \; 10} \end{array} \qquad 400 \; \div \; 3 \; = \; 133 \; \text{R } 1$$

$$\begin{array}{c} 133 \quad \text{R } 1 \\ \overline{50 \; + \; 80 \; + \; 3} \\ 3)\,\overline{400} \; = \; 3)\,\overline{150 \; + \; 240 \; + \; 10} \end{array} \qquad 400 \; \div \; 3 \; = \; 133 \; \text{R } 1$$

$$\begin{array}{c} 133 \quad \text{R } 1 \\ \overline{130 \; + \; 3} \\ 3)\,\overline{400} \; = \; 3)\,\overline{390 \; + \; 10} \end{array} \qquad 400 \; \div \; 3 \; = \; 133 \; \text{R } 1$$

ACTIVITY 11.15

Have students choose any two numbers they wish to divide. The only condition is that the quotient needs to include 2 as one of its digits. Students then create a story to match their division.

Building Number Sense

ACTIVITY 11.16

Ask students to create and solve a story problem involving division that involves one number greater than 200 and another less than 10.

Critical Thinking

Algorithms for Dividing with 5 and 25

As with multiplication, these algorithms are not meant for telling; rather, students might be encouraged to find simpler ways to divide by 5 and 25 and these might emerge.

ALGORITHM	EXAMPLE
Dividing by 5 This algorithm is based on the principle that to divide two numbers, you can multiply both numbers by the same amount, without changing the quotient. To divide by 5, you can multiply both numbers by 2, in order to change the divisor to 10, which is easy to divide mentally. The explanation of this strategy is in Chapter 8, on page 176.	Multiply dividend and divisor by 2: $460 \div 5 = 920 \div 10$ $ = 92$
Dividing by 25 This algorithm is also based on the principle that to divide two numbers, you can multiply both numbers by the same amount, without changing the quotient. To divide by 25, you can multiply both numbers by 4 in order to change the divisor to 100, which is easy to divide by mentally. Depending on the numbers involved, it may be easier to multiply by 2 twice instead of multiplying by 4.	Multiply dividend and divisor by 4: $3800 \div 25 = 15\ 200 \div 100$ $ = 152$ Multiply dividend and divisor by 2, then by 2 again: $3800 \div 25 = 7600 \div 50$ $ = 15\ 200 \div 100$ $ = 152$

> ## ACTIVITY 11.17
>
> Students could solve a number of "personal" division problems. For example,
>
> - How many times would you have to write your first name to have more than 1000 letters?
> - How long would it take to walk 1000 paces if you know your time for walking 10 paces?
> - Determine the "average" distance you can throw a ball by averaging 5 throws.
>
> _____
>
> **Proportional Reasoning**

Treatment of Remainders When dividing whole numbers, there are sometimes leftover amounts. These form the "remainder." Students need to learn to make sense of the remainder conceptually as well as how to account for the remainder symbolically when using a division algorithm. Context is what determines how the remainder should be treated.

Interpreting Remainders

INTERPRETATION	EXAMPLE
Remainder as a Whole Number Suppose students are using a traditional algorithm to find the share size when 3 people share 34 marbles. Students will end up recording the remainder and reporting the answer as "11 Remainder 1," because each person would get 11 marbles and there would be 1 marble left over. Marbles cannot be divided up, so it makes sense that there would be a whole number remainder given the context.	34 marbles shared among 3 children: $34 \div 3 = 11 \, R \, 1$ It does not make sense to divide 1 marble further. So, each child gets 11 marbles, and there is 1 marble left over.
Remainder as a Fraction If the problem were the amount of time each person would have to work if 3 people shared a job that took 34 hours total, the quotient could be reported as $11\frac{1}{3}$ hours; the remainder is included in the quotient.	34 hours shared among 3 workers: $$\begin{array}{r} 11\frac{1}{3} \\ \hline 3{\overline{)34}} \\ -33 \\ \hline 1 \end{array}$$ $\frac{1}{3}$ of an hour makes sense; it is 20 minutes. So, each person works $11\frac{1}{3}$ hours.
Remainder as a Decimal If the problem were the amount of money each person would get if 3 people shared $34, each person would get $11 and there would be $1 left over. Because of the money context, you would continue to divide the $1 left to find that each person gets $11.33, but there is still 1 penny left over. Again, because of the context, the quotient is reported as a decimal, but only to the hundredths place because it is dollar notation. In this case, the leftover penny remains.	$34 shared among 3 people: $$\begin{array}{r} 11.33 \\ \hline 3{\overline{)34.00}} \\ -33 \\ \hline 10 \\ -9 \\ \hline 10 \\ -9 \\ \hline 1 \end{array}$$ It does not make sense to divide 1 cent further as there is no such thing as $11.333. So, each person gets $11.33 (and there is 1 cent left over).

Rounding a Remainder Up	34 children, at 3 per car: how many cars?
There are contexts when a quotient might be "rounded up," for example, to solve the following problem: How many cars are needed to transport 34 children if 3 children can go in each car?	$34 \div 3 = 11 \text{ R } 1$ An additional car is needed because of the remainder. It does not make sense to leave one child behind, and 11.33 or $11\frac{1}{3}$ cars does not make sense either. So, 12 cars will be needed to transport 34 children.
Ignoring the Remainder	$34 to spend on toys at $3 each:
There are contexts for which the remainder is ignored. For example, how many $3 toys can you buy with $34?	$34 \div 3 = 11 \text{ R } 1$ You can't use the left-over $1 to buy another toy, so the answer is 11 toys, and the remainder is ignored.

There are 80 Grade 5 students going on a field trip.

Each van can seat 6 children.

To find out how many vans were needed, John divided $80 \div 6$.

Why did he say that 14 vans were needed, even though $80 \div 6$ is not 14?

$$\begin{array}{r} 13 \\ 6\overline{)80} \\ -6 \\ \hline 2\,0 \\ -1\,8 \\ \hline 2 \end{array}$$

when you divide 6 by 80 it equals 13 and 2 are left so you need one more van which makes 14 vans.

Student Response

This student understands that you must consider context when discussing a remainder.

ACTIVITY 11.18

Students can play a game where they roll two decadice to create a dividend and one die to create a divisor. They score 1 point if the remainder is 0 and/or 2 points if the quotient is 20 or greater. Later students might use three or four dice to create greater dividends.

Building Number Sense

Communicating about Multiplying and Dividing

As with addition and subtraction, teachers need to be careful with their words and must encourage students to be clear and accurate, too.

- Language such as "3 into 2 doesn't go," for a division such as $3\overline{)214}$, is not appropriate, nor is it correct. In fact, it is 200 and not 2 that you are dividing by 3.
- For a multiplication sentence like 34×25, it is important to use the appropriate place value language and say "2 tens times 3 tens" instead of "2 times 3," when multiplying the tens.
- When multiplying or dividing by powers of 10, it is important to avoid talking about "adding or dropping zeros," but instead to use more meaningful language, such as 3 groups of 4 tens is 12 tens.

Explain the steps you would follow to find the answer to $\overset{64}{\underset{}{32}} \times \overset{3}{6} = 192$

first half and double then times 60 x3 it equals 180. then 4 x3 it equals 12. add 12 + 180 it equals 192 and that is your answer.

Student Response

This explanation by a student shows that a combination of principles and strategies was used to multiply.

Use of Calculators

Although students might use calculators to solve problems where the computation itself is not the focus, if calculation is the focus it makes more sense to take these actions:

- Provide many situations where computations can be performed mentally, if desired.
- Provide some opportunities for students to perform calculations on paper, limiting the size of the numbers to what is appropriate for the student's grade level and encouraging students to vary strategies depending on the numbers being used and the student's preferences.

Common Errors and Misconceptions

Many of the common errors in performing multiplication and division algorithms stem from a lack of understanding of the underlying principles (numeration, multiplication, and division principles). If students continue to make these kinds of errors and do not seem to understand what they are doing wrong, they should be using concrete models to work through the algorithms while recording the written algorithms.

Multiplication and Division Algorithms: Common Errors, Misconceptions, and Strategies

COMMON ERROR OR MISCONCEPTION	SUGGESTED STRATEGY
Multiplying by the Incorrect Amount Students do not multiply by the correct amount when multiplying by a 2-digit number. For instance, as in the example below, a student might multiply the 3 in 34 as a 3 and not as 30. $\begin{array}{rl} 28 & \\ \times\,34 & \\ \hline 60 & (3 \times 20) \\ 24 & (3 \times 8) \\ 80 & (4 \times 20) \\ +\,32 & (4 \times 8) \\ \hline 196 & \end{array}$ instead of $\begin{array}{rl} 28 & \\ \times\,34 & \\ \hline 600 & (30 \times 20) \\ 240 & (30 \times 8) \\ 80 & (4 \times 20) \\ +\,32 & (4 \times 8) \\ \hline 952 & \end{array}$	Estimating will help here. For example, $30 \times 30 = 900$, and 196 is a long way from 900, so the student should be able to catch his or her error. Another strategy is to have students model the calculation with base ten blocks using an area model (see the base ten block area model for Algorithm 2 on page 241). Sometimes this sort of error is a result of teaching that focuses too much on the digits of the number, rather than on the value of the number. Rather than saying or having students say, "Multiply the 3 by the 8, and then the 3 by the 2," instead use "Multiply the 30 by the 8, and then the 30 by the 20."
Internal Zeros Students ignore internal zeros in a number; for example, $\begin{array}{r} 302 \\ \times\,4 \\ \hline 128 \end{array}$ instead of $\begin{array}{r} 302 \\ \times\,4 \\ \hline 1208 \end{array}$	By encouraging students to estimate, this sort of mistake is likely to be caught. For example, 4×302 is just a bit more than $4 \times 300 = 1200$. So, an incorrect answer like 128 should indicate an error.
Aligning Partial Product Digits Students do not align the digits on the partial products as they record them (see Algorithm 2 on page 241), resulting in an error when they add the partial products.	Students can use grid paper or lined paper turned sideways (see *Common Errors and Misconceptions* for addition and subtraction algorithms on page 232).

Including Incorrect Regrouped Values

Students use a regrouped value from a partial calculation in the wrong subsequent calculation. In the example below, the regrouping that resulted from multiplying 4 by 8 (3 tens) was used when multiplying the 30 by 20.

$$
\begin{array}{r}
{}^{3} \\
28 \\
\times\ 34 \\
\hline
112 \\
+\ 940 \\
\hline
1052
\end{array}
\qquad \text{instead of} \qquad
\begin{array}{r}
{}^{2} \\
{}^{3\!/} \\
28 \\
\times\ 34 \\
\hline
112 \\
+\ 840 \\
\hline
952
\end{array}
$$

Estimating may or may not be helpful, depending on how close the actual and incorrect products are.

Students who use a partial product method (Algorithm 2 for multiplication) are less likely to make this error. This algorithm could also be modelled using an area model and base ten blocks (see the base ten block area model for Algorithm 2 on page 241).

$$
\begin{array}{r}
28 \\
\times\ 34 \\
\hline
32 \\
80 \\
240 \\
+\ 600 \\
\hline
952
\end{array}
$$

Forgetting Remainders and Regrouping

Students forget required regrouping or remainders when dividing; for example:

Divide 21 by 4 to get 5 (forgetting the 1).

Then divide 5 by 4 to get 1 (forgetting the remainder).

$$
\begin{array}{r}
51 \\
4\overline{)215}
\end{array}
\qquad \text{instead of} \qquad
\begin{array}{r}
53\ \text{R}\ 3 \\
4\overline{)215}
\end{array}
$$

Estimating will not reveal the error, since $215 \div 4$ is about the same as the most likely estimate, which is $200 \div 4 = 50$. But, if students multiply $4 \times 51 = 204$ to check, they will see that the result is not 215.

Understanding Principles of Multiplication

Students confuse some of the principles of addition with those of multiplication. Multiplication is different from addition in that, in multiplication, the digit in a particular place value in one number is combined with all of the digits in the other number, not just with the digit in the same place value. Many students get confused and end up making errors like those shown below.

$$
\begin{array}{r}
{}^{1} \\
412 \\
\times 8 \\
\hline
6 \\
\\
36 \\
\times 25 \\
\hline
30
\end{array}
\quad\longrightarrow\quad
\begin{array}{r}
{}^{1} \\
412 \\
\times 8 \\
\hline
426 \\
\\
36 \\
\times 25 \\
\hline
630
\end{array}
\quad
\begin{array}{l}
(41 + 1 = 42) \\
\\
\\
(2 \times 3 = 6 \text{ and} \\
\ 5 \times 6 = 30)
\end{array}
$$

These students might benefit from the partial product algorithm (Algorithm 2):

$$
\begin{array}{r}
412 \\
\times\ 8 \\
\hline
3200 \\
80 \\
+\ 16 \\
\hline
3296
\end{array}
$$

They could also sketch an area model to represent the problem (see the pictorial area model for Algorithm 2 on page 241).

Internal Zeros

Students ignore internal zeros when dividing; for example,

$$
\begin{array}{r}
21 \\
3\overline{)6003}
\end{array}
\qquad \text{instead of} \qquad
\begin{array}{r}
 \\
3\overline{)6003}
\end{array}
$$

Estimation or multiplication would reveal this error:

$3 \times 20 = 60$ or $3 \times 21 = 63$

Both 60 and 63 are considerably less than 6003.

Appropriate Manipulatives

Any of the algorithms described on the previous pages can and should be modelled with manipulatives initially so that students understand the procedure and why it works. Students might continue to use the manipulative language even when they are no longer using the manipulatives.

Multiplication and Division Algorithms: Examples of Manipulatives

BASE TEN MATERIALS

All of the algorithms shown on the previous pages can be modelled using base ten materials. (See the discussion about base ten blocks under *Appropriate Manipulatives* for working with larger whole numbers on page 207.)

This model shows Algorithm 3 for division on page 245 using base ten blocks.

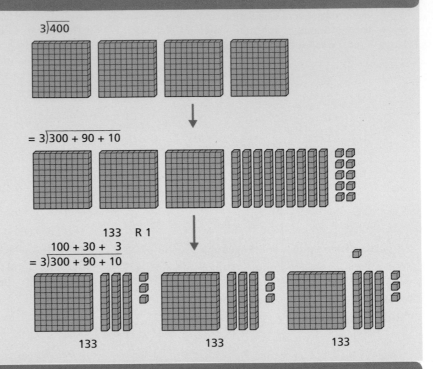

PLAY MONEY

Play money, as a substitute for base ten materials, is particularly useful for students who have internalized place value money concepts. (See the discussion about play money on page 234, under *Appropriate Manipulatives* for addition and subtraction algorithms.) This model shows Step 1 of Algorithm 1 for division on page 243, using coins instead of blocks.

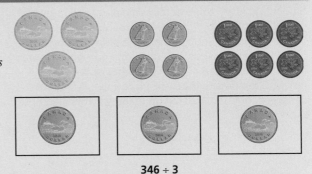

$$346 \div 3$$

PLACE VALUE MATS

Place value mats can be used with base ten materials or money for modelling multiplication algorithms, but they are optional. This model shows Step 1 of Algorithm 1 for multiplication, shown on page 240, using coins instead of blocks on a place value mat.

$$\begin{array}{r} 423 \\ \times 5 \end{array}$$

Hundreds	Tens	Ones

Appropriate Children's Books

Greater Estimations (Goldstone, 2008).

This book encourages students to estimate larger amounts, for example, the number of kernels in a giant tub of movie popcorn or the number of leaves on a pictured tree. These calculations involve both estimation and proportional reasoning, generally relying on the use of multiplication.

The Lion's Share (McElligott, 2009).

This book relates fractions and multiplication by 2. One of the focuses is on how much "twice as many" is. Students get to explore what turn out to be the powers of 2 (4, 8, 16, etc.) in the course of considering how many cakes are baked for the king.

The Rajah's Rice: A Mathematical Folktale from India (Barry, 1994).

This version of the ancient Indian folktale, which can be found under many titles, allows students to explore multiplicative growth as compared to additive growth. Students learn that, eventually, you gain a lot more if you start with less and let it keep doubling than if you start with more and just add a fixed amount repeatedly.

Ten Times Better (Michelson and Baskin, 2000).

This book focuses on multiplying by 10 by using the rate meaning of multiplication, for example, "I'm ten times wetter." The book educates the reader, through watercolour illustrations and text, about various interesting animals. The book also provides some problems for students to explore and lots of visual representations for comparing numbers to 10 times as many, for example, 3 to 30.

Appropriate Digital Resources

See the MindTap site for a selection of appropriate digital resources.

Assessing Student Understanding

- Although students may meet many algorithms, it is not necessary that they use all of them. The idea is to use the one or ones that makes the most sense to them.

- Students should sometimes show their understanding by performing the algorithm with manipulatives and not only using pencil-and-paper approaches. They might also explain their thinking verbally.

- Observe whether students use mental algorithms when appropriate. This provides insight into their number sense.

- Ask estimating questions frequently. For example, ask how they know that $356 - 296$ has to be less than 100.

- The following three student samples show three different responses to the question "Why does it make sense that $10 \times 50 = 500$?" Compare the responses. Would you assess them as equal in quality? Explain.

Student Response 1

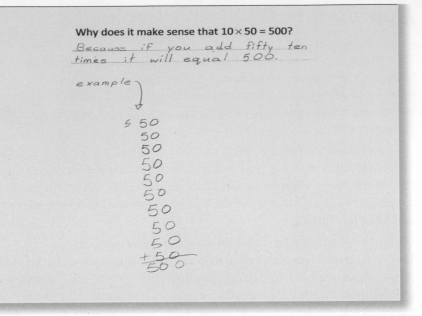

Why does it make sense that 10 × 50 = 500?

Because if you add fifty ten times it will equal 500.

example

```
5 50
  50
  50
  50
  50
  50
  50
  50
  50
+ 50
─────
 500
```

Student Response 2

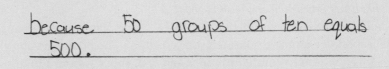

because 50 groups of ten equals 500.

Student Response 3

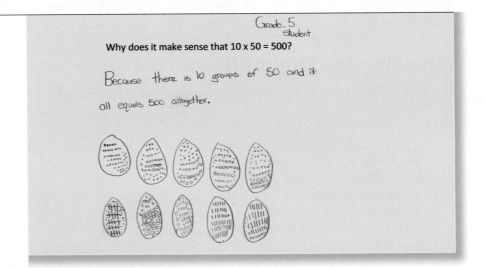

Grade 5
student

Why does it make sense that 10 × 50 = 500?

Because there is 10 groups of 50 and it all equals 500 altogether.

Applying What You've Learned

1. What was your solution to the chapter problem? Were you able to explain why your "rule" worked?

2. Select one of the children's literature suggestions offered. Read the book. Describe how you would follow up its reading to engage students in a valuable mathematical task.

3. Many people argue that base ten blocks are an essential manipulative to explain the algorithms for the four operations. Do you agree or not? Explain.

4. Some parents are concerned when they see a child coming home performing a calculation differently from what the parent knows. How would you handle a complaint about this?

5. To calculate $5002 - 3189$, a teacher suggested changing the question to $4999 - 3189$, and then adding 3 to the answer.

    a) Why might she do this?

    b) Do you think it is a good idea to make that suggestion?

6. Select a current elementary school text. Select a lesson about subtracting or adding multi-digit numbers that you think is particularly well constructed. Explain why you think it is a good lesson.

7. You want to teach students how to approach a 2-digit by 2-digit multiplication problem. How would you introduce the lesson and how would you summarize it?

8. Choose one of the division algorithms. What prerequisite skills would a student need to successfully perform that algorithm? How would you find out if they had those skills?

9. Would your main goal in developing computational algorithms be to foster skill with the paper-and-pencil algorithm, with estimating, or with mental algorithms? Explain your thinking.

10. If you had to assess what your Grade 4 students knew about adding 3-digit and 4-digit numbers and you could only ask three questions, what would they be? Why?

Interact with a K–8 Student:

11. Work with a student who knows how to subtract multi-digit numbers. Ask the student to explain to you how he or she would solve, for example, $91 - 43$, or $901 - 478$.

    a) What kinds of errors, if any, did you observe? Did they surprise you?

    b) If the student did not explain his or her actions, choose one of the steps performed and ask why it was done. See if the student simply repeats rules or if he or she explains why the action makes sense.

Interact with a K–8 Teacher:

12. Talk with a Grade 3 to 7 teacher about whether she or he encourages students to use alternate algorithms, or even invent their own, and why she or he holds that point of view.

Selected References

Baek, J.M. (**2005**). Research, reflection, practice: Children's mathematical understandings and invented strategies for multidigit multiplication. *Teaching Children Mathematics, 12*, 242–247.

Barry, D. (**1994**). *The rajah's rice.* New York: W. H. Freeman and Co.

Bass, H. (**2003**). Computational fluency, algorithms and mathematical proficiency: One mathematician's perspective. *Teaching Children Mathematics, 9*, 322–327.

Bobis, J. (**2007**). The empty number line: A useful tool or just another procedure? *Teaching Children Mathematics, 13*, 410–413.

Flowers, J., Kline, K., and Rubenstein, R.N. (**2003**). Developing teachers' computational fluency: Examples in subtraction. *Teaching Children Mathematics, 9,* 330–334.

Fuson, K.C. (**2003**). Toward computational fluency in multidigit multiplication and division. *Teaching Children Mathematics, 9,* 300–305.

Goldstone, B. (**2008**). **Greater estimations**. New York: Henry Holt and Company, LLC.

Gregg, J., and Gregg, D.U. (**2007**). Interpreting the standard division algorithm in a "candy factory" context. *Teaching Children Mathematics, 14,* 25–31.

Hillen, A.F., and Watanabe, T. (2013). Mysterious subtraction. *Teaching Children Mathematics, 20*, 294–301.

Huinker, D., Freckman, J.L., and Steinmeyer, M.B. (2003). Subtraction strategies from children's thinking: Moving toward fluency with greater numbers. *Teaching Children Mathematics, 9*, 347–353.

Jacobs, V.R., and Philipp, R.A. (2004). Mathematical thinking: Helping prospective and practicing teachers focus. *Teaching Children Mathematics, 11*, 194–201.

Keiser, J.M. (2010). Shifting our computational focus. *Mathematics Teaching in the Middle School, 16*, 216–223.

Kinzer, C.J., and Stanford, T. (2013). The distributive property: The core of multiplication. *Teaching Children Mathematics, 20*, 302–309.

Lamberg, T., and Wiest, L.R. (2012). Conceptualizing division with remainders. Teaching Children Mathematics, 18, 426–433.

Matney, G.T., and Daugherty, B.N. (2013). Seeing spots and developing multiplicative sense making. Mathematics *Teaching in the Middle School, 19*, 148–155.

McElligott, M. (2009). *The lion's share.* New York: Walker and Company.

Michelson, R., and Baskin, L. (2000). *Ten times better.* Tarrytown, NY: Marshall Cavendish Children's Books.

Onslow, B., Adams, L., Edmunds, G., Waters, J., Chapple, N., Healey, B., and Eady, J. (2005). Are you in the zone? *Teaching Children Mathematics, 11*, 458–463.

Scharton, S. (2004). "I did it my way": Providing opportunities for students to create, explain and analyze computation procedures. *Teaching Children Mathematics, 10*, 278–283.

Sellers, P.A. (2010). The trouble with long division. *Teaching Children Mathematics, 16*, 516–520.

Star, J.R., Kenyon, M., Joiner, R.M., and Rittle-Johnson, B. (2010). Comparison helps students learn to be better estimators. *Teaching Children Mathematics, 16*, 557–563.

Taylor, A.R., Breck, S.E., and Aljets, C.M. (2004). What Nathan teaches us about transitional thinking. *Teaching Children Mathematics, 11*, 138–142.

Chapter 12

Fractions

IN A NUTSHELL

The main ideas in this chapter are listed below:

1. A fraction is a number. It might be used to represent part of a continuous measure, such as an area, a capacity, a length, a volume, a mass, or an interval of time, or it might represent part of a countable set of items.

   It can also represent a quotient of two integers, describe a comparison of two integers, or describe a scale factor used to shrink or stretch an amount or item.

2. When a fraction represents part of a measure, the fraction is not meaningful without knowing what the whole is.

3. Renaming fractions is often the key to comparing them or computing with them. Every fraction can be renamed in an infinite number of ways.

4. Operations with fractions have the same meanings as operations with whole numbers, even though the algorithms are different.

5. There are multiple models and/or procedures for computing with fractions, just as with whole numbers.

CHAPTER PROBLEM

What is the fraction between $\frac{2}{7}$ and $\frac{5}{12}$ with the lowest denominator possible?

Representing and Comparing Fractions

Fractions in the Child's World

A fraction is a number that can be located on a number line. A fraction might be used to describe part of a continuous measure such as area, length, volume, time, or mass, or part of a discrete set of objects.

A fraction might also be used to represent a division, and describe a ratio or describe the factor by which a measure is stretched or shrunk. (Some use the term "operator" to name this last meaning of a fraction. However, others believe that it is actually the process of multiplying that is the operator and that the fraction is the scale factor.)

It is important that students meet various representations of fractions early on, with different meanings and different types of wholes represented.

It is also important that they practise partitioning wholes of various types. Note that it is often easier to partition lengths or rectangular areas than circular areas, so rectangular models and length models are important to use in early fraction work.

The first fraction that students meet is usually $\frac{1}{2}$, but, ideally, written as "one half" rather than in symbolic form. This helps students think of one half as a single quantity rather than as the two different numbers they see in the symbolic representation. Generally, they work next with other unit fractions, such as $\frac{1}{4}$ and $\frac{1}{3}$, and then $\frac{1}{8}, \frac{1}{6}, \frac{1}{5}, \frac{1}{10}$, and others, initially written in words. Once students have a firm grasp of the commonly used unit fractions, they typically extend their work to other proper fractions, such as $\frac{2}{3}, \frac{3}{4}$, and $\frac{5}{8}$, again, initially written in words. In later grades, they meet improper fractions like $\frac{1}{3}$, and mixed numbers such as $1\frac{1}{3}$ and $2\frac{2}{3}$. Eventually, students work with fraction operations, but usually not until middle or junior high school. Critical skills for students to develop when working with fractions are partitioning (to divide wholes into equal parts) and iterating (to combine unit fractions to create other fractions).

ACTIVITY 12.1

Ask upper elementary or middle school/junior high students to draw, on paper or using a digital tool, as many different pictures as they can or create as many models as they can to show the fraction $\frac{2}{5}$. See what meanings of fractions they choose to model. By sharing pictures and models, the notions of multiple representations and multiple meanings are reinforced.

Building Number Sense

ACTIVITY 12.2

Show or have students create non-examples of fractions and explain why they are non-examples. They might explain their thinking using an app.

For example, why does each model not represent each fraction?

Is $\frac{1}{3}$ of the area red?

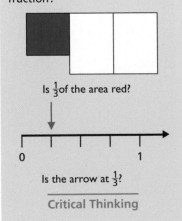

Is the arrow at $\frac{1}{3}$?

Critical Thinking

Meanings of Fractions

MEANING	EXAMPLE
A number	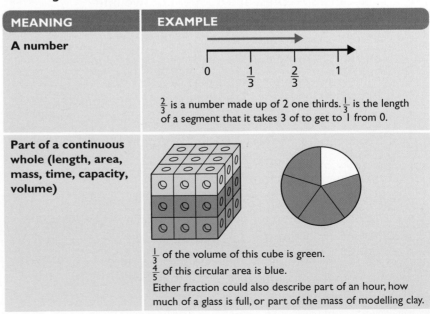$\frac{2}{3}$ is a number made up of 2 one thirds. $\frac{1}{3}$ is the length of a segment that it takes 3 of to get to 1 from 0.
Part of a continuous whole (length, area, mass, time, capacity, volume)	$\frac{1}{3}$ of the volume of this cube is green. $\frac{4}{5}$ of this circular area is blue. Either fraction could also describe part of an hour, how much of a glass is full, or part of the mass of modelling clay.

MEANING	EXAMPLE
Part of a whole set	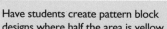 $\frac{3}{5}$ of the group of counters are red.
Division	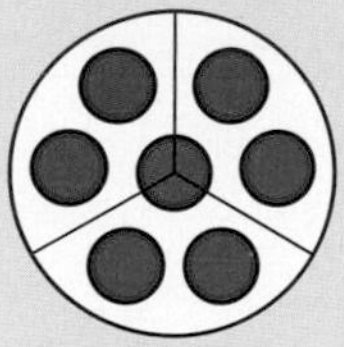 If you divide 7 counters among the three equal parts of this circle, there are $2\frac{1}{3}$ counters in each part. $7 : 3 = 2\frac{1}{3}$
Comparison/ratio	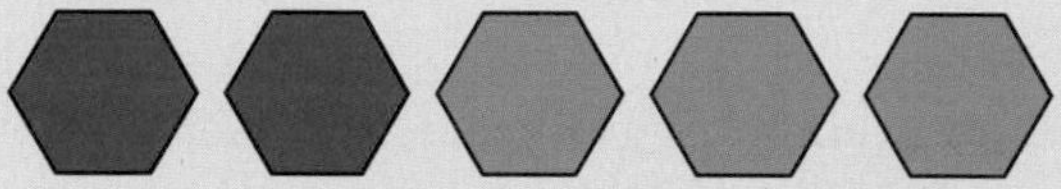 $\frac{2}{5}$ tells the part of the whole set of hexagons that is red. $\frac{2}{3}$ describes a comparison between the number of red hexagons and the number of blue ones (there are $\frac{2}{3}$ as many red hexagons as blue ones).
Stretch (shrink) factor	 $\frac{3}{4}$ describes the scale factor that shrank the original length of the line to its new reduced length.

How the Fraction Meanings Are Equivalent

Because fractions have different meanings, at some point, students will have to put these meanings together and see that they are all equivalent. Some of the methods teachers can use to help students bring some of these meanings together are shown below.

How Is a Fraction of a Set Like a Fraction of a Region?

EXAMPLE 1

Here is a model that shows the relationship between a fraction of a set and a fraction of a region:

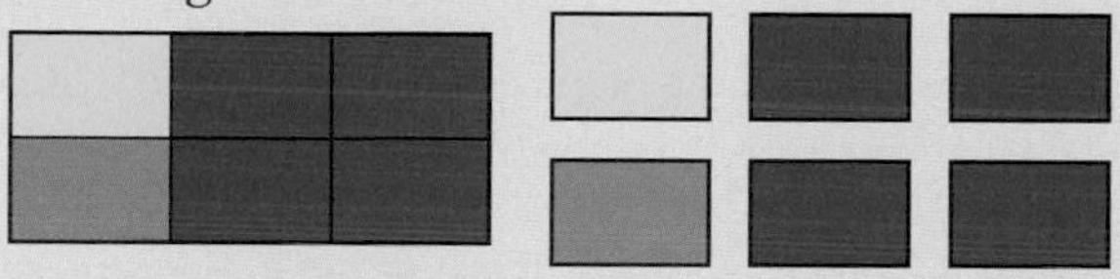

$\frac{1}{6}$ of the area of the rectangular region is yellow; $\frac{1}{6}$ of the set of rectangles is yellow.

EXAMPLE 2

Here is another model that shows the relationship between a fraction of a set and a fraction of a region:

- To show $\frac{1}{3}$ of a region, divide a rectangle into 3 equal parts and colour 1 part blue.
- To show $\frac{1}{3}$ of a set, or group, divide a group of 15 counters into 3 equal parts and consider 1 part.

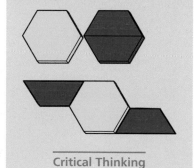

ACTIVITY 12.3

Have students create pattern block designs where half the area is yellow.

Encourage students to realize that the shapes do not need to display symmetry; many young students think, for example, that the area of the first design is half yellow, but that the bottom design is not.

Critical Thinking

Be careful of the language used to describe or name fractions. "Two thirds," emphasizing that there are 2 one thirds, is more meaningful than "two over three," which suggests that there are two separate numbers, not one number that suggests a relationship between two numbers. Note that you might say "two out of three" in some circumstances, for example, to describe a part of a whole (set), but using this phrasing indiscriminately might overemphasize the part of whole meaning of a fraction to a student.

The relationship between the two meanings becomes more apparent when you combine them in the same model as shown below.

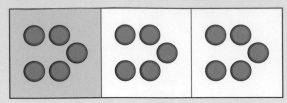

$\frac{1}{3}$ of the area of the rectangle is blue; $\frac{1}{3}$ of 15 counters is 5.

How Is a Fraction of a Region the Same as Division?

Division is about sharing. To show $\frac{1}{3}$, you take 1 whole and "share" it into 3 parts; thus, the relationship between $1 \div 3$ and $\frac{1}{3}$ is easy to see. But the question is how this generalizes to other fractions, particularly non-unit fractions such as $\frac{2}{3}$. The following model uses the context of sharing 2 rectangular cakes among 3 people ($2 \div 3$) to show why $\frac{2}{3}$ is the same as $2 \div 3$.

FRACTIONS AND DIVISION

$\frac{2}{3}$ is the same as $2 \div 3$, or 2 shared 3 ways.

Each cake can be divided into 3 thirds. Each of the 3 people sharing gets 1 third from each cake —either 2 blue, 2 white, or 2 red pieces—which is equivalent to 2 thirds of one cake.

ACTIVITY **12.4**

Display circle graphs like this one to students. Ask questions related to fractions about them. For example,

• *About what fraction of the school population is in each grade? How do you know?*

• *What is the probability that a student chosen at random is a Grade 1 student?*

• *How might the graph change if about $\frac{1}{4}$ of the students were in kindergarten?*

Students in K to Grade 3

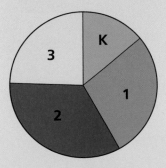

Spatial Reasoning

Fraction Definitions and Principles

Some of the important definitions and principles that students must learn about fractions are listed below.

SOME FRACTION DEFINITIONS

$$3 \rightarrow \text{numerator}$$
$$4 \rightarrow \text{denominator}$$

• the denominator tells how many equal parts there are in a line segment from 0 to 1, or how many equal parts a whole measure is partitioned into, or how many equal parts there are in a whole set, or what to divide by

• the numerator tells how many of the equal parts in the whole measure (length, area, mass, time, volume, set, etc.) are being described, or what amount is being divided

• a unit fraction has a numerator of 1, as in $\frac{1}{3}$

• a proper fraction, such as $\frac{4}{5}$, is less than 1

• an improper fraction, such as $\frac{7}{4}$, has a numerator equal to or greater than the denominator

• a mixed number, such as $5\frac{7}{8}$, has a whole number and a proper fraction part

FRACTION PRINCIPLES

1. When describing a fraction as part of a whole, the attribute that is being considered should be indicated.

2. You have to know what a whole is to say what the part represents.

3. The equal parts into which a whole is divided are equal with respect to the relevant attribute, but do not have to be identical. For parts of a set, this means that the members of the set do not have to be the same area or volume.

4. Fraction parts do not have to be adjacent.

5. If the numerator and denominator of a fraction are equal, the fraction represents one whole, or 1. Therefore, all whole numbers can be represented as fractions.

6. Fractions have more than one name.

7. Fractions with numerators greater than their denominators are greater than 1.

Principle 1: When describing a fraction as part of a whole, the attribute that is being considered should be indicated.

When looking at a partially filled glass of water, students should know whether the fraction they are using to describe how full the glass is describes the fraction of the height of the glass or the fraction of the capacity; these might be different.

When looking at a design made up of one yellow and two red pattern blocks, the yellow is $\frac{1}{2}$ only if considering area; it is $\frac{1}{3}$ in terms of number of blocks.

HEIGHT VS. CAPACITY

The water might reach $\frac{1}{2}$ the height, but it's not $\frac{1}{2}$ the capacity of the tapered glass.

NUMBER VS. AREA

$\frac{1}{2}$ the area of the design is yellow, but $\frac{1}{3}$ of the set of blocks is yellow.

Principle 2: You have to know what the whole is to say what the part represents.

If, for example, we say the blue rectangle at the top of page 260 is $\frac{1}{4}$, it is only in relation to the first rectangle, on the left. If it were in relation to the second rectangle, on the right, the blue rectangle becomes $\frac{1}{6}$. In the example of the family below, the fraction used to describe the girl also depends on what is considered the whole.

TEACHING TIP

When we say $\frac{1}{2} > \frac{1}{4}$, we assume that the fractions are parts of the same whole or that they represent numbers, not parts of wholes.

FRACTIONS OF A REGION EXAMPLE

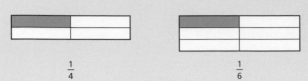

$\frac{1}{4}$ $\frac{1}{6}$

The blue rectangle is $\frac{1}{4}$ of the first rectangle, but it is $\frac{1}{6}$ of the second rectangle.

FRACTIONS OF A SET EXAMPLE

This girl is $\frac{1}{2}$ of the children in her family, but $\frac{1}{4}$ of the whole family.

Students might find it interesting to explore how fraction names change if the whole changes. For example, the blue rhombus is $\frac{2}{3}$ if the red trapezoid is the whole, and, therefore, called 1, but if the blue rhombus is the whole, or 1, the red trapezoid is $\frac{3}{2}$.

The blue block is $\frac{2}{3}$ of the red one; the red block is $\frac{3}{2}$ of the blue one.

Principle 3: The equal parts into which a whole is divided are equal with respect to the relevant attribute, but do not have to be identical. For parts of a set, this means that the members of the set do not have to be the same area or volume.

The rectangle below on the left is divided into four equal parts, each a fourth, but notice that not all of the fourths are congruent (same size and shape); for example, the yellow fourth is wide and short and the green fourth is narrower and taller. However, they are still equal parts because each fourth has the same area. On the right, below, you can see that the rectangle's yellow and green fourths are both made up of the same two congruent triangles. This shows that the fourths are equal in area.

ACTIVITY 12.5

Students can use fractions in probability experiments. For example, ask a student how many green cubes she or he is likely to draw in 10 tries, if a bag contains 4 green, 2 yellow, and 2 blue cubes, and to explain the prediction.

Proportional Reasoning

The green part and the yellow part of the rectangle may not be congruent, but they are equal in area (as each is made up of the same two congruent right triangles). That means that each is a fourth of the rectangle.

In the group of shapes below, $\frac{3}{5}$ are red because, even though each fifth is a different shape and size, the whole is considered the set of 5 shapes, so each shape is 1 fifth of the set of shapes.

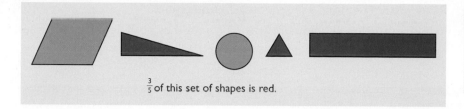

$\frac{3}{5}$ of this set of shapes is red.

> **TEACHING TIP**
>
> It is important to say "$\frac{3}{5}$ of the set of shapes are red," not just "$\frac{3}{5}$ are red," since it is not true that $\frac{3}{5}$ of the total area is red.

Principle 4: Fraction parts do not need to be adjacent.

In this four-coloured rectangle, the two sections that make up the yellow fourth are not adjacent; neither are the two sections that make up the blue fourth. It is important for teachers to attend to this. In some cases, teachers so rarely show fractions with non-adjacent parts that students are uncomfortable when they encounter them.

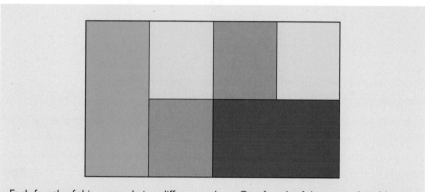

Each fourth of this rectangle is a different colour. One fourth of the rectangle is blue and one fourth is yellow, even though the sections that make up the blue fourth and the yellow fourth are not adjacent.

Principle 5: If the numerator and denominator of a fraction are equal, the fraction represents one whole, or 1. Therefore, all whole numbers can be represented as fractions.

This principle is true for $\frac{2}{2}, \frac{3}{3}, \frac{4}{4}, \frac{5}{5}, \frac{6}{6}$, etc.

FRACTION OF A REGION EXAMPLE

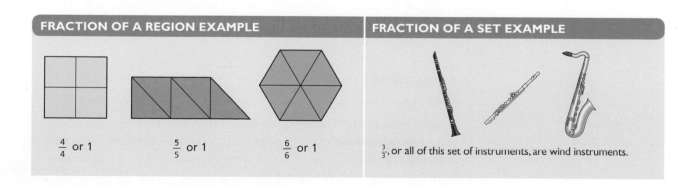

$\frac{4}{4}$ or 1 $\frac{5}{5}$ or 1 $\frac{6}{6}$ or 1

FRACTION OF A SET EXAMPLE

$\frac{3}{3}$, or all of this set of instruments, are wind instruments.

Principle 6: Fractions have more than one name.

In both examples, $\frac{1}{2}$ is another name for $\frac{2}{4}$ since they both describe the same location on a number line or the same part of the same whole (set).

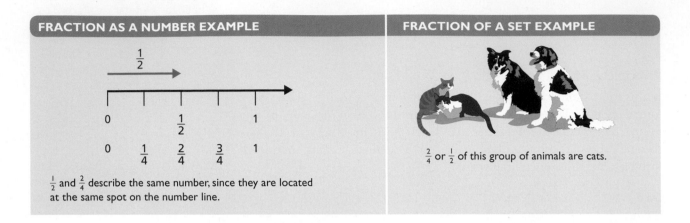

FRACTION AS A NUMBER EXAMPLE	FRACTION OF A SET EXAMPLE

$\frac{1}{2}$ and $\frac{2}{4}$ describe the same number, since they are located at the same spot on the number line.

$\frac{2}{4}$ or $\frac{1}{2}$ of this group of animals are cats.

Principle 7: Fractions with numerators greater than their denominators are greater than 1.

The red portion of the pair of circles below could be described as $\frac{7}{4}$, or 7 fourths, if one circle is considered the whole. Since it only takes 4 fourths to make a whole (a circle), 7 fourths must be greater than a whole, or 1. The 17 eggs in the two egg cartons below could be described as $\frac{17}{12}$, or 17 twelfths of a carton of eggs, if one carton is considered the whole. Since one carton is 12 twelfths, 17 twelfths must be greater than a whole, or 1. Fractions of this type are called improper fractions.

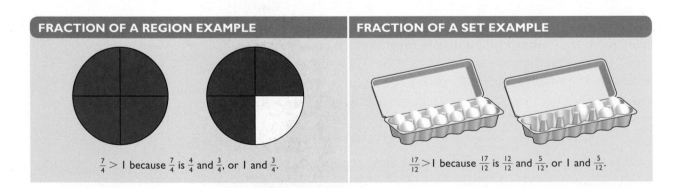

FRACTION OF A REGION EXAMPLE	FRACTION OF A SET EXAMPLE

$\frac{7}{4} > 1$ because $\frac{7}{4}$ is $\frac{4}{4}$ and $\frac{3}{4}$, or 1 and $\frac{3}{4}$.

$\frac{17}{12} > 1$ because $\frac{17}{12}$ is $\frac{12}{12}$ and $\frac{5}{12}$, or 1 and $\frac{5}{12}$.

Equivalent Fractions

As described above in Principle 6, fractions have more than one name.

Proper Fractions To determine an equivalent name for a proper fraction, you can subdivide the existing parts to create more equal-size parts, which symbolically has the effect of multiplying the numerator and denominator by the same amount. For example:

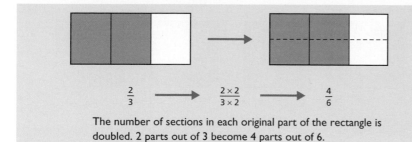

$$\frac{2}{3} \longrightarrow \frac{2 \times 2}{3 \times 2} \longrightarrow \frac{4}{6}$$

The number of sections in each original part of the rectangle is doubled. 2 parts out of 3 become 4 parts out of 6.

One way to accomplish this is to fold a piece of paper.

For example, if you start with a sheet of paper folded in half lengthwise, mark or shade one of the halves, and then fold the paper again in half widthwise, students will see the half becoming $\frac{2}{4}$.

To determine an equivalent name for a fraction, you can also combine parts, which symbolically has the same effect as dividing the numerator and denominator by the same amount. For example:

ACTIVITY 12.6

Students might consider equivalence in terms of musical notes. For example, a whole note is equivalent to 2 half notes, 4 quarter notes, 8 eighth notes, or 16 sixteenth notes. Using this idea, they might be asked to create measures of music with as many different combinations of notes as they can.

Creative Thinking

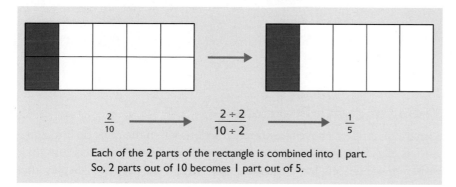

$$\frac{2}{10} \longrightarrow \frac{2 \div 2}{10 \div 2} \longrightarrow \frac{1}{5}$$

Each of the 2 parts of the rectangle is combined into 1 part. So, 2 parts out of 10 becomes 1 part out of 5.

Students should come to realize that fractions are only equivalent when the multiplicative relationships between the numerators and denominators are the same, which is a result of the suggested partitioning. For example, $\frac{2}{4} = \frac{4}{8}$, since both times the denominator is twice the numerator.

Mixed Numbers and Improper Fractions

One of the equivalences students need to learn about is the relationship between mixed numbers and equivalent improper fractions. For example, $\frac{15}{4} = 3\frac{3}{4}$ since 15 fourths makes 3 wholes (4 fourths + 4 fourths + 4 fourths) and 3 fourths. Symbolically, this has the effect of dividing 15 by 4 to determine the number of wholes. The remainder is the number of fourths in the fraction part of the mixed number. However, students should not rush into the procedure until the meaning is clear.

ACTIVITY 12.7

Older students can try to use all the digits from 1 to 9 to create a fraction equivalent to $\frac{1}{2}$. This sort of activity exercises students' number sense. For example, they must realize that the numerator must be 4 digits and the denominator 5 digits. They must also recognize that the rightmost digit of the denominator must be even, or the fraction could not be equivalent to $\frac{1}{2}$.

Building Number Sense

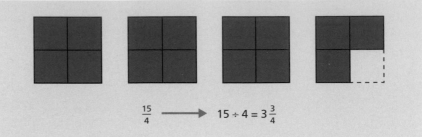

$$\frac{15}{4} \longrightarrow 15 \div 4 = 3\frac{3}{4}$$

Divide the 15 parts by 4 (because there are 4 parts per whole) to determine the number of wholes. The remainder becomes the fraction part of the mixed number.

Student Response

This student renamed the improper fraction as a mixed number in order to compare the fractions. This student also made a very common error in transposing the dividend and divisor when recording the division.

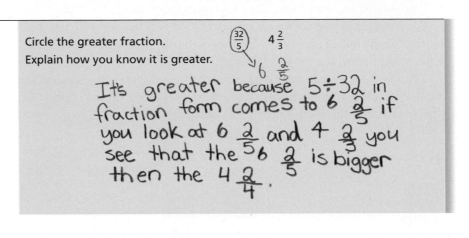

Circle the greater fraction.
Explain how you know it is greater.

It's greater because 5÷32 in fraction form comes to 6 2/5 if you look at 6 2/5 and 4 2/3 you see that the 6 2/5 is bigger then the 4 2/4.

Visualizing with Fractions

Sometimes students have to estimate fractions when the division into equal parts is either incomplete or not displayed, or when students create their own representations for a fraction. **Activities 12.8** and **12.9** display that type of situation.

Another useful skill for students is visualizing the whole when given the fraction. The task in **Activity 12.10** is an example of a task that forces students to "think the other way around," that is, instead of working from a known whole and finding the part, students must work from the known part to find the unknown whole.

ACTIVITY 12.9

Post pictures like these. Ask students to estimate what fraction of each whole is coloured. Pay attention to students' use of spatial visualization skills. For example, a student might look at the triangle and imagine three more small red triangles filling the white space. This would lead the student to estimate the red section as $\frac{1}{4}$.

Spatial Reasoning

ACTIVITY 12.8

Provide tangram sets. Tell students it costs 5¢ to make one small tangram triangle. Ask how much each other piece would cost to make.

Spatial Reasoning

Principles for Comparing Fractions

Some of the important principles that students must understand in order to compare fractions are listed below.

PRINCIPLES FOR COMPARING FRACTIONS

1. Fractions representing parts of wholes can be compared only if the whole is known in each case or assumed to be the number 1.

2. If two fractions have the same denominator, the one with the greater numerator is greater, for example, $\frac{4}{5} > \frac{3}{5}$.

3. If two fractions have the same numerator, the one with the greater denominator is less, for example, $\frac{3}{5} < \frac{3}{4}$.

4. Some fractions can be compared by relating them to benchmark numbers such as 0, 1, and $\frac{1}{2}$.

5. Fractions can be compared by renaming them with common denominators, or by renaming them with common numerators.

6. No matter what two different fractions are selected, there is a fraction in between. For example, $\frac{3}{6}$ is between $\frac{1}{3}$ and $\frac{2}{3}$.

Principle 1: Fractions representing parts of wholes can be compared only if the whole is known in each case or assumed to be the number 1.

ACTIVITY 12.10

Display a picture of a cube.

Tell students that this represents $\frac{1}{3}$ of a cake. The other $\frac{2}{3}$ has been eaten. Ask students:

• *What did the whole cake look like?*

• *Is only one shape possible?*

You might follow up by changing the dimensions of the original displayed shape (e.g., use a rectangular prism that is not a cube), or by changing the fraction that it represents.

Spatial Reasoning

SAME WHOLE	DIFFERENT WHOLES

SAME WHOLE

You can easily compare the two fractions shown below, $\frac{1}{3}$ and $\frac{1}{2}$, because they are $\frac{1}{3}$ and $\frac{1}{2}$ of the same whole.1

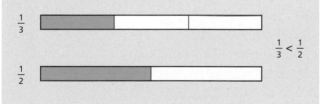

$\frac{1}{3} < \frac{1}{2}$

$\frac{1}{3}$ is less than $\frac{1}{2}$ of the same rectangle.

DIFFERENT WHOLES

Although the fraction $\frac{1}{4}$ is less than the fraction $\frac{1}{2}$, the green square representing $\frac{1}{4}$ of the first area is not less area than the green rectangle representing $\frac{1}{2}$ of the second area. This is because the wholes are different in each case.

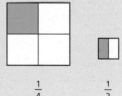

$\frac{1}{4} \qquad \frac{1}{2}$

$\frac{1}{4}$ and $\frac{1}{2}$ cannot be compared without considering the wholes.

Jeff says the pictures show that $\frac{2}{3}$ is greater than $\frac{3}{4}$.

Do you agree with Jeff? Explain your thinking.0

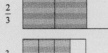

$\frac{2}{3}$

$\frac{3}{4}$

I disagree with Jeff because the pictures should be the same size to show the real answer.

Student Response

This student can tell from the model that $\frac{2}{3}$ and $\frac{3}{4}$ are not fractions of the same whole, and, therefore, cannot be compared as if they were.

Principle 2: If two fractions have the same denominator, the one with the greater numerator is greater.

If the fractions represent numbers on a number line, the jumps would all be the same size, but there would have been more jumps with a greater numerator, so the result is farther to the right, or greater.

If the fractions represent parts of a whole, then the wholes must be the same. In this case, the denominator tells the total number of equal parts the whole is divided into, and the numerator tells the number of parts accounted for. If the denominators of two fractions are the same, then the parts are the same. So, the fraction with the greater number of parts accounted for is the greater fraction.

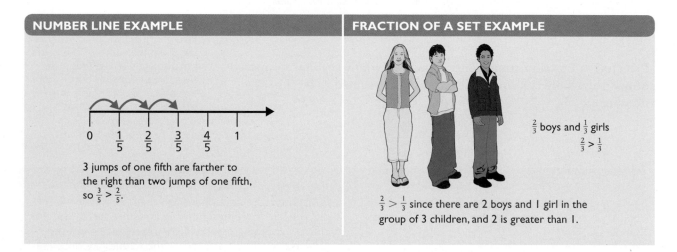

NUMBER LINE EXAMPLE

3 jumps of one fifth are farther to the right than two jumps of one fifth, so $\frac{3}{5} > \frac{2}{5}$.

FRACTION OF A SET EXAMPLE

$\frac{2}{3}$ boys and $\frac{1}{3}$ girls
$\frac{2}{3} > \frac{1}{3}$

$\frac{2}{3} > \frac{1}{3}$ since there are 2 boys and 1 girl in the group of 3 children, and 2 is greater than 1.

Student Response

This student understands why you can compare fractions with the same denominator by comparing their numerators.

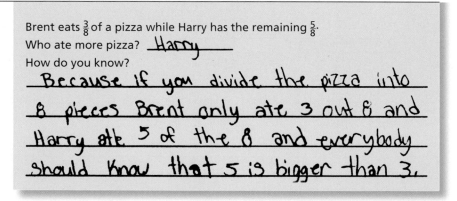

Brent eats $\frac{3}{8}$ of a pizza while Harry has the remaining $\frac{5}{8}$.
Who ate more pizza? __Harry__
How do you know?
Because if you divide the pizza into 8 pieces Brent only ate 3 out 8 and Harry ate 5 of the 8 and everybody should know that 5 is bigger than 3.

Principle 3: If two fractions have the same numerator, the one with the greater denominator is less.

If both fractions represent a division, then dividing an amount into more shares results in smaller shares, or a smaller fraction.

If the fractions represent parts of the same whole, the denominator tells the total number of equal parts that the whole is divided into, and the numerator tells the number of parts accounted for. If the numerators are the same, then the number of parts accounted for is the same. But, if the denominators are different, then the fraction with the greater denominator is less, because the greater the number of parts, the smaller the parts.

Many students assume $\frac{1}{3} > \frac{1}{2}$ because they are using whole number thinking. The fact that a greater denominator means a smaller fraction needs different thinking and careful attention.

FRACTION OF A REGION EXAMPLE	FRACTION AS DIVISION EXAMPLE

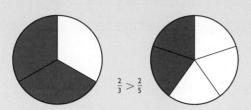

$\frac{2}{3} > \frac{2}{5}$

$\frac{2}{3} > \frac{2}{5}$ because 2 parts of a circle divided into 3 is greater than 2 parts of the same circle divided into 5.

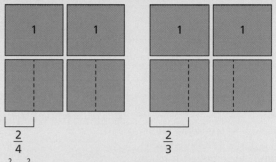

$\frac{2}{4}$

$\frac{2}{3}$

$\frac{2}{4} < \frac{2}{3}$ since dividing 2 wholes into 4 shares results in smaller share sizes than dividing 2 wholes into 3 shares.

Principle 4: Some fractions can be compared by relating them to benchmark numbers such as 0, 1, and $\frac{1}{2}$.

If one fraction is greater than $\frac{1}{2}$ (or 1) and the other is less, it is easy to compare them.

USING BENCHMARKS TO COMPARE FRACTIONS

Using $\frac{1}{2}$ to compare: $\frac{2}{5} < \frac{3}{4}$ since $\frac{2}{5} < \frac{1}{2}$ and $\frac{3}{4} > \frac{1}{2}$.

Using 1 to compare: $\frac{7}{3} > \frac{3}{4}$ since $\frac{7}{3} > 1$ and $\frac{3}{4} < 1$.

Principle 5: Fractions can be compared by renaming them with common denominators, or by renaming them with common numerators.

Here are two ways to compare $\frac{3}{8}$ and $\frac{4}{10}$. The first method is based on Principle 2, and the second method is based on Principle 3.

RENAMING WITH COMMON DENOMINATORS

Comparing $\frac{3}{8}$ and $\frac{4}{10}$: $\frac{3}{8} = \frac{30}{80}$ $\frac{4}{10} = \frac{32}{80}$

$\frac{30}{80} < \frac{32}{80}$

$\frac{3}{8} < \frac{4}{10}$

RENAMING WITH COMMON NUMERATORS

Comparing $\frac{3}{8}$ and $\frac{4}{10}$: $\frac{3}{8} = \frac{12}{32}$ $\frac{4}{10} = \frac{12}{30}$

$\frac{12}{32} < \frac{12}{30}$

$\frac{3}{8} < \frac{4}{10}$

The strategy of using common numerators to compare fractions (that is, comparing the denominators of fractions if the numerators are the same) is often overlooked. In fact, students will often rename fractions, for instance,

ACTIVITY 12.11

One tool students can use to compare fractions, whether with the same numerator or denominator or as they relate to 0, $\frac{1}{2}$, or 1, is a fraction tower (or fraction strips).

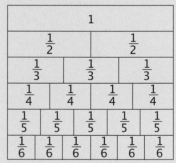

Students might be asked to describe 5 different fraction comparisons that the tower shows them.

Spatial Reasoning

$\frac{2}{3}$ and $\frac{2}{5}$ as $\frac{10}{15}$ and $\frac{6}{15}$, in order to compare them instead of simply comparing the denominators without doing any renaming at all.

Student Response

This student understands that because the denominator of 5 is less, it means the parts are larger, and so the two parts are more of the whole (Principle 3).

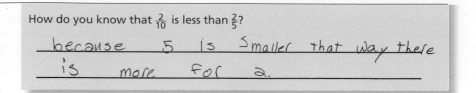

How do you know that $\frac{2}{10}$ is less than $\frac{2}{5}$?

because 5 is smaller that way there is more for 2.

TEACHING TIP

Students should be helped to see that one of the main differences between fractions and counting numbers is the fact that there are always in-between fractions, but there are not always in-between counting numbers. You might ask students whether there are fractions between $\frac{2}{5}$ and $\frac{3}{5}$. Many will realize that $\frac{1}{2}$ works.

Principle 6: No matter what two different fractions are selected, there is a fraction in between.

Between $\frac{3}{5}$ and $\frac{4}{5}$ are an infinite number of fractions. You can rename $\frac{3}{5}$ and $\frac{4}{5}$ with greater denominators to find those in-between fractions, as shown below.

$\frac{3}{5} = \frac{6}{10}$ and $\frac{4}{5} = \frac{8}{10}$, so $\frac{7}{10}$ is between.

$\frac{3}{5} = \frac{12}{20}$ and $\frac{4}{5} = \frac{16}{20}$, so $\frac{13}{20}$, $\frac{14}{20}$, and $\frac{15}{20}$ are between, etc.

Relating Fractions to Decimals

At some point, students will be ready to write a fraction as a decimal quantity. At the K–8 level, students begin by writing fractions like $\frac{3}{10}$ or $\frac{3}{100}$, with denominators as powers of ten, in decimal form. Then they write other fractions, with equivalents in this form, as decimals, for example, $\frac{1}{8} = \frac{125}{1000}$ as 0.125. But eventually, they learn to write any fraction as a decimal, using the division meaning for fractions. Since $\frac{2}{3}$ means $2 \div 3$, then the decimal for $\frac{2}{3}$ is calculated by dividing 2 by 3, usually using a calculator.

Common Errors and Misconceptions

Many of the common errors in fraction work stem from a lack of understanding of the underlying principles. If students continue to make these kinds of errors and do not seem to understand what they are doing wrong, they should be using concrete and pictorial models of the fractions.

Fractions: Common Errors, Misconceptions, and Strategies

COMMON ERROR OR MISCONCEPTION	STRATEGY
Understanding the Whole in Fractions Students do not understand the importance of the whole in describing a fraction. For example, in the situation below, 2 cakes are each divided into thirds. Even though there are 6 shares, $\frac{1}{3}$ still describes $\frac{1}{3}$ of one cake. Many students see 6 parts and call each part $\frac{1}{6}$. 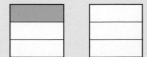	Students should be encouraged to circle or highlight the whole unit and use language to reinforce the whole. In this case, the green rectangle is $\frac{1}{3}$ of 1 cake. one → whole cake 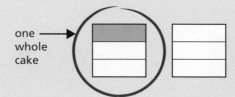

COMMON ERROR OR MISCONCEPTION	STRATEGY
Equal Parts of a Region or Measure Students do not pay attention to the need for all parts to be equal when talking about parts of a length, area, volume, mass, or time. (Note that this is not the case when talking about parts of a set.) For example, the blue part of the rectangle below is not $\frac{1}{3}$ of the area even though it is 1 of 3 parts. 	Ensure that students have many opportunities to work with incorrectly divided wholes in context. For the example shown here, you might relate the fraction to a real context, such as a cake divided into 3 pieces. Ask if students think that the recipients will each be happy with their "thirds."
Parts of Sets Can Be Different Students are confused by sets containing different items. For example, students might not recognize the circle below as $\frac{1}{3}$ of the set of shapes.  The circle is $\frac{1}{3}$ of the set of shapes.	Many students do not have enough experience working with parts of sets. This can be remedied by providing more of these opportunities. Using pattern blocks for both fractions of a set and region can help; for example, the green block is $\frac{1}{6}$ of the yellow block (fraction of a region) but $\frac{1}{4}$ of the set of 4 blocks below (fraction of a set).  The green block is $\frac{1}{4}$ of this set of blocks.
Increasing the Value of a Fraction Students have the misconception that a fraction always increases in value if the numerator and denominator are increased.	There are specific circumstances when this is true; for example, if both the numerator and denominator of a proper fraction increase by the same amount, the value of the fraction increases. It is only by using a counter-example that students will see that adding (different) amounts to the numerator and denominator does not always increase the value of the fraction. For example, $$\frac{5}{8} \rightarrow \frac{5+1}{8+2} = \frac{6}{10} \quad \frac{6}{10} < \frac{5}{8}$$
Fractions Can Be Greater Than 1 Students have the misconception that all fractions are less than 1.	Clearly, many fractions are greater than 1. There are many real-world examples of fractions greater than 1, such as $1\frac{1}{2}$ hours and $2\frac{1}{2}$ dozen cookies. Students need many opportunities to work with mixed numbers and improper fractions in a variety of contexts.
Modelling Improper Fractions on Number Lines Students have difficulty placing fractions on number lines when the fractions are greater than 1.	It might be helpful for students to count on a number line labelled with improper fractions only, and only later add the whole number equivalents. For example, 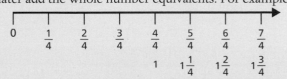 Later, students can think of an improper fraction as a mixed number, choose the segment in which to work, and then mentally translate what they would do in the segment from 0 to 1 to represent the fraction part of the mixed number.

Appropriate Manipulatives

Many appropriate manipulative materials are available for work with fractions. It is essential that all students work with at least some of these materials and not rely on pictures. Even older students should be encouraged to use physical representations of fractions.

Fractions: Examples of Manipulatives

FRACTION PIECES

Fraction pieces are shapes, whether plastic, paper, or some other material, that are pre-cut to show various fractions and are used to represent fractions of regions. Usually, the different fractions are different colours. The wholes upon which these fractions are based are not always the same shape. Often they are square, rectangular, or circular.

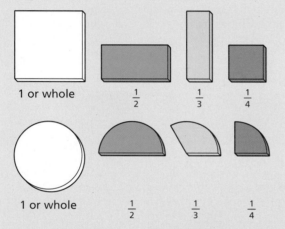

1 or whole $\frac{1}{2}$ $\frac{1}{3}$ $\frac{1}{4}$

1 or whole $\frac{1}{2}$ $\frac{1}{3}$ $\frac{1}{4}$

PATTERN BLOCKS

Pattern blocks provide another model for representing fractions of a region. Pattern blocks work particularly well for showing halves, thirds, and sixths if the yellow hexagon block is considered 1 or the whole.

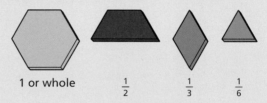

1 or whole $\frac{1}{2}$ $\frac{1}{3}$ $\frac{1}{6}$

Note that the fraction representations can change, depending on which block is considered the whole.

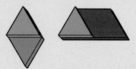

The green block is $\frac{1}{2}$ of the blue block.

The green block is $\frac{1}{3}$ of the red block.

SQUARE TILES

Square tiles come in different colours, and can be used to show many different fractions of a region. They can also be used to show fractions of a set.

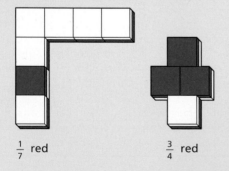

$\frac{1}{7}$ red $\frac{3}{4}$ red

EGG CARTONS

Egg cartons are useful for showing fractions with denominators that are factors of 12 (halves, thirds, fourths, sixths, and twelfths).

$\frac{13}{12}$, or $\frac{1}{4}$, of the carton is filled.

COUNTERS

Counters in a variety of colours and shapes can be used to show fractions of sets. Two-sided counters with a different colour on each side are also useful.

$\frac{3}{5}$ of the counters are white. $\frac{3}{5}$ of the counters are square.

GEOBOARDS AND SQUARE DOT OR GRID PAPER

Geoboards allow students to represent fractions as parts of regions in a variety of ways. Square dot paper or grid paper can be used to record what is shown on the geoboard or as a pictorial equivalent. One of the advantages of the geoboard is that more unusual shapes and fractions, such as $\frac{2}{7}$, can be shown.

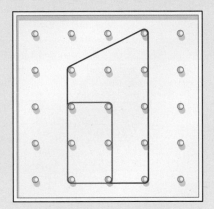

If the whole is 7 squares, 2 squares are $\frac{2}{7}$.

CUISENAIRE RODS

Cuisenaire rods are useful to show the concepts of fraction of a length and fraction as a ratio or comparison. As with pattern blocks, any rod can be considered the whole, so the fraction that each rod represents varies, depending on what is considered the whole, for example:

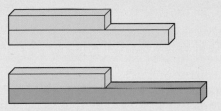

The light green rod is $\frac{3}{5}$ of the yellow rod but $\frac{1}{2}$ of the dark green rod.

The rods can also be used to show improper fractions and mixed numbers, for example:

The yellow rod is $\frac{5}{3}$, or $1\frac{2}{3}$ of the light green rod.

NUMBER LINES

Number lines are useful for comparing and ordering fractions. Students can place fractions at appropriate spots on a number line using the benchmarks $0, \frac{1}{2},$ and 1.

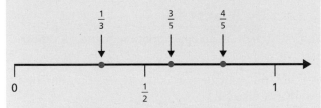

$\frac{4}{5}$ can be placed using its size relative to 0 $\left(\frac{0}{5}\right)$ and 1 $\left(\frac{5}{5}\right)$.

$\frac{1}{3}$ can be placed using its size relative to 0 and $\frac{1}{2}$.

$\frac{3}{5}$ can be placed using its size relative to $\frac{1}{2}$ and 1.

MONEY

Money provides a value model that is very effective for students who have internalized money concepts.

3 quarters is $\frac{3}{4}$ or $\frac{75}{100}$, of a dollar.

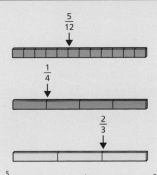

4 dimes is $\frac{4}{10}, \frac{40}{100},$ or $\frac{2}{5}$ of a dollar.

FRACTION BARS (OR STRIPS OR RECTANGLES)

Fraction bars are another length model for showing fractions of a measure. They can be made of plastic or paper and are sometimes called fraction strips or rectangles. The bars are all the same length, are pre-divided, and are sometimes colour-coordinated to show halves, thirds, fourths, fifths, sixths, eighths, tenths, and twelfths. These strips might be cut out of a fraction tower. If the tower is used on an interactive white board, the fraction strips can be superimposed.

$\frac{5}{12}$ is greater than $\frac{1}{4}$ but less than $\frac{2}{3}$.

Modelling with Manipulatives

MODELLING EQUIVALENCE

The equivalence of fractions can be shown using manipulatives.
For example, using pattern blocks:

If the yellow block is 1 or the whole, each green block is $\frac{1}{6}$.
So, 3 green blocks make up $\frac{3}{6}$, or $\frac{1}{2}$, of the yellow block.

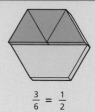

$$\frac{3}{6} = \frac{1}{2}$$

MODELLING FRACTIONS GREATER THAN 1

Fractions greater than 1 can also be modelled using manipulatives.
The equivalence of improper fractions and mixed numbers also
becomes apparent. For example, using pattern blocks:

If the yellow block is 1, then each blue block is $\frac{1}{3}$.
So, 5 blue blocks are $\frac{5}{3}$, or $1\frac{2}{3}$, yellow blocks.

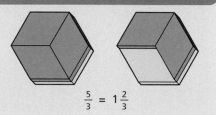

$$\frac{5}{3} = 1\frac{2}{3}$$

Fraction Operations

Although decimal algorithms closely parallel whole number algorithms, that is not the case with fraction algorithms. For this reason, although many students learn the fraction procedures, they are not comfortable with why they are doing what they are doing. It is essential to continue to help students see that the meaning of the operations has not changed just because students are now working with fractions.

Adding and Subtracting Fractions

As students add and subtract fractions, an appropriate sequence of types of questions might be

- fractions less than 1 with the same denominator, where the sum, or the minuend, is less than 1, like $\frac{3}{8} + \frac{4}{8}$
- any fractions less than 1 with the same denominator, like $\frac{5}{8} + \frac{7}{8}$
- fractions less than 1 with a sum, or minuend, less than 1, initially where the denominators have a factor in common (e.g., $\frac{1}{4} + \frac{1}{2}$), and then where they don't, like $\frac{1}{4} + \frac{2}{3}$
- any fractions less than 1, like $\frac{3}{5} + \frac{7}{8}$
- mixed numbers and/or improper fractions, such as $1\frac{2}{3} + \frac{1}{5}$ or $\frac{9}{8} + \frac{7}{5}$

One way to begin the topic is to use what students already know about representations. For example, since students know that $\frac{5}{8}$ can be represented as 5 sections out of 8, they can colour different sections to create different addition expressions.

TEACHING TIP

Most students find the details of the addition and subtraction algorithms for fractions more complex than the details for fraction multiplication and division. However, addition and subtraction are normally introduced first since, conceptually, addition and subtraction contexts for fractions are easier for many students to recognize than multiplication and division contexts for fractions.

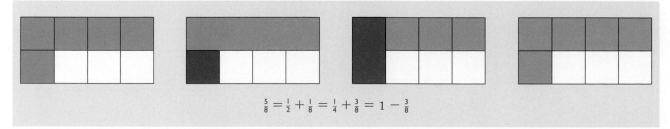

$$\frac{5}{8} = \frac{1}{2} + \frac{1}{8} = \frac{1}{4} + \frac{3}{8} = 1 - \frac{3}{8}$$

ACTIVITY 12.12

Present pictures of start and end positions for containers from which liquid has been drained in some way. Ask students to write subtraction sentences to describe the pictures. For example, the pictures below show how much of a pitcher of lemonade has been poured out and how much of a gas tank in a car has been used.

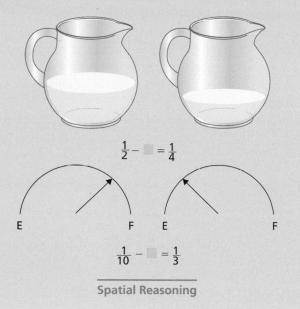

$$\frac{1}{2} - \blacksquare = \frac{1}{4}$$

$$\frac{1}{10} - \blacksquare = \frac{1}{3}$$

Spatial Reasoning

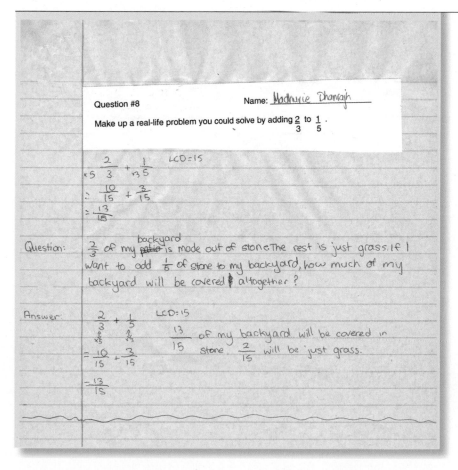

Question #8   Name: Madhurie Dhanraj

Make up a real-life problem you could solve by adding $\frac{2}{3}$ to $\frac{1}{5}$.

$$\frac{2}{3} + \frac{1}{5} \qquad LCD = 15$$
$$= \frac{10}{15} + \frac{3}{15}$$
$$= \frac{13}{15}$$

Question: $\frac{2}{3}$ of my ~~patio~~ backyard is made out of stone. The rest is just grass. If I want to add $\frac{1}{5}$ of stone to my backyard, how much of my backyard will be covered altogether?

Answer: $\frac{2}{3} + \frac{1}{5} \qquad LCD = 15$

$\frac{13}{15}$ of my backyard will be covered in stone. $\frac{2}{15}$ will be just grass.

$$= \frac{10}{15} + \frac{3}{15}$$
$$= \frac{13}{15}$$

Student Response

Although it is unclear what $\frac{1}{5}$ of stone actually means (Is it $\frac{1}{5}$ of the area of the yard or $\frac{1}{5}$ of the area of the existing stone?), if we assume it is $\frac{1}{5}$ of the yard, and we assume that the student means "covered in stone," the problem meets the criterion.

Once students see that $\frac{5}{8}$ can be represented as $\frac{1}{4} + \frac{3}{8}$, it makes sense that the sum of $\frac{1}{4} + \frac{3}{8}$ is $\frac{5}{8}$.

Whenever calculating sums and differences, students should be estimating using benchmarks, for example, is the sum closer to $\frac{1}{2}$ or 1? Is the difference closer to 0 or $\frac{1}{2}$? It is also important that different meanings of subtraction arise in problems that students meet—sometimes take away, sometimes comparison, and sometimes missing addend.

It makes sense to expose students to addition and subtraction of improper fractions after mixed numbers have been introduced, since then it is possible for students to check the reasonableness of the sum or difference. It also makes sense to repeatedly focus on the relationship between addition and subtraction.

Different models and approaches can and should be used to show addition and subtraction of fractions. Some examples are shown below:

Model 1: Think of the denominator as a unit when fractions have the same denominator.

Adding $\frac{3}{5} + \frac{1}{5}$

Fifths are just like any other unit. Three of them and one more of them is four of them, so 3 fifths + 1 fifth = 4 fifths, or $\frac{3}{5} + \frac{1}{5} = \frac{4}{5}$.

Subtracting $\frac{3}{5} - \frac{1}{5}$

Again, think of fifths as the "unit." Three of them are two more than one of them, so 3 fifths − 1 fifth = 2 fifths, or $\frac{3}{5} - \frac{1}{5} = \frac{2}{5}$.

Model 2: Number Lines

Adding $\frac{3}{5} + \frac{1}{5}$

Use the resulting position when a distance of $\frac{1}{5}$ is added to the $\frac{3}{5}$ position on a number line:

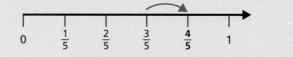

Subtracting $\frac{3}{5} - \frac{1}{5}$

This can be thought of in two ways:

i) the distance from $\frac{1}{5}$ to $\frac{3}{5}$ on the number line ($\frac{2}{5}$, in this case, represents the length of the arrow).

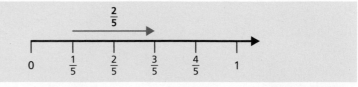

ii) the resulting position when you move $\frac{1}{5}$ to the left instead of the right from the $\frac{3}{5}$ position

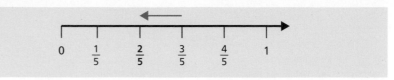

The context of the problem might suggest which approach to use, although either is correct in any subtraction situation.

For example, if the problem were: *I had 1 of the 5 reports done, but I promised 3 of them. What fraction of the work do I have left?*, the first model might make more sense.

If the problem were: *$\frac{3}{5}$ of the work was done. I decided to redo $\frac{1}{5}$ of it. How much did I not have to redo?*, the second model might seem to fit better.

Model 3: Fraction Strips

Adding $\frac{2}{3} + \frac{1}{4}$

$\frac{2}{3} + \frac{1}{4}$ is the length of a fraction strip with the same total length as the $\frac{2}{3}$ and $\frac{1}{4}$ strips placed end-to-end.

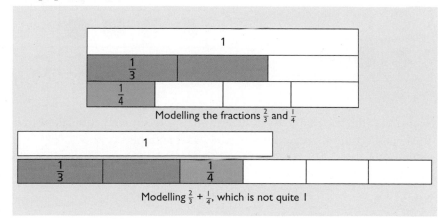

Modelling the fractions $\frac{2}{3}$ and $\frac{1}{4}$

Modelling $\frac{2}{3} + \frac{1}{4}$, which is not quite 1

It is not hard to see that the sum is less than 1, but it is hard to see exactly what it is since the pieces are different sizes.

Students might use the idea that thirds and fourths can both be represented as twelfths to complete the problem. 12 was chosen since it is a common multiple of the two denominators.

Before expecting students to add fractions, it is important to be sure that they are comfortable creating equivalent fractions and that they are comfortable with the concept of a common multiple.

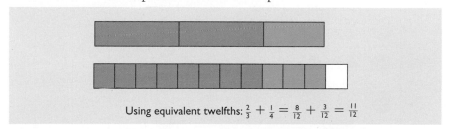

Using equivalent twelfths: $\frac{2}{3} + \frac{1}{4} = \frac{8}{12} + \frac{3}{12} = \frac{11}{12}$

Subtracting $\frac{2}{3} - \frac{1}{4}$

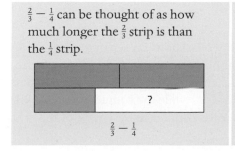

$\frac{2}{3} - \frac{1}{4}$ can be thought of as how much longer the $\frac{2}{3}$ strip is than the $\frac{1}{4}$ strip.

$\frac{2}{3} - \frac{1}{4}$

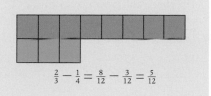

Again, it is hard to see without the equivalent twelfths, as shown here.

$\frac{2}{3} - \frac{1}{4} = \frac{8}{12} - \frac{3}{12} = \frac{5}{12}$

Model 4: Grids and Counters

Adding $\frac{3}{5} + \frac{1}{3}$

- Use a 3 × 5 grid since it nicely shows both fifths (as columns) and thirds (as rows).
- $\frac{3}{5}$ of the grid is 3 of the 5 columns; $\frac{1}{3}$ of the grid is one of the 3 rows.
- First model the first fraction: $\frac{3}{5}$.

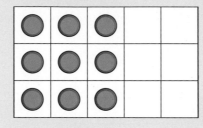

- Adding $\frac{1}{3}$ means adding the number of counters in one row.
- Move some of the blue counters in order to have room to fill a full row ($\frac{1}{3}$).
- $\frac{14}{15}$ of the grid is full, so $\frac{3}{5} + \frac{1}{3} = \frac{14}{15}$.

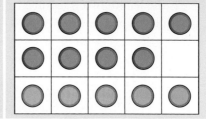

Notice that the use of a 3 × 5 grid automatically showed equivalent fractions with a common denominator, the $\frac{3}{5}$ as $\frac{9}{15}$ and the $\frac{1}{3}$ as $\frac{5}{15}$.

This will always be true. So, for example, if students want to add sixths and fifths, they could use a 6 × 5 grid, or for fourths and fifths, a 4 × 5 grid.

Subtracting $\frac{3}{4} - \frac{2}{5}$

- Use a 3 × 4 grid since the denominators are 4 and 3. $\frac{3}{4}$ of the grid is 3 of the 4 columns. $\frac{2}{3}$ of the grid is 2 of the 3 rows.
- Model the first fraction, $\frac{3}{4}$, by filling 3 of the 4 columns.

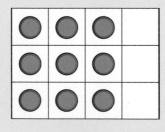

Modelling $\frac{3}{4}$

- Subtracting $\frac{2}{3}$ means taking away all of the counters in 2 full rows.
- Move some of the $\frac{3}{4}$ counters so 2 rows are full.
- Then remove all the counters in the 2 rows and see what is left. It is $\frac{1}{12}$.

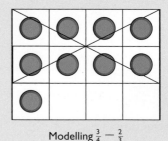

Modelling $\frac{3}{4} - \frac{2}{3}$

Alternatively, you could model the two fractions on separate 3 by 4 grids and see how many extra counters are on one of the grids. If you model $\frac{3}{4}$ as above, but model $\frac{2}{3}$ as filling 2 of 3 rows, you can see that the counters representing $\frac{3}{4}$ take up 9 of the 12 parts ($\frac{9}{12}$), while the counters representing $\frac{2}{3}$ take up 8 of the 12 parts ($\frac{8}{12}$). Since each counter represents $\frac{1}{12}$ of the grid, the difference is $\frac{1}{12}$.

ACTIVITY 12.14

Students can explore the sums and differences of fractions that form a pattern. For example, they could calculate the sums for each pair of neighbouring fractions shown below:

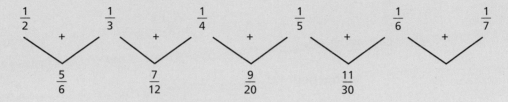

You can create other situations to explore by replacing this pattern with other fraction patterns, for example, $\frac{1}{2}, \frac{1}{4}, \frac{1}{8}, \frac{1}{16}, \dots,$ or asking students to subtract instead of add.

Algebraic Thinking

Adding and Subtracting Mixed Numbers

When adding and subtracting mixed numbers, the same models can be used as with proper fractions. Often, the whole-number amounts are added or subtracted separately from the fraction amounts. For example:

Subtracting $1 - \frac{2}{3}$

USING A NUMBER LINE	USING A GRID
$1 - \frac{2}{3}$ is the distance from $\frac{2}{3}$ to 1, which is, $\frac{1}{3}$.	$1 - \frac{2}{3}$ tells how much of a grid is not filled if $\frac{2}{3}$ is filled. Here it is easy to see that it is $\frac{1}{3}$ of the grid.

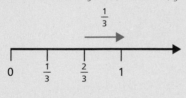

$$1 - \frac{2}{3} = ? \rightarrow \frac{2}{3} + ? = 1$$

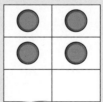

Notice that a grid with 3 rows and 2 columns was used, but any grid with either 3 rows or 3 columns could have been used to model thirds.

Subtracting $4 - \frac{2}{3}$

USING A NUMBER LINE	USING EQUIVALENT FRACTIONS
$4 - \frac{2}{3}$ is the combined distance from $\frac{2}{3}$ to 1, and then from 1 to 4. The total jump is $3\frac{1}{3}$.	$4 = \frac{12}{3}$, so $4 - \frac{2}{3} = 12 \text{ thirds} - 2 \text{ thirds}$ $= 10 \text{ thirds}$ $= 3\frac{1}{3}$

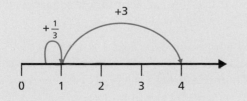

Adding $1\frac{1}{2} + 3\frac{4}{5}$

The whole-number parts might be added first, and then the fraction parts.

$$1 + 3 = 4$$

$$\frac{1}{2} + \frac{4}{5} = \frac{5}{10} + \frac{8}{10} \qquad 4 + 1\frac{3}{10} = 5\frac{3}{10}$$
$$= \frac{13}{10}$$
$$= 1\frac{3}{10}$$

So, $1\frac{1}{2} + 3\frac{4}{5} = 5\frac{3}{10}$.

Subtracting $3\frac{1}{4} - 1\frac{3}{5}$

ADDING UP USING A NUMBER LINE	REGROUP AND SUBTRACT
Add $\frac{2}{5}$ to get to 2. Add $1\frac{1}{4}$ to get to $3\frac{1}{4}$. 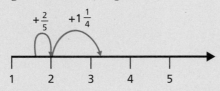 The total move is $\frac{2}{5} + 1\frac{1}{4}$. $\frac{1}{4} + \frac{2}{5} = \frac{5}{20} + \frac{8}{20} = \frac{13}{20}$, so $3\frac{1}{4} - 1\frac{3}{5} = 1\frac{13}{20}$	Because $\frac{3}{5} > \frac{1}{4}$, without using negatives, it is not possible to subtract the whole parts and fraction parts separately. So rename $3\frac{1}{4} = 2 + \frac{4}{4} + \frac{1}{4} = 2\frac{5}{4}$. Now subtract: $$\begin{array}{r} 2\frac{5}{4} \\ -\ 1\frac{3}{5} \\ \hline 1\frac{13}{20} \end{array}$$ (since $2 - 1 = 1$ and $\frac{5}{4} - \frac{3}{5} = \frac{25}{20} - \frac{12}{20} = \frac{13}{20}$)

ACTIVITY 12.16

Students can use pattern blocks to create a design, choose a block to call 1, and then name the design using fraction addition. For example, if the yellow block is 1, the design below can be written as $2 + \frac{2}{6} + \frac{2}{3} + \frac{1}{2}$. The student sees that this is equivalent to $3\frac{1}{2}$ by rearranging the blocks.

 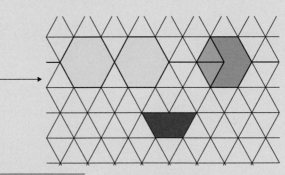

Proportional Reasoning

Multiplying and Dividing Fractions

As students multiply and divide fractions, an appropriate sequence of types of problems might be

- multiplying fractions by whole numbers, e.g., $5 \times \frac{2}{3}$, or $\frac{2}{3} \times 5$
- multiplying a fraction less than one by a unit fraction with a denominator a factor of the other numerator, e.g. $\frac{1}{4} \times \frac{8}{3}$
- multiplying a fraction less than 1 by any unit fraction, e.g., $\frac{1}{5} \times \frac{3}{8}$
- multiplying two fractions less than 1, e.g., $\frac{2}{3} \times \frac{4}{5}$

- dividing fractions by whole numbers that are factors of the numerator, e.g., $\frac{6}{10} \div 3$
- dividing fractions by any whole number, e.g., $\frac{3}{4} \div 6$
- dividing whole numbers by fractions, initially unit fractions, e.g., $6 \div \frac{1}{3}$
- dividing a fraction less than 1 by a lesser one, e.g., $\frac{3}{4} \div \frac{1}{3}$
- dividing any two fractions, e.g., $\frac{1}{8} \div \frac{2}{5}$
- dividing mixed numbers, e.g., $4\frac{2}{3} \div 1\frac{3}{4}$

Multiplying a Fraction by a Whole Number

Students can interpret the multiplication of a fraction by a whole number as repeated addition. For example, $4 \times \frac{3}{5}$ means 4 sets of $\frac{3}{5}$, so it is $\frac{3}{5} + \frac{3}{5} + \frac{3}{5} + \frac{3}{5} = \frac{12}{5}$ or $2\frac{2}{5}$. Alternatively, students can think of $4 \times \frac{3}{5}$ as stretching a length of $\frac{3}{5}$ to be 4 times as long, leading to the same result.

When considering $\frac{2}{3} \times 6$, students think of separating a total length of 6 into three equal parts (each part would be $6 \div 3 = 2$) and counting two of them for a total of 4.

Multiplying Two Fractions

One of the most difficult aspects of multiplying two fractions for students is the fact that the product is less than the factors; this is something they had rarely experienced using whole numbers and is quite troublesome for some students.

To begin, it is important to help remind students of what multiplication means. One of the things it means is "of," that is, 3×4 means 3 [sets] of 4, or 8×9 means 8 [sets] of 9. It only makes sense that the same is true with fractions, that is $\frac{1}{2} \times \frac{2}{5}$ means $\frac{1}{2}$ [set] of $\frac{2}{5}$, or $\frac{1}{5}$ or, $\frac{1}{2} \times \frac{3}{5}$, means $\frac{1}{2}$ [set] of $\frac{3}{5}$.

Using fraction strips helps students see that $\frac{1}{2}$ of $\frac{3}{5}$, or $\frac{1}{2} \times \frac{3}{5}$, means $\frac{3}{10}$. The same model could be looked at in terms of the fraction as a scale factor. $\frac{1}{2}$ changed a length of $\frac{3}{5}$ into a length that is half as long.

$$\frac{2}{3} \times \frac{2}{3} = \frac{3}{10}$$

Another meaning of multiplication that students used with whole numbers is the notion that multiplication represents the area of a rectangle with given dimensions. That concept can be used to model, for example, $\frac{3}{5} \times \frac{2}{3}$, as shown on the following page.

A rectangle representing 1 whole unit by 1 whole unit is created. This can be done using grid paper, forming a whole that is 5×3 (since the denominators are 5 and 3), or by folding paper to form thirds in one direction and fifths in the other. Then the rectangle representing the multiplication is shaded or coloured in. The blue part is a rectangle with dimensions $\frac{2}{3}$ and $\frac{3}{5}$ representing $\frac{2}{3} \times \frac{3}{5}$, or $\frac{6}{15}$ of one whole unit.

> **TEACHING TIP**
>
> Notice that a calculation like $\frac{3}{8} \times 4$ means $\frac{3}{8}$ of 4 and so is generally not treated as repeated addition. It could be, however, if the commutative property were invoked. Otherwise students might realize that $\frac{1}{8}$ of 4 is $\frac{1}{2}$, so $\frac{3}{8}$ of 4 is $\frac{3}{2}$.

ACTIVITY 12.17

Students can use fraction strips and try to describe a variety of fractions as parts of other fractions. For example, looking at the strips below, they could see that $\frac{1}{6}$ is $\frac{1}{2}$ of $\frac{1}{3}$ or $\frac{1}{3}$ of $\frac{1}{2}$.

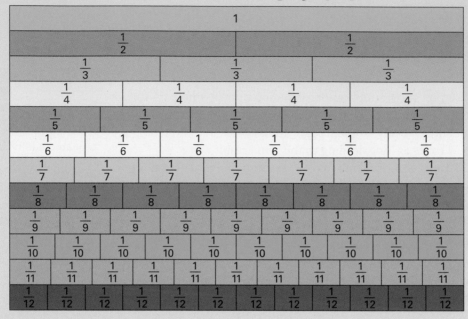

Building Number Sense

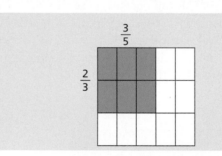

Notice that it is also $\frac{3}{5}$ of $\frac{2}{3}$, or $\frac{3}{5} \times \frac{2}{3}$, if you think of the blue rectangle as part of this combined blue and green one representing $\frac{2}{3}$.

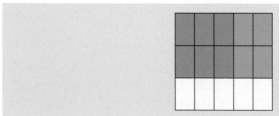

Students observe that the numerator of the resulting fraction product, $\frac{6}{15}$, is 3×2 since there are 3 columns with 2 rows in each, and the denominator is 5×3 since the whole is made up of 5 columns with 3 rows in each.

In general, when you multiply two fractions, the numerator is the product of the numerators, and the denominator is the product of the denominators. The total area of the rectangle has $b \times d$ sections, so each section has area $\frac{1}{(b \times d)}$. There are $a \times c$ of those sections in the shaded part. So the area of the shaded part is $a \times c \times \frac{1}{(b \times d)}$, which is $\frac{(a \times c)}{(b \times d)}$.

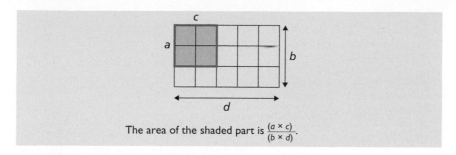

The area of the shaded part is $\frac{(a \times c)}{(b \times d)}$.

Even if the fractions are greater than 1, this algorithm can be used. For example, to show $\frac{5}{4} \times \frac{2}{3}$, you would create a rectangle, using two of the grids, with dimensions 5×2, so there would still be 10 sections in the rectangle and each grid would still be divided into 12.

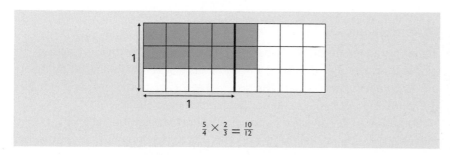

$$\frac{5}{4} \times \frac{2}{3} = \frac{10}{12}$$

Once students understand how to multiply fractions, it is possible to revisit the concept of creating equivalent fractions in a new way.

Students know that to create an equivalent fraction, they could multiply the numerator and denominator by the same amount. For example, $\frac{2}{3} = \frac{6}{9}$ since both numerator and denominator were multiplied by 3.

Now they can see that they have really completed the question $\frac{2}{3} \times \frac{2}{3} = \frac{6}{9}$.

Since $\frac{3}{3} = 1$, they have actually multiplied by 1, which they know does not change an amount.

Multiplying Mixed Numbers

Students can multiply mixed numbers, either using an area model, or multiplying the equivalent improper fractions.

Multiplying $2\frac{1}{2} \times 3\frac{1}{3}$

USING AN AREA MODEL

$2\frac{1}{2} \times 3\frac{1}{3}$ is the area of a rectangle that has those dimensions.

Separate the rectangle into four smaller rectangles, separating the whole part and fraction part of each mixed number, and add the four areas.

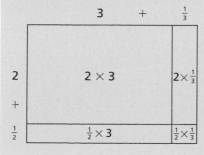

$$\begin{aligned} \text{Area} &= 6 + \frac{2}{3} + \frac{3}{2} + \frac{1}{6} \\ &= 6 + \frac{4}{6} + \frac{9}{6} + \frac{1}{6} \\ &= 6 + \frac{14}{6} \\ &= 6 + 2 + \frac{2}{6} \\ &= 8\frac{2}{6} \end{aligned}$$

> **TEACHING TIP**
>
> When more than one grid is used, it is important that they are separated so that the whole, and therefore the value of each section, is clear, but they should be fairly close together so that the coloured section seems almost like a rectangle.

This model will only be useful if students are fairly competent at multiplying two proper fractions as well as multiplying whole numbers by proper fractions.

USING IMPROPER FRACTIONS

Use equivalent improper fractions.

$2\frac{1}{2} \times 3\frac{1}{3} = \frac{5}{2} \times \frac{10}{3} = \frac{50}{6} = 8\frac{2}{6}$

If students use the improper-fraction approach, they should be encouraged to use mixed-number equivalents to estimate the answer to see if their product is reasonable.

Dividing a Fraction by a Whole Number

Thinking about division as sharing helps students to divide fractions by whole numbers. For example, $\frac{6}{7} \div 3$ means 6 sevenths is shared by 3 people. Each person gets 2 sevenths, so $\frac{6}{7} \div 3 = \frac{2}{7}$. The numerator is divided by the whole number and the denominator does not change.

Sometimes, the division is not as straightforward. For example, $\frac{6}{7} \div 4$ means 6 sevenths is shared by 4 people. Each person gets $1\frac{1}{2}$ sevenths, but this is awkward to write. If an equivalent for $\frac{6}{7}$ is written where the numerator is divisible by 4, the problem is much easier to grasp.

$$\frac{6}{7} = \frac{12}{14} \text{ so } \frac{6}{7} \div 4 = \frac{12}{14} \div 4 = \frac{(12 \div 4)}{14} = \frac{3}{14}$$

This can be modelled as shown below:

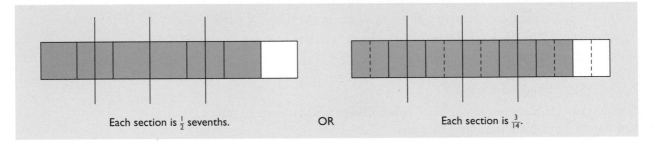

Each section is $\frac{1}{2}$ sevenths.　　OR　　Each section is $\frac{3}{14}$.

Dividing a Whole Number by a Fraction

Thinking about division as how many of one thing fits into another helps students to divide whole numbers by fractions. For example,

- $4 \div \frac{1}{3}$ asks how many $\frac{1}{3}$s fit in 4. Since 3 thirds fit in 1, clearly $4 \times 3 = 12$ thirds fit in 4.

- so, to divide 4 by $\frac{2}{3}$, the answer would be half as much as dividing by $\frac{1}{3}$, so $4 \div \frac{2}{3} = 4 \times 3 \div 2$, or 6.

Notice that, since $4 = \frac{12}{3}$, $\div \frac{2}{3}$ is asking how many 2 thirds fit in 12 thirds, so it's $4 \times 3 \div 2$ (which is $4 \times \frac{3}{2}$).

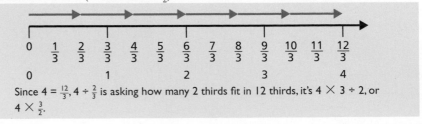

Since $4 = \frac{12}{3}$, $4 \div \frac{2}{3}$ is asking how many 2 thirds fit in 12 thirds, it's $4 \times 3 \div 2$, or $4 \times \frac{3}{2}$.

Dividing Two Fractions

Some division of fraction questions can be very easy for students without knowing any formal procedures. This is particularly the case if the division is "read" to them meaningfully. For example, reading $\frac{1}{2} \div \frac{1}{4}$ as *How many fourths are in $\frac{1}{2}$?* allows students who do not know any formal procedure to calculate a quotient of 2.

Estimating Quotients With the use of manipulatives and a recognition that $a \div b$ means how many bs are in a, students can easily estimate quotients.

For example, $\frac{2}{3} \div \frac{1}{10}$ means how many $\frac{1}{10}$s are in $\frac{2}{3}$. Just looking at the diagram below, it is clear that the answer is about 7. To get the exact answer, though, students need to use more exact procedures, such as those that follow.

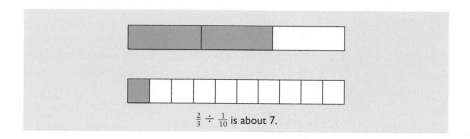

$\frac{2}{3} \div \frac{1}{10}$ is about 7.

Algorithm 1: Using Common Denominators Among the easiest types of fraction division for students are questions like $\frac{6}{7} \div \frac{2}{7}$ (*How many 2 sevenths are in 6 sevenths?*) or $\frac{8}{9} \div \frac{2}{9}$ (*How many 2 ninths are in 8 ninths?*), where the denominators are the same and one numerator is a factor of the other. Students readily see that the quotient is simply the quotient of the numerators; the denominator is not used in the computation; it simply describes the unit that was used.

The question is only slightly more difficult if the denominators are the same, but one numerator is not a factor of another.

For example, $\frac{3}{5} \div \frac{2}{5}$ is really about how many 2s (in this case, 2 fifths) are in 3 (in this case, 3 fifths). The diagram below shows that 1 set of 2 fifths does not go far enough and 2 sets of 2 fifths would go too far, so an answer of $1\frac{1}{2}$ makes sense. Notice that $1\frac{1}{2} = 3 \div 2$ is the quotient of the two numerators. In general: $\frac{a}{c} \div \frac{b}{c} = a \div b = \frac{a}{b}$, since we divide a by b to find out how many b units fit into a units.

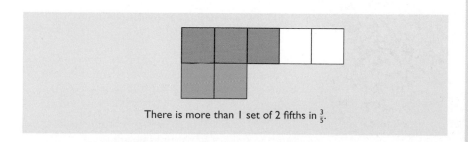

There is more than 1 set of 2 fifths in $\frac{3}{5}$.

Dividing using common denominators works even when fractions have different denominators if equivalent fractions are substituted.

For example, $\frac{3}{4} \div \frac{2}{3} = \frac{9}{12} \div \frac{8}{12} = 9 \div 8$ or $\frac{9}{8}$.

Problems involving rates are a good way to see why the invert and multiply algorithm makes sense. For example, if you ask, "If you can tile $\frac{1}{3}$ of a room in $\frac{3}{4}$ of an hour, how much can you tile in 1 hour?", you are looking for a unit rate, so you divide $\frac{1}{3}$ by $\frac{3}{4}$. One way to do this is to a divide $\frac{1}{3}$ by 3 to figure out how much can be done in $\frac{1}{4}$ of an hour and then multiply by 4 to see how much can be done in a whole hour. In other words, you can multiply $\frac{1}{3}$ by $\frac{4}{3}$ to divide $\frac{1}{3} \div \frac{3}{4}$.

Algorithm 2: Inverting and Multiplying The more "traditional" algorithm for dividing fractions is inverting and multiplying.

For example, $\frac{3}{4} \div \frac{2}{3} = \frac{3}{4} \times \frac{3}{2} = \frac{9}{8}$.

This algorithm can be explained in several ways. One meaningful approach is this one.

- $1 \div \frac{1}{3} = 3$ since there are 3 thirds in 1.
- $\frac{3}{4} \div \frac{1}{3} = \frac{3}{4}$ of 3 since there can only be $\frac{3}{4}$ as many thirds in $\frac{3}{4}$ as there are in 1. That is the same as $\frac{3}{4} \times 3$.
- Since $\frac{2}{3}$ is twice as much as $\frac{1}{3}$, only half as many $\frac{2}{3}$s can fit into a whole as $\frac{1}{3}$s, so $\frac{3}{4} \div \frac{2}{3} = \frac{1}{2}$ of $(\frac{3}{4} \times 3) = \frac{3}{4} \times \frac{3}{2}$.

The invert and multiply is the better-known algorithm, probably because it is easier to use in algebraic situations in later grades, but either the common denominator or the invert and multiply algorithm is appropriate for students to use.

Dividing Mixed Numbers

The easiest way to divide mixed numbers is to use the equivalent improper fractions and apply one of the division algorithms to these values.

For example, $2\frac{1}{2} \div 1\frac{1}{3} = \frac{5}{2} \div \frac{4}{3}$

$$= \frac{5}{2} \times \frac{3}{4} = \frac{15}{8} = 1\frac{7}{8}$$

Students should be asked to look back to see if an answer makes sense. This answer does make sense since $1\frac{1}{3}$ is slightly bigger than $1\frac{1}{4}$, and $1\frac{1}{4}$ fits into $2\frac{1}{2}$ twice.

Common Errors and Misconceptions

Fraction Operations: Common Errors, Misconceptions, and Strategies

COMMON ERROR OR MISCONCEPTION	STRATEGY
Adding Denominators Students add or subtract numerators and denominators to add or subtract fractions. For example, they add $\frac{3}{5} + \frac{2}{3}$ as $\frac{5}{8}$.	Focus students on the size of the fractions being added. Ask students to estimate: *If you are starting at a number greater than $\frac{1}{2}$ ($\frac{3}{5}$) and adding a number greater than $\frac{1}{2}$ ($\frac{5}{8}$), about how much should the sum be? Is $\frac{5}{8}$ reasonable?*
Forgetting What the Whole Is When students draw diagrams to show the addition of fractions when the result is greater than 1, they forget what the whole is. For example, a student adds $\frac{2}{5} + \frac{4}{5}$ and reports the answer as $\frac{6}{10}$. 	It is easy for students to forget what the whole is. What the student sees in this situation are 6 coloured pieces out of 10, so it is natural to say $\frac{6}{10}$. Encourage students to estimate answers before they begin. For example, ask whether 2 fifths and 4 fifths should be more or less than 1. Then if the error is made, it will be easier to convince the student that there is a problem. Another strategy is to have students circle the whole in their diagrams.
Subtracting Mixed Numbers Incorrectly When subtracting mixed numbers, students separately subtract the whole numbers and mixed numbers, but not always in the same direction. For example, a student records: $\begin{array}{r} 4\frac{1}{4} \\ -1\frac{1}{2} \\ \hline 3\frac{1}{4} \end{array}$	Students who calculate using rote procedures and who know that the fractions and whole numbers can be subtracted separately might make this sort of error. Encourage students to estimate. $4\frac{1}{4}$ is about 4. To get from $1\frac{1}{2}$ to 4, go $\frac{1}{2}$ to get to 2 and another 2, so the answer should be about $2\frac{1}{2}$. $3\frac{1}{4}$ is too high. Ask students to model with manipulatives.

(continued)

Fraction Operations: Common Errors, Misconceptions, and Strategies (Continued)

COMMON ERROR OR MISCONCEPTION	STRATEGY
Multipying Fractions Students believe you must use a common denominator to multiply two fractions. For example, $$\frac{2}{3} \times \frac{1}{2} = \frac{4}{6} \times \frac{3}{6} = \frac{12}{36}$$	This approach is not efficient, but it is not incorrect. If students draw an area diagram to model the problem, they will see that equivalent fractions are not required.
Dividing Fractions Incorrectly When dividing fractions, students invert the wrong fraction. For example, $$\frac{2}{3} \div \frac{3}{4} = \frac{3}{2} \times \frac{3}{4} = \frac{9}{8}$$	Suggest that students read a division problem in terms of "how many," e.g., $\frac{2}{3} \div \frac{3}{4}$ as how many $\frac{3}{4}$s are in $\frac{2}{3}$. Recognizing that $\frac{3}{4}$ is more than $\frac{2}{3}$, the answer of $\frac{9}{8}$ will not seem reasonable.

Appropriate Manipulatives

Fraction Operations: Examples of Manipulatives

FRACTION STRIPS

Fraction strips can be used to add, subtract, multiply, or divide fractions.

For example, $\frac{2}{3} \times \frac{3}{5}$ is $\frac{2}{3}$ of $\frac{3}{5}$.

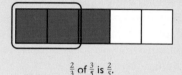

$\frac{2}{3}$ of $\frac{3}{5}$ is $\frac{2}{5}$.

NUMBER LINES

Number lines can be used to add, subtract, multiply, or divide fractions.

For example, to calculate $1\frac{1}{4} - \frac{3}{8}$, jump from $\frac{3}{8}$ to 1, and then another $\frac{1}{4}$, and total the amount jumped.

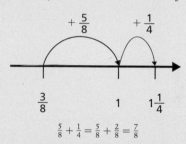

$$\frac{5}{8} + \frac{1}{4} = \frac{5}{8} + \frac{2}{8} = \frac{7}{8}$$

GRIDS AND COUNTERS

Grids and counters can be used for all four operations.

For example, $\frac{5}{8} \div \frac{1}{3}$ tells how many $\frac{1}{3}$s fit in $\frac{5}{8}$.

Cover $\frac{5}{8}$ of a 3-by-8 grid.

$\frac{1}{3}$ of the grid is 1 row of 8, so the question is really how many groups of 8 counters can be formed.

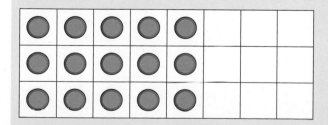

$$15 \div 8 = 1\frac{7}{8}$$

GEOBOARDS

Geoboards can be used in the same way as grids and counters, but rather than using counters, sections of the geoboard are circled with elastics.

For example, $\frac{2}{3} \times \frac{1}{5}$ is shown by using an elastic to enclose a 3×5 rectangle, another elastic to enclose 1 column of the rectangle, and then another to enclose 2 of the 3 rows in that column.

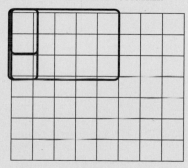

$$\frac{2}{3} \times \frac{1}{5} = \frac{2}{15}$$

Appropriate Children's Books

My Half Day (Fisher, Sneed, 2008).

Lots of fractions are used to describe the day of a boy and his friend. The illustrations are fun and the story appropriately silly.

Whole-y Cow! Fractions are Fun (Souders, 2010).

This is a fun book using rhymes and visuals to entice children into the use of fractions.

Jump, Kangaroo, Jump! (Murphy, 1998).

A group of 12 kangaroos divide themselves into different numbers of teams for some field-day events. The fractions associated with these groupings are shown visually and symbolically.

Appropriate Digital Resources

See the MindTap site for a selection of appropriate digital resources.

Assessing Student Understanding

- Although typically teachers ask students to describe the fraction associated with a picture, it is equally important to have students draw a picture for a fraction. This provides insight into a child's understanding of the need for equal parts for fractions of a whole or fractions of a measure.
- Assessment of fraction understanding should include an appropriate balance of conceptual, procedural, and problem-solving questions. For example, to find out what students understand about subtracting fractions, include questions in which
  - they are asked to draw models to represent a particular subtraction
  - they are given a model and asked to provide the associated computation
  - they explain why a difference might be in a particular range of numbers, for example, why $\frac{3}{4} - \frac{1}{3}$ is between $\frac{1}{2}$ and $\frac{2}{3}$

Student Response

This student was asked to compare 2/3 and 6/9.

Elisa thinks that $\frac{6}{9}$ is more than $\frac{2}{3}$ since 6 and 9 are more than 2 and 3. What do you think? Explain why.

– they solve a problem involving subtraction of fractions
– they create a problem to match a particular subtraction calculation

- Examine this student's response. What is good about what the student does? What are the problems? What feedback would you offer?
- Make sure not to focus only on fractions as parts of a whole, but to include consideration of fractions as parts of a set, fractions as comparisons, fractions as division, and, certainly, fractions as numbers.
- It is important to encourage students to use alternative models and alternative algorithms so that when they are assessed on their understanding of fraction concepts or operations, they can select the model or algorithm that makes the most sense to them.

Applying What You've Learned

1. Many young children have an understanding of $\frac{1}{2}$ much earlier than other simple fractions, for example, $\frac{1}{3}$ or $\frac{1}{4}$. Why do you think this might be?

2. We often focus on the part-of-a-whole meaning for fractions. Make a case for why the other meanings are also important to use.

3. Develop a plan for a lesson using pattern blocks to demonstrate the importance of knowing what the whole is in naming a fraction.

4. How would you help a student understand why the wholes need to be considered in order to compare two fractions?

5. One of the ways we later use the notion that fractions represent division is to divide a numerator by a denominator to create a decimal equivalent. For example, we get the decimal for $\frac{3}{7}$ by dividing 3 by 7. Set up an activity that would make this approach make sense to a Grade 7 student.

6. Consider each of the fraction operations. In what ways is an understanding of fraction equivalence fundamental to success with each operation? Be as specific as you can.

7. Consider each of the fraction operations. In what ways is visualization fundamental to success with the operations? Be as specific as you can.

8. Which is usually greater: the sum, difference, product, or quotient of two fractions? Explain.

9. Find a journal article either from the reference list or elsewhere that documents the difficulties students have in learning about fractions.
   a) What reasons are proposed for these difficulties?
   b) What remedies are suggested?

10. You are creating an assessment tool for multiplication of fractions.
    a) What understandings are important to get at?
    b) How would you make sure these are part of the assessment?

Interact with a K–8 Student:

11. Try Activity 11.8 with students in Grade 4 or higher. What strategies do they use to figure out the fractions? How might you (or did you) intervene to help a student whose estimates are not reasonable?

Discuss with a K–8 Teacher:

12. Ask a teacher what fraction topics cause the most difficulty for his or her students. Ask how he or she tries to avoid those difficulties.

Selected References

Barnett–Clarke, C., Fisher, W., Marks, R., and Ross, S. (2010). *Developing essential understanding of rational numbers for teaching mathematics in grades 3–5.* Reston, VA: National Council of Teachers of Mathematics.

Behr, M., Harel, G., Post, T., and Lesh, R. (1993). Rational numbers: Toward a semantic analysis-emphasis on the operator construct. In T.P. Carpenter, E. Fennema, and T.A. Romberg (Eds.), *Rational numbers: An integration of research* (pp. 13–47). Hillsdale, NJ: Erlbaum.

Bray, W.S., and Abreu-Sanchez, L. (2010). Using number sense to compare fractions. *Teaching Children Mathematics, 17,* 90–97.

Bruce, C., Chang, D., Flynn, T., and Yearley, S. (2013). *Foundations to learning and teaching fractions: Addition and subtraction.* Retrieved June 29, 2014, from http://www.edugains.ca/resourcesDP/Resources/Planning-Supports/FINALFoundationstoLearningandTeaching-Fractions.pdf.

Cengiz, N., and Rathouz, M. (2011). Take a bite out of fraction division. *Mathematics Teaching in the Middle School, 17(3),* 146–153.

Clarke, D., and Roche, A. (2011). Some advice for making the teaching of fractions a research-based, practical, effective and enjoyable experience in the middle years. *Australian Catholic University.* Retrieved on July 4, 2014, from http://gippslandtandlcoaches.wikispaces.com/file/view/fractions.pdf.

Coughlin, H. (2010). Dividing fractions: What is the role of the divisor? *Mathematics Teaching in the Middle School, 16,* 280–287.

Cramer, K., Monson, D., Whitney, S., Leavitt, S., and Wyberg, T. (2010). Dividing fractions and problem solving. *Mathematics Teaching in the Middle School, 15,* 338–346.

Dixon, J.K., and Tobias, J.M. (2013). The whole story: Understanding fraction computation. *Mathematics Teaching in the Middle School, 19(3),* 156–163.

Empson, S., and Levi, L. (2011). *Extending children's mathematics: Fractions and decimals: Innovations in cognitively guided instruction* (pp. 178–216). Portsmouth, NH: Heinemann.

Fennell, F., Kobett, B.M., and Wray, J.A. (2014). Fractions are numbers, too! *Mathematics Teaching in the Middle School, 19(8),* 486–493.

Fisher, D., and Sneed, D. (2008). *My half day,* Mount Pleasant, SC: Sylvan Dell Publishing.

Gregg, J., and Gregg, D.U. (2007). Measurement and fair-sharing models for dividing fractions. *Mathematics Teaching in the Middle School, 12,* 490–496.

Johanning, D.I. (2011). *Estimation's role in calculations with fractions. Mathematics Teaching in the Middle School,* 17(2), 96–102.

Kieren, T. (1995). Creating spaces for learning fractions. In J.T. Sowder and B.P. Schappelle (Eds.), *Providing a foundation for teaching mathematics in the middle grades* (pp. 31–65). New York: State University of New York Press.

Lamon, S.J. (1999). *Teaching fractions and ratios for understanding: Essential content knowledge and instructional strategies for teachers* (2nd ed.). Mahwah, NJ: Lawrence Erlbaum Associates.

McCloskey, A., and Norton, A.H. (2009). Using Steffe's advanced fraction schemes. *Mathematics Teaching in the Middle School, 15,* 44–50.

Moss, J., and Case, R. (1999). Developing children's understanding of the rational numbers: A new model and an experimental curriculum. *Journal for Research in Mathematics Education, 30,* 122–147.

Murphy, S. (1998). *Jump, kangaroo, jump!* Toronto: Harper-Collins Canada.

Norton, A., and McCloskey, A. (2008). Modeling students' mathematics using Steffe's fraction schemes. *Teaching Children Mathematics, 15(1),* 48–54.

Petit, M.M., Laird, R.E., and Marsden, E.L. (2010). *A focus on fractions: Bringing research to the classroom.* New York: Routledge.

Reys, B.J., Kim, O., and Bay, J.M. (1999). Establishing fraction benchmarks. *Mathematics Teaching in the Middle School, 4,* 530–532.

Sharp, J., and Welder, R.M. (2014). Reveal limitations through fraction division problem posing. *Mathematics Teaching in the Middle School, 19,* 540–547.

Siegler, R.S., Carpenter, T., Fennell, F., Geary, D., Lewis, J., Okamoto, Y., Thompson, L., and Wray, J. (2010). *Developing effective fractions instruction for kindergarten through 8th grade: A practice guide (NCEE #2010-4039).* Washington, D.C.: National Center for Education Evaluation and Regional Assistance, Institute of Education Sciences, U.S. Department of Education. Available at www.whatworks.ed.gov/publications/practiceguides.

Small, M. (2013). Uncomplicating fractions to meet common core standards in math, K–7. New York: Teachers College Press.

Souders, T. (2010). Whole-y cow! Fractions are fun. Chelsea, MI: Sleeping Bear Press.

Tobias, J.M. (2014). Mixing strategies to compare fractions. Mathematics Teaching in the Middle School, 19, 376–381.

Wilson, P.H., Myers, M., Edgington, C., and Confrey, J. (2012). Fair shares, matey, or walk the plank. *Teaching Children Mathematics, 18(8),* 482–489.

Witherspoon, T.F. (2014). Using constructed knowledge to multiply fractions. *Teaching Children Mathematics, 20(7),* 444–451.

Chapter 13

Decimals

IN A NUTSHELL

The main ideas in this chapter are listed below:

1. A decimal is an alternative representation of a fraction, but one that allows for calculations that are consistent with whole number calculations.

2. A decimal can be read and interpreted in different ways; sometimes one representation is more useful than another in explaining a computation.

3. Algorithms for computing with decimals are derived directly from algorithms for computing with whole numbers.

CHAPTER PROBLEM

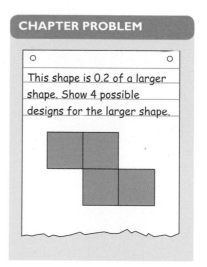

This shape is 0.2 of a larger shape. Show 4 possible designs for the larger shape.

Representing Decimals

Since we often need to describe parts of objects in real life, for example, parts of metres or parts of litres, it is important for students to learn about decimals. Decimals are not unfamiliar to students who have seen prices in dollar-and-cents form even before they get to school. However, students' understanding of this notation, for example, $3.14, is in terms of 3 dollars and 14 cents and not 3 dollars and 14 hundredths of a dollar, which is the underlying decimal meaning.

It is not really possible for students to make sense of decimals without some understanding of fractions. An introduction to decimals requires familiarity with the concept of fraction tenths. It is natural to begin with items that come in tens to begin renaming fraction tenths as decimal tenths.

TEACHING TIP

Although hundredths may be more familiar to students because of money amounts, it is easier to model tenths concretely, so it may be a better place to start.

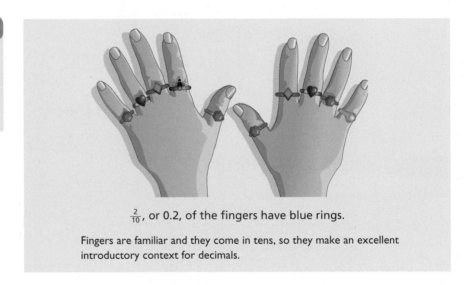

$\frac{2}{10}$, or 0.2, of the fingers have blue rings.

Fingers are familiar and they come in tens, so they make an excellent introductory context for decimals.

A possible model for hundredths might be a 10 × 10 grid or a base ten flat (which is a 10 × 10 grid of base ten unit cubes), since each section of the grid shows one hundredth.

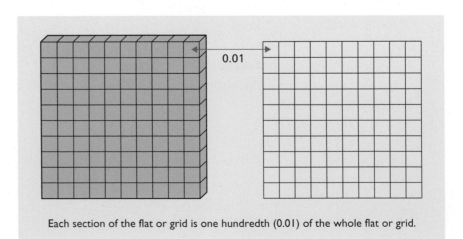

0.01

Each section of the flat or grid is one hundredth (0.01) of the whole flat or grid.

Some students who are fairly comfortable with decimal tenths and hundredths become less comfortable with decimal thousandths. It is important not to hurry the introduction of thousandths until students are ready, or at least to use concrete or pictorial support.

A good pictorial representation of thousandths is possible using thousandths grids like the one below.

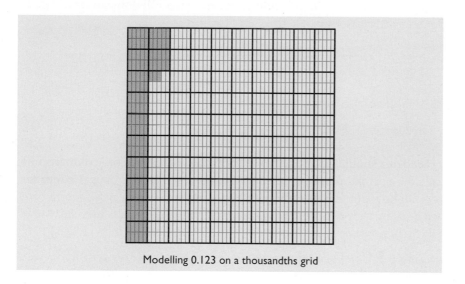

Modelling 0.123 on a thousandths grid

Decimal Contexts

Some valuable contexts that can be used to teach decimals are

- fingers and toes (for tenths)
- items that are packaged in tens, such as pencils (for tenths)
- food that can be shared in tenths, for example, pizza and cake
- money: dollars as the whole, dimes as tenths, and pennies as hundredths
- the metric system: the metre as the whole or 1, decimetres as tenths, centimetres as hundredths, and millimetres as thousandths
- gas prices, which are posted to the tenth of a cent (Note that prices are shown to the thousandths of a dollar on the pumps.)
- scores that are in decimal form in various sports events

Decimal Principles

Some of the important principles that students must learn about decimals are listed and described below.

DECIMAL PRINCIPLES

1. Using decimals extends the place value system to represent parts of a whole or values between whole numbers.
2. Our base ten place value system is built on symmetry around the ones place.
3. Decimals can represent parts of a whole, as well as mixed numbers.
4. Decimals can be read in more than one way.
5. Decimals can be renamed as other decimals or fractions.

ACTIVITY 13.1

Students might enjoy hearing an amusing poem about "toe painting," "High on the Wall" by Charles Causley (1986). They could then colour toes on an activity sheet to represent different decimal tenths. For example, paint the toenails so that 0.2 of them are green.

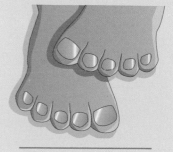

Building Number Sense

Principle 1: Using decimals extends the place value system to represent parts of a whole or values between whole numbers.

The use of decimal notation is an extension of the whole number place value system. The convention of writing the tenths after the decimal point must be explicitly addressed since it is simply a convention. It is important, though, to show why this convention makes sense, given the way whole numbers are written. If you follow the base ten relationship from left to right, a pattern appears.

Hundreds	Tens	Ones	Tenths
100	$\frac{1}{10}$ of 100, or 10	$\frac{1}{10}$ of 10, or 1	$\frac{1}{10}$ of 1, or 0.1e

Each time you move one place to the right, the value decreases by a factor of $\frac{1}{10}$. It makes sense that the next place after the ones is $\frac{1}{10}$ of 1, or 0.1.

Students should also be led to see why there must be some demarcation (called a decimal point) to separate the tenths from the ones. Otherwise, you might assume that 42 means 42 ones, even if 4 ones and 2 tenths (4.2) had been intended. Note that in some systems, a comma is used instead of a decimal point.

Principle 2: The base ten place value system is built on symmetry around the ones place.

The base ten system is built on symmetry. The tens and the tenths and the hundreds and the hundredths are "reflections" across the line of symmetry.

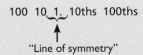

100 10 1. 10ths 100ths

"Line of symmetry"

There is symmetry in our place value system. The "line of symmetry" includes the ones place and the decimal point, which essentially is a marker for the ones place.

Principle 3: Decimals can represent parts of a whole, as well as whole numbers or mixed numbers.

Decimals can be used to represent improper or mixed fractions or whole numbers. For example, 3.2 means $\frac{32}{10}$ or $3\frac{2}{10}$, and 3.0 means $3\frac{0}{10}$ or 3. Any decimal tenth, hundredth, or thousandth can be written as a fraction with a denominator of 10, 100, or 1000.

Principle 4: Decimals can be read in more than one way.

Decimals can be renamed just as can whole numbers. Students should become comfortable both reading and representing decimals in alternative forms. The first example on the next page uses a full 10-frame as the whole, or 1. As with fractions, it is critical that the whole be identified.

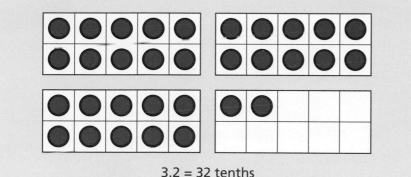

3.2 = 32 tenths

If one 10-frame is the whole, or 1, this model shows that 3.2 is
3 ones and 2 tenths, or 32 tenths.

In the example below that one, the base ten block that is used to represent 100 when modelling whole numbers is now used to represent the whole, or 1 (see *Appropriate Manipulatives* on page 305). For some students, this is a difficulty, and using a new colour of block, if available, might be helpful.

Representing 2.35 in Different Ways

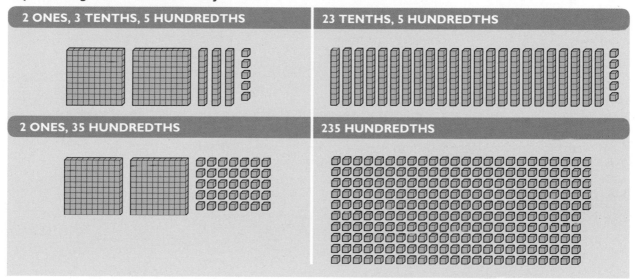

Principle 5: Decimals can be renamed as other decimals or fractions.

Just like fractions, decimals have multiple names, including both fraction and decimal equivalents.

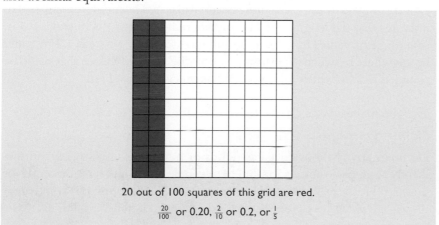

20 out of 100 squares of this grid are red.

$\frac{20}{100}$ or 0.20, $\frac{2}{10}$ or 0.2, or $\frac{1}{5}$

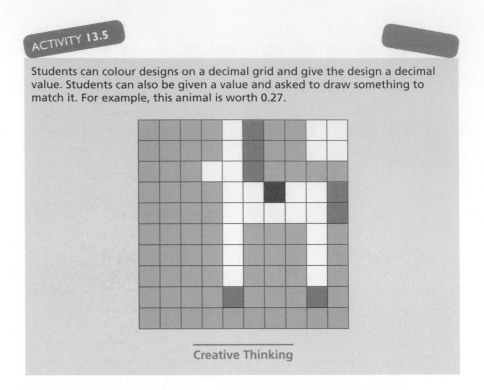

Students can colour designs on a decimal grid and give the design a decimal value. Students can also be given a value and asked to draw something to match it. For example, this animal is worth 0.27.

Creative Thinking

Equivalent Decimals

Explaining Equivalence of Decimals

USING FRACTIONS	USING PLACE VALUE
One way to explain equivalence of decimals is to appeal to fraction descriptions for each decimal. **0.2** $= \frac{2}{10}$ If each tenth section is split into 10 equal parts, then 2 tenths would be 20 hundredths. Therefore, 0.2 = 0.20.	Another way to explain equivalence of decimals is to use place value language and expanded notation. 0.2 = 2 tenths 0.20 = 2 tenths + 0 hundredths Since the 0 hundredths has no effect, 0.20 must be the same as 0.2.

Equivalent Decimals and Precision

It should be noted that, when you speak about measurement units, you cannot equate, for example, 3.2 m and 3.20 m, since different levels of precision are implied by the use of more decimal places. The measurement 3.20 m indicates that the length could be anywhere between 3.195 m and 3.205 m (the range of values that could be rounded to 3.20); whereas 3.2 m could be anywhere between 3.15 m and 3.25 m (the range of values that could be rounded to 3.2), which makes 3.2 m less precise than 3.20 m.

Equivalent Fractions and Decimals

Simpler Fractions

Decimals are first introduced as tenths or hundredths, so students immediately recognize the relationship between decimals and fraction tenths or hundredths: for example, $\frac{2}{10}$ is 0.2, and 0.34 is $\frac{34}{100}$. But often it is convenient to take advantage of other fraction and decimal relationships. For example, you want students to know that

TEACHING TIP

Notice that some decimal equivalents for fractions are infinite decimals, like 0.333 .... Make sure students realize that 0.33 is not $\frac{1}{3}$, since 0.33 = $\frac{33}{100}$ but $\frac{1}{3} = \frac{33}{99}$.

- 0.5 or 0.50 is another name for $\frac{1}{2}$
- 0.25 is another name for $\frac{1}{4}$
- 0.125 is another name for $\frac{1}{8}$
- 0.333 ... is another name for $\frac{1}{3}$

Knowing these relationships helps students interpret decimals meaningfully. For example, they see 0.48 and realize that it is almost $\frac{1}{2}$.

Explaining Equivalence of Decimals and Fractions

USING A MONEY MODEL

One way to explain equivalent fractions and decimals is using a money model. For example:

- Since a quarter is 25¢, or $\frac{25}{100}$, of a dollar, and 4 quarters make a dollar, 0.25 is $\frac{1}{4}$.

- A dime is $\frac{1}{10}$ $\left(\frac{102}{100}\right)$, or 0.1 (0.10), of a dollar.

USING DIVISION

Another way to explain equivalent fractions and decimals is to use the quotient or division meaning of fractions. For example:

You can think of $\frac{1}{2}$ as $1 \div 2$. When you divide 1 by 2 on a calculator, the display reads 0.5. You read this as "5 tenths" and realize that this makes sense since 5 is half of 10.

$\frac{1}{2}$ as $1 \div 2$ makes sense because 0.5 is 5 tenths, 1 is 10 tenths, and 5 is half of 10.

USING DECIMAL GRID MODELS

Some of these relationships can be shown visually using decimal grids. For example,

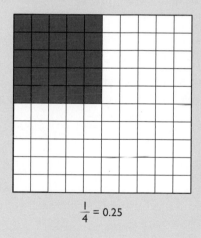

$$\frac{1}{4} = 0.25$$

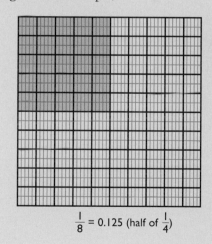

$$\frac{1}{8} = 0.125 \text{ (half of } \frac{1}{4}\text{)}$$

A useful activity for relating fractions and decimals might be to ask students to place decimals and fractions on the same number line. For example,

Where would 0.8, $\frac{3}{5}$, $\frac{3}{4}$, 1.1, and 0.1 go?

ACTIVITY 13.6

Encourage students to explore the decimal equivalents to these sets of fractions and notice the patterns.

$\frac{1}{9}, \frac{2}{9}, \frac{3}{9}, \frac{4}{9}, \frac{5}{9}, \frac{6}{9}, \frac{7}{9}, \frac{8}{9}$

$\frac{1}{11}, \frac{2}{11}, \frac{3}{11}, \frac{4}{11}, \frac{5}{11}, \frac{6}{11}, \frac{7}{11}, \frac{8}{11}, \frac{9}{11}, \frac{10}{11}$

$\frac{1}{7}, \frac{2}{7}, \frac{3}{7}, \frac{4}{7}, \frac{5}{7}, \frac{6}{7}$

Proportional Reasoning

ACTIVITY 13.7

Have students play a concentration game where they use a deck of turned-over cards, some with decimals and some with fractions. Their job is to make matches by turning over two cards. They keep the cards if they match. They turn them back over if they do not match. A card set might include the fractions $\frac{1}{10}, \frac{1}{5}, \frac{1}{4}, \frac{1}{2}, \frac{3}{4}, \frac{7}{10}, \frac{1}{100}, \frac{1}{50}, \frac{1}{25}, \frac{3}{5}, \frac{4}{5}$, and $\frac{9}{10}$ and the decimals 0.1, 0.2, 0.25, 0.5, 0.75, 0.7, 0.01, 0.02, 0.04, 0.6, 0.8, and 0.9.

Building Number Sense

TEACHING TIP

Students should recognize that estimating using only the whole number part of the decimal makes sense unless they are comparing decimals that are close in value.

More Complex Fraction/Decimal Relationships

In about Grade 7 or 8, students are asked to apply the fraction/decimal relationship even when fractions are not as easy to interpret as decimals.

For example, students are asked to think of $\frac{1}{3}$ as a decimal. In general, you use the division meaning of fraction to make this make sense. Since $\frac{1}{3} = 1 \div 3$, students use either a calculator or a pencil-and-paper algorithm to see that $\frac{1}{3} = 0.3333\ldots$. Students observe that, unlike other decimals they had met before, this decimal **repeats**, and does not **terminate**. Since the calculator screen only shows part of the infinite decimal, it is important to appeal to reasoning to convince students why the decimal goes on forever. For example, the following "story" might help students understand:

Imagine trying to divide 1 whole so that 3 people can share it.

Each person cannot get a whole, so rename the whole as 10 tenths.

Now each person gets 3 tenths, but there is 1 tenth left over that cannot be shared.

So rename the 1 tenth as 10 hundredths.

Now each person gets 3 hundredths, but there is 1 hundredth left over that cannot be shared.

So rename the 1 hundredth as 10 thousandths....

Students soon see that every time there will be one piece left over, so the process will never end. They also see that every time, each person sharing gets 3 of the new and smaller unit. So, $\frac{1}{3} = 0.333 \ldots$ makes sense.

At this point, you usually introduce notation for a repeating decimal. For example, you can write 0.3333 as 0.3 or as 0.$\dot{3}$.

In later grades, students learn how to convert a repeating decimal to a fraction.

Rounding and Estimating Decimals

Students should be able to round decimals to simpler decimals, such as 2.567 to 2.6 or 2.567 to 3. The conventions, or rules, for rounding are just like the ones for whole numbers. For example:

Rounding Decimals

Decimal	Nearest Thousandth	Nearest Hundredth	Nearest Tenth	Nearest Whole
2.9375	2.938	2.94	2.9	3
6.0693	6.069	6.07	6.1	6

You might round decimals when you are describing measurements with different units. For example, suppose a wall is 2.367 m long. The length can be estimated as 2.37 m (2 m and 37 cm) or 2.4 m (2 m and 4 dm) or as 2 m. These would be meaningful examples of rounding to the nearest hundredth, tenth, and whole, respectively.

Student Response

This student has rounded to "convenient" numbers that are easy to calculate with mentally. It might be good to ask why she or he rounded one number down and the other up.

Round each number to estimate.

32.46 − 17.48 is about ___30.50___ − ___20.50___ = ___10.00___

Students should also have the opportunity to estimate decimals using simple fractions; for example, 3.24 is about $3\frac{1}{4}$, and 2.17 is almost $2\frac{1}{5}$. To do this type of estimating, the common fraction–decimal equivalents below come in handy. Students can estimate the decimal as any nearby common fraction–decimal equivalent; for example, 5.81 is about 5.75, or $5\frac{3}{4}$.

Some Common Fraction–Decimal Equivalents

$\frac{1}{5}$	$\frac{1}{4}$	$\frac{2}{5}$	$\frac{1}{2}$	$\frac{3}{5}$	$\frac{3}{4}$	$\frac{4}{5}$
0.2	0.25	0.4	0.5	0.6	0.75	0.8

Reading and Writing Decimals

Reading Decimals

Students should read a decimal like 3.2 as "3 and 2 tenths," not as "3 point 2" or "3 decimal 2." Reading a decimal like 7.23 as "7 and 23 hundredths" reveals the important connection between fractions and decimals, but the language "seven point two three" does not.

However, you rarely read decimals with more than 3 digits after the decimal place in this meaningful way, although you could. For example, a decimal number like 0.4578 could be read as "four thousand five hundred seventy-eight ten thousandths," but is more likely to be read as "point four five seven eight." Once students are working comfortably with decimals of this many digits, the value of reading the decimal as a fraction is no longer as great.

Note that the decimal point is represented by the word "and." That is why it is recommended that students be taught to read whole numbers without using "and"; for example, it might be preferable to read 547 as "five hundred forty-seven" rather than "five hundred *and* forty-seven," although using "and" in this case is not incorrect. As well, teachers and students should also be careful to read the digit 0 as "zero," not "oh," in order to emphasize its mathematical "value."

Writing Decimals

Decimals can be greater than 1 or less than 1. For this reason, encourage students to record decimals less than 1 using a zero in the ones place, for example, 0.2, rather than just .2. This reinforces that the decimal is less than 1 and eliminates the confusion when decimal points are written indistinctly. Note that, for assessment purposes, writing 0.2 as .2 is not incorrect unless the purpose of the assessment is to determine if the student can apply the convention of recording a 0 in the ones place. Numbers such as 3 can be written as 3 or as 3.0, depending on the context and level of precision required.

Comparing Decimals

Strategies for comparing decimals relate more closely to strategies for comparing whole numbers than to strategies for comparing fractions. This is, in fact, one of the reasons that a decimal system is used—to make comparison easy. The trick, as with whole numbers, is to ensure that values in the same places are being compared. In the examples at the top of the next page, each decimal pair is compared two different ways.

0.78 > 0.39 since almost 8 tenths > almost 4 tenths	43.8 > 8.27 since more than 4 tens > not even 1 ten
0.78 > 0.39 since 78 hundredths > 39 hundredths	43.8 > 8.27 since almost 44 ones > less than 9 ones

Note that with whole numbers, you can rely on the number of digits to provide a sense of the relative size of numbers—a 3-digit whole number is always greater than a 2-digit whole number. This is not the case with decimals. When comparing decimals, the number of digits is irrelevant; it is the place value of the digits that matters. For example:

> 0.021 < 0.2 because not even 1 tenth < 2 tenths
> 0.021 > 0.01 because more than 2 hundredths > only 1 hundredth

Many students find it easier to compare decimals if the number of digits is the same. This is always possible using equivalent decimals, but should not be considered necessary. For example:

> 0.34 > 0.3 because 0.34 > 0.30 (34 hundredths > 30 hundredths)
> 8.302 < 8.32 because 8.302 < 8.320 (302 thousandths < 320 thousandths)

Students might be encouraged to use number lines to locate decimals once they have comparison strategies that make sense to them.

ACTIVITY 13.8

Students can represent decimal tenths using base ten blocks. If the flat is worth 1, they might observe that 2.3 can be represented with fewer blocks than 1.8, even though it has a greater value.

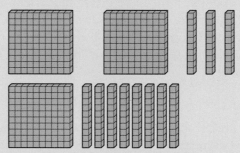

Ask students to build other decimals that are not great in value, but require a lot of blocks to model.

———————————

Proportional Reasoning

Creating In-between Decimals

Sometimes, students need to determine a decimal value between two other values. This is always possible with decimals, as it is with fractions (see Principle 6 on page 268). For example:

BETWEEN 3.2 AND 3.6	BETWEEN 3.2 AND 3.3	BETWEEN 3.2 AND 3.21
To create decimals between 3.2 and 3.6 is simple because there are decimal tenths in between:	To create decimals between 3.2 and 3.3 requires looking to the hundredths:	To create decimals between 3.2 (3.20) and 3.21 requires looking to the thousandths:
3.2, 3.3, 3.4, 3.5, 3.6	3.2, 3.21, 3.22, 3.23, ..., 3.29, 3.3	3.2, 3.201, 3.202, ..., 3.209, 3.21

Decimal Operations

As students learn to add, subtract, multiply, and divide with decimals, they should be using what they learned about whole numbers.

- Each principle related to whole number operations continues to apply (see page 162 for *Addition and Subtraction Principles*, and page 174 for *Multiplication and Division Principles*).
- Each algorithm students learned for whole numbers continues to apply (see pages 224–231, and pages 239–245). There are virtually no changes to the explanations for the algorithms when dealing with addition and subtraction of decimals rather than whole numbers. The changes required to deal with multiplication and division with decimals relate more to the subtleties of how things are said than to changes in how the procedures are carried out.
- What students learned about estimating whole numbers also applies to decimals (see page 220 for *Estimating Sums and Differences*, and page 237 for *Estimating Products and Quotients*).

Adding and Subtracting Decimals

Just as with whole numbers, students have a choice of algorithms for adding and subtracting decimals. Many of the following algorithms translate well into mental algorithms, depending on the numbers involved.

The Traditional Algorithm for Addition

This algorithm follows the same steps as it does for whole numbers (see Algorithm 1 for Addition on page 224).

Step 1 of the procedure has been modelled below to show how the algorithm could be modelled for decimals.

ACTIVITY 13.9

Provide decks of cards to students with each of the numbers 0.1, 0.2, ..., 0.9 on a card. Ask students to choose three cards to add to various values, for example, the sum of 1.2.

Building Number Sense

Step 1 Model both numbers with blocks, on a decimal place value mat, if available.

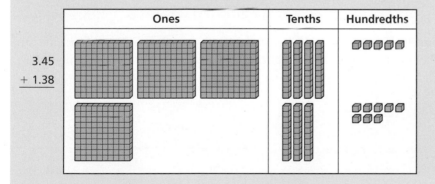

	Ones	Tenths	Hundredths

3.45
+ 1.38

Steps 2 to 4 See Algorithm 1 for Addition on pages 224–225.

Note how the values of the blocks have changed with respect to what they represent:

This block is now 1.   This block is now 0.1.

Encourage students to subtract to compare sports statistics, for example, batting averages for baseball players.

Building Number Sense

The Traditional Algorithm for Subtraction

As with addition, this subtraction algorithm follows the same steps as it does for whole numbers (see Algorithm 1 for Subtraction on page 228). Step 1 of the procedure has been modelled to show how the algorithm could be modelled for decimals using base ten blocks.

Step 1 Model the minuend, on a decimal place value mat, if available.

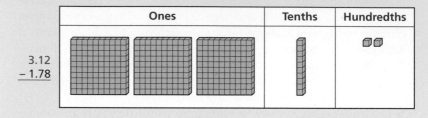

	Ones	Tenths	Hundredths
3.12 − 1.78			

Steps 2 to 4 See Algorithm 1 for Subtraction on pages 228–229.

Alternative Algorithms

All of the other algorithms available to students for adding and subtracting whole numbers can be applied to those operations with decimals.

"Making Change" to Subtract Students can add on to subtract (see Algorithm 5 for Subtraction on page 230). For example:

Step 1 Think of the subtraction as a missing addend number sentence:

$50 − 22.8 = \blacksquare$, so $22.8 + \blacksquare = 50$

Step 2 Count up:

a) Add 0.2 to get to the next whole number: $\quad 22.8 + 0.2 = 23$
b) Add 7 to get to a multiple of 10: $\qquad\qquad 23 + 7 = 30$
c) Add 20 to get to the minuend, or total: $\qquad\qquad 30 + 20 = 50$
d) Add up the "change": $\qquad\qquad 0.2 \quad + 7 \quad + 20 = 27.2$

Adding Too Much and Then Subtracting to Compensate Students can also use the compensating algorithms that they use for whole numbers (see Algorithm 3 for Addition on page 227). For example:

$4.25 + 3.97 \rightarrow 4.25 + (3.97 + 0.03)$ (Add 0.03 too many.)
$\quad = 4.25 + 4$
$\quad = 8.25 \rightarrow 8.25 - 0.03$ (Take away the extra 0.03.)
$\quad = 8.22$

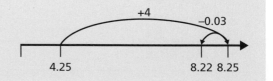

Student Response

This student is adding too much and then subtracting to compensate.

Describe the steps you would follow to add 4.87 + 3.154.

I would round 4.87 to 5 and add that to 3.154. Then take away 0.13 that I added on and get 8.024.

Adding or Subtracting in Parts Students can also add and subtract in parts (see Algorithm 5 for Addition on page 228 and Algorithm 3 for Subtraction on page 230), for example:

(see Algorithm 5 for Addition on page 228 and Algorithm 3 for Subtraction on page 230)

ADDING IN PARTS

5.68 + 3.2

Start with 5.68 and add 3.2 in parts:
First add 3:   5.68 + 3 = 8.68
Then add 0.2:   8.68 + 0.2 = 8.88

SUBTRACTING IN PARTS

8.46 − 3.7

Start with 8.46 and subtract 3.7 in parts:
First subtract 3:   8.46 − 3 = 5.46
Then subtract 0.4:   5.46 − 0.4 = 5.06
Then subtract 0.3:   5.06 − 0.3 = 4.76

Often students are taught that to add and subtract decimals, the critical thing to remember is to line up the decimal points. Notice that this is not an issue with many of the alternative algorithms.

Multiplying and Dividing Decimals

Multiplying by Powers of 10

Before students begin multiplying with decimals, it is useful to look at patterns with respect to the effect of multiplying whole numbers by 0.1 and 0.01, and decimals by 10, 100, and 1000.

Multiplying Whole Numbers by Decimal Powers of 10

MULTIPLYING 400 BY 0.1 AND 0.01

$100 \times 400 = 40\,000$
$10 \times 400 = 4000$ (One factor is $\frac{1}{10}$ as much, so the product is $\frac{1}{10}$ as much.)
$1 \times 400 = 400$ (One factor is $\frac{1}{10}$ as much, so the product is $\frac{1}{10}$ as much again.)
$0.1 \times 400 = 40$ (One factor is $\frac{1}{10}$ as much, so the product is $\frac{1}{10}$ as much again.)
$0.01 \times 400 = 4$ (One factor is $\frac{1}{10}$ as much, so the product is $\frac{1}{10}$ as much again.)

Multiplying Decimals by Whole Number Powers of 10

MULTIPLYING 2.5 BY 10, 100, AND 1000

$1 \times 2.5 = 2.5$
$10 \times 2.5 = 25$ (One factor is 10 times as much, so the product is 10 times as much again.)
$100 \times 2.5 = 250$ (One factor is 10 times as much, so the product is 10 times as much again.)
$1000 \times 2.5 = 2500$ (One factor is 10 times as much, so the product is 10 times as much again.)

Moving Digits, Not the Decimal Note that multiplying or dividing by powers of 10 does not change the digits of a number, only the position of each digit within the number. If, for example, you begin with 3.4, dividing by 10 or multiplying by 0.1 decreases the value of each part of the

---

ACTIVITY 13.11

Encourage a huff-and-puff contest where two students blow cotton balls across a table and measure how much farther, in hundredths of a metre, one ball went than the other.

Building Number Sense

ACTIVITY 13.12

Encourage students to bring in grocery receipts. They can sort the items into categories of their choosing and figure out how much was spent in the various categories.

Building Number Sense

number by a factor of 10, and so the digits in the product change value and move over one place to the right. 3 ones are now 3 tenths; 4 tenths are now 4 hundredths. It is actually the digits that move, not the decimal point.

Alternative Multiplication Algorithms

Many of the multiplication and division algorithms for whole numbers can also be applied to decimals, often with the same models. Many of the following algorithms translate well into mental algorithms, depending on the numbers involved.

Modelling Multiplication of Decimals This algorithm follows the same steps as it does for whole numbers (see Algorithm 2 for Multiplication on page 241). As with whole number multiplication, this algorithm, too, can be modelled using the area model and base ten blocks.

see Algorithm 2 for Multiplication on page 241

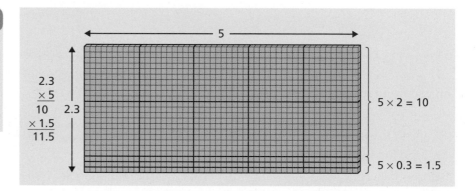

TEACHING TIP

Help students see that the model shows why 5 × 23 and 5 × 2.3 involve exactly the same digits. All that's different is what each of the blocks represents.

"Ignoring" the Decimal Often students pretend that the decimal is not there while calculating, and then compensate at the end. This is appropriate since the digits do not change; only their placement within the number changes. The algorithm shown below could be performed mentally, depending on the numbers involved.

"IGNORE" THE DECIMAL (× 10)	COMPENSATE (÷ 10)	ESTIMATE TO CHECK
5 × 2.3 → 5 × 23 = 5 × 20 + 5 × 3		5 × 2.3 is a bit more than 5 × 2 = 10.
= 100 + 15		
= 115 ⟶	115 ÷ 10 = 11.5	11.5 is a bit more than 10.

Student Response

This student uses her or his understanding of fractions and money to multiply decimals.

To multiply 8 × 0.25, Jeff thought of it as 8 fourths. How might that help him multiply?

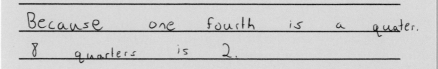

Because one fourth is a quater.
8 quarters is 2.

When multiplying two decimals rather than a decimal and a whole number, students use the same approaches as above, but must interpret what the factors mean. For example, 0.2×0.4 means two-tenths of four-tenths. Since 0.1×0.4 is $\frac{1}{10}$ of $\frac{4}{10}$, or $\frac{4}{100}$, then 0.2×0.4 must be twice as much, or 0.08.

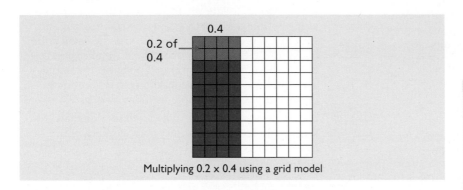

Multiplying 0.2 × 0.4 using a grid model

Alternative Division Algorithms

As with multiplication, many of the whole number division algorithms can also be applied to decimals, often with the same models. Many of the following algorithms also translate well into mental algorithms.

Written Division Algorithms The algorithms shown below follow the same steps as they do for whole numbers (see Algorithms 1 and 2 for division on pages 243–244). Because some students experience difficulty in lining up the partial quotients correctly using the algorithm on the right, many teachers prefer the one on the left when dealing with decimals.

$$
\begin{array}{r}
2.6 \\
6\overline{)15.6} \\
-12.0 \\
\hline
3.6 \\
-3.6 \\
\hline
0
\end{array}
\qquad
\begin{array}{r|l}
6\overline{)15.6} & \\
-12.0 & 2.0 \\
\hline
3.6 & \\
-3.6 & 0.6 \\
\hline
0 & \\
& \overline{2.6}
\end{array}
$$

Mental Math Algorithms for Decimals

There are many division algorithms that lend themselves to mental math. For example:

USING PLACE VALUE CONCEPTS	USING A DIVISION PRINCIPLE
Renaming each decimal (note that it is important to make the place value units the same):	Multiplying both numbers by the same amount:
$3.0 \div 0.6 = 30 \text{ tenths} \div 6 \text{ tenths}$ $= 5$	$3.0 \div 0.6 = (3.0 \times 10) \div (0.6 \times 10)$ $= 30 \div 6$ $= 5$
$3.2 \div 0.08 = 32 \text{ tenths} \div 8 \text{ hundredths}$ $= 320 \text{ hundredths} \div 8 \text{ hundredths}$ $= 40$	$3.2 \div 0.08 = (3.2 \times 100) \div (0.08 \times 100)$ $= 320 \div 8$ $= 40$

ACTIVITY 13.13

Students can solve problems of the form $13.25 \div 0.25$ by thinking about how many quarters are in $13.25. Pose a variety of questions like this involving dividing by 0.10 (to count dimes), 0.05 (to count nickels), or 0.25 (to count quarters).

Proportional Reasoning

ACTIVITY 13.14

Students can calculate the averages (means) of a variety of measurements that are in decimal form. For example, to figure out how far they can jump, they might jump 5 times, and calculate their average.

Building Number Sense

ACTIVITY 13.15

Students might use decimal calculations to determine how much C$1 is worth in U.S. dollars. Use the most current exchange rate, if possible.

Proportional Reasoning

Common Errors and Misconceptions

Decimals: Common Errors, Misconceptions, and Strategies

COMMON ERROR OR MISCONCEPTION	SUGGESTED STRATEGY
Models for Whole Numbers versus Decimals Students struggle with using the same models for whole numbers as for decimals. If the flat represents 100 with whole numbers, they have difficulty switching to a flat representing the whole, or 1, for decimals. 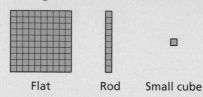 Whole numbers: The flat is 100, the rod is 10, and the small cube is 1. The large cube is not used. Decimals: If the flat is 1, the rod is 0.1, and the small cube is 0.01.	Ensure that students do not refer to the flat as 100 but as one whole. Relate the flat to everyday items such as one whole cake. In this case, the rod becomes a slice that is one tenth of the cake, and the small cube becomes a piece that is one tenth of the slice and one hundredth of the whole cake. If possible, try to use a set of blocks of a different colour to differentiate decimal blocks from whole number blocks. If students struggle with this model for decimals, they might feel more comfortable working with hundredths grids instead.
Switching the Model for 1 Students struggle with switching from using a flat to represent 1 to using a large cube to represent 1. This switch is often done when students begin working with thousandths, for which they need a model that has different blocks for 1, 0.1, 0.01, and 0.001. 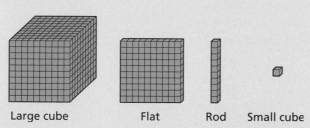 For thousandths: If the large cube is 1, the flat is 0.1, the rod is 0.01, and the small cube is 0.001. For hundredths: The flat is 1, the rod is 0.1, and the small cube is 0.01. The large cube is not used.	It is helpful to use real-life analogies, for example, by thinking of the large cube as a big piece of cheese, the flat as a wide slice, the rod as a strip, and the small cube as a bite. However, if students are struggling, it may be preferable to switch to a different model, such as thousandths grids.
Counting in Tenths Students have difficulty counting in tenths as they bridge whole numbers; for example, instead of 0.8, 0.9, 1.0, 1.1, 1.2, many students write 0.8, 0.9, 0.10, 0.11, 0.12 and read them incorrectly as 8 tenths, 9 tenths, 10 tenths, 11 tenths, and 12 tenths.	If students read 0.10 as 10 tenths, present them with a 10 × 10 grid, and ask them to show you 10 hundredths and to write the decimal. Have them look at the decimal that they read as 10 tenths to see and hear the contradiction.
Reading Decimals Students do not recognize the difference between decimals like 3.04 and 3.004.	If students are encouraged to read decimals meaningfully, this is less likely to occur: 3.04 would be read as "3 and 4 hundredths." 3.004 would be read as "3 and 4 thousandths."
Understanding and Comparing Decimals Students do not see the difference between 3.05 and 3.50. This is natural, particularly if they had been told that you can "add zeros after the decimal point" without changing the answer.	Students can use place value language and expanded notation to understand and compare the numbers: 3.05 is 3 ones, and 0 tenths, 5 hundredths. 3.50 is 3 ones, and 5 tenths, 0 hundredths.

(continued)

Decimals: Common Errors, Misconceptions, and Strategies (Continued)

COMMON ERROR OR MISCONCEPTION	SUGGESTED STRATEGY
Interpreting Decimal Digits Students think that decimal numbers with a greater number of digits or with digits that are greater are "bigger" than they really are. For example, when comparing 0.8211 and 23, a student might think that 0.8211 is greater because of the digit 8 or because it has more digits.	Place value language and estimation is helpful here. The focus for students should be on thinking of 0.8211 as about 8 tenths (not even 1 whole) and 23 as more than 2 tens, or 20 wholes. Another strategy is to allow students to record zeros to align the numbers along the decimal: <div align="center">00.8211 23.0000</div>
Aligning Digits Students forget to line up the decimals when adding and subtracting. Consequently, the answer does not make sense; for example: <div align="center">4.2 +15 5.7</div>	Students should be given exercises in horizontal form, for example, 1.5 + 1.85 + 1.787, so they can practise aligning digits when calculating. As well, estimating is particularly important in this situation to help determine the reasonableness of an answer. For example, if a student adds 4.2 + 15 as shown to the left, an estimate of 15 + 4 = 19 should indicate an error.
Renaming Decimals Students do not know how to handle a question like 3.4 × 100 since there are not enough digits in 3.4 to easily move the digits over 2 places, as is necessary when multiplying by 100.	Students who have lots of experience renaming decimals, for example, 3.4, 3.40, and 3.400, will know that 3.4 can be written as an equivalent decimal with as many places as desired.
Interpreting Division Students use place value to calculate, but they interpret division incorrectly. For example: <div align="center">30 tenths ÷ 6 tenths = 5 tenths instead of 30 tenths ÷ 6 tenths = 5</div>	A comparison might be made to a more familiar situation. For example, if you ask how many groups of 2 trucks are in 4 trucks, the answer is 2, not 2 trucks. <div align="center">4 trucks ÷ 2 trucks = 2</div>

Appropriate Manipulatives

Decimals: Examples of Manipulatives

10-FRAMES

10-frames can be used to show decimal tenths, both less than 1 and greater than 1, as shown below.

 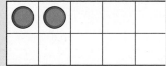

1.2 is 12 tenths.

BASE TEN BLOCKS

Base ten blocks can be used to model decimals. If it is necessary to model thousandths, the large cube can be treated as the whole. If it is only necessary to model hundredths, the flat can be treated as the whole. (See *Common Errors and Misconceptions* on page 304.)

DECIMAL STRIPS

Decimal strips divide the unit 1.0 into different numbers of equal pieces (like fraction strips or a fraction tower). Only certain decimals, associated with unit fractions, are shown.

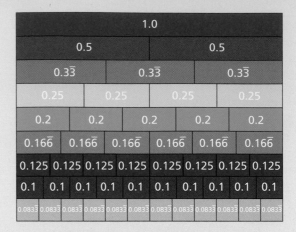

DECIMAL GRIDS

Decimal grids divided into one hundred squares can be used to model decimal hundredths and show equivalent decimals and fractions. Decimal grids can also be used for tenths and thousandths.

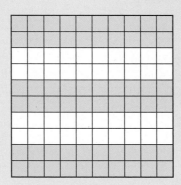

White: 0.40, 0.4, $\frac{40}{100}$, $\frac{4}{10}$, $\frac{2}{5}$

Yellow: 0.60, 0.6, $\frac{60}{100}$, $\frac{6}{10}$, $\frac{3}{5}$

NUMBER LINES

Number lines are useful for comparing and relating numbers. Students can relate decimals to benchmark numbers such as 0, 0.5, 1.5, and 2.0:

(continued)

Decimals: Examples of Manipulatives (Continued)

MONEY

Coins can be used to model decimals. A loonie could be used for 1, a dime for 0.1, and a play penny for 0.01.

1   0.1   0.01

MEASUREMENT MODEL

Metre sticks and base ten blocks can be used to model decimals:

- The metre could be the whole, or 1, and is modelled with a metre stick.
- The decimetre would be a tenth (represented by a rod, which is 1 dm long).
- The centimetre would be a hundredth (represented by a small cube, which is 1 cm long).

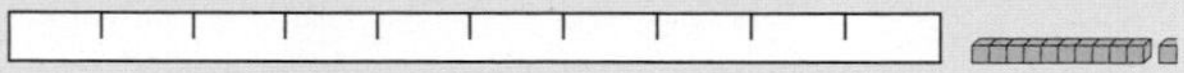

1.11 m
1 m. 1 dm. 1 cm

PLACE VALUE MATS

Place value mats, which up until now have been used for whole numbers, can be extended to include decimals to the thousandths place. Both money and base ten blocks can be modelled on the mat.

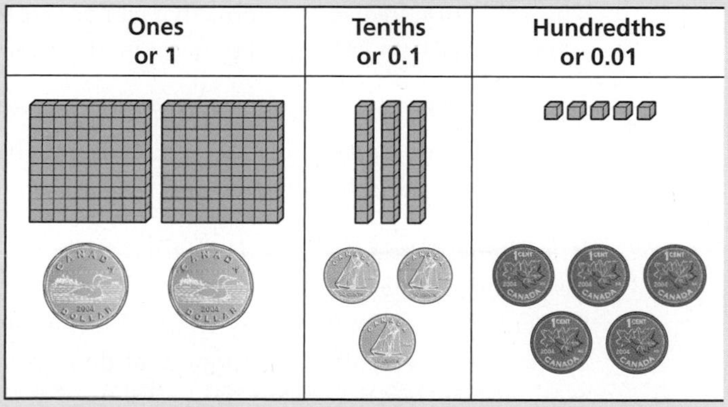

Ones or 1	Tenths or 0.1	Hundredths or 0.01

2.35

HUNDREDTHS CIRCLES

Circles divided into 10 sections but with small tick marks dividing each tenth into 10 are useful to model both tenths and hundredths.

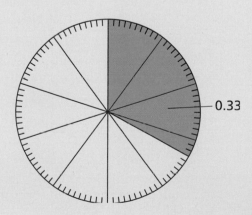

0.33

Student Response

This student has used a decimal hundredths grid model to show that he or she understands that a decimal does not have to be modelled as adjacent parts.

Finish colouring the grid so that seventeen hundredths of the grid is shaded altogether.

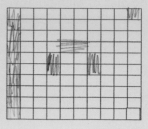

Appropriate Children's Books

10 for Dinner (Bogart, 1989).
This humorous book about a very interesting group of 10 children provides an excellent context for dealing with decimal tenths. The decimals could describe subgroups of the 10 children.

100th Day Worries (Cuyler, 2000).
This silly book focuses on items that can be put together to make a total of 100. Decimals could be used to describe the subgroups of items.

The Father Who Had Ten Children (Guettier, 1999).
As with *10 for Dinner,* this is another book that focuses on a group of 10 children. These children can form the basis for problems related to tenths.

If the World Were a Village: A Book about the World's People (Smith and Armstong, 2002).
Students have an opportunity to use decimal hundredths in a meaningful context as they explore this book that describes the demographics of our world. They can follow up on a variety of websites that explore similar activities where village sizes of both 100 and 1000 are used.

Appropriate Digital Resources

See the MindTap site for a selection of appropriate digital resources.

Assessing Student Understanding

- Make sure to assess students' conceptual understanding of decimals and not just their ability to perform algorithms. For example,
  - What misconceptions are these two students exhibiting? How would you intervene?
  - A student might know that you can calculate 1.3×1.4 by multiplying 13 by 14 and placing the decimal point so that the answer is about 2, but not know why this is appropriate.
  - Avoid questions like 3.25 = __ ones + ___ tenths + ___ hundredths. Even students who do not understand place value are likely to put the number 3, 2, and 5, respectively, in the correct spaces.

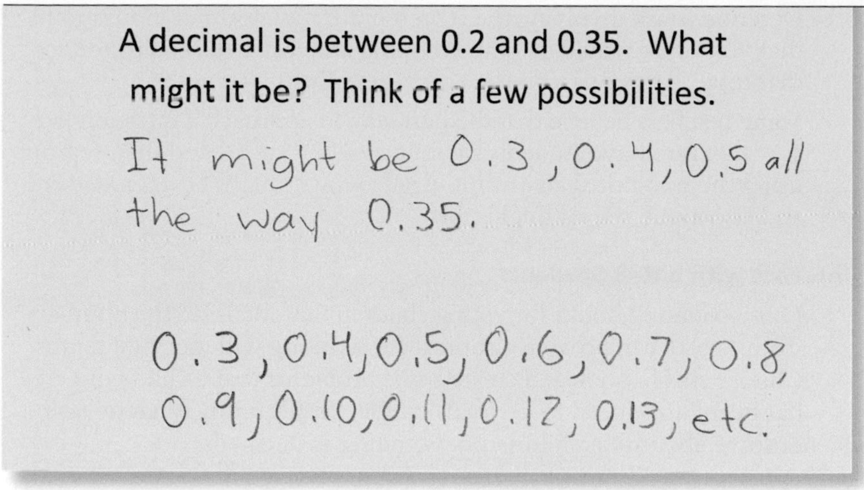

A decimal is between 0.2 and 0.35. What might it be? Think of a few possibilities.

It might be 0.3, 0.4, 0.5 all the way 0.35.

0.3, 0.4, 0.5, 0.6, 0.7, 0.8, 0.9, 0.10, 0.11, 0.12, 0.13, etc.

Student Response 1

This student has some significant misconceptions about decimals.

Which is more : 0.3, 0.30 or 0.03 ?

How do you know?

0.30 is more because 30 is more then 3 so 0.30 must be more then 0.3 and 0.03

Student Response 2

This student has some significant misconceptions about decimals.

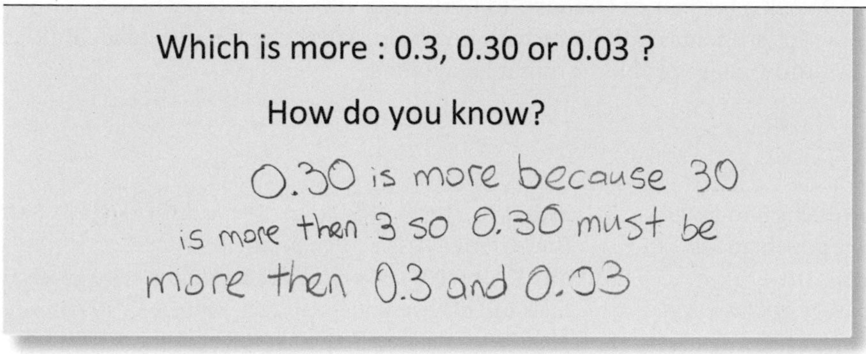

- Make sure that students understand the effect of multiplying and dividing by decimals. For example, you might ask which of these is true:

  ■ × 0.4 is less than ■
  ■ ÷ 0.4 is less than ■
  ■ × 1.4 is less than ■
  ■ ÷ 1.4 is less than ■

Applying What You've Learned

1. What was your solution to the chapter problem? What would a student need to understand about decimals to solve this problem?
2. What ideas about fractions do you think students should understand before you introduce decimals? Why?
3. We often introduce decimal tenths before decimal hundredths. Some people believe that we should start with hundredths first since students are familiar with prices. What would your position be? Why?
4. Some people believe that it confuses students to use base ten blocks as decimal representations when they had previously been used for whole numbers. How would you (or, would you) argue that they are still an important manipulative for understanding and carrying out decimal operations?
5. How would you first introduce multiplication by a decimal less than 1?

6. Describe a task involving the representation of decimal thousandths that you think would be both engaging and instructive to introduce that topic. After describing the task, describe its strengths.

7. Some teachers believe that the best way to approach a question like 4 − 1.23 is to have students set it up as 4.00 − 1.23, and then regroup using the traditional algorithm. Argue why it might be a good idea, and also argue why it might not.

Interact with a K–8 Student:

8. Many counting books for young children that focus on the numbers from 1 to 10 can provide a context for working with decimal tenths. Choose such a book and create some problems that a child who has been introduced to decimals might grapple with. What do you observe about that child's understanding of decimals?

Discuss with a K–8 Teacher:

9. Ask a teacher of Grades 3 to 8 students what sorts of problems her or his students experience with decimals. Ask the teacher to talk about how these problems might be avoided.

Selected References

Baturo, A., and Cooper, J. (1997). Reunitising hundredths: Prototypic and non-prototypic representations. In Pehkonen, E. (Ed.). *Proceedings of the 21st Conference of the International Group for the Psychology of Mathematics Education,* Lahti, Finland: PME, 2-57–2-64.

Behr, M., Harel, G., Post, T., and Lesh, R. (1992). Rational number, ratio and proportion. In Grouws, D. (Ed.). *Handbook of research on mathematics teaching and learning.* New York: MacMillan, 296-333.

Bogart, J.E. (1989). *10 for dinner.* Richmond Hill, ON: North Winds Press.

Causley, C. (1986). High on the wall. In *Early in the morning.* London: Puffin.

Cramer, K.A., Monson, D.S., Wyberg, T., Leavitt, S., and Whitney, S.B. (2009). Models for initial decimal ideas. *Teaching Children Mathematics, 16,* 106–117.

Cuyler, M. (2000). *100th day worries.* New York: Simon and Schuster.

Glasgow, R., Ragan, G., and Fields, W.M. (2000). The decimal dilemma. *Teaching Children Mathematics, 7,* 89–93.

Guettier, B. (1999). *The father who had ten children.* East Rutherford, NJ: Dial/Penguin.

Irwin, K.C. (2001). Using everyday knowledge of decimals to enhance understanding. *Journal for Research in Mathematics Education, 32,* 399–420.

Martinie, S.L., and Bay-William, J.M. (2003). Investigating students' conceptual understanding of decimal fractions using multiple representations. *Mathematics Teaching in the Middle School, 8,* 244-247.

Michaelidou, N., Gagatsis, A., and Pitta-Pantazi, D. (2004). The number line as a representation of decimal numbers: A research with sixth grade students. *Proceedings of the 28th Conference of the Internal Group for the Psychology of Mathematics Education, 3,* 305–312.

Oppenheimer, L., and Hunting, O. (1999). Relating fractions and decimals: Listening to students talk. *Mathematics Teaching in the Middle School, 4,* 318–321.

Smith, D.J., and Armstrong, S. (2002). *If the world were a village: A book about the world's people.* Toronto, ON: Kids Can Press.

Chapter 14

Ratio and Proportion

IN A NUTSHELL

The main ideas in this chapter are listed below:

1. Ratios, rates, and percents, just like fractions, are multiplicative comparisons of quantities.

2. Solving rate, ratio, or percent problems generally involves representing the rate or ratio in a different, but equivalent, form.

3. A proportion is a statement of equality relating two ratios. Proportional thinking is key to solving many rate, ratio, and percent problems.

CHAPTER PROBLEM

On average, people lose about 70 scalp hairs each day.

a) About how many hairs does a person lose in a lifetime?

b) If a typical scalp is covered by 100 000 follicles, then a person loses the equivalent of how many heads of hair in a lifetime?

Proportional Reasoning

Proportional reasoning focuses on how two amounts are related multiplicatively (as described in Chapter 2 on page 22). Recall that when students think proportionally, they think of, for example, the number 56 as 7 groups of 8 rather than as 50 + 6, or they realize that if 2 cookies cost $3, then 4 cookies cost $6. Developing proportional reasoning is a significant goal of Grades 4 and 5 curriculum in terms of work with fractions, multiplication, and division. But it is particularly important in Grades 6 to 8, where concepts of ratio, rate, and percent are explicitly taught.

Post et al. (1988) call proportional reasoning the capstone of arithmetic thinking. There is a lot of evidence that this type of thinking is difficult for many children (Behr, Harel, Post, and Lesh, 1992).

This chapter focuses on a subset of the topic of proportional reasoning: concepts of rate, ratio, proportions, and percent.

Ratio

A ratio is a multiplicative comparison between two numbers. For example, 3:4 is the ratio of red to blue circles. It can be read *three to four* and denotes that for every three blue counters there will be four red counters. The 3 is called the first term of the ratio and the 4 the second term. Notice that a colon is used between the numbers to represent the ratio. What matters is not that there is 1 fewer blue counter than red ones (an additive comparison), but that there are $\frac{3}{4}$ as many blue counters as red ones (a multiplicative comparison).

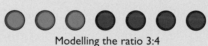

Modelling the ratio 3:4
There are $\frac{3}{4}$ as many blue counters as red ones.

Whenever a situation can be described by one ratio, it can be described by several ratios. For example, the picture on page 313 shows that for every three boys, there are two girls. All of these ratios describe the situation:

- 3:2 describes boys:girls.
- 3:5 describes boys:runners.
- 2:5 describes girls:runners.
- 2:3 describes girls:boys.
- 5:3 describes runners:boys.
- 5:2 describes runners:girls.

The two ratios in the first line are called part-to-part ratios. These ratios compare two parts of something. The remaining ratios are called part-to-whole ratios. They compare one part of something (the boys or the girls) to the whole thing—in this case the whole group of runners.

Many ratios can be expressed as fractions. If the second term in the ratio describes the whole, the fraction tells what fraction of the whole group the part represents. But even expressing the ratio 3:2 as the fraction $\frac{3}{2}$ in the runner situation above is meaningful. It says that there are $\frac{3}{2}$ as many boys as girls.

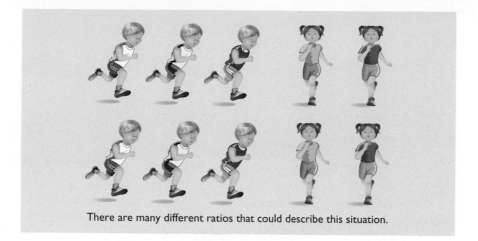

There are many different ratios that could describe this situation.

Not every ratio is a fraction, though. For example, $\frac{\pi}{2}$ is the ratio of the circumference of a quarter circle to its radius but is not a fraction since π is not an integer and fractions are a comparison of two integers.

Although ratios are often not formally introduced until Grade 6, they are actually considered much earlier, in informal ways. For example, to teach a student about number in Kindergarten, teachers often describe 2 by saying that there are 2 eyes for every person; this is a ratio. When multiplication is introduced in Grade 2 or 3, ratio is implicit. For example, to determine how many wheels are on 5 bicycles, students implicitly use the ratio of 2:1 to solve that problem. Young students also use "ratio thinking" when measuring. For example, when a student realizes that an area can be covered with 12 green pattern blocks if it can be covered with 2 yellow ones, he or she is using the 6:1 ratio of green to yellow blocks. Whenever they compare the number of times one unit is required as compared to a different unit, they are using ratio principles.

Equivalent Ratios

Two ratios are equivalent if they represent the same relationship. For example, 3:4 and 6:8 represent the same relationship since if there are 4 red counters for every 3 blue ones, there would have to be 8 red ones for every 6 blue ones.

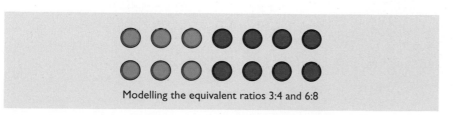

Modelling the equivalent ratios 3:4 and 6:8

Calculating equivalent ratios is handled in the same ways as calculating equivalent fractions. To help students make sense of those equivalents, ratio tables are useful. The tables can be either vertical or horizontal and include any equivalent ratios students choose to include and in any order (e.g., not necessarily ascending).

For example, to clarify the ratio 2:3, think about 2 red counters for each 3 blue ones.

If there are … red ones	there are … blue ones
2	3
4	6
6	9
8	12
10	15

TEACHING TIP

It is important to describe equivalent ratios meaningfully, and not just call upon knowledge of how to form equivalent fractions.

3:4 is equivalent to 6:8 not just because $\frac{3}{4}$ and $\frac{6}{8}$ are equivalent fractions, but because, if there are to be 3 blues for each 4 reds, there have to be 6 blues for each 8 reds.

To assess understanding, you might ask students to draw a picture either to show why 3:4 is not equivalent to 4:5 or why 3:4 is equivalent to 9:12.

Students initially focus on the fact that the values in each column change by adding, but eventually realize that the relationship is really a multiplicative one. Each row is a multiple of every other row.

Another tool to model equivalent ratios is the double number line. The student uses each term of the ratio as a unit on one of the lines. For example, the model below shows that 3:4 = 6:8 = 9:12.

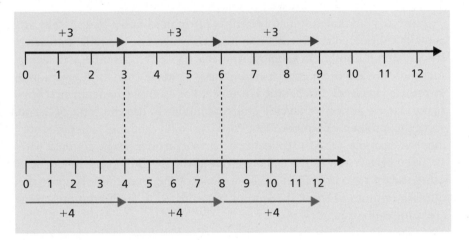

Students can also use graphs to represent ratios. For example, the graph below represents the ratio 1:3, comparing the number of cans of juice concentrate to cans of water to make orange juice from frozen concentrate.

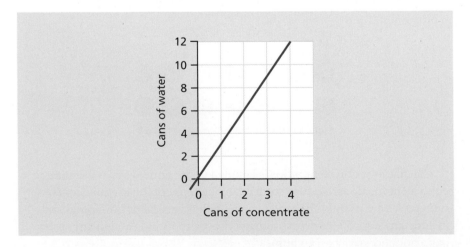

The graph can be used to write other equivalent ratios. Each ordered pair representing a point on the line describes terms of a ratio equivalent to 1:3.

Students can use ratio tables or graphs to solve simple problems. For example, suppose the ratio of red counters to blue ones is 3:5. You can use ratio tables to calculate the number of red counters if there are 45 blue ones by creating equivalent ratios until the number 45 appears in the blue row. Notice that columns in the ratio tables can be combined (i.e., added) to make other equivalent ratios. For example, since 3:5 = 6:10, then 3:5 = (3 + 6): (5 + 10).

A Table Built on Doubles

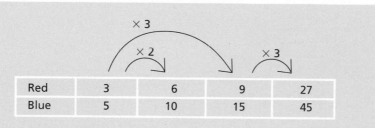

| Red | 3 | 6 | 12 | 24 |
| Blue | 5 | 10 | 20 | 40 |

45 = 40 + 5

There are (24 + 3) 27 reds if there are (40 + 5) 45 blues.

A Table Built on Equivalent Ratios That Are Not Necessarily Doubles

| Red | 3 | 6 | 9 | 27 |
| Blue | 5 | 10 | 15 | 45 |

45 blues = 3 × 15 blues
so the number of reds = 3 × 9
= 27 reds

TEACHING **TIP**

The value of using ratio tables is that students can move as quickly or as slowly as is comfortable for them to get from one form of a ratio to a desired equivalent form.

An Excel spreadsheet can be used to create the tables, if desired.

ACTIVITY 14.2

Students can use multiplication tables to look for equivalent ratios. For example, ratios equivalent to 3:4 (6:8, 9:12, etc.) are found by looking at numbers in the same column of the ×3 and ×4 rows of the table:

×	0	1	2	3	4	5	6
0	0	0	0	0	0	0	0
1	0	1	2	3	4	5	6
2	0	2	4	6	8	10	12
3	0	3	6	9	12	15	18
4	0	4	8	12	16	20	24
5	0	5	10	15	20	25	30
6	0	6	12	18	24	30	36

Proportional Reasoning

You can also look for the y-coordinate on a graph of $y = \frac{3}{5}x$, where x represents the number of blue counters and the corresponding y represents the corresponding number of red counters. This latter approach is more likely to be used at higher grade levels.

Types of Ratio Problems

Ratios can be used to solve a variety of problems.

Some teachers begin using problems that do not require a numerical answer, but a qualitative answer instead. The idea is for students to get a sense of what the ratio situations actually mean. For example, a student is presented with two glasses of liquid. One is made using 1 part orange juice to 1 part water, and the other is 1 part orange juice to 2 parts water. Students are asked which will taste sweeter.

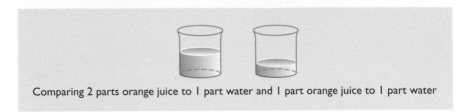

Comparing 2 parts orange juice to 1 part water and 1 part orange juice to 1 part water

In a similar way, Kent, Arnosky, and McMonagle (2002) cite a problem where students are asked to identify which parking lot is "more full."

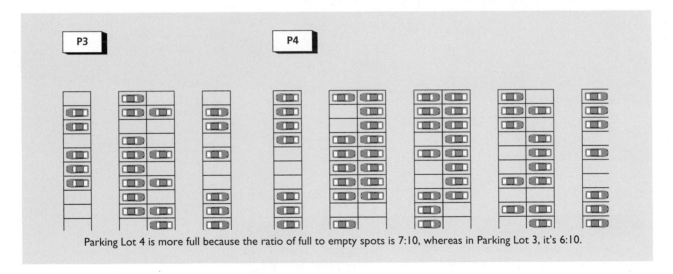

Parking Lot 4 is more full because the ratio of full to empty spots is 7:10, whereas in Parking Lot 3, it's 6:10.

Students cannot just count cars since the lots are of different sizes; they must use proportional thinking.

Different Types of Ratio Problems

Different researchers catagorize ratio problems in different ways. For example, Lamon (1993) categorizes ratio problems into four types: "well-chunked measures," "part-part-whole," "associated sets," or "stretchers and shrinkers." Examples of each are listed below.

Well-Chunked Measures These types of problems involve the comparison of two or more measures that result in another meaningful measure.

> Example 1: After 2, 5, and 7 hours of driving, the distances travelled by three drivers were 260 km, 650 km, and 890 km. Did the three drivers travel at the same rate?

> Example 2: Casey spent $37.38 for 42 L of gasoline. At that rate, could she get another 40 L for less than $35?

Part-Part-Whole These types of problems involve the number of items in a subset of a larger group.

Example 1: Which group has a greater proportion of girls?

Group A   Group B

Example 2: A teacher divided her 25 students into 5 equal size groups. Each group had 3 girls in it. How many boys are in the class?

Associated Sets These types of problems involve creating a connection between two groups that might, initially, seem unconnected.

Example 1: 7 girls are sharing 3 vegetarian pizzas. 3 boys are sharing 1 pepperoni pizza. Who gets more pizza, a boy or a girl?

Example 2: There are 25 students in Amy's school of 400 who are taking karate, and 30 students in Brad's school of 420 who are taking karate. In which school does karate seem more popular?

Stretchers and Shrinkers These problems involve growth, usually linear, where one or more particular ratios are maintained.

Example 1: If you double both the width and length of a rectangle, is the resulting rectangle similar to the original?

Example 2: Is an 8 × 10 enlargement of a 5 × 7 picture exactly the same as the original picture?

Solving Ratio Problems

The problems below are provided to give a fuller sense of the kinds of problems that Grades 6 to 8 students are likely to confront based on current Canadian curricula and to share some of the strategies that are typically used to solve them.

Problem 1 You know that the ratio of boys to girls in a Grade 5 class is 5:4. Determine how many students could be in the class.

This problem is likely to be solved using a ratio table. The class sizes that make the most sense are 18 or 27.

BOYS	GIRLS	TOTAL SIZE OF CLASS
5	4	9
10	8	18
15	12	27

Problem 2 A recipe uses 375 g of flour for every 250 g of sugar. If a large batch is made and 1000 g of sugar is used, how much flour is used?

This problem might be solved in a variety of ways. One way is to set up a **proportion**, which is an equation that says that two ratios are equivalent. In this case, the proportion might be $\frac{375}{250} = \frac{x}{1000}$, where x represents the number of grams of flour. This states that the ratio of 375:250 must be maintained, even though the 250 has been changed to 1000.

One student might look **across** the equal sign or **between** the two ratios and notice that 250 was multiplied by 4 to get 1000, so 375 must be multiplied by 4 to get x. The result would be $4 \times 375 = 1500$ g.

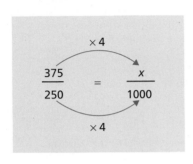

One student might look **within** the first ratio and notice that 375 is $1\frac{1}{2}$ times as much as 250, so x must be $1\frac{1}{2}$ times as much as 1000. That would be $1000 + 500 = 1500$. The result, again, would be 1500 g.

One student might multiply both sides of the equation by 1000, resulting in the equation: $\frac{375}{250} \times 1000 = x$. Solving that equation results in $x = 4 \times 375$, or 1500.

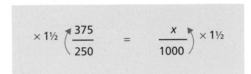

One student might multiply both sides of the equation by 250×1000. This results in the equation $375 \times 1000 = 250x$. This is called **cross-multiplying** since it comes from multiplying each numerator by the opposite denominator. To solve this equation, the student must divide both sides of the equation by 250, resulting in $375 \times \frac{1000}{250} = x$ (or $375 \times 4 = x$).

Problem 3 Suppose you learned that, on average, there are 105 males born in Canada for every 100 females. Officials in Alberta predicted about 25 000 births in 2016. About how many of these babies would be boys?

This problem might be solved as follows:

If there are 105 males for every 100 females, the fraction of babies that are male is $\frac{105}{205}$. You can multiply this fraction by 25 000 to estimate the number of boys.

$\frac{105}{205} \times 25\ 000 = \frac{2625\ 000}{205} = 12\ 804.9$, so about 12 800 are likely to be boys.

You could also have written $\frac{105}{205}$ as the decimal 0.5122 and multiplied it by 25 000 to get the same result.

Problem 4 Sometimes, a problem involves combining ratios. For example, suppose you know that in one class the ratio of boys to girls is 3:4, and in another it is 4:3. You are asked what the ratio of boys to girls is in the whole group.

If the groups are the same size, you can actually add first terms and second terms. For example, if both classes had 28 students, the ratio of boys to girls would be 7:7, which is the same as 1:1, in the total group. You can explain this visually:

Class 1

BBB GGGG
BBB GGGG
BBB GGGG
BBB GGGG

Class 2

BBBB GGG
BBBB GGG
BBBB GGG
BBBB GGG

Combined, there are four groups of

BBB GGGG BBBB GGG, which is the same as

BBBBBBB GGGGGGG.

You can see that if the sizes of the classes were different, this would not be the case. For example, if there were an extra 7 students in Class 2, there would be a total of 32 boys and 31 girls. The ratio is no longer 1:1.

The fact that terms of ratios can be added actually creates difficulties for students since numerators and denominators of fractions cannot normally be added. Over-emphasis of the relationship between ratios and fractions can actually create learning difficulties.

Problem 5 Ratios are often used in geometric situations. In fact, shapes are similar only if the linear measures of one are proportional (in the same ratio) to the linear measures of the other. **Activities 14.7, 14.8,** and **14.9** provide examples of geometric problems based on ratio.

More about Solving Proportions

A number of different methods for dealing with proportions were described above. It is worth pointing out that which way a student chooses to solve proportions may just be a personal preference, but might change depending on the numbers involved.

Notice that to solve $\frac{5}{8} = \frac{x}{16}$, it makes more sense to look **across** or **between** the ratios to see that the 8 was multiplied by 2 and so it makes sense to multiply the 5 by 2 to solve for the missing value.

But to solve $\frac{4}{8} = \frac{x}{30}$, it makes more sense to look **within** the first ratio and notice that 4 is half of 8 to realize that x would need to be half of 30, or 15.

Multiplying both sides by 16 or by 8 × 16 (to cross-multiply) is, of course, still an option.

Rates

Some mathematicians define a rate as like a ratio, only with different units. For example, a rate could be \$5.50/person to represent the cost of a movie, 6 for \$5 to represent the cost of an item, or 12 oranges/litre to represent the number of oranges that have to be squeezed to make 1 L of orange juice. Other mathematicians do not make a distinction between rates and ratios (as mentioned above, rates can be considered well-chunked measures). The notion is that although the units may be different, the mathematics used to talk about rates is identical to the mathematics used to talk about ratios.

ACTIVITY 14.7

Ask students to enlarge a picture of this dog so that it is twice as wide and twice as high.

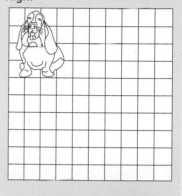

Spatial Reasoning

ACTIVITY 14.8

Tell students that a map of Canada is to be drawn. Have them decide on the paper size and then decide what ratio would be a good one for the scale.

Proportional Reasoning

ACTIVITY 14.9

Provide students a group of rectangles, some of which are similar and some of which are not, and ask them to determine which are enlargements of which. Point out that you can tell whether rectangles are similar by seeing if the length and width were changed by the same factor OR if the ratio of length to width remained the same.

Proportional Reasoning

Thompson argues that rate is defined as a set of infinitely many equivalent ratios (Lobato and Ellis, 2010). For example, knowing that 3:4 = 6:8 demonstrates some understanding of equivalent ratios, but it is understanding how 3:4 can be altered more generally into an equivalent ratio that indicates that the student fully has the idea of 3 per 4 as a rate.

Rates can have two terms, just as ratios do. They represent comparisons, just as ratios do, and can and usually are written as fractions, as ratios can be. There are equivalent rates, for example, 6 for $5 is equivalent to 3 for $2.50, and rates can be compared.

Problems involving rates can be solved using the same technique as problems involving ratios. There is more emphasis, though, in solving rate problems on what is called the unit rate.

Using Unit Rates

A unit rate is an equivalent rate where the second term is 1. For example, if you drive 30 km in 20 minutes, the unit rate is 1.5 km/min. The second term is 1 minute; unit implies 1. Unit rates are calculated by dividing, so division skills are important when working with ratios and rates.

Unit rates are not the only way to solve rate problems, but they are often used.

For example, consider the problem: Which is the better buy: 3.6 L of dishwashing soap for $3.69, or 4 L for $4.29?

If you think of the rate as litres/dollar, you want to know how many litres you can buy for $1 in each case. If you get more litres for your dollar, it is a better buy.

If 3.6 L cost $3.69, you need to divide 3.6 by 3.69 to see how much you get for $1.

$$3.6 \div 3.69 = 0.9756 \text{ L}$$

If 4 L cost $4.29, you divide 4 by 4.29 to see how much you get for $1.

$$4 \div 4.29 = 0.9324 \text{ L}$$

The first soap is the better buy—you get more for each $1.

You could have written the rate as dollars/litre and solved the problem by determining how many dollars 1 L of each costs.

If $3.69 gets you 3.6 L, then 1 L costs 3.69 ÷ 3.6 = $1.025, about $1.03.

If $4.29 gets you 4 L, then 1 L costs 4.29 ÷ 4 = $1.0725, about $1.07.

Fermi Problems

One set of problems that people find interesting are called Fermi problems. They are problems that require realistic estimates to solve, and they always relate to objects in the real world. They are named after the physicist Enrico Fermi. An example is: Choose a tree in the school yard in the springtime or summertime. Estimate the number of leaves on the tree.

To solve these problems, students use ratios. For example, they might count the number of branches, count the number of leaves on

ACTIVITY 14.10

Tell students that 4 books cost $18.99. Ask them to:

a) change the 4 so that the new price would be cheaper

b) change the $18.99 so that the new price would be cheaper

c) change both 4 and $18.99 so that the new price would be cheaper.

For purposes of assessment, note whether students calculate the unit rate or use a more conceptual approach.

_____

Proportional Reasoning

one branch, and multiply. They are assuming the ratio of leaves to branch is constant.

Another problem might be to estimate how large an area $10 000 worth of loonies, laid out flat on a floor, would cover. The ratio here is the ratio of value to a given area. More examples of Fermi problems are available in Kenton (2008) and Nugent (2006).

Role of Proportional Reasoning in Other Strands

As has already been seen incidentally in this chapter and throughout other chapters in this resource, proportional reasoning plays a significant role in all strands in mathematics. A few very specific examples are listed here.

Measurement

When a young student measures using a non-standard unit or an older student using a standard unit, he or she might be asked to use that unit to measure a part of something and predict how many units will be required to measure the full thing. The student uses proportional reasoning to estimate how many of those units will be required by thinking of the full item as "so many of" the partial items.

For example, a student might estimate that the red distance is 8 paper clips based on the fact that the red length looks like about 4 times as long as the length the paper clips go.

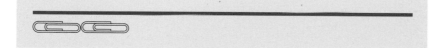

Or a student might estimate this angle size as about half of a benchmark 90° angle, and recognize it as about 45°.

When a student is asked to recreate a yellow pattern block design using only red blocks, she or he uses the relationship between the yellow and red blocks to realize it will take twice as many red blocks as yellow ones. When an area is measured in a unit half the size, it will take twice as many of them to cover the same space.

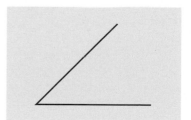

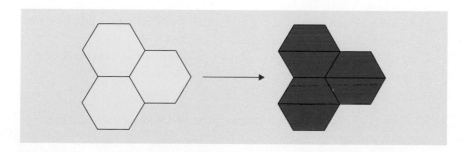

Geometry

The concept of similar shapes is fully based in the notion of proportion. Two shapes are similar if the ratios of all of their linear measurements are identical. For example, the ratio for the width to length for both rectangles below is 2:3. It turns out that the perimeter ratio is also 2:3.

Because dilations are about forming similar shapes, they, too, are all about proportional thinking.

Scale drawings are another geometric example of using proportional thinking. The scale rate or ratio tells exactly what the ratio of linear measures relating the real item and the drawing must be.

Data

Students frequently use concepts of proportionality when interpreting graphs, for example, noticing that one bar in a bar graph is about double the width of another or one section of a circle graph triple the area of another.

They use proportional thinking when they create scatter plots to decide if two variables are related in a linear fashion. If they are, the variables might be related proportionally.

They use proportional thinking when they realize that if all values in a data set are doubled, so are the mean and median.

They often use proportional reasoning to interpret sports statistics (e.g., what does a basketball player's assist to turnover ratio mean?).

Probability

Probability is, by nature, rooted in proportional thinking, although the randomness of outcomes often wreaks havoc with that thinking. For example, it is because the probability of rolling a 1 on a die is $\frac{1}{6}$ that we assume that, in 36 rolls, we are likely to get six 1s, even though that may not happen.

Algebra

There is a significant amount of proportional thinking related to predicting subsequent terms in what are called linear growing patterns (i.e., patterns that increase by a constant amount). For example, to predict what the 40th term of 3, 6, 9, 12, … is, the student thinks about what 40 units of 3 are.

Proportional thinking is also used when looking at two variables whose relationship, when graphed, forms a line through the origin. That line provides information about equivalent ratios connected to that relationship.

And proportional thinking is used when solving linear equations. For example, we multiply an equation through by 3, or divide it through by 4, because what we know about proportional thinking allows us to realize that if two different items are identical, 3 copies or $\frac{1}{4}$ of a copy of each are also identical.

Financial Literacy

Increasing attention is being paid to the importance of including financial literacy topics in students' mathematical education. Understanding interest rates, debt rates, percents for budgeting, currency conversion, etc., all evoke proportional reasoning.

Percent

Percents are a special sort of ratio, a ratio where the second term is 100. The concept of 50% or 100% is rarely new to students. They are familiar with both from talk about test scores and everyday situations like weather reports. In fact, some teachers choose to teach percent before they teach other ratios. Some students may note the connection to the word "cent," where a cent is $\frac{1}{100}$ of a dollar, just like 1 cm is $\frac{1}{100}$ of 1 m.

Principles for Percent

PRINCIPLES FOR PERCENT

1. A percent is a ratio or a comparison of a number to 100 and can be written as ■:100 or $\frac{[\ ]}{100}$ or as an equivalent decimal. It can be represented with a variety of models.
2. The actual amount that a percent represents is based on the whole of which it is a percent.
3. Comparing percents is as easy as comparing decimals, as in many instances, you only need to compare whole number values.
4. Percents can be as low as 0, but can go higher than 100.
5. Sometimes percents are used to describe change.
6. There are a variety of strategies appropriate for solving any problem involving percent.

These principles can be explored using a variety of approaches.

Principle 1: A percent is a ratio or a comparison of a number to 100 and can be written as ■:100 or $\frac{[\ ]}{100}$ or as an equivalent decimal. It can be represented with a variety of models.

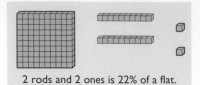

2 rods and 2 ones is 22% of a flat.

Early on, any model for a percent should involve something that has 100 parts; this will reinforce the meaning of percent as a comparison to 100. One obvious model is a base ten block flat. To show, for example, 22%, you can cover a base ten block with 2 tens and 2 ones.

Adults often think of percents as sections of a circle, because of the prominence of pie charts or circle graphs. Nonetheless, a decimal hundredths grid is an excellent model for percents, particularly if grids have been used previously to model decimal hundredths.

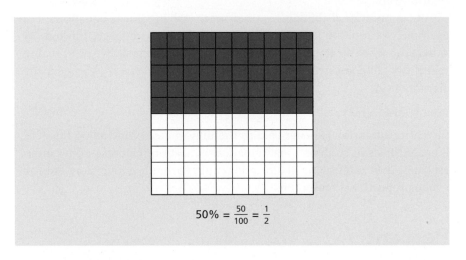

$$50\% = \frac{50}{100} = \frac{1}{2}$$

Eventually, students can simply sketch approximate models. For example, a student might represent 30% like this:

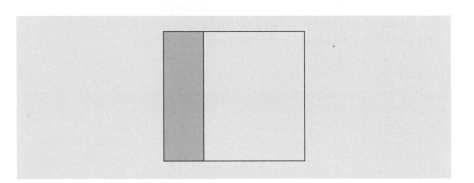

ACTIVITY 14.11

Pose the following question to students: It is really easy to figure out 20% of this number. What might the number be?

_____

Proportional Reasoning

A percent can always be written as a decimal, or vice versa. For example, 48% is the same as 0.48; both mean 48 hundredths. If a number is written as a decimal, the first two places to the right of the decimal point can be written as a whole number percent. For example, 0.235 can be written as 23.5%.

Initially, students should relate certain percents to some comfortable fractions, for example, 50% to $\frac{1}{2}$, 25% to $\frac{1}{4}$, 10% to $\frac{1}{10}$, and perhaps 33% to about $\frac{1}{3}$. Later, students use relationships to relate a broader group of percents to related fractions or fractions to related percents. For example, the fraction $\frac{3}{4}$ is related to 75% since it is the same as three groups of $\frac{1}{4}$, or $3 \times 25\%$.

ACTIVITY 14.12

Present various statements involving percent. Ask students which make sense. For example,

– The percent of males in the world is 42%.

– The percent of the floor in a living room covered by furniture is usually 50%.

– The percent of red on the Canadian flag is 75%.

Shutterstock/Edwin Verin

Proportional Reasoning

If you know 20% of a number, what other percents of it do you also know?

I think if you know 20% of a number, you will know also the 10%, 40%, 60%, 80%. The reason I said that because if you already know 20%, to find 10% you just need to divide the number you get from the 20% by 2. If you want to find 40% you multiply by 2, then if you want to find 60% you multiply by 3, and for 80% you multiply by 4.

Student Response

This student responds, like many others, by figuring out the "easy" percents you would know if you know 20%. She doesn't seem to realize that, if you know 20%, you can figure out any percent.

Principle 2: The actual amount that a percent represents is based on the whole of which it is a percent.

1% can be a lot or a little; it depends what it is 1% of. For example, 1% of all the water on the planet is a lot of water, but 1% of a juice glass full of water is not very much water at all. However, in both circumstances, 1% is definitely not a lot when compared to each whole.

The same quantity can represent different amounts depending on the whole. For example, 20 is 50% of 40, but it is 100% of 20 and only 10% of 200.

10% percent is not a lot if you are considering 10% out of 100%. 10% is not even half of 100%.

Student Response

This student is not concerned with the size of the whole and focuses on 10% as relative to a whole; 10% is not a lot, relative to any whole.

Principle 3: Comparing whole number percents is as easy as comparing two decimals or two whole numbers.

Although comparing two fractions with different numerators and denominators is not always straightforward, comparing two percents is as easy as comparing whole numbers or decimals.

For example, although the fraction $\frac{27}{40}$ is greater than the fraction $\frac{21}{32}$, it is not immediately obvious. However, if they are both written as decimals (0.675 and 0.65625) or percents (67.5% and 65.625%), it is clearer that the first fraction is greater.

Principle 4: Percents can be as low as 0, but can go higher than 100.

Fractions and decimals less than 1 can be compared to 100. For example, 0.5% means half of 1%. It actually represents the fraction $\frac{1}{200}$ since there would be 200 half-squares and only 1 is coloured.

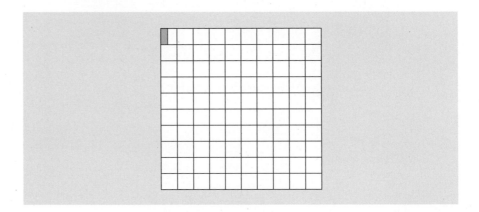

TEACHING TIP

It might be useful to have students circle the 100% amount each time when percents greater than 100 are used. That way they remember why they are using a denominator of 100.

To show more than 100%, it is necessary to use more than one grid, assuming each single grid is defined as 100%.

For example, the diagram below shows 125% if one grid is considered the whole (although it is 5/8, or 62.5% if the double grid is considered the whole).

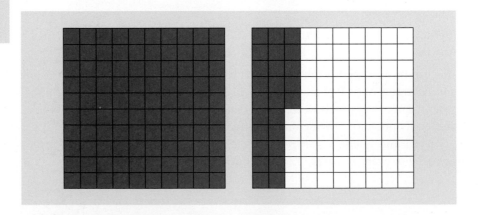

Principle 5: Sometimes percents are used to describe change.

A newspaper headline might read, "Population grew by 8%." One of the important ideas for students to understand is that the 8% represents the change, but the new population is actually 108% of the old one. The ability to represent a percent increase (or decrease) has many practical everyday applications. For example, tax has to be added to the price of an item that you purchase. It is the new price, not just the tax, that you are interested in; the new price might be 114% of the marked price, depending on taxes.

Sometimes prices are decreased. For example, a store is having a sale and marks 40% off. A customer should realize that the new price is actually 60% of the original price in order to make a quick estimate of the new price.

One of the situations where percents are used to describe change is currency conversion. If C$1 is worth US$0.92, you can use rates or percents to figure out the appropriate conversion. If the Canadian dollar is worth only 92% of the U.S. dollar, a dollar amount in Canadian dollars must be multiplied by 0.92 to determine its worth in U.S. dollars. On the other hand, a U.S. dollar amount must be divided by 0.92 to determine its worth in Canadian dollars. It turns out that US$1 is worth $1.09 at this exchange rate. Many students, and adults, are surprised that you do not gain the same number of cents as you lose when you make a currency conversion. The reason is based on **Principle 2** above. The whole that you are taking a percent of has changed; in one case, the whole is the Canadian dollar, but in the other case, it is the U.S. dollar, which is worth more—a greater whole.

Principle 6: There are a variety of strategies appropriate for solving any problem involving percent.

Sometimes, in solving a percent problem, you want to calculate the percent. Other times, you want to calculate the amount the percent represents, and still other times the value of the whole.

Problem 1 For example, the price of a $60 item has been reduced by 20% and you want to know your savings. You must calculate 20% of $60. One way is to write 20% as the decimal 0.2 and multiply by 60.

$0.2 \times 60 = 12.0$. You save $12.

Another way is to think of 20% as $\frac{1}{5}$. You can divide 60 by 5 or multiply 60 by $\frac{1}{5}$ to calculate the savings.

Another way to calculate your savings is to use a ratio table. Your goal is to have a percent of 20 in the bottom row and to find the corresponding price in the top row. You can divide both terms by 5, and read off the $12 saved.

TEACHING TIP

It is important for students to be given freedom to set up the solution strategy in whatever way makes the most sense to them. There is no one best approach.

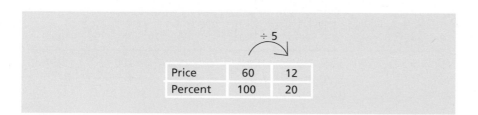

	÷ 5	
Price	60	12
Percent	100	20

Yet another way to solve the problem is to use a hundredths grid. If the original item cost $60, 100% of the grid is worth $60, so each column is worth $6. If you save 20%, you save the value of two columns, or $12.

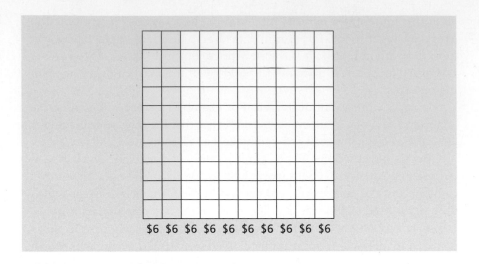

$6 $6 $6 $6 $6 $6 $6 $6 $6 $6

Problem 2 During another sale, you know that you paid $50 for an $80 item. You want to know what the discount was.

You know you saved $30, so you could compare 30 to the original price of 80. (You compare to the original price since the discount is applied to that price.) Since $\frac{30}{80} = 0.375$, the savings is 37.5%.

Another way to solve this is to realize that an $8 savings is a 10% discount. But you saved $30. Since $30 \div 8 = 3\frac{3}{4}$, the percent you want is 10% $\times 3\frac{3}{4} = 37.5\%$.

Yet another strategy is to solve the proportion: $\frac{30}{80} = \frac{x}{100}$, since $\frac{x}{100}$ is a ratio that can easily be written as a percent. To solve the proportion, you can multiply $\frac{30}{80}$ by 100. You use 30 in the numerator and not 50 since it is the percent saved that you are interested in.

Problem 3 Suppose, at yet another sale, the discount was 40% and you know that you saved $50. You want to know what the original price was.

You can use strategies similar to those described for the other two problems. You might realize that if a discount of 40% is worth $50, then a discount of 20% is worth $25. If 20% is $25, then the original price, which is 100%, must be 5 times as much, or $125.

You could use a matching percent/number line and take equal step sizes on each line.

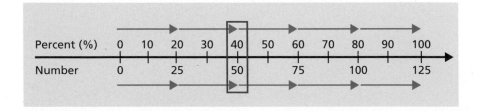

You might divide 50 directly by 0.4 since the original price was multiplied by 0.4 to get 50. The result is still $125.

You could set up a ratio table and manipulate the values to get 100% in the bottom row; 100%, the original price, would be $125.

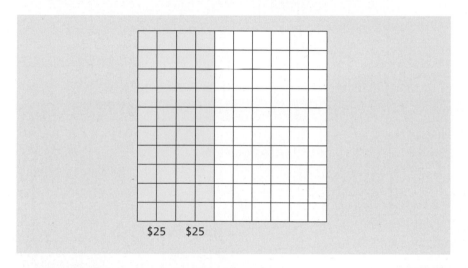

	÷ 2		× 5
Amount	50	25	125
Percent	40	20	100

You might use a hundredths grid. In this situation, since you saved $50 based on 40 squares of the grid, each set of 20 squares represents a saving of $25. That means the full grid, or the original price, would be 5 sets of $25, or $125.

$25 $25

Or, again, you can set up and solve a proportion: $\frac{40}{100} = \frac{50}{x}$. To solve, you can multiply both sides of the equation by 100 x and then divide by 40, and the result is, again $125.

Common Errors and Misconceptions

Ratio, Rate, and Percent: Common Errors, Misconceptions, and Strategies

COMMON ERROR OR MISCONCEPTION	SUGGESTED STRATEGY
Percents Greater than 100% Some students who are focused on the concept of "out of 100" find percents greater than 100% difficult to deal with. A percent greater than 100 would be equivalent to an improper fraction.	Students might look at hundredths grids where first 10, then 20, then 30, ... up to 100 squares are coloured. Then bring out a second grid and colour another 10 squares in that grid. Talk about how this is 100% and another 10%, so the total would be 110%.
Writing Decimals Students write a decimal like 0.5 as 0.50%.	This is similar to the confusion around writing 0.25¢ instead of $0.25. Students need to know that 0.5 is equivalent to 50 out of 100, or 50%.
Describing Percent Change Students sometimes do not relate to the correct whole (or 100%) when describing a percent change. For example, when calculating the original price after a discount of 20% that results in a price of $40, they forget that the 20% discount was based on a different whole than a 20% increase of $40 would be.	Having students check an answer usually shows them that they calculated incorrectly. But what is even more important is that they always identify what 100% represents before they perform any calculation. *(continued)*

Ratio, Rate, and Percent: Common Errors, Misconceptions, and Strategies (Continued)

COMMON ERROR OR MISCONCEPTION	SUGGESTED STRATEGY
Relating Percent to Multiplication Inappropriately Some students solve the problem 4 = ___ % of 8, by noticing that 8 = 2 × 4, so they write 2% instead of 50%.	When students first consider a percent problem, they should focus on meaning. For example, in this case, if the answer were 100%, it would be all of the 8. If it were 10%, it would be less than 1 since 10% of 10 is 1 and 8 is less than 10. In this way, they would see that an answer of 2% does not make sense. Help students see that it is because 8 = 4 × 2 that 4 is half of 8, and thus 50% of it.

Appropriate Manipulatives

Ratio, Rate, and Percent: Examples of Manipulatives

COUNTERS

Counters can be used to represent ratios.

For example, the counters below show the ratios 6:4, 4:6, 4:10, 10:4, 6:10, and 10:6.

DECIMAL HUNDREDTHS GRIDS

Decimal hundredths grids are particularly appropriate to represent percents and some ratios. For example, this hundredths grid shows clearly why 75%, or 75 out of 100, is the same ratio as 3 out of 4:

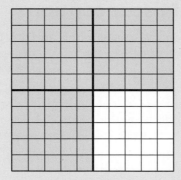

75% is 75:100, or 3:4.

PERCENT CIRCLES

Percent circles can be used to model percent. Ideally, if the circle is large enough, the ticks could be placed around the circumference to show each hundredth, or at least every 5 hundredths. This model is a good one to show the relationship between percent and fractions.

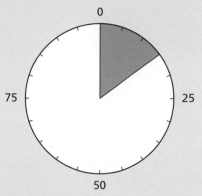

This circle shows that the 15% that is blue is less than $\frac{1}{4}$.

Appropriate Children's Books

Pythagoras and the Ratios: A Math Adventure (Ellis, 2010).
Ellis and her illustrator invite students to learn about Pythagoras and note frequencies and instrument ratios.

If Dogs Were Dinosaurs (Schwartz, 2005).
This book compares the relative sizes of items. For example, it says, "If your hair were as thick as spaghetti, the meatballs would be as big as bowling balls." Most of the comparisons are surprising and interesting. Schwartz actually includes the calculations at the back of the book to explain his thinking.

If You Hopped Like a Frog (Schwartz, 1999).
This book also allows students to explore relative proportions. For example, if a person jumped as high, proportionally, as a flea, the person could reach the torch of the Statue of Liberty. It compares how much a person could eat compared to a shrew and even compares growth rates of people during the nine months before they were born to their growth rate after birth.

If … A Mind-Bending New Way of Looking at Big Ideas and Numbers (Smith, 2014).
This book offers so many different ways for students to look at proportions. For example, one spread likens the human timeline to a 36-inch tape measure to show where different things would have been invented. Another uses percent concepts to show how salt water and fresh water would be divided up into 100 glasses. Another likens a student's life to a 12-slice pizza.

Appropriate Digital Resources

See the MindTap site for a selection of appropriate digital resources.

Assessing Student Understanding

- Make sure to focus on students' reasoning in assessing their proportional thinking. Reasoning is fundamental to proportional thinking. For example, pose a question like this: In a certain class, the ratio of boys to girls was 4:5. In another class, the ratio was 6:5. What would the ratios be if a boy and a girl from the second class move to the first class?
- Encourage students to use a variety of strategies to solve problems, not always a single strategy. For example, if they solve one problem using a unit rate, ask them to solve the next problem a different way.
- Examine how this student responded to the open question: 72 is _____ % of _____.
  - What does it show that the student understands?
  - How was this question useful in assessing this student's understanding?

Student Response

This student recognized that there were many possible responses to the provided prompt.

```
B.      72 is 72% of 100
        72 is 36% of 50
        72 is 18% of 25
        72 is 100% of 72
        72 is 200% of 36
        72 is 400% of 18
        72 is 800% of 9
        72 is 1600% of 4.5
        72 is 2000% of 3.6
        72 is 4000% of 1.8
        72 is 8000% of 0.9
        72 is 16000% of 0.45
        72 is 20000% of 0.36
        72 is 40000% of 0.18
        72 is 80000% of 0.09
        72 is 160000% of 0.045
        72 is 10% of 7200
        72 is 200000% of 0.036
            etc.
```

- Ask students to describe situations where rates, ratios, and proportions are used to show that they have a sense of when these mathematical concepts apply.
- Make sure students can relate various rates, ratios, and percents to known benchmarks. For example, you might ask them to draw a sketch to show what the ratio 4:9 might mean and what that ratio might really describe.

Applying What You've Learned

1. Some students are troubled by a problem like the chapter problem since there is some ambiguity; they worry that it is not definitive how long a lifetime actually is.
   a) What are the advantages and disadvantages of this sort of ambiguity?
   b) Were you surprised by the solution to the problem? Explain why or why not.

2. a) Describe three different ways that you might solve this problem: 72% of students in a school participated in the food drive. If 198 students participated, how many students are in the school?

   b) Which of those ways do you personally find most comfortable? Why?

3. Many students struggle with the introduction of percents greater than 100 and that is why the topic is usually left until Grade 8. List one or two ways to introduce these percents that you think will make their use more meaningful to students.

4. It was mentioned in the chapter that there is some informal proportional thinking that happens in Grades K to 5. Cite as many examples as you can think of and explain how several of them really are about proportional thinking.

5. What are some of the advantages of differentiating between *a:b* and the fraction? Explain your thinking.

6. Create a lesson plan built around a piece of children's literature related to ratio and proportion. What ideas about proportion does your lesson plan bring out? How?

7. There are some educators who advocate the introduction of percent prior to formal work with ratios of the form *a:b*. What might be some arguments for this? What might be some arguments against this?

Interact with a K–8 Student:

8. Prepare a set of percent statements with which a Grade 5 to 8 student can agree or disagree. See how reasonable this student's responses are. An example might be: 20% of Grade 5 students play sports.

Discuss with a K–8 Teacher:

9. Ask a teacher to share with you one or two of his or her favourite problems that require the use of ratio, rate, and percent. Ask why he or she particularly likes these problems. What is your response to the problems?

Selected References

Abrahamson, D., and Cigan, C. (2003). A design for ratio and proportion instruction. *Mathematics Teaching in the Middle School, 9,* 493–501.

Attia, T.L. (2003). Using school lunches to study proportion. *Mathematics Teaching in the Middle School, 9,* 17–21.

Beckmann, C.E., Thompson, D.R., and Austin, R.A. (2004). Exploring proportional reasoning through movies and literature. *Mathematics Teaching in the Middle School, 9,* 256–262.

Behr, M.J., Harel, G., Post, T., and Lesh, R. (1992). Rational number, ratio and proportion. In Grouws, D.A. (Ed.). *Handbook of research on mathematics teaching and learning.* Toronto, ON: Maxwell Macmillan Canada, 296–333.

Che, S.M. (2009). Giant pencils: Developing proportional reasoning. *Mathematics Teaching in the Middle School, 14,* 404-408.

Clark, M.R., Berenson, S.B., and Cavey, L.O. (2003). A comparison of ratios and fractions and their roles as tools in proportional reasoning. *Journal of Mathematical Behavior, 22,* 297–317.

Cohen, J.S. (2013). Strip diagrams: Illuminating proportion. *Mathematics Teaching in the Middle School, 19,* 536–542.

Ellis, J. (2010). *Pythagoras and the ratios: A math adventure.* Watertown, MA: Charlesbridge Publishing.

Ercole, L.K., Frantz, M., and Ashline, G. (2011). Multiple ways to solve proportions. *Mathematics Teaching in the Middle School, 16,* 482–491.

Griffith, H.V. (1999). *How many candles?* New York: Greenwillow Books.

Hunter, A.E., Bush, S.B., and Karp, K. (2014). Systematic interventions for teaching ratio. *Mathematics Teaching in the Middle School, 19,* 360–367.

Kent, L.B., Arnosky, J., and McMonagle, J. (2002). Using representational contexts to support multiplicative reasoning. In Litwiller, B., and Bright, G. (Eds.). *Making sense of fractions, ratios, and proportions: 2002 yearbook.* Reston, VA: National Council of Teachers of Mathematics, 145–152.

Kenton, G.C. (2008). How many piano tuners are in our city? *Mathematics Teaching in the Middle School, 14,* 280–283.

Lamon, S.J. (1993). Ratio and proportion: Connecting content and children's thinking. *Journal for Research in Mathematics Education, 24,* 41–61.

Langrall, C.W., and Swafford, J. (2000). Three balloons for two dollars: Developing proportional reasoning. *Mathematics Teaching in the Middle School, 6,* 254–261.

Lo, J.J., Watanabe, T., and Cai, J. (2004). Developing ratio concepts: An Asian perspective. *Mathematics Teaching in the Middle School, 7,* 362–367.

Lobato, J., and Ellis, A.B. (2010). *Developing essential understanding of ratios, proportions and proportional reasoning.* Reston, VA: National Council of Teachers of Mathematics.

Martinie, S.L., and Bay-Williams, J.M. (2003). Using literature to engage students in proportional reasoning. *Mathematics Teaching in the Middle School, 9,* 142–147.

Ministry of Eduction (Ontario) (2012). *Paying attention to proportional reasoning.* Toronto: Queens Printer for Ontario.

Moss, J., and Case, R. (1999). Developing children's understanding of the rational numbers: A new model and an experimental curriculum. *Journal for Research in Mathematics Education, 30,* 122–147.

Moss, J., and Caswell, B. (2004). Building percent dolls: Connecting linear measurement to learning ratio and proportion. *Mathematics Teaching in the Middle School, 10,* 68–74.

Nugent, C. (2006). How many blades of grass are on a football field? *Teaching Children Mathematics, 12,* 283–289.

Pagni, D. (2005). Angles, time, and proportion. *Mathematics Teaching in the Middle School, 10,* 436–441.

Post, T., Behr, M.J., and Lesh, R. (1988). Proportionality and the development of prealgebra understandings. In Coxford, A.F., and Shulte, A.P. (Eds.). *The ideas of algebra, K–12.* Reston, VA: National Council of Teachers of Mathematics, 78–90.

Reeder, S. (2009). Are we golden? *Mathematics Teaching in the Middle School, 13,* 150–155.

Riehl, S.M., and Steinthorsdottir, O.B. (2014). Revisiting Mr. Tall and Mr. Short. *Mathematics Teaching in the Middle School, 20,* 220–228.

Roberge, M.C., and Cooper, L.L. (2010). Map, scale, proportion, and Google Earth. *Mathematics Teaching in the Middle School, 15,* 448–457.

Schwartz, D. (1999). *If you hopped like a frog.* New York: Scholastic Press.

Schwartz, D. (2005). *If dogs were dinosaurs.* New York: Scholastic Press.

Sinn, R., Spence, D.J., and Poitevint, M. (2010). A geometric approach to solving rate problems. *Mathematics Teaching in the Middle School, 16,* 302–310.

Slovin, H. (2000). Moving to proportional reasoning. *Mathematics Teaching in the Middle School, 6,* 58-60.

Smith, D.J. (2014). *If ... a mind-bending new way of looking at big ideas and numbers.* Toronto: Kids Can Press.

Thompson, C.S., and Bush, W.S. (2003). Improving middle school teachers' reasoning about proportional reasoning. *Mathematics Teaching in the Middle School, 8,* 398–403.

Van Dooren, W., De Bock, D., Hessels, A., Janssens, D., and Verscaffel, L. (2005). Not everything is proportional: Effects of age and problem type on propensities for over-generalization. *Cognition and Instruction, 23,* 57–86.

Chapter 15

Extending the Number System to Negative and Irrational Numbers

IN A NUTSHELL

The main ideas in this chapter are listed below:

1. The negative integers are the "opposites" of the whole numbers. Each integer is the reflection of its opposite across a line perpendicular to and cutting the number line at 0.

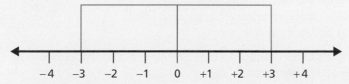

−3 and +3 are opposites

−4 −3 −2 −1 0 +1 +2 +3 +4

2. Integer operations are based upon the zero principle, the fact that $(-1) + (+1) = 0$.

3. The meanings for the operations that apply to whole numbers, fractions, and decimals also apply to negative integers. Each meaning can be represented by a model, although some models suit some meanings better than others.

CHAPTER PROBLEM

You represent an integer using some positive counters and 4 times as many negative counters. What integer might you be representing?

4. Exponents are used to shorten multiplication notation.

5. Conventions for the order in which operations are performed must be shared to ensure consistency.

6. There are numbers, called irrational numbers, which cannot be written as rational numbers (i.e. positive or negative fractions or integers). When written as decimals, the decimal digits of these numbers do not repeat.

Introducing Integers

The concept of negative integers is generally introduced near the end of the elementary school years or in early middle/junior high school. Many students are quite comfortable interpreting these numbers, particularly because of their familiarity with negative temperatures, although operations with integers may be less familiar. In fact, there is evidence (Wilcox, 2008, and Behrend and Mohs, 2006) that young students are quite successful understanding negative numbers, even adding them.

Integer Contexts

Useful contexts for making work with integers meaningful, depending on the interest and experience of students, include

- temperatures
- floors below or above a main floor
- being below or above sea level or ground level
- golf scores below or above par

However, often integer operations make more sense to students using purely mathematical contexts.

ACTIVITY 15.1

Have students bring in clippings from newspapers that include negative numbers and discuss the variety of situations. They might also listen to weather reports and attend to how negative numbers are read, whether as "minus 5" or "negative 5."

Building Number Sense

Student Response

This student has an interesting interpretation of the number −2.

What does −2 mean?

It means you have 2 things you lost or got robbed.

Reading and Writing Integers

It is desirable to use either a raised + or − sign or brackets around the number to write an integer, to make the distinction between these symbols and the operations symbols for addition and subtraction. However, even though making this distinction is helpful when students are first working with integers, later on they will learn that there is a connection between subtraction and the negative symbol and between addition and the positive symbol; for example, ⁻3 or (−3) is 0 − 3, and ⁺3 (or +3) is 0 + 3. Students can use the + symbol to indicate a positive integer, even though it is not necessary, as the symbol is assumed if there is no symbol.

Comparing Integers

When comparing integers, it is helpful if students think about the placement of each integer on a number line rather than trying to memorize rules. In this way, students are much less likely to make the mistake of thinking that −9 > −7.

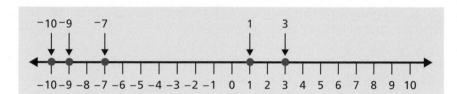

PRINCIPLES FOR COMPARING INTEGERS

1. Any negative integer is less than any positive integer.
2. A positive integer closer to 0 is always less than a positive integer farther away from 0; for example, +1 < +3.
3. A negative integer closer to 0 is always greater than a negative integer farther away from 0; for example, −7 > −10.

These principles can be developed using the number line.

Principle 1: Any negative integer is less than any positive integer.

Every negative value is to the left of 0, or below it, on a vertical number line. Every positive value is to the right, or above it on a vertical number line. Since the number line is built so that greater numbers are to the right or above, any positive integer must be greater than any negative integer.

Principle 2: A positive integer closer to 0 is always less than a positive integer farther away from 0.

On a horizontal number line, 0 is to the left of all of the positive integers. So a positive integer closer to 0 is farther left than one farther from 0. Since it is farther left, it is less.

Principle 3: A negative integer closer to 0 is always greater than a negative integer farther away from 0.

On a horizontal number line, 0 is to the right of all of the negative integers. So a negative integer closer to 0 is farther right and, therefore, greater.

The Zero Property

Mathematicians have defined (−1) as the number that you add to +1 to result in 0; that is, by definition, (−1) + (+1) = 0.

Representing the Zero Property

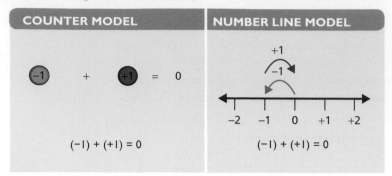

COUNTER MODEL	NUMBER LINE MODEL

$(-1) + (+1) = 0$ $(-1) + (+1) = 0$

This is referred to as the zero property and is the foundation for computations involving negative numbers. As a consequence of this definition, any number can be added to its opposite to result in a value of 0. For example, $(-3) = (-1) + (-1) + (-1)$ and $(+3) = (+1) + (+1) + (+1)$. So $(-3) + (+3) = (-1) + (-1) + (-1) + (+1) + (+1) + (+1)$. The order of adding numbers is irrelevant, so the total is the same as $[(-1) + (+1)] + [(-1) + (+1)] + [(-1) + (+1)]$. The sum of zeros is just zero.

Adding Integers

Just as with whole numbers, adding means putting together. Therefore, $(-5) + (+3)$ means putting together an amount representing $+3$ with an amount representing (-5). This can be modelled in several ways:

• using a number line

Start at (-5) and move 3 forward. You land at (-2).

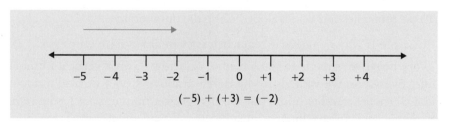

$(-5) + (+3) = (-2)$

• using counters where one colour, for example, blue, represents (-1) and another colour, for example, red, represents $(+1)$

Use the fact that $(-3) + (+3) = 0$ to simplify $(-5) + (+3)$ to (-2).

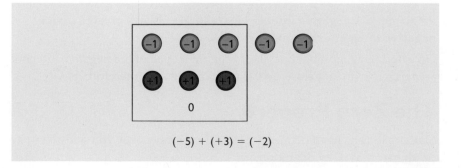

$(-5) + (+3) = (-2)$

These two models can be used to help students discover the principles that underlie integer addition.

PRINCIPLES FOR ADDING INTEGERS

1. The sum of two negatives is negative.
2. The sum of two positives is positive.
3. The sum of a negative and a positive can be either positive or negative. The sum takes the sign of the number that is farther from 0.

Principle 1: The sum of two negatives is negative.

By modelling with counters, students see that they are putting blue counters together with other blue counters. The result is blue counters.

Principle 2: The sum of two positives is positive.

Starting to the right of 0 on a number line and continuing farther to the right results in a value to the right of 0, or a positive value.

Principle 3: The sum of a negative and a positive can be either positive or negative. The sum takes the sign of the number that is farther from 0.

For example, $(-3) + (+4)$ is positive since there are more reds than blues, so a red is left over when 0s are created by pairing up reds and blues. But $(+3) + (-4)$ is negative since there are more blues than reds, so a blue is left over when zeros are created.

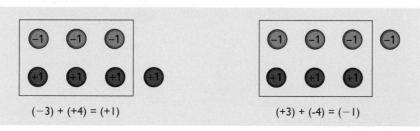

$$(-3) + (+4) = (+1) \qquad (+3) + (-4) = (-1)$$

More generally, there are more of one colour counter than another, pairs can be created, but there will be left-overs of one colour; that means the sum has the sign of the number with more counters.

Encourage students to apply this principle and use a variety of mental math strategies when adding two or more integers. For example, to add $(-32) + (-39) + (42) + (30)$, it might make sense to combine $(+42) + (-32)$ to get $(+10)$ to add to (-9), the result of adding (-39) and $(+30)$.

ACTIVITY 15.5

Integrate integer work with probability.

Have students toss a coin.

- If the coin lands heads, they gain a point $(+1)$.
- If it lands tails, they lose a point (-1).

After students have tossed 20 times, they indicate their final score.

Ask how many tails someone whose final score is -2 could have tossed and why.

Building Number Sense

ACTIVITY 15.4

Ask students to select two integers and add them. The only condition is that the sum has to be close to but to the left of 0.

Building Number Sense

ACTIVITY 15.6

Display a number line. Ask students to determine how to get from 2 to -3 if the only allowable moves are moving left 2 spaces or right 5 spaces. Then ask students to use a number sentence to describe what they did.

Critical Thinking

ACTIVITY 15.7

Provide a magic square partially filled in. All columns, rows, and diagonals add to the same total. Ask students to complete the square.

+8		−5	+5
	+3	+2	
	−1		+4
−4			−7

Critical Thinking

Subtracting Integers

As with adding integers, it is important for students to develop a conceptual understanding of the principles that underpin integer subtraction.

PRINCIPLES FOR SUBTRACTING INTEGERS

1. To subtract an integer, you can use either a take away meaning or a missing addend meaning.
2. To subtract an integer, you can use the zero property to add enough to the minuend (the starting amount) to take away the subtrahend.
3. To subtract an integer, you can determine what to add to the subtrahend to get to the minuend; sometimes you need to use the zero property.
4. To subtract an integer, you can add its opposite.

Principle 1: To subtract an integer, you can use either a take away meaning or a missing addend meaning.

As with whole numbers and decimals, subtraction can mean take away or how much must be added to one number to get another.

You might model subtraction of integers with two-coloured counters.

- $(-5) - (-2)$ means you have 5 blues and want to take away 2 of them.

$$(-5) - (-2) = (-3)$$

- $(-5) - (-2)$ tells how much to add to (-2) to get to (-5) (just as $4 - 3$ tells how much to add to 3 to get to 4). If you already have (-2), 2 blues, you have to add 3 more blues (-3) to get to (-5). Again, $(-5) - (-2) = (-3)$.

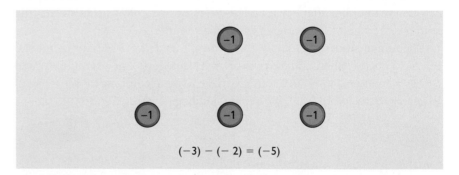

$$(-3) - (-2) = (-5)$$

Principle 2: To subtract an integer, you can use the zero property to add enough to the minuend (the starting amount) to take away the subtrahend.

Both meanings of subtraction can also be used to subtract numbers like $(-2) - (-6)$ or $(+2) - (-6)$, where taking away is not immediately possible. (If you only have 2 blues, how do you take away 6?)

- $(-2) - (-6)$ can mean you have 2 blues, but want to take away 6 blues. To get more blues to take away, you can add four pairs of 0 in the form of $(+1) + (-1)$, that is, 4 reds and 4 blues. Because you are adding 0, you are not changing the total, but now there are 6 blues to take away. Once they are removed, the result is 4 reds, or $(+4)$.

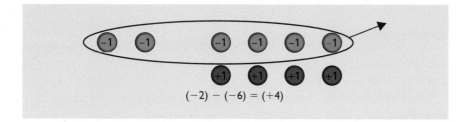

$$(-2) - (-6) = (+4)$$

- $(+2) - (-6)$ tells how much to add to (-6) to get to $(+2)$. That means you start with 6 blues and want to figure out what to add to end up with 2 reds. You want to add 6 reds (to pair up with the 6 blues) and another 2 reds so you end up with 2 reds.

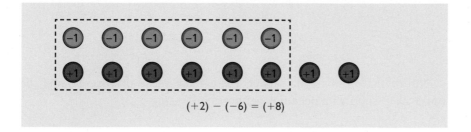

$$(+2) - (-6) = (+8)$$

Subtraction of integers can also be modelled using a number line. The take away model is difficult to explain meaningfully on a number line, but the missing addend model works well. For example, $(-7) - (-1)$ tells what to add to (-1) to get to (-7). Start at (-1) and see what you have to add to get to (-7). You have to go left, 6 spaces, so the result is (-6).

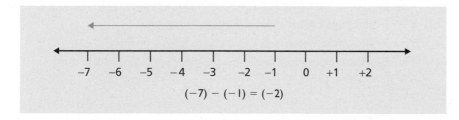

$$(-7) - (-1) = (-2)$$

Principle 3: To subtract an integer, you can add its opposite.

When you subtract a negative from a positive, it is easy to see, using the number line model, why you can add the opposite to subtract. For example, $(+4) - (-5)$ is a way to ask what to add to (-5) to get to $(+4)$. It is clear that you need to move 5 to the right to get to 0, and another 4 to the right to get to $(+4)$, so the total amount to be added is $4 + 5$.

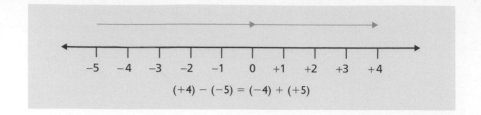

$$(+4) - (-5) = (-4) + (+5)$$

The concept that subtraction can be accomplished by adding the opposite can be modelled with other types of questions, too, for example, $(-3) - (-2)$, but it tends to be a little less obvious.

Here's another way to show the same idea. What has to be added to –5 to get to 4 is the same as what has to be added to 5 more than –5 (that is, 0) to get to 5 more than 4, which is 9. That amount is 5 + 4.

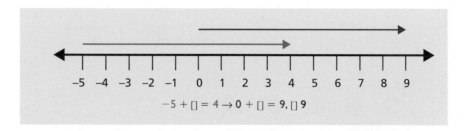

$$-5 + [] = 4 \rightarrow 0 + [] = 9, [] 9$$

Notice that both of the models used make sense of why we add the opposite to subtract a negative; neither is just a rule.

Multiplying Integers

As with integer addition and subtraction, counter models and number line models can be used to help students make sense of multiplication and division of integers.

PRINCIPLES FOR MULTIPLYING INTEGERS

1. Integers can be multiplied in any order without affecting the product.
2. The product of a positive and a negative is negative.
3. The product of two positives or two negatives is positive.
4. The distributive property applies to multiplication and addition of integers, that is, $a(b + c) = ab + ac$.

Principle 1: Integers can be multiplied in any order without affecting the product.

Mathematicians have defined the set of integers to ensure that they obey the same properties as the set of whole numbers. One example is the commutative property. For example, $(+3) \times (-2) = (-2) \times (+3)$. Knowing this property will be key to explaining Principle 2.

Principle 2: The product of a positive and a negative is negative.

A variety of models can be used to explain why a positive multiplied by a negative is negative. For example,

- One can model $3 \times (-2)$ as 3 groups of (-2) using counters. Clearly 3 groups of (-2) is modelled by the same number of counters as 3×2, but the counters are all blue, so the product is negative.

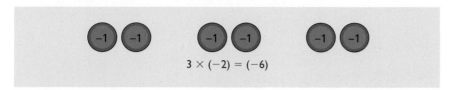

$$3 \times (-2) = (-6)$$

- The number line model is based on repeated addition, that is, $3 \times (-2) = (-2) + (-2) + (-2)$, and so the result is negative.

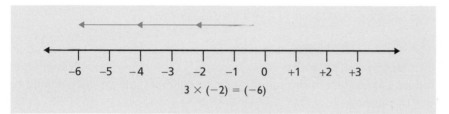

$$3 \times (-2) = (-6)$$

It is harder to model $(-3) \times (+2)$ since it is not clear what (-3) groups means. However, students can use the commutative property of multiplication:

- $(-3) \times (+2)$ can be represented as $(+2) \times (-3)$, and 2 groups of (-3) can be modelled.

- Another way to model $(-3) \times (+2)$ is symbolically through patterns.

$$(+3) \times (+2) = (+6)$$
$$(+2) \times (+2) = (+4)$$
$$(+1) \times (+2) = (+2)$$
$$(0) \times (+2) = (0)$$
$$(-1) \times (+2) = (?)$$
$$(-2) \times (+2) = (?)$$
$$(-3) \times (+2) = (?)$$

A student observes that the product decreases by 2 as the left-hand factor decreases by 1. This makes sense: each time there is one less 2. If the pattern were to continue, the products would be (-2), (-4), and then (-6).

Yet another approach is to think of $(-3) \times 2$ as $0 - 3 \times 2$, since $-3 = 0 - 3$.

Students would show 0 in such a way that it would be easy to take away 3 sets of $+2$ [most likely as $6 + (-6)$]. They would observe that 6 negative counters are left when the 3 sets of $+2$ are removed.

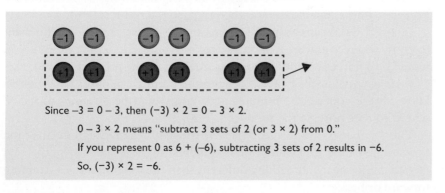

Since $-3 = 0 - 3$, then $(-3) \times 2 = 0 - 3 \times 2$.

$0 - 3 \times 2$ means "subtract 3 sets of 2 (or 3×2) from 0."

If you represent 0 as $6 + (-6)$, subtracting 3 sets of 2 results in -6.

So, $(-3) \times 2 = -6$.

ACTIVITY 15.8

Tell students that the product of five integers is -120. Ask them what the least possible sum of the integers could be. Ask, as well, if it is possible for the product of four different integers to be -120.

Critical Thinking

TEACHING TIP

Recall that the principles are not simply stated to students. They will uncover them as they work with patterns, models, and the meaning of the operations.

Principle 3: The product of two positives or two negatives is positive.

One way for students to understand why, for example, $(-3) \times (-2) = (+6)$ is to use patterns. You can set up a pattern that will ultimately include the desired factors. For example:

$$(+3) \times (-2) = (-6)$$
$$(+2) \times (-2) = (-4)$$
$$(+1) \times (-2) = (-2)$$
$$(0) \times (-2) = (0)$$
$$(-1) \times (-2) = (?)$$
$$(-2) \times (-2) = (?)$$
$$(-3) \times (-2) = (?)$$

The student would notice that as the first factor decreases by 1, the product increases by 2. This makes sense since each time there is one less (-2) to reduce the product. If the pattern were to continue, the products would be $(+2), (+4)$, and $(+6)$, so $(-3) \times (-2) = (+6)$.

Another approach is to think of $(-3) \times (-2)$ as $0 - 3 \times (-2)$, since $-3 = 0 - 3$.

Students would show 0 in such a way that it would be easy to take away 3 sets of -2 [most likely as $6 + (-6)$] and would observe that 6 positive counters are left when the 3 sets of (-2) are removed.

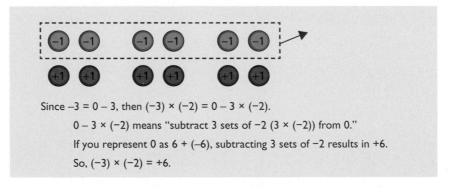

Since $-3 = 0 - 3$, then $(-3) \times (-2) = 0 - 3 \times (-2)$.

$0 - 3 \times (-2)$ means "subtract 3 sets of -2 ($3 \times (-2)$) from 0."

If you represent 0 as $6 + (-6)$, subtracting 3 sets of -2 results in $+6$.

So, $(-3) \times (-2) = +6$.

Some teachers use "stories" to explain why two negatives make a positive. Generally, although they capture students' attention, the logic on which they are based is a little vague for the student. One example is the idea of a videotape:

$(+2) \times (+3)$ means a tape is fastforwarded 3 frames a minute for 2 minutes. You are 6 frames ahead, so the result is $+6$.

$(+2) \times (-3)$ means a tape is rewound 3 frames a minute for 2 minutes. You are 6 frames behind the starting point, so the result is (-6).

$(-2) \times (+3)$ means a tape is fastforwarded 3 frames a minute. You want to know where you were 2 minutes ago (-2 represents a time of -2). You would be 6 frames behind where you are now, so the product is (-6).

$(-2) \times (-3)$ means a tape is rewound 3 frames a minute. You want to know where you were 2 minutes ago. You would be 6 frames ahead of where you are now, so the product is $(+6)$.

The "vagueness" in this story is why the first negative sign means time forward and time backward. Some students might wonder why the first negative sign means something different than the other one does (running forward or backward).

TEACHING TIP

Although there are not many realistic situations involving the multiplication of two negatives, one possibility is determining the prior location of an object moving in a negative direction. For example, using the context of sea level depths, the following problem can be modelled using $(-3) \times (-20)$: Where was an object 3 hours ago, if it has been travelling at 20 m/h downward and it is now at sea level?

Principle 4: The distributive property applies to multiplication and addition of integers, that is, $a(b + c) = ab + ac$.

Students are likely simply to assume that this principle holds. It is useful in a situation like this one: The student knows that $-2 \times 34 = -68$ and wants to calculate -2×37. He or she would think of this as $-2 \times 34 + (-2) \times 3$, and would add the two values together. Indeed, this principle does hold for integers.

Dividing Integers

As with multiplying integers, using models helps make sense of where the quotients come from.

> **PRINCIPLES FOR DIVIDING INTEGERS**
>
> 1. Division of integers can be modelled using a sharing, a grouping (measurement), or an inverse multiplication meaning.
> 2. The rules for assigning signs to the quotient of two integers are based on the rules for products.
>   - The quotient of two positives or two negatives is positive.
>   - The quotient of a positive and a negative is negative.

Principle 1: Division of integers can be modelled using a sharing, a grouping (measurement), or an inverse multiplication meaning.

One of the meanings of a quotient like $14 \div 2$ is the size of the share if 2 people share 14. That approach can also be used to describe the quotient of a negative divided by a positive and can be modelled using counters or a number line.

For example, $(-10) \div 2 = (-5)$.

- 10 blue counters can be shared by 2 people. Each gets 5 blue counters.

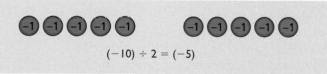

$$(-10) \div 2 = (-5)$$

- A jump of 10 to the left on the number line can be divided into 2 jumps of 5 to the left

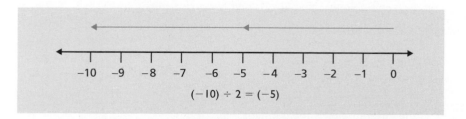

$$(-10) \div 2 = (-5)$$

Another meaning of division is grouping or measurement. It is useful to explain a positive divided by a positive, or a negative divided by a negative. For example, $(-10) \div (-2)$ can mean how many groups of (-2) can be found in a group of (-10). There are 5 groups. This can be modelled using counters or a number line (as shown at the top of the next page).

ACTIVITY 15.9

Students can practise division of integers by calculating the average score per hole in a golf game if the values are reported as scores above and below par.

Building Number Sense

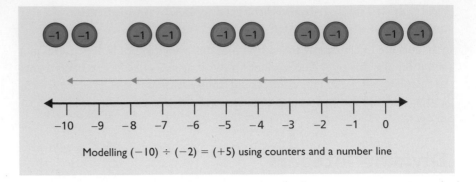

Modelling $(-10) \div (-2) = (+5)$ using counters and a number line

ACTIVITY 15.10

Tell students you divided two integers and the result was -8. Ask what the integers might have been and how they know.

Building Number Sense

A third meaning of division is inverse multiplication. The quotient of two numbers is the number you must multiply the divisor by to achieve a product that is the dividend. For example, $12 \div 2 = 6$ since $6 \times 2 = 12$. It is this meaning of division that best explains the quotient of integers with different signs.

For example, $(-12) \div 2$ describes the number by which you must multiply 2 to get a product of (-12). From the rules for multiplying, it is clear that the number is negative. $(-12) \div 2 = -6$ since $2 \times (-6) = (-12)$.

Principle 2: The rules for assigning signs to the quotient of two integers are based on the rules for products.

- The quotient of two positives or two negatives is positive.
- The quotient of a positive and a negative is negative.

Because of the relationship between multiplication and division, the sign rules are the same for division as for multiplication.

For example, $(-12) \div (-4)$ must be $(+3)$ since $(-4) \times (+3) = (-12)$.

$(-12) \div (+4)$ must be (-3) since $(+4) \times (-3) = (-12)$.

$(+12) \div (-4)$ must be (-3) since $(-4) \times (-3) = +12$.

ACTIVITY 15.11

Students will enjoy playing Mystery Integers as described below:

Select four integers. Do not tell anyone what they are.

Make up a set of eight clues that will allow someone to guess the integers you chose. All eight clues must be necessary. The clues must

- use all four operations somewhere in the eight clues
- include some clues that involve comparing integers

For example, suppose that your integers are -8, 7, 5, and -3. Here are three possible clues:

- The sum of the four integers is 1.
- If you order the integers from least to greatest, the product of the two middle integers is -15.
- If you subtract the least integer from the greatest integer, and divide the difference by 3, the quotient is 5.

The three clues above do not give enough information to figure out the integers. What five additional clues would give enough information? Remember that all five clues must be necessary.

Creative Thinking

Rational Numbers

Rational numbers are the quotients of two integers. They might be thought of as fractions (which include positive integers and 0) and their opposites on the number line. For example, $-\frac{2}{3}$ is a rational number, as is $\frac{2}{3}$.

There are an infinite number of rational numbers on the number line, and, in fact, there is always another rational number between any two given ones. For example, between $-\frac{3}{4}$ and $-\frac{9}{10}$ is $-\frac{6}{7}$.

The rules for operations with rational numbers simply combine the sign rules for operations with integers and the procedures for operating with fractions or decimals. For example, $-\frac{1}{3} + (-\frac{4}{5})$ is negative, just as would be the case when adding two negative integers, but the distance from 0 is $\frac{1}{3} + \frac{4}{5}$, so the sum is $-\frac{17}{15}$. Or $-\frac{2}{3} \times \frac{3}{4}$ is negative, just as would be the case when multiplying a negative integer by a positive one, but the distance from 0 is $\frac{2}{3} \times \frac{3}{4} = \frac{2}{4}$, or $\frac{1}{2}$. The product is $-\frac{1}{2}$.

Exponents

Just as the multiplication sign is a shortcut so that a long expression involving the repeated addition of the same number, like $2 + 2 + 2 + 2$, can be written more succinctly (as 4×2), the exponent is a shortcut so that a long expression involving the repeated multiplication of the same number, like $2 \times 2 \times 2 \times 2 \times 2$, can be written more succinctly, in this situation, as 2^5.

The 5 is called the exponent; it tells how many of the base, 2, are multiplied together. The entire expression, 2^5, is called a power.

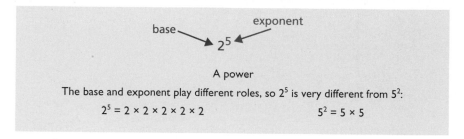

base → 2^5 ← exponent

A power

The base and exponent play different roles, so 2^5 is very different from 5^2:

$$2^5 = 2 \times 2 \times 2 \times 2 \times 2 \qquad 5^2 = 5 \times 5$$

In later grades, students learn what are called exponent or power laws, where they observe, for example, that $2^5 \times 2^3 = 2^{(5+3)}$. Although these are taught formally later, many students will understand, for example, that if five 2s were multiplied by an additional three 2s, there would be eight 2s multiplied together; that is 2^8.

It would be valuable to make the link to the superscripts (i.e., exponents) used in metric units of area and volume. The reason we write 4 cm^2 (which is 2^2 cm^2 for the area of a 2 cm × 2 cm square) is that we are multiplying 2 × 2 and creating squares that are 1 cm × 1 cm, in a sense, multiplying centimetre by centimetre. The reason we write 8 cm^3 (which is 2^3 cm^3 for the volume of a 2 cm × 2 cm × 2 cm cube) is that we are multiplying 2 × 2 × 2 and creating cubes that are 1 cm × 1 cm × 1 cm.

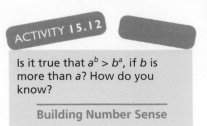

ACTIVITY 15.12

Is it true that $a^b > b^a$, if b is more than a? How do you know?

Building Number Sense

Relating Powers to Metric Measurement

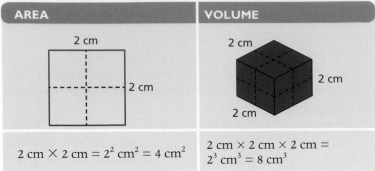

AREA	VOLUME
$2 \text{ cm} \times 2 \text{ cm} = 2^2 \text{ cm}^2 = 4 \text{ cm}^2$	$2 \text{ cm} \times 2 \text{ cm} \times 2 \text{ cm} = 2^3 \text{ cm}^3 = 8 \text{ cm}^3$

Using Powers of 10 to Give a Sense of Number Size

The pattern in the place value system is built on powers of 10. Some students might notice that, since $10 \times 10 = 10^2$, and $10 \times 10 = 100$, then it makes sense that the hundreds place can also be described as 10^2. Since each place, as you move to the left in a place value chart, is multiplied by 1 more 10, the exponent increases by 1 in each column going left. This can also help students make sense of negative and zero exponents; it will make sense that, since each place to the right is multiplied by 1 fewer 10, the exponent will be 1 less.

10^5	10^4	10^3	10^2	10^1	10^0	10^{-1}	10^{-2}	10^{-3}
Hundred thousands	Ten thousands	Thousands	Hundreds	Tens	Ones	Tenths	Hundredths	Thousandths

Using powers of 10 to describe the columns of the place value chart

Order of Operations Including Exponents

Sometimes students are confronted with a long series of computations in one expression, for example, $3 \times 4 + (5^2 - 3) \div 2$. Since all four operations and exponentiation are included, students need direction as to what to do.

Because different people might calculate in a different order, resulting in different answers, students need to learn conventions for the order. It is often described using either of the shortcuts BEDMAS or PEDMAS.

ORDER OF OPERATIONS RULES	
B (or P)	Do anything that is in brackets (or parentheses) first.
E	Do exponentiation next.
DM	Do division and multiplication, in the order they appear left to right.
AS	Do addition and subtraction, in the order they appear left to right.

For example, to calculate $3 \times 4 + (5^2 - 3) \div 2$:

B. Do $5^2 - 3$ first, since it is in Brackets:
    a) Calculate 5^2 first, since it has an Exponent: $5^2 = 5 \times 5 = 25$
    b) Then subtract 3: $25 - 3 = 22$

DM. Multiply 3×4 next: $3 \times 4 = 12$
    Divide $22 \div 2$ next: $22 \div 2 = 11$

AS. Add $12 + 11$: $12 + 11 = 23$
    So, $3 \times 4 + (5^2 - 3) \div 2 = 23$

Even this simple question might be problematic for some students, since, in a way, the exponentiation was done before the value in the brackets was evaluated (because it could not be evaluated without doing exponentiation first). This can be troubling for some students who feel that the rules were violated. Notice that, if the rules had not been used and students simply calculated moving from left to right, the answer would be incorrect: $12 + 25 = 37 \rightarrow 37 - 3 = 34 \rightarrow 34 \div 2 = 17$.

Although the rules may seem clear-cut, there are nuances, which sometimes escape some students. For example, even though the acronym puts division before multiplication (DM in BEDMAS), multiplications and divisions should be completed in order from left to right, even if the multiplications come first; similarly for addition and subtraction. More problematic might be "implicit" parentheses or brackets. For example, in writing the fraction with a numerator of $4 + 5$ and denominator of $5 + 5$, the intent is that each is "implicitly" bracketed, so the value is $\frac{9}{10}$. Some students will think $\frac{4+5}{5+5} = 4 + 1 \,(5 \div 5) + 5 = 10$.

If an expression involves only addition and subtraction (e.g., $4 + 18 - 12$), only multiplication and division (e.g., $4 \times 5 \times 12 \div 2$), or has all multiplication and division to the left of addition and subtraction without brackets or exponentiation (e.g., $4 \times 3 \div 2 + 8 - 3$), the results will be the same going left to right or using BEDMAS.

Depending on the type of calculator a student has, she or he may have to think about how to enter a complex expression so it is calculated correctly.

Rational versus Irrational Numbers

In Chapter 13, on page 296, there was a discussion about some fractions that, when written as decimals, end with repeating digits. For example, $\frac{1}{6}$ is 0.16666... and $\frac{4}{99}$ is 0.040 404 04.... We can show the repetition in the digits using a bar, $0.1\overline{6}$ and $0.\overline{04}$. $0.1\overline{6}$ and $0.\overline{04}$ are rational numbers, since they can be written as a fraction of two integers. (Note that fractions resulting in terminating decimals are also rational, for example, $\frac{1}{8}$ is 0.125.)

But there are decimals that continue but do not repeat. These numbers are called irrational numbers. An example might be 0.123 456 791 011 121 3..., with successive whole numbers, one after the other, appearing to the right of the decimal point. Since the numbers keep changing, there will never be repetition of digits. Any number on a number line that is not rational (a quotient or fraction of two integers) is irrational. It turns out that most numbers are actually irrational.

ACTIVITY 15.13

Create a complicated expression that would be calculated incorrectly by going from left to right, compared to applying the rules for the order of operations.

Then create a complicated expression that has the same result whether going from left to right or using the order of operations.

Critical Thinking

In middle/junior high/late elementary school, students meet some of these irrational numbers. One of them is 3.141 59..., a number called π (pi), which is discussed in Chapter 19 in the context of circle measurements.

Square Roots

Another set of irrational numbers they will meet are the square roots, for example, the square root of 2 ($\sqrt{2}$) or the square root of 18 ($\sqrt{18}$). Note that there are also rational square roots, such as $\sqrt{4}$, which is 2 and $\sqrt{16}$, which is 4.

The symbol for square root is $\sqrt{}$ and so $\sqrt{2}$ means the square root of 2. The numerical definition of the square root of a number is the number that can be multiplied by itself to result in the number. For example, $\sqrt{2}$ is a bit more than 1.414 since $1.414 \times 1.414 = 1.999396$, almost 2.

The geometric definition of a square root (whether rational or irrational), probably a more meaningful one for many students, is the length of the side of a square with an area of the number in question. For example,

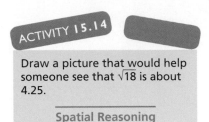

ACTIVITY 15.14

Draw a picture that would help someone see that $\sqrt{18}$ is about 4.25.

_____

Spatial Reasoning

Square Roots

A RATIONAL EXAMPLE	AN IRRATIONAL EXAMPLE
4 cm; 16 cm²	4.123 cm; 4.123 cm; 17 cm²
$\sqrt{16}$ is the side length of a square with area 16, $\sqrt{16} = 4$.	$\sqrt{17}$ is the side length of a square with area 17. $\sqrt{17} = 4.123\ ...$

Students will learn that square roots of what are called perfect squares are whole numbers. For example, 16 is a perfect square, since $16 = 4 \times 4$. They learn that the square root of the rational number $\frac{4}{9}$, the quotient of two whole number perfect squares, is $\frac{2}{3}$, a rational number, as well. But many square roots of fractions and whole numbers are irrational, for example, $\sqrt{2}$, $\sqrt{7}$, or $\sqrt{\frac{2}{7}}$.

Common Errors and Misconceptions

Integers, Exponents, and Irrational Numbers: Common Errors, Misconceptions, and Strategies

COMMON ERROR OR MISCONCEPTION	SUGGESTED STRATEGY
A student assumes $(-9) > (-4)$ since $9 > 4$.	Focus students on the number line model for integers. Some students respond better to a vertical number line than a horizontal one. It seems clearer to them that "up" means greater. When asked to compare numbers, students can locate both numbers and then look for the one that is farther up.
A student adds $(-3) + (-8)$ and gets 11. He says that the rule is "two negatives make a positive."	Frequently, to simplify the mathematics for students, "rules" are created for them to remember. This student remembered, all too well, that two negatives make a positive. He or she did not think about when that rules applies (for multiplication and division, not addition and subtraction). Rather than memorizing rules, students should always be thinking about what the operation means. They should be reading this as "(-3) and another (-8)", rather than simply as "(-3) plus (-8)."
A student subtracts $(-3) - (-8)$ and gets $+11$. She or he reasons that you add when there are two negatives, so $8 + 3 = 11$.	Again, the student is applying a rule where it does not apply. The student should be reading $(-3) - (-8)$ as "How far is it from (-8) to (-3)?" Then the error is much less likely.
A student calculates 3^5 as $5 \times 5 \times 5$.	It is easy for students to mix up the roles of the base and exponent in a power. It is a matter of remembering how the notation works. But it is essential that students realize that the values are not reversible.
A student misapplies BEDMAS by not recognizing that it is always implied that the value of the numerator or denominator of a fraction is in brackets. So, for example, the student calculates $\frac{3+4}{5 \times 8 - 2}$ as $3 + 4 \div 5 \times 8 - 2 = 9.2$, instead of as $(3 + 4) \div (5 \times 8 - 2) = 0.184\ldots$.	It is easy for students to be literal and always look for brackets. They need to learn that, implicitly, there are brackets describing the numerator and describing the denominator of any fraction.
A student misapplies BEDMAS by not recognizing that a fraction is a single value, since division is implied.	It is easy for students to be literal and always look for a division symbol. They need to learn that, implicitly, a fraction is another way to show a division, for example, $\frac{1}{8} = 1 \div 8 = 0.125$.
A student calculates $\sqrt{36}$ as 18 since 18 is half of 36.	Some students see the process of finding two numbers to multiply to result in a particular answer as taking half of it. And, in fact, it is true that half of 4 is $\sqrt{4}$. Use an example like 9. Ask students what† two numbers multiply to make 9 (3×3). Then ask for the value that was repeated to create 9, that is, the square root (3). Ask how they know it's not the same as half of 9. In this case, since half of 9 is not even a whole number, the difference may be more compelling than if an even value had been selected for the perfect square.

Appropriate Manipulatives

Integers, Exponents, and Irrational Numbers: Examples of
Manipulatives

NUMBER LINES

The negative of a number is defined to be the number equally distant from
zero as its positive opposite. Because of this, integers are usually modelled
first with a number line, whether horizontal or vertical. The vertical
number line more closely resembles a thermometer, making it perhaps a
more "contextual" model if students are working with a context such as
temperature or altitude.

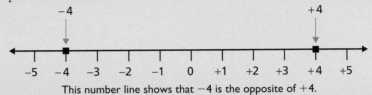

This number line shows that -4 is the opposite of $+4$.

INTEGER TILES

Another common model for integers is two-sided coloured tiles, where one
colour represents a positive and a different colour represents a negative. In
later work, when adding integers, students pair up negative tiles and positive tiles to create pairs with a value of 0, and what is left over is the sum.

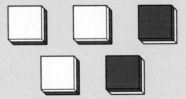

$+3$ and -2 are modelled with white positive and red negative tiles.

COUNTERS

Two colours of counters can be used in the same way as integer tiles.
For example, $(-3) + (+8)$ is modelled below

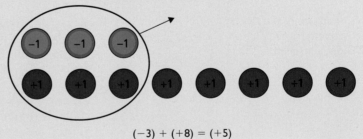

$$(-3) + (+8) = (+5)$$

SQUARE TILES

Square tiles can be used to model powers with an exponent of 2 and square roots. For example, to show 3^2, a student can make a 3×3 square and count the number of square tiles making up the area. Conversely, to show $\sqrt{9}$, a student could arrange 9 square tiles into a square and determine the side length.

Representing $3^2 = 9$ and $\sqrt{9} = 3$

LINKING CUBES

Linking cubes can be used to model powers with an exponent of 3. For example, to show 4^3, a student can make a $4 \times 4 \times 4$ cube and count the number of small cubes required to make it.

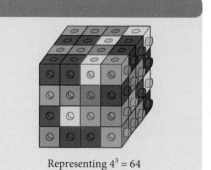

Representing $4^3 = 64$

Appropriate Children's Books

The King's Chessboard (Birch, 1993).
This book, based on an ancient tale about repeated doubling, acquaints students with the powers of two, that is, $2^1, 2^2, 2^3, 2^4, \ldots$, in an intriguing way. Students could follow up by exploring what would have happened had the number of rice grains been tripled each time instead of doubled.

One Grain of Rice: A Mathematical Folk Tale (Demi, 1997).
This book tells essentially the same story as *The King's Chessboard*, above, but the artwork and some of the story details are quite different.

Appropriate Digital Resources

See the MindTap site for a selection of appropriate digital resources.

Assessing Student Understanding

- Include conceptual and problem-solving questions in your assessment plan.

  A conceptual question might be:

  Explain why the product of two negative integers has to be greater than their sum.

A problem-solving question might be:

A certain negative integer fits these clues:
- *It is greater than −20.*
- *It is less than −4.*
- *It is farther from −4 than −20.*
What is the greatest value it could be?

- Rather than asking for a series of calculations, ask questions "backward." For example, indicate that you had added three integers and the result was (−16). Ask what those integers could have been and why. Similarly, you could ask why two integers could have been subtracted, multiplied, or divided to result in (−16), and ask why.
- Have students reflect on how operations with integers are like those with whole numbers, and how they are different.
- What feedback would you give to this student?
- Ask students why it makes sense that 2^{10} is a big number, while 10^2 is not that big.
- Encourage students to use diagrams to help them explain what numbers like $\sqrt{24}$ and $\sqrt{32}$ mean.

Student Response

This student explains how to calculate −3 − (−8) using models.

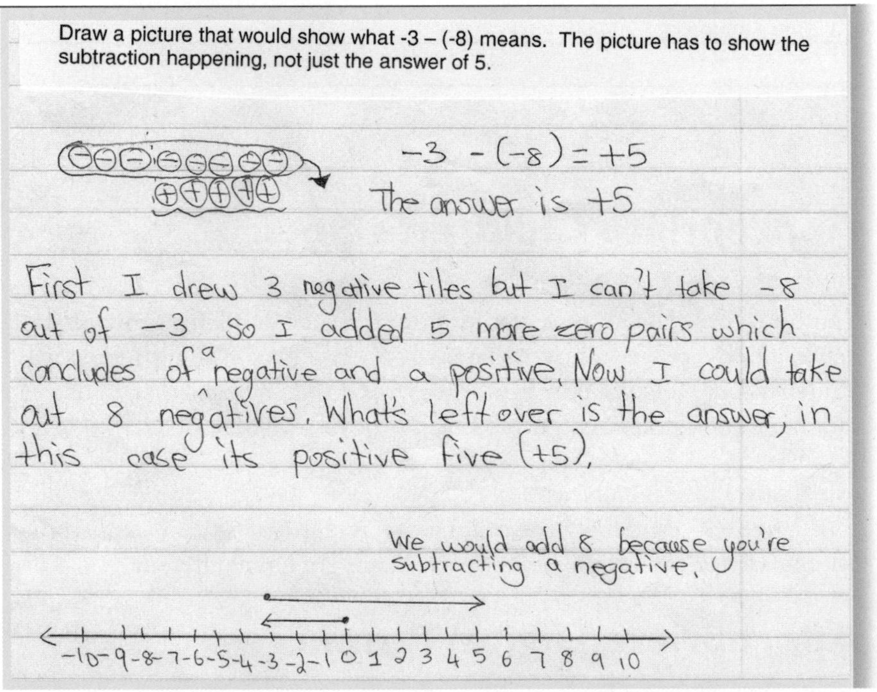

> Draw a picture that would show what -3 – (-8) means. The picture has to show the subtraction happening, not just the answer of 5.

$$-3 - (-8) = +5$$

The answer is +5

First I drew 3 negative tiles but I can't take -8 out of -3 so I added 5 more zero pairs which concludes of a negative and a positive. Now I could take out 8 negatives. What's left over is the answer, in this case its positive five (+5).

We would add 8 because you're subtracting a negative.

Applying What You've Learned

1. Ask students to explain why a number like −10 cannot be a solution to the chapter problem.

2. What do you see as the advantages and what do you see as the disadvantages of insisting that students use the + sign in describing positive integers?

3. It was mentioned in the chapter that the zero property is fundamental to all four operations. Show why this is the case for each operation.

4. Create a lesson plan to help students gain an understanding of how and why you subtract integers the way you do. Set your lesson plan in a problem-solving context.

5. Some people who think the rules for multiplying and dividing integers are easier than the rules for adding think we should start integer operations with multiplying and dividing rather than adding and subtracting. What do you think? Why?

6. What problem might you suggest to students to help them practise the various skills and concepts around powers in an interesting way?

7. Would a student need a set of rules like BEDMAS to solve story problems involving a lot of computations, or is it just for complicated expressions involving only numbers?

Interact with a K–8 Student:

8. Ask a student to show you how they use two-coloured counters for integer operations. Have them share which operation they think the counters help with the most and why.

Discuss with a K–8 Teacher:

9. Ask a middle school/junior high teacher what struggles her or his students have in learning integer operations and how she or he handles those challenges. Think about the teacher's choices and describe what you might differently and why.

Selected References

Andrews, D.R. (2011). Integer operations using a whiteboard. *Mathematics Teaching in the Middle School, 16,* 474–479.

Behrend, J.L., and Mohs, L.C. (2006). From simple to powerful conversations: A two-year conversation about negative numbers. *Teaching Children Mathematics, 12,* 260–264.

Birch. D. (1993). *The king's chessboard.* New York: Puffin Books.

Cooke, M.B. (1993). A videotaping project to explore the multiplication of integers. *Arithmetic Teacher, 41,* 170–171.

Demi (1997). *One grain of rice: A mathematical folk tale.* New York: Scholastic Press.

Flores, A. (2008). Subtraction of positive and negative numbers: The difference and completion approaches with chips. *Mathematics Teaching in the Middle School, 14,* 21–23.

Friedmann, P. (2008). The zero box. *Mathematics Teaching in the Middle School, 14,* 222–223.

Jeon, K. (2012). Reflecting on PEDMAS. *Teaching Children Mathematics, 18,* 370–377.

Karp, K., Bush, S.B., and Dougherty, B.J. (2014). 13 rules that expire. *Teaching Children Mathematics, 21,* 18–25.

Kent, L.B. (2000). Connecting integers to meaningful contexts. *Mathematics Teaching in the Middle School, 6,* 62–66.

Lamb, L.C., and Thanheiser, E. (2006). Understanding integers: Using balloons and weights software. In Alatorre, S., Cortina, J.L., Sáiz, M., and Méndez, A.

(Eds.). *Proceedings of the 28th Annual Meeting of the North American Chapter of the International Group for the Psychology of Mathematics Education, 2,* 163–164.

Linchevski, L., and Williams, J. (1999). Using intuition from everyday life in "filling" the gap in children's extension of their number concept to include the negative numbers. *Educational Studies in Mathematics, 39,* 131–147.

Nunes, B., and Nunes, T. (1999). Young children's representations of negative numbers. *Proceedings of the British Society for Research into Learning Mathematics, 19,* 7–12.

Petrealla, G. (2001). Subtracting integers: An affective lesson. *Mathematics Teaching in the Middle School, 7,* 150–151.

Reeves, C.A., and Webb, D. (2004). Balloons on the rise: A problem solving introduction to integers. *Mathematics Teaching in the Middle School, 9,* 476–482.

Streefland, L. (1996). Negative numbers: Reflections of a learning researcher. *Journal of Mathematical Behavior, 15,* 57–77.

Whitacre, I., Pierson Bishop, J., Lamb, L.L.C., Philipp, R.A., Schappelle, B.P., and Lewis, M.L. (2012). Happy and sad thoughts: An exploration of children's integer reasoning. *The Journal of Mathematical Behavior, 31,* 356–365.

Wilcox, V.B. (2008). Questioning zero and negative numbers. *Teaching Children Mathematics, 15,* 202–206.

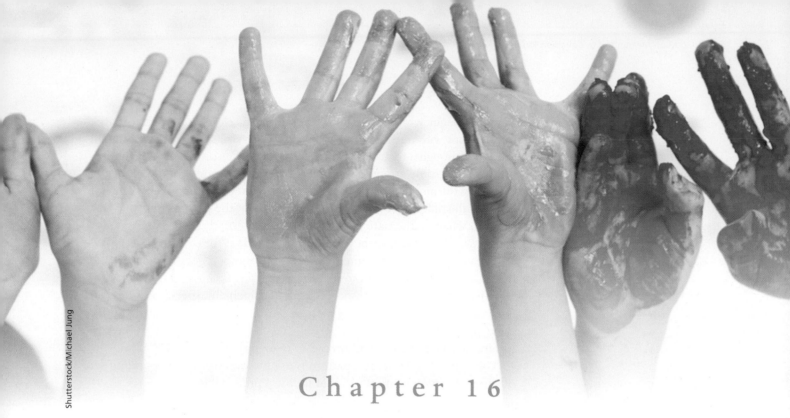

Shutterstock/Michael Jung

Chapter 16

Patterns and Algebra

IN A NUTSHELL

The main ideas in this chapter are listed below:

1. Patterns represent identified regularities. There is always an element of repetition, whether the same items repeat over and over, or whether a "transformation," for example, adding 1, is what repeats.

2. Patterns can be represented in a variety of ways.

3. Patterns underlie much of the learning in other strands in math.

4. Generalizing pattern is a way into algebraic thinking.

5. Generalizing number relationships is a way into algebraic thinking.

6. Algebraic notation is often a convenient way to represent mathematical relationships and useful to facilitate an understanding of how quantities change.

CHAPTER PROBLEM

There are 20 students in a class. On the first day, the teacher asks each student to shake hands with each other student. How many handshakes were there?

Patterns

Students begin working with patterns in early elementary school, and, unlike work with numbers, pattern work follows all the way through high school. Although a focus on algebra replaces a focus on patterns at the secondary level, some attention to patterns remains throughout the grades.

One of the most fundamental concepts in pattern work, but also one not clear to all students, is that, although the part of the pattern that they see is finite, when mathematicians talk about a pattern, they are talking about something that continues beyond what the student sees.

The notion of pattern is integrated into the number, geometry, measurement, and data strands in most of the curriculums across the country. In fact, there is an underlying aspect of data management, specifically classifying and sorting, inherent in any pattern. This is why, in some curriculums, the expectations/outcomes for sorting and classifying are found in the patterning strand of the curriculum rather than in the data strand.

Throughout this chapter, pattern is used to describe a never-ending set of sounds, shapes, or numbers that follow a predictable rule.

Types of Patterns

Repeating Patterns

Students' first experiences with patterns generally involve repeating patterns. Initially, the repeating patterns are "intuitive." Students hear rhythmic patterns in sounds, songs, and stories, and recognize patterns in physical actions. They also observe patterns in their environment. They use these patterns to help them predict. Soon after, they are explicitly introduced to repeating colour, shape, size, and position patterns, and usually somewhat later to repeating number patterns.

Core of a Repeating Pattern The shortest part of the pattern that repeats is called the core. In the pattern below, the core is the set of three shapes found at the start of the pattern since this is the shortest string that repeats.

The core

Sometimes determining the core can be difficult for students. For example, the following pattern has a five-element core. A student might see the small circle repeating in the 4th spot and guess that the core is 1 small circle and 2 large circles. When the student checks farther along in the pattern, however, he or she will realize that this is not correct and may look for the next small circle in the pattern to see if the core ends there.

The core

ACTIVITY 16.1

Encourage students to look for repeating patterns in nature, for example, flowers, gardens, and leaves, or in man-made products like clothing.

Creative Thinking

TEACHING TIP

Although the core is the shortest repeating piece of a repeating pattern, if we ask students "What repeats?" they might well suggest 2 or 3 copies of the core, not just 1. This is not really incorrect, so be careful of language used if the core is meant to be the focus.

It is good practice to show at least three full repetitions of the core of a pattern to make it reasonable for a student to identify it. One of the reasons for this is to remove some of the inherent ambiguity. For example, a pattern beginning 5, 10, … could be 5, 10, 15, 20, … or 5, 10, 20, 40, …. The complexity of recognizing patterns is increased when patterns repeat in more than one direction or dimension. For example, students need to think about more than one aspect of these shapes to identify the pattern below.

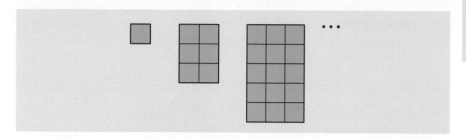

Representing a Repeating Pattern Repeating patterns are sometimes described using a letter code. An AB pattern has a core of two different elements that repeat over and over (e.g., 1, 2, 1, 2, 1, 2, …). An AABC pattern has a core of four elements, where the first two are the same and the others are different (e.g., 3, 3, 4, 5, 3, 3, 4, 5, 3, 3, 4, 5, …). This is, of course, much simpler for students than recording the repetitions and remembering to use the … notation to show that the pattern continues. Mathematically, all AB patterns are the same, but to a student, the specific elements are the focus. Younger students view a pattern made up of a repeating circle and square as different from a repeating number pattern like 1, 2, 1, 2, 1, 2, … because they are focused on the actual items rather than the underlying pattern. They may fail to see that the cores of all AB patterns are similar, that is, two different items.

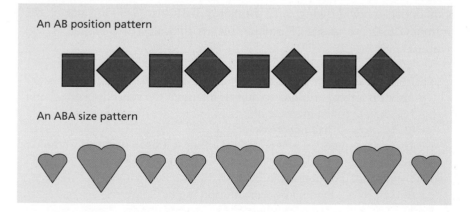

Multi-Attribute Patterns In the early grades, the patterns students observe are built on a single attribute, such as colour, shape, or sound. Eventually, students deal with more complex patterns with two attributes. For example, the pattern below involves change with respect to both shape and colour.

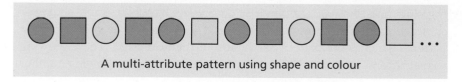

A multi-attribute pattern using shape and colour

ACTIVITY 16.2

Ask students to create a shape pattern so that the numbers form an ABA pattern, but the shapes form an AB pattern.

Critical Thinking

It is possible for students to deal with patterns with even more than two attributes. When the attributes are highly visual, such as colour or size, the task is easier for students. It is often a challenge for students, however, to identify a pattern with multiple changing attributes that have different core sizes. The above pattern changes colour in an AAB pattern but changes shape in an AB pattern, thus causing difficulty for students unless they analyze the pattern attributes separately. It is for this reason that many teachers use pattern blocks as a manipulative when they begin work with multi-attribute patterns. For example, the pattern below changes with respect to both shape and colour, but the changes are concurrent.

The colour pattern is ABB. The shape pattern is also ABB.

For students to really understand multi-attribute patterns, it is important to move to other materials like the attribute blocks shown below, so that they learn to look at the two changing attributes separately.

The size/shape pattern is AB while the colour pattern is AABA.

Growing and Shrinking Patterns

Some growing patterns are quite familiar to students, particularly the number pattern 1, 2, 3, 4, ... As children develop mathematically, they experience other growing (and shrinking) patterns. Growing means the numbers increase in size. Shrinking means they decrease in size. These patterns may be

TEACHING TIP

Sometimes teachers overemphasize growing patterns over shrinking. It is good to provide practice in both shrinking and growing patterns.

- arithmetic sequences, also called linear growing patterns, where each number is a fixed amount greater or less than the preceding one
  - 3, 5, 7, 9, ... (fixed increase of 2)
  - 12, 10, 8, 6, ... (fixed decrease of 2)
- geometric sequences, where each number is a fixed multiple of the preceding one
  - 2, 4, 8, 16, ... (doubling pattern)
  - 100, 20, 4, ... (dividing by 5 or multiplying by $\frac{1}{5}$ pattern)
- other number sequences where the growth is not constant
  - 3, 4, 6, 9, 13, ... (increase by 1 more each time)
  - 20, 18, 14, 8, ... (decrease by 2 more each time)

Students are generally able to recognize and extend arithmetic sequences before they are comfortable with the other types of growing and shrinking sequences, because arithmetic sequences are based on simply adding or subtracting the same amount each time. There can also be growing shape patterns, such as the patterns at the top of the next page. These growing shape patterns can often be represented and described as growing number patterns: 1, 3, 5, ... and 1, 4, 9, ...

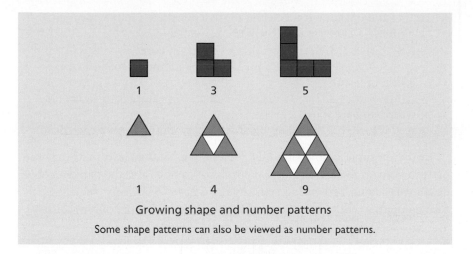

Growing shape and number patterns

Some shape patterns can also be viewed as number patterns.

Recursive Patterns

A recursive pattern is one where each element in the pattern is defined based on a previous element or elements. Some of the growing patterns described in the previous section can be defined recursively. For example, for the sequence 2, 4, 6, 8, ..., each term is defined as 2 greater than the preceding term. However, some recursive patterns are more complex. For example, for the pattern 2, 3, 6, 18, 108, ..., each term is defined as the product of the two preceding numbers.

Some particularly famous recursive sequences include:

- the triangular numbers—beginning at 1, each term is found by adding 1 greater than was added previously: 1, 3, 6, 10, 15, ... (Start at 1, add 2, then 3, then 4, then 5, ...)
- the Fibonacci sequence—beginning with 1 and 1, add two terms to get the next term: 1, 1, 2, 3, 5, 8, 13, 21, 34, ... (Start with 1 and 1; add the first two terms to get the 3rd term; then add the 2nd and 3rd terms to get the 4th term, then add the 3rd and 4th terms to get the 5th term, ...)

Describing and Extending Patterns

Extending Patterns

Once students have identified a pattern, you normally ask them to either extend it or describe it so that you can see that they "understood" the pattern. It is often easier for students to demonstrate their recognition of the pattern by extending it rather than describing it.

Sometimes when you ask students to extend a pattern, there is ambiguity in terms of what you expect and what students understand or perceive. For example:

- Students seem to find it easier to extend a repeating pattern that ends at the end of a full repetition of the core, than to start in the middle of a repetition. For example, students might be asked to extend *clap, clap, snap, clap, clap, snap, clap, clap, snap, ...* Many students do not find this difficult, and they respond *clap, clap, snap*. However, if students are asked to extend *clap, clap, snap, clap, clap, snap, clap, ...*, they will often repeat the entire core of *clap, clap, snap*, ignoring the fact that there was already one clap of the core included.
- Students legitimately view the pattern in a different way than you expect because no pattern rule is provided. For example, a teacher asks a student to extend the pattern 2, 3, 5, 8, ... The teacher is expecting the student to say 13, 21, ... (where each term of the pattern

ACTIVITY 16.3

Students can explore some of the properties of the Fibonacci sequence (1, 1, 2, 3, 5, 8, 13, 21, 34, ...) with these tasks:

- Choose a number in the sequence. Multiply it by itself. Then multiply the next number in the sequence by itself. Add the two products (e.g., 3 × 3 = 9; 5 × 5 = 25; 9 + 25 = 34). What do you notice?

- Choose a number in the sequence. Divide it by the previous one. Repeat several times. What do you notice?

Algebraic Reasoning

is the sum of the two preceding terms), but there are many other legitimate ways to extend the pattern, such as

– 2, 3, 5, 8, 2, 3, 5, 8, … (repeating a four-term core)

– 2, 3, 5, 8, 12, 13, 15, 18, 22, 23, 25, 28, … (adding 10 to each of a group of terms)

– 2, 3, 5, 8, 8, 5, 3, 2, 2, 3, 5, 8, 8, 5, 3, 2, … (repeating four terms forward and backward)

– 2, 3, 5, 8, 12, 17, … (adding 1 first, and then adding 1 more each time)

In the example below of a 2-D pattern, the student assumed that the pattern going right was adding 2 columns of squares and the pattern going down was adding 1 row of squares. Again, there is ambiguity, since the pattern going right could have been to double the number of columns instead.

Student Response

This student is able to extend a pattern in more than one direction.

Draw out or explain the next three figures to continue the pattern.

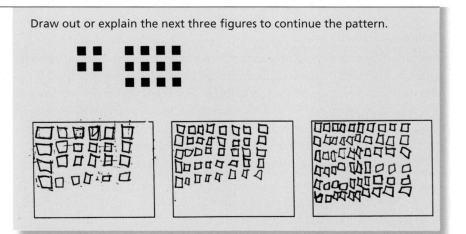

ACTIVITY 16.4

Ask students to continue a pattern in two dimensions such as this one:

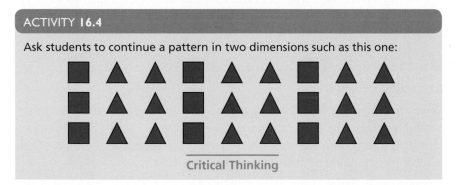

Critical Thinking

Be aware that asking students to extend a pattern by writing the next few terms is quite different from asking them to tell what the 100th or 1000th term is, even though that is a type of extension as well.

Extending to much later terms in the sequence requires students to use algebraic reasoning to develop some sort of rule between the term position of the term in the pattern (often called the term number) and the related term value.

Describing Patterns

Teachers often ask students to describe a pattern to ensure that they understand it. Ideally, a pattern's description is a *pattern rule*, whether described verbally, pictorially, or symbolically. The rule is an unambiguous description of the pattern.

Use words to describe this pattern:

3, 7, 11, 15,....

Start at 3 and keep adding 4.

Frequently, students focus on one aspect of the rule, but forget another important part of it. For example, if a student describes the pattern 4, 7, 10, 13, ... as "an add 3 pattern" without indicating that it starts at 4, the pattern rule is incomplete. Clearly, this is not a problem if the first part of the pattern is shown, so it may seem superfluous to say that it starts at 4. Formally, students should learn that a pattern rule must describe how each and every element of the pattern is described (including the first element).

Sometimes students find it easier to describe a pattern by comparing it to another one. For example, they describe the pattern 3, 6, 9, 12, 15, ... by suggesting that it is like 2, 4, 6, 8, ... but the numbers start at 3 and go up by 3 instead of by 2.

Eventually, as mentioned above, we expect the rule to be described in such a way as to relate the term position to its value (e.g., for the pattern 5, 7, 9, 11, ..., to determine the term value, you multiply the term position by 2 and add 3). This requires deeper reasoning. These types of rules will be discussed on page 369.

Translating Patterns

To determine whether a student is focused on the mathematical structure of a pattern, ask her or him to translate a pattern into a different, but equivalent, form. For example, a student might be shown the original pattern below and be asked to show the same pattern using red, yellow, and green circles and squares. There are many possibilities, as shown below.

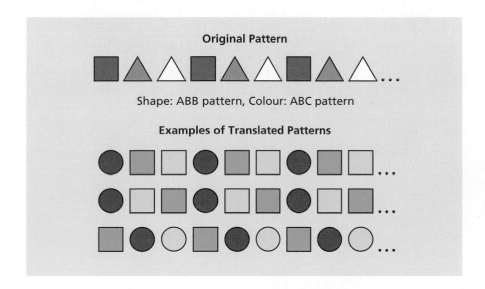

Original Pattern

Shape: ABB pattern, Colour: ABC pattern

Examples of Translated Patterns

ACTIVITY 16.5

Ask students to choose a criterion from the list below for creating a pattern:

- Use three colours of counters to create a pattern.
- Create a repeating pattern that has a core of three elements.
- Create a repeating pattern where the 5th element is a large blue square.
- Create a growing pattern where the 10th term is 100.
- Create a pattern that grows but not by the same amount each time.
- Create a shrinking pattern where the 4th term is 16.

Critical Thinking

Creating Patterns

Students should be encouraged to create patterns as soon as they have an understanding of what patterns are. By exposure to many types of patterns, and patterns of various structures based on many different attributes, students' patterns will be richer.

Most young students will need to first create patterns with concrete materials, then pictorial representations, and then number patterns.

Sample Criteria for Creating Patterns

There are many criteria that can be used to structure students' pattern creation. There can be less or more structure imposed on what is required. Some examples are shown in **Activity 16.5**.

Mathematical Situations Rich in Patterns

A number of charts and tables rich in patterns are regularly used in mathematics classrooms. One example is the 100 chart.

The 100 Chart

The 100 chart is a tool students use through many elementary and middle school grades. Some of the patterns found in the 100 chart are shown below.

PATTERNS INHERENT IN THE PLACE VALUE SYSTEM

- Every 10th number ends in a 0.
- The pattern of ones digits is always 1, 2, 3, 4, 5, 6, 7, 8, 9, 0, repeating over and over.
- The tens digits form groups of 10 numbers that repeat and then jump by 1; then another 10 repeat followed by another jump of 1, etc.:
  1, 1, 1, 1, 1, 1, 1, 1, 1, 1; 2, 2, 2, 2, 2, 2, 2, 2, 2, 2;
  3, 3, 3, 3, 3, 3, 3, 3, 3, 3; 4, 4, 4, 4, 4, 4, 4, 4, 4, 4; ....
- If you go down a column, you keep adding 10.
- If you go across a row to the right, you keep adding 1.

1	2	3	4	5	6	7	8	9	10
11	12	13	14	15	16	17	18	19	20
21	22	23	24	25	26	27	28	29	30
31	32	33	34	35	36	37	38	39	40
41	42	43	44	45	46	47	48	49	50
51	52	53	54	55	56	57	58	59	60
61	62	63	64	65	66	67	68	69	70
71	72	73	74	75	76	77	78	79	80
81	82	83	84	85	86	87	88	89	90
91	92	93	94	95	96	97	98	99	100

PATTERNS IN 3-BY-3 GRIDS

If you take the mean (average) value of all the numbers in any 3-by-3 square, the result is in the middle of the square. For example, the mean average of 72, 73, 74, 82, 83, 84, 92, 93, and 94 is 83.

72	73	74
82	83	84
92	93	94

MULTIPLES-OF-9 PATTERNS

If students put counters on every multiple of 9, two diagonals going down to the left are formed. This makes sense since each multiple of 9 is 9 more than the preceding multiple, so you add 10 by going down 1, and then left 1 to subtract the extra 1 that was added when just going down 1.

1	2	3	4	5	6	7	8	9	10
11	12	13	14	15	16	17	18	19	20
21	22	23	24	25	26	27	28	29	30
31	32	33	34	35	36	37	38	39	40
41	42	43	44	45	46	47	48	49	50
51	52	53	54	55	56	57	58	59	60
61	62	63	64	65	66	67	68	69	70
71	72	73	74	75	76	77	78	79	80
81	82	83	84	85	86	87	88	89	90
91	92	93	94	95	96	97	98	99	100

Using Patterns to Develop Mathematical Concepts

A rich mathematics program at the K–8 level is full of opportunities for teachers to use patterns to develop and clarify mathematical concepts, as well as to provide insight into how the number system works. The examples below should provide some understanding of the important role that pattern plays in developing mathematical thinking.

ACTIVITY 16.6

Ask students to explore an addition or multiplication table to find as many patterns as they can in the table. Encourage them to explain why it makes sense for those patterns to have occurred in terms of what they know about number.

Creative Thinking

Computational Patterns

Sometimes patterns are useful to help set up a computational relationship that students can explore. Some people call patterns like the first three examples *strings*.

Using Patterns to Explore Computational Relationships

EXAMPLE	COMPUTATIONAL RELATIONSHIP
31 + 5 = 36 41 + 5 = 46 51 + 5 = 56 61 + 5 = ▨	As students complete each answer, the patterns inherent in the place value system should become apparent. When adding the same amount to a number that is 10 greater, the sum is 10 greater; the tens digit changes, but the ones digit does not. Thus, the sum of 61 + 5 must be 66.
32 − 18 = 14 42 − 28 = 14 52 − 38 = 14 62 − 48 = ▨	As students complete the subtractions, they should notice that when both the minuend and the subtrahend increase by the same amount, the difference is the same. Thus, the difference for 62 − 48 would be 14.
4 × 3 = 12 4 × 30 = 120 4 × 300 = 1200 4 × 3000 = ▨	As students determine each answer, they should observe that each time an additional 0 appears at the end of the second factor, there is an additional 0 at the end of the product. Thus, the product of 4 × 3000 should be 12 000. Although this pattern does not explain why this is so, it is an appropriate model to start off the conversation about multiplying by powers of 10.

(continued)

Measurement and Geometry Patterns

Patterns can be useful to help students either come up with or understand measurement formulas. For example, observing the pattern of how the perimeter of a square increases consistently as the side length increases by 1 could help lead students to the formula $P = 4s$ or help them understand the formula that they have been given.

Side Length	1	2	3	4
Perimeter	4	8	12	16

Organizing data into a pattern to look at the various combinations of lengths and widths that result in a rectangle with a perimeter of 20 cm could help students see that the length and width must add to 10 cm.

PERIMETER	20	20	20	20	20
LENGTH	1	2	3	4	5
WIDTH	9	8	7	6	5

Observing the number of edges on prisms with different bases can lead students to notice that the number of edges on a prism is always triple the number of sides of its base. They can then reason about why that has to be.

PRISM TYPE	TRIANGULAR	RECTANGULAR	PENTAGONAL	HEXAGONAL
Sides of base	3	4	5	6
Edges of prism	9	12	15	18

Common Errors and Misconceptions

Patterns: Common Errors, Misconceptions, and Strategies

COMMON ERROR OR MISCONCEPTION	SUGGESTED STRATEGY
Being Unaware of Multiple Possible Patterns Students do not recognize that there are different ways to continue a pattern if a pattern rule is not described. For example, if given 5, 10, 15 … as the beginning of the pattern, they may only see it as a repeating pattern and will not consider that it might be a growing pattern.	Students who only relate to repeating patterns need many opportunities to work with growing patterns using concrete materials and pictures before working with numbers. For example, provide blocks for students to make a growing pattern of 1 row of 5 blocks, then 2 rows of 5 blocks, and then 3 rows of 5 blocks. Discuss how there can be more than one correct pattern. For example: 5, 10, 15, 20, 25, 30, … 5, 10, 15, 25, 35, 50, 65, …
Using Incomplete Pattern Rules Students omit important information in describing a pattern rule. For example, for the pattern 4, 6, 9, 13, 18, … , a student might state the rule as "Just keep adding 1 more."	Follow students' rules literally to show them the incomplete nature of their rules. For example, with the rule "Just keep adding 1 more," you might continue the pattern by writing down 4, 6, 9, 13, 18, 19, 20, 21, …, literally adding 1 more. This should help the student see the need for a clearer and more complete rule such as, "Start with 4 and add 2, then add 3, then add 4, each time adding a number that is 1 greater than the number added the time before."

Multi-Attribute Patterns with Different Cores

Students have difficulty fully describing a pattern that changes by multiple attributes. For example, the pattern below changes by colour, size, and shape, but the description must account for the different core lengths for each attribute.

Have students begin by listing the attributes that change: colour, size, and shape. Then, for each attribute, have them identify the pattern (ignoring the other attributes as they focus on one at a time).

Colour: red, green, yellow, red (ABCA)

Size: small, big (AB)

Shape: star, diamond (AB)

Make a pattern that follows this pattern rule:
Start at 4 and add 3 each time.
Write the numbers in the blanks.

4   3   4   3   4   3

Student Response

This student has incorrectly interpreted the pattern rule as a description of a repeating pattern. This may be because the student is still more comfortable with repeating patterns.

Make a pattern that follows this pattern rule:
Start at 4 and add 1, then 2, then 3, and so on.
Write the numbers in the blanks.

__4__ , __14__ , __24__, __34__, __44__, __54__, __64__

Student Response

This student has applied the pattern rule incorrectly. This may be because the student is still more comfortable with arithmetic patterns that grow by a constant amount.

Appropriate Manipulatives

Patterns: Examples of Manipulatives

COUNTERS	EXAMPLE
Counters can be used for sorting work. For example, counters of the same type but different colours can be used for simple sorting by colour. Counters of different shapes, for example, square and circular, can be used for simple sorting by shape. Counters are also useful to model number patterns or repeating colour patterns.	Counters can be used to show that each successive odd number is "one pair" more than the preceding one. 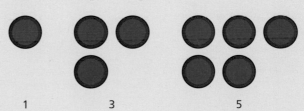

ATTRIBUTE BLOCKS

Attribute, or logic, blocks are ideal for sorting because of their many attributes: size, colour, shape, and thickness. Because of the number of potential attributes, they can also be used to show a variety of simple patterns based on colour, size, thickness, and shape.

EXAMPLE

This repeating attribute block pattern is based on size (small, big; small, big; small, big; ...), shape (square, triangle; square, triangle; square, triangle; ...), and colour (blue, blue, red, blue; blue, blue, red, blue; blue, blue, red, blue, ...).

The size/shape pattern is AB while the colour pattern is AABA.

PATTERN BLOCKS

Pattern blocks are useful for students to create patterns using the attributes of shape, colour, number, or position.

EXAMPLE

This pattern changes with respect to shape and colour as well as number.

Shape: ABA, Colour: ABA, Number: AAB

SORTING MATERIALS

Items that are often used for sorting, such as the commercial set shown here, can also be used to create patterns because of the deliberate variety of attributes and characteristics. They can be used in the same way as attribute blocks, but are more fanciful and, therefore, more interesting to some students.

Students can begin by sorting to focus on the attributes, and then create patterns based on those attributes.

EXAMPLE

The sorting tiles shown below have many attributes to use for sorting and patterning: size, colour, type of animal, and design (stripes or polka dot). This pattern shows what is called a one-difference train—each element differs from the preceding one in only one way.

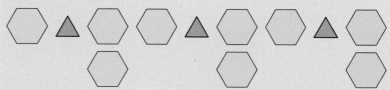

Changes: size, colour, design, size

LINKING CUBES

Linking cubes can be used to show both shape and number patterns. They can also be used for simple colour sorting activities.

EXAMPLE

These linking cubes show the odd number pattern.

1   3   5

TOOTHPICKS	EXAMPLE
Toothpicks can be used to create shape patterns of various sorts, whether repeating patterns or growing ones.	Growing patterns (4, 7, 10, 13, ...) and repeating patterns (3, 6; 3, 6; 3, 6; ...) can be created with toothpicks.

Algebra

Algebra involves generalized thinking about relationships and how quantities change. It evolves from generalizing work in number and pattern to address the broader picture, rather than individual situations. Although we think of algebra as math with letters or symbols, it is really the fact that it addresses the general rather than the specific that makes a situation algebraic. There is a natural progression for students to move from number and pattern work to algebra.

Moving from Pattern to Algebra

When students are younger and look at a "linear growing pattern"—that is, a pattern that increases or decreases by a constant amount, like the one below,

5, 8, 11, 14, 17, ...,

—they tend to describe it recursively, that is, tell how to move from one term to the next. They might say the pattern rule is "Start with 5 and keep adding 3 each time." But this recursive approach does not help them easily figure out, say, the 30th term, or the 100th term. To be able to do this, it is helpful for a student to build a relationship between the term number and the term value.

TERM NUMBER (POSITION)	TERM VALUE
1	5
2	8
3	11
4	14
5	17

One way for them to do this is to use a table (sometimes informally referred to as a T–chart) as an organizer. In this case, the first column would tell the term number and the second number the term value.

Students are then asked to see how they could "act on" the number in the first column, the term number, to determine the number in the second column, the term value.

Some students might even add a third column to help. By noticing that the original term values go up by 3s, they think about the easiest pattern that they know that goes up by 3s, namely the 3 × table. They use this set of values in the third column.

TERM NUMBER (POSITION)	TERM VALUE	HELPER VALUE
1	5	3
2	8	6
3	11	9
4	14	12
5	17	15

They might notice that the helper value is always 3 × the term number and that the term value is always 2 more than the helper value. So, to determine, for example, the 30th term in the original pattern, they would calculate 3 × 30 + 2. Students might write the pattern rule: term value = 3 × term number + 2.

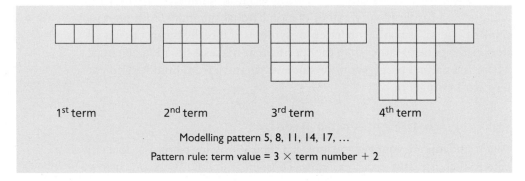

1st term   2nd term   3rd term   4th term

Modelling pattern 5, 8, 11, 14, 17, …
Pattern rule: term value = 3 × term number + 2

Others might view the pattern geometrically to come up with the same rule. They would show figures to relate the term value to the term number, focusing on the fact that each figure has 3 more parts than the previous one. By recolouring, it becomes clear that the total number of squares each time is 3 × term number (the number of yellow squares = 3 × the number of rows) + 2 (the number of green squares).

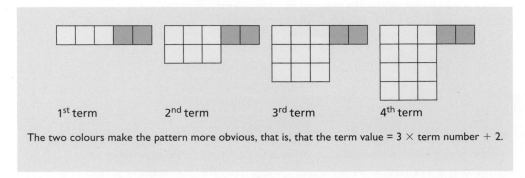

1st term   2nd term   3rd term   4th term

The two colours make the pattern more obvious, that is, that the term value = 3 × term number + 2.

The picture could vary. For example, it could look like the one below, but it's clearly useful to use colour to distinguish between what stays constant and what changes.

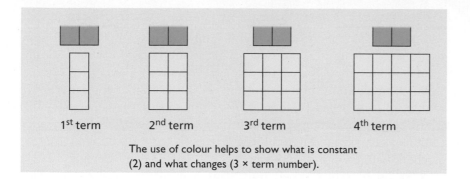

1st term   2nd term   3rd term   4th term

The use of colour helps to show what is constant
(2) and what changes (3 × term number).

Eventually the algebraic expression $3n + 2$ describes the pattern rule.

Once students move to later grades, they would break up the array of yellow rectangles and the two green rectangles to place them vertically, so the height each time is the y-value in the expression $y = 3x + 2$, where x is the term value when it is a counting number.

ACTIVITY 16.7

Ask students to use coloured tiles or linking cubes in two different ways to show that the rule for the pattern 4, 7, 10, 13 could be described as either 3 × term position + 1 or 3 × (term position −1) + 4.

_____

Critical Thinking

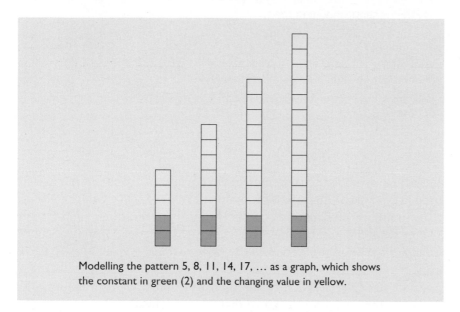

Modelling the pattern 5, 8, 11, 14, 17, ... as a graph, which shows
the constant in green (2) and the changing value in yellow.

This turns into what is called a scatterplot, since the data is not continuous, showing the relationship between term number and term value.

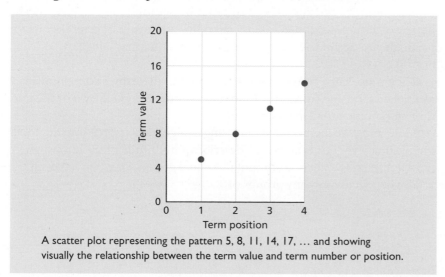

A scatter plot representing the pattern 5, 8, 11, 14, 17, ... and showing
visually the relationship between the term value and term number or position.

Algebra as Generalizing Number Relationships

Although people tend to think that it's only when symbols or letters are used that it is really algebra, students in earlier grades think algebraically, even without symbols, when they generalize number ideas.

For example, in the primary grades, students learn that you can add two numbers in any order. As soon as they think of this as a generality—that it's true for any two numbers, not just a particular two—they are starting to think algebraically. Later, this is written as $a + b = b + a$, but it is just as algebraic before writing it this way.

A few other number generalizations students might come to in K–8 (and there are many more) include:

GENERALIZATION	HOW IT IS LATER WRITTEN ALGEBRAICALLY
You can multiply two numbers in either order.	$ab = ba$
You can increase one number and decrease another without changing the sum.	$a + b = (a + c) + (b - c)$
You can triple a sum by tripling the parts and adding.	$3(a + b) = 3a + 3b$
You can add two fractions with the same denominator by adding the numerators.	$\frac{a}{b} + \frac{c}{b} = \frac{(a + c)}{b}$
You can subtract a negative by adding its opposite.	$a - (-b) = a + b$

Algebraic Notation

Variables—symbols used to represent unknown and/or varying values—are used in *expressions*. An expression is something like $3m + 5$, which indicates that a number is changed by multiplying it by 3 and then adding 5, no matter what the number m is. The choice of the letter for the variable is often arbitrary and students need to realize that $3m + 5$ and $3t + 5$ say the same thing.

Students must learn how to interpret algebraic expressions. For example, they need to recognize that "$n - 10$" means "take 10 from the value of n," as compared to "$10 - n$," which means "how much less n is than 10." They will create algebraic expressions to describe a computational rule (e.g., writing $bh \div 2$ to describe multiplying the base by the height of a shape and then taking half of it), and evaluate expressions for particular values of the variable (e.g., recognizing that $2m - 8 = -6$ when $m = 1$).

They must learn conventions. For example, the expression $2n$ means 2 multiplied by n, and the expression $\frac{2}{n}$ means either 2 divided by n or the fraction with numerator 2 and denominator n.

They must recognize that any single algebraic expression describes many situations. For example, $5b$ describes a multitude of situations where we want to know the total amount in 5 equal groups, or when we want the total when we have many groups of 5.

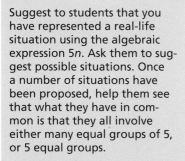

ACTIVITY 16.8

Suggest to students that you have represented a real-life situation using the algebraic expression $5n$. Ask them to suggest possible situations. Once a number of situations have been proposed, help them see that what they have in common is that they all involve either many equal groups of 5, or 5 equal groups.

Algebraic Reasoning

TEACHING **TIP**

When students are using symbols to represent variables, it is important for them to understand that when the same variable is referred to, the same symbol is used, but when two different variables are referred to, different symbols are used.

Is 2x + 3 usually more or less than x + 5?

I think usually x + 5 is ~~more~~ less than 2x + 3 because if you substitute x with 1 or 2, that's the only time x + 5 / 2x + 3 is higher. Otherwise, ~~for number~~ if x equalled ~~its~~ 4 and onward 2x + 3 would be more. This is because even though the 1st equation adds less than the second, the first still multiplying 's which gives (usually) a greater value.

However, if you're multiplying with negatives, x + 5 is always greater. This is because when you multiply a positive with a negative it equals a negative which is really low.

But, in my opinion, positive integers are much more common than negative ones so I would assume the variable would be a higher positive #.

You could also argue x + 5 would usually be higher because zero is the middle of all numbers and from 4 onwards only then 2x + 3 is greater. So more numbers would be variables that make x + 5 larger.

Student Response

Although there are a few technical errors in this explanation, this student shows some good symbol sense.

As described in the section above, they learn to use expressions to describe relationship rules in patterns. For example, $4n - 2$ describes the rule for the pattern 2, 6, 10, 14, … since each term is determined by multiplying its position by 4 and subtracting 2.

Variables are also used in *equations*. Equations, unlike expressions, describe relationships. For example, $m + 5 = 9$ is the statement of a relationship between m and 9, that is, that 9 is 5 more than m. Notice that in the expression, m can represent any value, but in the equation, m is an unknown, and this equation is true for only one particular value of m.

Initially, students are likely to use open boxes or frames to represent variables, rather than letters. For example the equation ■ $+ 5 = 9$ says exactly the same thing as the equation $m + 5 = 9$. Later, students are more likely to use letters.

Often students use variables to represent unknowns in story problems. For example, if a student knows that 3 identical shirts were purchased and the change from $20 was $2.33, the student could construct the equation $3t + 2.33 = 20$ to determine the unknown shirt price.

Later on in this section, there is a discussion of how students learn to determine these values by solving equations.

Using Variables to Describe Relationships

Mathematicians are always looking for succinct, symbolic ways to describe multiple situations. Sometimes that leads to algebraic descriptions of number generalizations as described in the previous chart on page 372.

ACTIVITY 16.9

Students can create situations involving variables that are true some of the time, but not all of the time, and others that are always true.

Critical Thinking

Sometimes it is a way to say that the same algebraic expression can be described differently. For example, writing $(3x + 7) + (2x + 2) = 5x + 9$ is a way to say that no matter what the value of x is, this relationship holds true. In a later section, there is discussion of how students learn to perform this simplification.

But writing the relationship $3x + 5 = 2x + 7$ is a different description of a relationship; this time, the student is seeking the value of x for which one would have to add 7 to its double to match 5 more than its triple. This is not always true; in fact, it is only true if $x = 2$, but it still describes a relationship between the double of x and the triple of x.

Sometimes the relationship is between two potentially unrelated quantities that are, all of a sudden, related. For example, suppose there is a variable called w representing the number of weeks old someone is and the variable d representing the number of days old someone is. Writing the equation $d = 7w$ is a way to say that the two variables were related after all. Measurement formulas are all examples of this sort of relationship between quantities. Some examples are:

- relating speed (or rate), time, and distance ($D = rt$)
- describing the volume of a rectangular prism ($V = l \times w \times h$)
- relating the value of a term in a pattern to its position in the pattern; for example, in the pattern 2, 4, 6, 8, 10, 12, ..., each term's value is double its position in the pattern: $t = 2p$

Sometimes the relationship is a way of asking what position in a pattern has a certain value. For example, the equation $2n + 6 = 24$ is asking which term in the pattern with the rule $2n + 6$ (i.e., 8, 10, 12, 14, ...) is 24.

Although most algebraic relationships students meet are equalities, these relationships can also be inequalities. For example, one might indicate that for certain values of x, $3x > 2x$, and ask students to figure out for which values of x this is true.

Equality and Inequality

The form of an equation is a mathematical sentence with an equals sign. For some students, the equality sign poses a difficulty. Although they are comfortable with, for example, the sentence $4 + 5 = \blacksquare$, they interpret the equality sign to mean "find the answer." Therefore, when students see the sentence $\blacksquare - 4 = 5$, they may not be sure what to do as they think the answer is already there. Similarly, students might solve $4 + \blacksquare = 5$ by adding 4 and 5 to "get the answer."

The notion of an equation as an expression of balance is not apparent to them. This long-standing problem is exacerbated by the fact that many calculators require the equals key to be pressed to get an answer, so students are reinforced in interpreting the $=$ sign as synonymous with "get the answer."

It is important for students to recognize that the equality sign should be viewed as a way to say that the same number has two different names, one on either side of the equals sign.

In the early grades, students meet equalities, or perhaps inequalities, using no symbols, but only numbers. For example, they meet an equation like $7 = 3 + 4$ or the equation $4 + 3 = 6 + 1$. Ideally, students do not merely

---

ACTIVITY 16.10

Encourage students to use either a pan balance or mental processes to figure out what values of [] and $\triangle$ can make these equations or inequalities true:

$[] + 8 = \triangle + 10$

$[] + 4 = \triangle - 5$

$[] + [] = \triangle + \triangle + \triangle$

$[] + 8 > \triangle + 10$

Algebraic Reasoning

---

realize that this second equation is true because $7 = 7$, but see that if the first value increased by 2, the only way the sums can be equal is if the second value decreases by 2. Students might model this on a pan balance; by using cubes of the same size, the student sees that the amounts do, in fact, balance.

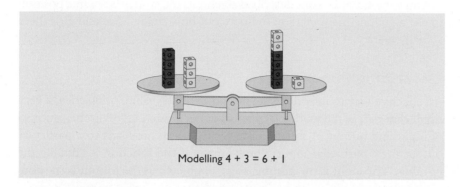

Modelling $4 + 3 = 6 + 1$

The inequality $4 + 2 > 5$ could be modelled in a similar way, but this time there is an imbalance, and not a balance. The model below shows that $4 + 2$ is somewhat more than 5.

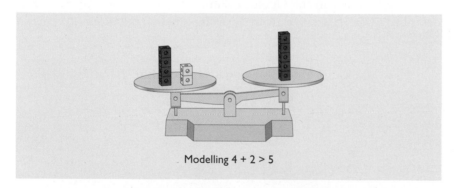

Modelling $4 + 2 > 5$

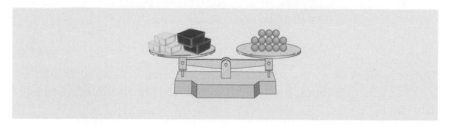

ACTIVITY 16.11

Ask students what number of marbles could be in each of the yellow boxes (same number in each yellow box) and what number in each red box (same number in each red box) to make this balance.

Algebraic Reasoning

Later, as was mentioned in an earlier section, they meet equations with symbols representing unknown values. For example, the equation might be $4 \times 3 = \blacksquare$ or it might be $4 \times \blacksquare = 20$. And at some point, they begin to use letters rather than symbols.

In later elementary grades and through secondary school, students learn to use equations to model real–life situations. Even earlier, to figure out how many children are in a class with 12 boys and 18 girls, the students could write the equation $12 + 18 = \blacksquare$ and solve it. To figure out the side length of a square knowing that the perimeter is 48 cm, a student could write $4 \times s = 48$ and solve the equation. Later, to represent the situation that there were 428 children in a school and there were

22 more boys than girls, the students might write any of these equations or pairs of equations:

$$b + g = 428 \text{ and } b = g + 22$$
$$(g + 22) + g = 428$$
$$b + (b - 22) = 428$$

Once the situations are described algebraically, students are in a position to use algebraic manipulation to figure out how many boys and girls there actually were.

Describing Functions

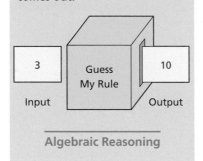

ACTIVITY 16.12

Determining the relationship in a table can be approached as a "guess my rule" game. You can dramatize this idea by building a box that, metaphorically, houses the rule. There is a hole in which inputs can be inserted on small pieces of paper, and a hole from which outputs emerge. The back of the box is open so that you can ensure the correct output number comes out.

3 | Guess My Rule | 10

Input | Output

_____

Algebraic Reasoning

An effective way to introduce the notion of relationship, or *function*, a very significant part of the work in algebra in upper grades, involves the concepts of input and output. A function is a relationship that leads to a particular output for a particular input. For example, if the function is "double the number," the input is the number to be doubled and the output is the double. Often these inputs and outputs are shown in a table to make it easier for students to infer relationships.

The table below shows the relationship "subtract 1 and double," as you subtract 1 from the number in the Input column, and then double the result to get the number in the Output column. In high school, this would be described as $f(x) = 2(x - 1)$, with $f(x)$ being function notation.

T-Chart Showing a Relationship

Input	Output
3	4
4	6
5	8
6	10

Subtract 1 from the number in the input column and then double to get the output value.

Not only does exploring functions build algebraic reasoning as students look for generalizations, but it tends to provide practice in number sense as well.

Students in K–8 tend to focus mostly on linear functions, where the input value is multiplied by a constant and perhaps a constant number is added or subtracted after the multiplication, but occasionally they might meet other kinds of functions like these.

Input	Output
1	1
2	4
3	9
4	16

Output = Input × Input

Input	Output
1	2
2	4
3	8
4	16

Output = 2^{Input}

Using Graphs to Describe Relationships

Graphs are valuable models for describing relationships between various variables or quantities. For example, Beatty (2010) has described very effective ways for students to link patterns represented numerically and geometrically to their related graphs. Some examples of functions are shown below.

Graphs That Show Relationships

RELATING NUMBERS OF TRICYCLES AND WHEELS

This graph shows the relationship between the number of tricycles and the total number of wheels; that is, as the number of tricycles increases by 1, the number of wheels increases by 3. By using the graph, the pattern inherent in counting tricycle wheels is highlighted.

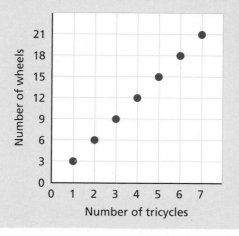

RELATING SIDE LENGTH AND PERIMETER OF A SQUARE

This graph shows that the perimeter of a square is related to its side length; that is, as the side length increases, the perimeter increases in a linear pattern. By using the graph, the linear relationship between side length and perimeter is highlighted.

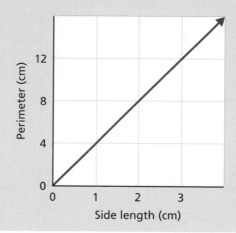

RELATING SIDE LENGTH AND AREA OF A SQUARE

This graph shows that the area of a square is related to its side length and that the relationship is not linear.

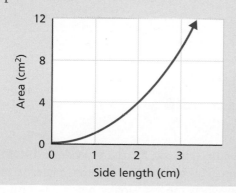

RELATING MONTHS OF THE YEAR AND HOURS OF DAYLIGHT

This graph shows that the length of daylight increases until June, and then decreases until the end of December. If the graph is continued, a cyclical pattern will emerge.

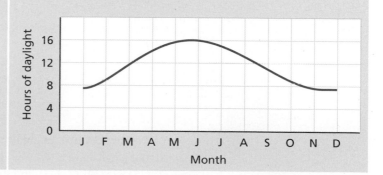

In introducing graphs to represent functions, it will be necessary to introduce students to the convention that the independent variable is usually graphed on the x-axis and the dependent variable on the y-axis, and to distinguish between graphs of discrete data (usually graphed with dots as in the first graph in the previous table) and graphs of continuous data (graphed as continuous lines or curves).

Students will learn that linear relationships—that is, those where one variable is multiplied by a constant with, perhaps, another constant added or subtracted—always result in a line or points in a line when graphed and that, in particular, when the line goes through the origin, the two variables are related proportionally, that is, one is a multiple of the other.

An example might be a student graphing the relationship $m = 12y$, relating the number of years to the number of months in that many years. The graph will be a line going through the points (0, 0), (1, 12), (2, 24), ..., where the first variable represents the number of years and the second the number of months. A continuous line graph makes sense, since, for example, 2.5 years is 30 months.

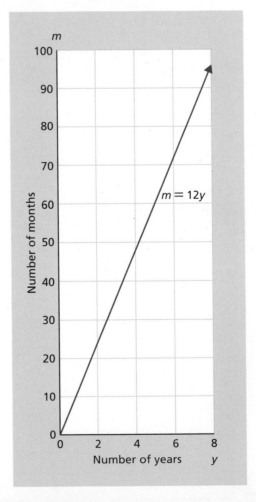

Another example might be a graph of the cost for a party where it costs $200 to rent a hall and $15 for each guest. This will result in points in a line, (0, 200), (1, 215), (2, 230), (3, 245), and so on, where the first variable represents the number of guests and the second the cost for the event. A discrete graph (of points) makes sense, since you cannot have, for example, 4.5 guests.

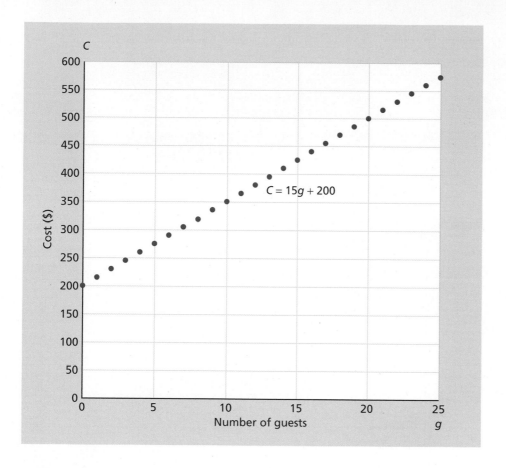

The fact that each of these is a line or points in a line makes sense since, if a fixed increase in one variable always leads to the same increase in the other, the result looks like a line.

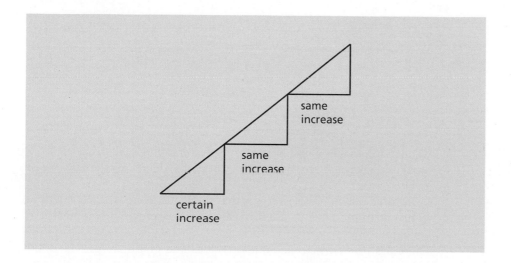

It is valuable for students to flexibly move between the representations of a function as a graph, an equation, and a table of values. Any one of these representations can be more useful in a particular situation.

For example, the table of values, graph, and equation below all describe how much money is left, m, after w weeks, if someone has $400 in the bank and removes $20 in one withdrawal each week.

Weeks of Withdrawal, w	Money Left ($), m
0	400
1	380
2	360
3	340
4	320
5	300

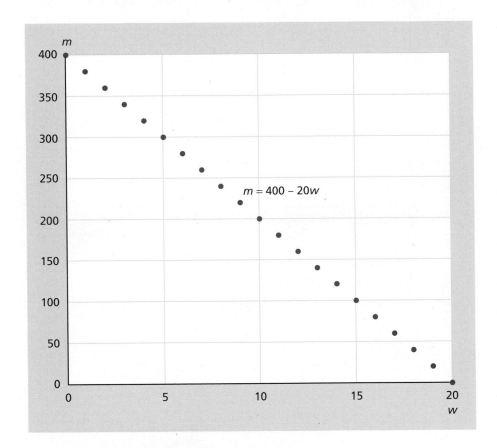

$m = 400 - 20w$

- The graph makes it easiest to see when the money will be gone. It makes it fairly easy to see that the value of m decreases as the value of w increases.
- The table makes it easiest to see that the value decreases $20 at a time.
- The equation makes it easiest to calculate the remaining money for a given number of weeks.

There are times when the table of values and graph are provided, but not the situation or equation, and the student must ascertain what they can about the relationship between the variables.

For example, if provided with the graph below about the relationship between the number of items manufactured by a company and the amount of profit, the student can quickly ascertain that the relationship is not linear. He or she might realize that the profit, y, will be low, if too few or too many items, x, are manufactured and that profit is maximized at 100 items.

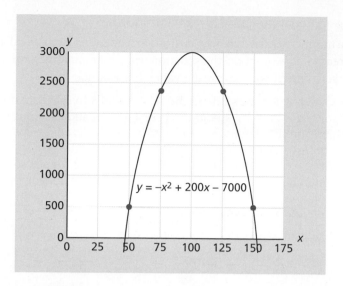

Algebraic Manipulation

The use of symbols to represent relationships and generalizations has the added benefit that symbols can be manipulated to deduce new information from given information. Often this involves taking what appears to be a complex relationship and writing it as a simpler relationship. This is true when simplifying expressions as well as when solving equations or inequalities.

Simplifying Expressions

Students working with expressions like $2n + 3n - 2$ might represent these using algebra tiles. If, for example, a rectangle is used to represent n, then students soon observe that $2n + 3n = 5n$. Usually, one colour is used to present positive amounts, for example, n or 1, and another colour to represent negative amounts, for example, $-2n$ or -4.

Below, two expressions have been modelled, $2n$ and $3n - 2$.

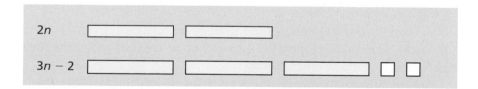

The zero property that is used to help students work with positive and negative integers is also applied to these algebraic expressions. So, for example, $2n - 3n = -n$ is shown below. Notice how the tiles for $+2n$ and the tiles for $-2n$ combine for a value of 0, leaving only one tile representing $-n$.

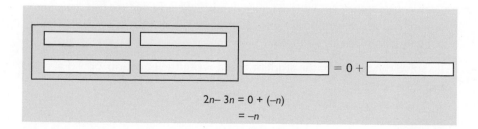

$$2n - 3n = 0 + (-n)$$
$$= -n$$

Solving an Equation Using Manipulatives

When a number sentence is simple enough, students can either call on a fact they already know or model the situation using manipulatives, for example, counters, to determine the missing value. For example:

- To solve $4 \times 5 = \blacksquare$, students model 4 sets of 5 to calculate the 20.
- To solve $4 \times \blacksquare = 24$, students create 4 groups and keep putting out counters until 24 counters are placed in 4 equal-sized groups. Students then observe that each group includes 6 items.
- To solve $3 \times \blacksquare + 6 = 21$, students distribute 21 counters so that an equal number are in each of three circles and 6 are outside the circles. The solution is the number of counters in one circle, 5 counters, so $3 \times 5 + 6 = 21$, as shown below.

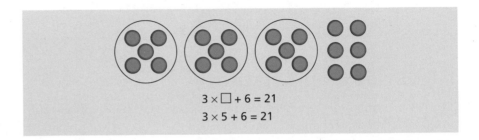

$$3 \times \square + 6 = 21$$
$$3 \times 5 + 6 = 21$$

Solving an Equation Using Opposite Operations

Students can think about working backward to solve an equation like $4 \times \blacksquare = 24$. What the equation says is that a number is multiplied by 4 to get 24. The "reverse" of multiplying by 4 is dividing by 4. So students can work backward and divide 24 by 4 to get 6.

Students might solve the more complex equation, $5 \times \blacksquare + 2 = 27$, by thinking "I multiply a number by 5, and then add 2 to get 27. So, if I work backward and subtract 2 ($27 - 2 = 25$), and then divide by 5 ($25 \div 5 = 5$), I will end up with the solution, 5."

A more involved example of this strategy is found in **Activity 16.13**, to the right. After students apply the steps in part (a), they can follow the steps in reverse to see how the trick works.

Some equations, such as $2n + 3 = n + 5$, do not lend themselves as easily to working backward. Other strategies that students can use to solve equations like this are guessing and checking, or balancing.

Solving an Equation by Guessing and Checking

A student might be faced with the following problem:

Amy built a structure made of two identical towers and had three blocks left over. Lisa started out with the same number of blocks and made a structure with a single tower just like one of Amy's and had 5 blocks left over. How many blocks were in each tower?

To solve the problem, the student could write the equation $2n + 3 = n + 5$ and then solve it.

Solving $2n + 3 = n + 5$

GUESS	REASONING	CHECK BY SUBSTITUTION $2n + 3 = n + 5$
First guess: 10	I'll start with 10 because it's an easy number to work with mentally.	$2 \times 10 + 3 = 23$ $10 + 5 = 15$ 23 is not equal to 15.
Second guess: 5	I'll try a number less than 10 because, if n is too great, doubling it and adding 3 (the left side of the equation) will make it a lot more than just adding 5 to it (the right side of the equation). I'll try 5.	$2 \times 5 + 3 = 13$ $5 + 5 = 10$ 13 is not equal to 10.
Third guess: 4	I'll try 4 because I notice that 13 and 10, the numbers I got when I used 5, were closer together than the numbers I got when I used 10.	$2 \times 4 + 3 = 11$ $4 + 5 = 9$ 11 is not equal to 9.
Fourth guess: 3	I'll try 3 to get numbers that are even closer together.	$2 \times 3 + 3 = 9$ $3 + 5 = 8$ 9 is not equal to 8.
Fifth guess: 2	I'll try 2 to get numbers that are even closer together.	$2 \times 2 + 3 = 7$ $2 + 5 = 7$ 7 is equal to 7. n must be 2.

Solving an Equation by Maintaining a Balance

Students could start out using manipulatives such as a balance scale with small, very light paper bags holding the unknown number of cubes. For example, to model $2n + 3 = n + 5$, students put 2 open empty paper bags ($2n$) and 3 cubes on one side of a balance, and 1 open empty paper bag (n) and 5 cubes on the other side (see the balance scale below). Students then put the same number of cubes in each bag, increasing the value until the sides of the scale balance. The number of cubes in each empty bag is the value of the unknown, n.

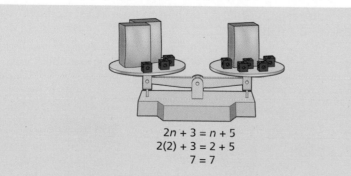

$$2n + 3 = n + 5$$
$$2(2) + 3 = 2 + 5$$
$$7 = 7$$

The scale is balanced when 2 cubes are put in each of the bags. Therefore, $n = 2$.

On a symbolic level, the equation $2n + 3 = n + 5$ can still be considered a balance. If either side of the equation is changed, the other side must be changed the same way to maintain a balance. Therefore, if 3 is subtracted from both sides of the equation, $2n + 3 - 3 = n + 5 - 3$, the balance is maintained. This also results in an equation that is easier to solve. For example:

$2n + 3 = n + 5$
$2n + 3 - 3 = n + 5 - 3$ (Subtract 3 from both sides.)
$2n = n + 2$
$n + n = n + 2$ (Substitute $n + n$ for $2n$ since $2n = n + n$.)
So, $n = 2$.

"Dividing" to Balance the Scale The equation representing the situation shown below on the balance scale on the left is $2b = 6$. The problem that motivated it might have been:

Two cans of juice cost $6. How much does each cost?

Note that, in this model, the bags are closed and each contains the same number of cubes. To find out how many cubes are in each bag, each side could be separated into 2 equal amounts. This is equivalent to dividing both sides by 2, as shown by the balance scale on the right.

"Subtracting" to Balance the Scale The equation representing the situation shown below on the balance scale on the left is $2b = 6 + b$. The problem that motivated it could have been:

Ian had some marbles, but Kyle had twice as many. If someone gave Ian 6 marbles, he would have as many as Kyle. How many marbles did Ian start with?

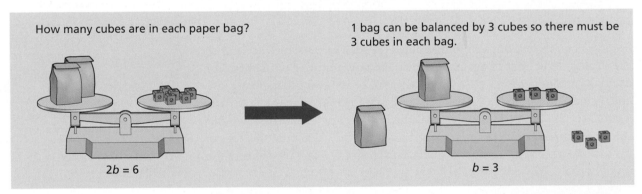

How many cubes are in each paper bag?

$2b = 6$

1 bag can be balanced by 3 cubes so there must be 3 cubes in each bag.

$b = 3$

To find out how many cubes are in each bag, a bag could be taken off each side. This is equivalent to subtracting b from both sides, as shown by the balance scale on the right.

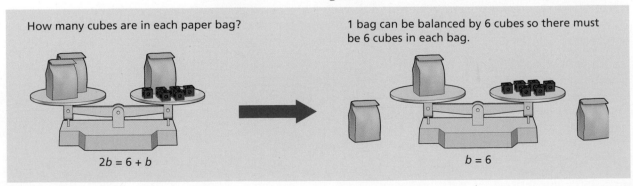

How many cubes are in each paper bag?

$2b = 6 + b$

1 bag can be balanced by 6 cubes so there must be 6 cubes in each bag.

$b = 6$

An Alternative Balance An alternative balance model for an equation involves balancing length, rather than mass. For example, the equation $2n + 3 = n + 5$ would be modelled as below:

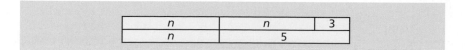

The student sees that the left two rectangles match, so they look at the right of the diagram. Since 5 is made up of an n and a 3, then n must be 2.

The model below shows that $3n - 2 = n + 8$ since it is a length that is 2 less than $3n$ that balances a length 8 more than n.

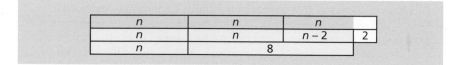

The student sees that the left two boxes (one in each row) match and give no real information. He or she then sees that if the 2 were added on to the bottom section to the right of the 8, then $8 + 2 = 10$ would match $2n$ rectangles. That means each n rectangle must have a length of 5; the solution is 5.

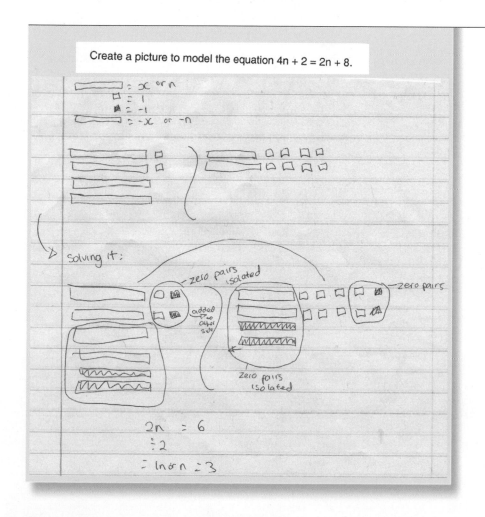

Student Response

This student effectively uses algebra tiles to model and solve a linear equation.

Common Errors and Misconceptions

Algebra: Common Errors, Misconceptions, and Strategies

COMMON ERROR OR MISCONCEPTION	SUGGESTED STRATEGY
Incorrectly Interpreting Equations Students often incorrectly interpret the equality sign. For example, to solve $3 \times 8 = \blacksquare \times 4$, they use 24 to replace the ▨ since 24 is 3×8.	Students need to participate in conversations about what the equals sign means; that is, both sides of the equation represent different names for the same amount. It also helps if students see a variety of equation types. For example: $8 + 7 = 15 \qquad 15 = 7 + 8 \qquad 6 + 9 = 10 + 5$
Switching the Variables in Relationships Students may misrepresent a relationship in words when using symbols. For example, to represent the fact that each teacher has 30 students, they might write $t = 30c$ instead of $c = 30t$ (where t stands for the number of teachers and c the number of children).	Provide students with practice in moving from verbal descriptions of a relationship to symbolic ones using familiar relationships. Trial and error with a familiar context is a reasonable strategy in this circumstance. For example, students know that there are 10 pennies in a dime. They can write the equations $d = 10p$ and $p = 10d$ and use different values for p to find corresponding values for d. They soon realize that the appropriate equation is $p = 10d$.
Interpreting a Multiplication Sign as the Variable _x_ When letters are used to represent variables, students are often confused between x as a variable and $\times$ as a multiplication sign. For example, if a student sees $3 \times y$, he might wonder if he should find the product of 3, x, and y, or the product of 3 and y.	One way around this problem is to avoid the use of the variable x in early stages of using literal variables. In early algebra work, n is often used to represent a whole number. As well, using variables that represent what they are modelling is also helpful. For example, if the variable represents the number of cubes in a bag (see page 383), perhaps b or c would be a more easily understandable variable. Another option is to clearly differentiate the symbols; for example, use a small italic x to represent a variable and a large non-italic capital X to represent multiplication. Once students become familiar with the notion that $ab = a \times b$, this will no longer be a problem.
Interpreting an Expression like 4x as a 2-Digit Number When letters are used to represent variables, students are often confused, for example, between $4n$ as the product of the numbers 4 and n, and a number in the 40s with a ones-digit of n. (See the **Student Response** below.)	It is not obvious to students why you omit the operation sign when you multiply a variable by a number. This requires specific discussion with students and practice with reading these values. A small dot could be used between two values as another way to represent multiplication and avoid confusion, for example, $4 \cdot n$.
Assuming –x Is a Negative Amount When faced with an expression like $4 - (-x)$, students assume the value is greater than 4, since they assume that they are subtracting a negative number, so adding a positive. But if x happens to be –3, then $-x$ is actually +3 and subtracting +3 leads to the value of 1, which is less than 4.	It is important to reinforce in many, many situations that whether a variable is positive or negative, is a fraction, or is a whole number cannot be determined without specific information about what possible values can be.

Can *x* be any number at all for this to be true? $2x - 6 = 18$

Circle (Yes) or No

Explain your answer. ___24 minus 6 equals 18___

___so you could change the X to a 4___

Student Response

This student appears to have incorrectly interpreted the variable *x* as the digit 4 (part of the number 24) instead of as the number 12 ($2x = 2 \times 12$).

Appropriate Manipulatives

Algebra: Examples of Manipulatives

COUNTERS, LINKING CUBES, OR SQUARE TILES	EXAMPLE
Counters are useful to model the solution of whole number equations.	Any of the suggested materials can be used to solve $2 \times \blacksquare + 8 = 16$ by distributing 16 of them so that an equal number are in each circle, and 8 are outside of both circles.

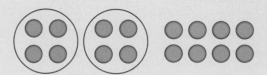

$$2 \times \square + 8 = 16 \longrightarrow 2 \times 4 + 8 = 16$$

Any of those materials can also be used to help determine pattern rules. For example, the arrangement below helps a student see why the rule for the pattern 4, 6, 8, 10, 12, …, is $2 \times$ term position $+ 2$.

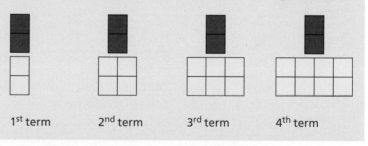

1st term   2nd term   3rd term   4th term

BALANCE SCALES AND PAPER BAGS	EXAMPLE
Balance scales and paper bags can be used to model solving equations.	To model $3n + 2 = 2n + 4$, put 3 empty paper bags and 2 cubes on one side of a balance scale, and 2 empty paper bags and 4 cubes on the other side. Then put the same number of cubes in each bag, increasing the number until the sides of the scale balance.

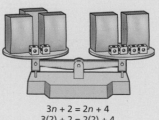

$$3n + 2 = 2n + 4$$
$$3(2) + 2 = 2(2) + 4$$
$$8 = 8$$

ALGEBRA TILES	EXAMPLE
Algebra tiles are useful for both simplifying expressions and solving equations.	**Simplifying an Expression** Tiles can be combined to show why $4x + 3 + (2x - 1) = 6x + 2$. 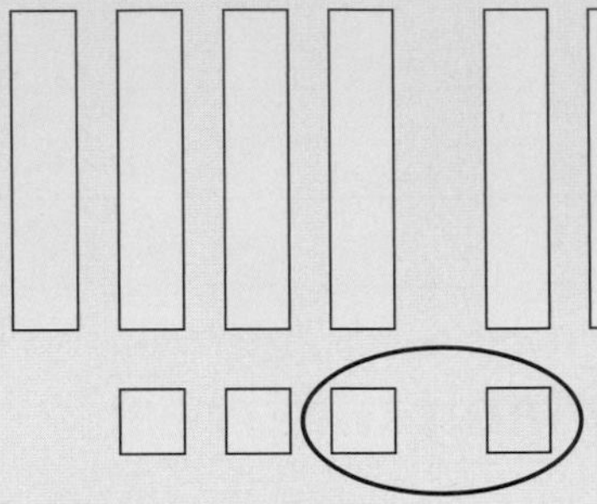 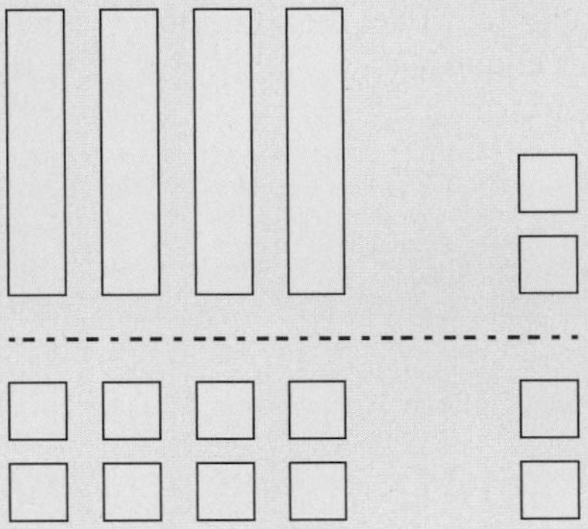

Solving an Equation

Clearly, x must have the value of 2 if $4x + 2 = 10$.

Appropriate Children's Books

The Rajah's Rice: A Mathematical Folktale from India (Barry, 1994), and *The Token Gift (McKibbon, 1996)*.

The exponential pattern (1, 2, 4, 8, 16, 32, ...) that comes from repeatedly doubling is explored in both versions of a very famous story about the wisdom of someone who recognizes how quickly numbers can grow when you multiply. Older students can use T-tables to predict the exact amount at various points in time.

Pattern Fish (Harris, 2000), and *Pattern Bugs (Harris, 2001)*.

Using these nicely illustrated books with few words, young students can explore a variety of types of repeating patterns, with each pattern being represented in a number of different ways.

Two of Everything (Hong, 2003).

In this ancient folk tale, a poor old man finds a pot that has the effect of doubling whatever is put into it. This situation would allow students to explore the algebraic relationship between numbers and their doubles.

Sea Squares (Hulme, 1999).

This attractive book allows students to explore the pattern of square numbers (1, 4, 9, 16, ...) in a visual way.

Lots and Lots of Zebra Stripes: Patterns in Nature (Swinburne, 1998).
Many patterns in nature can be explored by young students in this book, not only zebra stripes, but also ridges on pumpkins and scales on snakes.

Appropriate Digital Resources

See the MindTap site for a selection of appropriate digital resources.

Assessing Student Understanding

- Create opportunities for students to look for patterns in their environment as well as in the mathematics they are doing, and point them out, even when pattern is not the mathematical topic currently under discussion.

- Make sure to remember that unless a pattern rule is provided, there is no single way to extend a pattern. Thus, if you ask a student to continue, for example, 1, 3, 5, 7, ... and the extension is not 9, 11, 13, ... as expected, make sure to ask the student to explain his or her reasoning. It might be correct.

- Ask students to model a generalized relationship of their choice, for example, showing why 3 of something plus 2 of it is 5 of it, no matter what it is, or why multiplying by 4 is doubling a double, no matter what is being multiplied.

- As students respond to situations involving variables, make sure that the variables appear on the right side of the equals sign some of the time, and on the left side other times.

- This student has provided a thoughtful and perhaps even unexpected response. How would you use it to enhance your instruction?

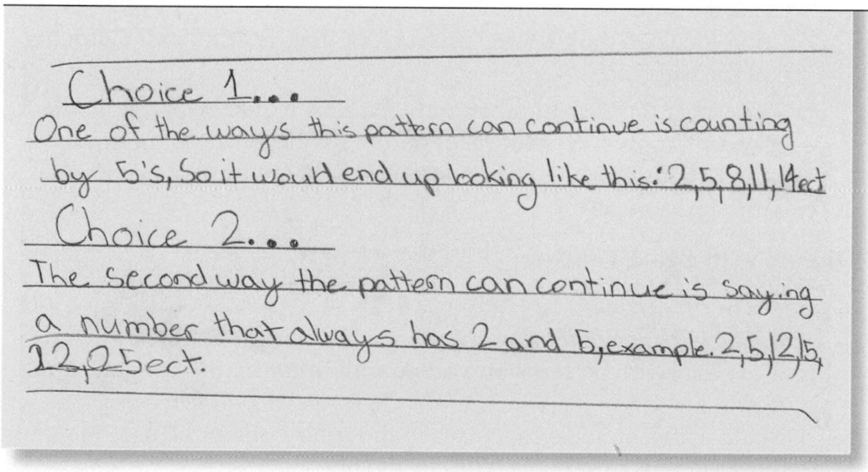

Choice 1...
One of the ways this pattern can continue is counting by 5's, so it would end up looking like this: 2,5,8,11,14ect

Choice 2...
The second way the pattern can continue is saying a number that always has 2 and 5, example. 2,5,12,5, 12,25ect.

Student Response

This student has answered the following question:
A pattern begins 2, 5, ... How could it continue?

Applying What You've Learned

1. What problem-solving strategy did you use to solve the chapter problem? Did you make a model? Draw a diagram? Use a pattern? How could the problem enhance a student's understanding of pattern?

2. Consider the two multi-attribute repeating patterns below. Why do you think the first might be easier for a student to extend than the second?

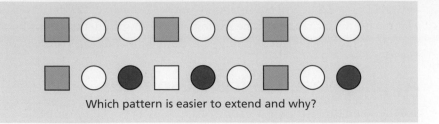

Which pattern is easier to extend and why?

3. Describe a variety of ways to use coloured multi-link cubes for students to work with both single-attribute and multi-attribute repeating patterns, as well as growing and shrinking patterns.

4. Develop an activity that will help students at about the Grade 4 level begin to recognize the relationship between where a number appears in a number pattern and its value.

5. Read several journal articles to get a sense of why the metaphor of a balance for an equation is important and powerful. List several of the important points that were raised.

6. The introduction of letter variables is difficult for students. What are some strategies you think would be helpful for them to deal better with letter variables?

7. Topics like solving equations of the form $[\ ] + b = c$ were once listed in curriculum documents as number topics; now they are listed in many documents as an algebra topic. How do you think that might affect the teaching of those topics?

Interact with a K–8 Student:

8. Ask a student to create three different patterns that include the numbers 10 and 12.

   a) Ask the student to compare the patterns. Does his or her description focus on the pattern structure, or does it simply list elements of the patterns?

   b) Ask what the 20th number in the pattern would be and how the student knows. What sorts of number concepts does the student use to determine his or her answers? What pattern concepts does the student use?

Discuss with a K–8 Teacher:

9. Choose one:

   Discuss with an elementary school teacher about how she or he integrates work with patterns into work with other mathematical strands.
   OR
   Discuss with a Grade 6 to 8 teacher about how she or he uses manipulative materials to support work in algebra.

Selected References

Barry, D. (1994). *The rajah's rice: A mathematical folktale from India.* Gordonsville, VA: W. H. Freeman & Co.

Beatty, R. (2010). Supporting algebraic thinking: Prioritizing visual representations. *Ontario Mathematics Gazette, 49, 28–33.*

Beatty, R., and Bruce, C. (2012). *From patterns to algebra.* Toronto: Nelson Education.

Beigie, D. (2011). The link from patterns to formulas. *Mathematics Teaching in the Middle School, 16, 329–335.*

Billings, E.M.H., Tiedt, T.L., and Slater, L.H. (2007). Algebraic thinking and pictorial growth patterns. *Teaching Children Mathematics, 13,* 302–308.

Blanton, M.L., and Kaput, J.J. (2003). Developing elementary teachers' "algebra eyes and ears." *Teaching Children Mathematics, 10,* 70–77.

Blanton, M., Levi, L., Crites, T., and Dougherty, B.J. (2011). *Developing essential understanding of algebraic thinking.* Reston, VA: National Council of Teachers of Mathematics.

Blanton, M. , Stephens, A., Knuth, E., Gardiner, A.M., Isler, I., and Kim, J-S. (2015). The development of children's algebraic thinking: The impact of a comprehensive early algebra intervention in third grade. *Journal for Research in Mathematics Education, 46,* 39–87.

Carpenter, T., Franke, M.L., and Levi, L. (2003). *Thinking mathematically: Integrating arithmetic and algebra in elementary school.* Portsmouth, NH: Heinemann.

Cuevas, G.J., and Yeatts, K. (2001). *Navigating through algebra, grades 3–5.* Reston, VA: National Council of Teachers of Mathematics.

Dubon, L.P., and Shafer, K.G. (2010). Storyboards for meaningful patterns. *Teaching Children Mathematics, 16,* 325–329.

Falkner, K.P., Levi, L., and Carpenter, T.C. (1999). Children's understanding of equality: A foundation for algebra. *Teaching Children Mathematics, 6,* 232–236.

Femiano, R. (2003). Algebraic problem solving in the primary grades. *Teaching Children Mathematics, 9,* 444–449.

Fosnot, C.T., and Jacob, B. (2010). *Young mathematicians at work: Constructing algebra.* Portsmouth, NH: Heinemann.

Friel, S., Rachlin, S., and Doyle, D. (2001). *Navigating through algebra, grades 6–8.* Reston, VA: National Council of Teachers of Mathematics.

Greenes, C., Cavanagh, M., Daccy, L., Findell, C., and Small, M. (2001). *Navigating through algebra in prekindergarten–grade 2.* Reston, VA: National Council of Teachers of Mathematics.

Greenes, C., and Rubenstein, R. (2008). *Algebra and algebraic thinking in school mathematics, 7th yearbook.* Reston, VA: National Council of Teachers of Mathematics.

Harris, T. (2000). *Pattern fish.* Brookfield, CN: Millbrook Press.

Harris, T. (2001). *Pattern bugs.* Brookfield, CN: Millbrook Press.

Hong, L.T. (2003). *Two of everything.* Morton Grove, IL: Albert Whitman & Company.

Hulme, J. (1999). *Sea squares.* New York: Hyperion.

Kaput, J.J., Carraher, D.W., and Blanton, M.L. (2007). *Algebra in the early grades.* New York: Routledge.

Kurz, T.L. (2013). Using technology to balance algebraic explorations. *Teaching Children Mathematics, 19,* 554–562.

Lee, L., and Freiman, V. (2006). Developing algebraic thinking through pattern exploration. *Mathematics Teaching in the Middle School, 11,* 428–433.

Lubinski, C.A., and Otto, A.D. (1997). Literature and algebraic reasoning. *Teaching Children Mathematics, 3,* 290–295.

Lubinski, C.A., and Otto, A.D. (2002). Meaningful mathematical representations and early algebraic reasoning. *Teaching Children Mathematics, 9,* 76–80.

Mason, J. , Graham, A., and Johnston–Wilder, S. (2005). *Developing thinking in algebra.* London: Sage Publications Ltd.

McKibbon, H.W. (1996). *The token gift.* Toronto, ON: Annick Press.

Schliemann, A.D., Carraher, D.W., and Brizuela, B. (2007). *Bringing out the algebraic character of arithmetic: From children's ideas to classroom practice. Studies in Mathematical Thinking and Learning Series.* London: Taylor & Francis.

Small, M. (2005). *PRIME: Patterns and algebra: Background and strategies.* Toronto, ON: Thomson Nelson.

———— (2014). *Uncomplicating algebra.* New York: Teachers College Press.

Stump, S. (2011). Patterns to develop algebraic reasoning. *Teaching Children Mathematics, 17,* 410–418.

Swinburne, S. (1998). *Lots and lots of zebra stripes.* Honesdale, PA: Boyds Mills Press.

Chapter 17
3-D and 2-D Shapes

CHAPTER PROBLEM

A mirror was placed on the original shape to create each of the other three shapes. Each time, indicate where the mirror was placed and how you know.

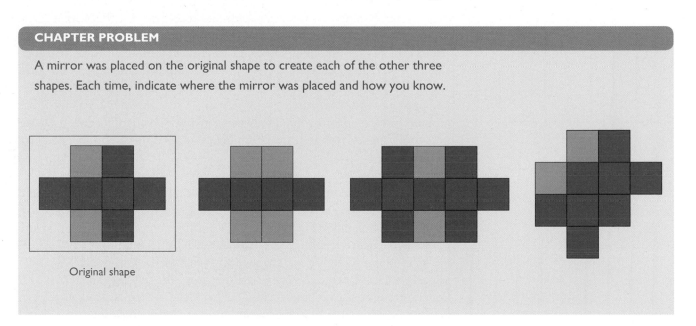

Original shape

IN A NUTSHELL

The main ideas in this chapter are listed below:

1. Researchers have described a taxonomy of geometric development that elaborates growth from the least sophisticated to the most sophisticated geometric understanding.

2. Properties and attributes of geometric shapes become the object of study in geometry. Many of the same properties and attributes that apply to 2-D shapes apply to 3-D shapes. The fact that every shape can be "cut up" and rearranged into other shapes is a fundamental part of this study.

3. Many geometric properties and attributes are related to measurements, for example, whether two sides are the same length, two faces the same area, and lines equally distant apart.

Geometry, which encompasses the study of shapes and spatial relationships, is an area of study that many students and teachers enjoy because it offers such a wide range of opportunities for hands-on exploration. K–8 students usually begin by examining 3-D shapes, and then broaden their investigations to include 2-D shapes and work with location and movement on grids. At higher levels of mathematics, students may go on to work with 3-D grids, or even explore what could happen in more than three dimensions. More importantly, spatial reasoning has been shown to be an important predictor of school success (Ministry of Education, Ontario, 2014). Work in geometry contributes to developing this reasoning, particularly in composition and decomposition tasks and viewing objects from different perspectives.

In this chapter, you will note that many topics are discussed in 2-D and 3-D situations in the same sections. Helping you, as the teacher, and students see the parallels between 2-D and 3-D geometry is important; it supports a focus on the underlying mathematical principles.

In some jurisdictions, 3-D shapes are called (3-D) objects or solids or (3-D) figures. 2-D shapes are also called (2-D) figures. The terms *2-D shapes* and *3-D shapes* are used throughout this chapter, but the vocabulary suggested in a particular curriculum might be best to use in that jurisdiction.

Fundamental Aspects of Geometry

Geometry is one, but not the only, aspect of mathematics where visualization is important. Whiteley (2004) speaks about visual reasoning as "seeing to think." Because visualization is such an obvious aspect of geometry, using geometric thinking as one tool to improve visual reasoning makes sense.

Fundamental aspects of geometry studied at the K–8 level include:

• recognizing and appreciating geometric shapes and actions in their world
• recognizing, describing, and making predictions about 3-D shapes, including their role in building structures

- recognizing, describing, and making predictions about 2-D shapes, including the representation of 3-D shapes in two dimensions
- exploring location and position, for example, using coordinate systems or map grids, and developing an understanding of relative position
- recognizing, describing, and making predictions about the effects of transformations on shapes, for example, predicting what a shape will look like after it is turned
- using visualization and spatial models to explore mathematical topics
- using reasoning to compare and contrast shapes, and to draw conclusions about them
- using geometric models and concepts to solve problems
- using mathematical language to communicate about geometric concepts
- representing shapes in different ways
- recognizing how geometric ideas connect to each other, and how they connect with other strands of mathematics, other subject areas, and the real world

Some of these topics will be examined in this chapter and some in Chapter 18.

Development of Geometric Thinking

It is important to note that children's ability to conceptualize shape develops through different stages, and that this development is fostered by each child's experience. Two researchers who explored these stages of development are Pierre van Hiele and Dina van Hiele-Geldof, who developed a taxonomy of geometric thinking (Teppo, 1991). At the initial level, Level 0: Visualization, students focus on what individual shapes "look like." A child at this level may identify a circle only because it "looks like" a circle. By Level 1: Analysis, children are ready to conceive of shapes as part of a group of similar shapes, and to begin taking note of their properties. By Level 2: Informal Deduction, they have a greater ability

The Van Hiele Taxonomy of Geometric Thought*

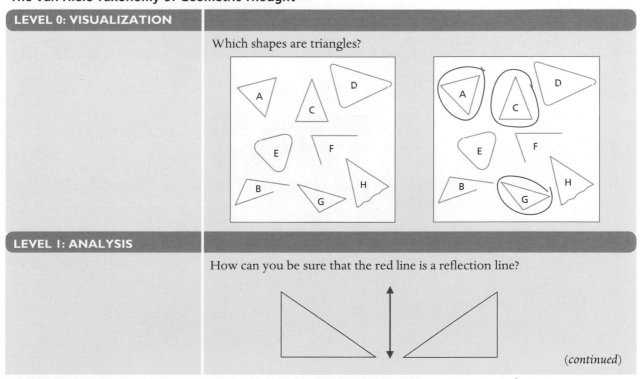

LEVEL 0: VISUALIZATION

Which shapes are triangles?

LEVEL 1: ANALYSIS

How can you be sure that the red line is a reflection line?

(continued)

---

*Pierre van Hiele and Dina van Hiele-Geldof, *Taxonomy of Geometric Thinking* (Teppo, 1991).

LEVEL 2: INFORMAL DEDUCTION

Do you think every triangle is half of a parallelogram? Explain.

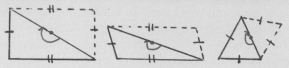

LEVEL 3: DEDUCTION

(not applicable to many elementary school students)

What is the sum of the angles in a triangle?

How can you use parallel lines and transversals to show that every triangle will have the same angle sum?

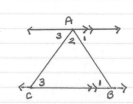

- The angles labeled 1 are equal because the line through A and side CB are parallel and side AB is a transversal.
- The angles labeled 3 are equal because the line through A and side CB are parallel and side AC is a transversal.
- Angles 1, 2, and 3 at the top form a straight angle so they have a sum of 180°.
- Therefore, angles 1, 2, and 3 inside the triangle have a sum of 180°.

LEVEL 4: RIGOUR

(not applicable to elementary school students)

Draw a triangle on a globe by joining the North Pole to two points on the equator. Show that the sum of the interior angles of this triangle is greater than 180°.

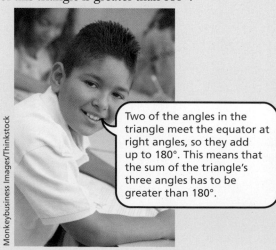

Monkeybusiness Images/Thinkstock

Two of the angles in the triangle meet the equator at right angles, so they add up to 180°. This means that the sum of the triangle's three angles has to be greater than 180°.

to apply "if–then" reasoning and are ready to consider simple logical arguments about shape properties. Van Hiele Levels 3 and 4 (Deduction and Rigour) apply to students in high school and beyond, and involve more formal work in which students are expected to use traditional Euclidean and also non-traditional axiom (premise) structures from which to deduce properties of shapes. Since this taxonomy was first proposed, there have been variations that describe the levels using different language—e.g. Level 0 as Pre-recognition, Level 1 as Visual, Level 2 as Descriptive/Analytic, Level 3 as Abstract/Relational, Level 4 as Formal Deduction, and Level 5 as Rigor/Mathematical (Clements and Battista, 1992).

It is children's spatial experiences more than their age that determines their level on the taxonomy. For that reason, it is incumbent on teachers to provide rich, spatial experiences using accessible strategies and language.

Identifying and Classifying Shapes

Younger students identify and name shapes on an intuitive level (van Hiele Level 0)—they just know that it is a "ball" (sphere) or a "box" (rectangle-based prism) or a square or a triangle. As students develop mathematically, they are increasingly able to identify and name a shape by examining its properties and using reasoning. For example, a student might say, "Both of these shapes are triangles because each has 3 straight sides. All shapes with 3 straight sides are triangles." This student recognizes that having 3 straight sides is a property of the class of shapes called triangles.

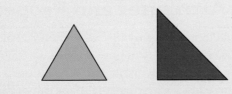

Both of these shapes can be named or classified as triangles because they have 3 straight sides.

Later, students' ability to identify and name/classify shapes becomes more sophisticated. These students are able to consider more and more geometric properties and more specific classifications. For example, a more advanced student might say, "The red triangle is a right isosceles triangle because it has 3 straight sides and two of them are equal, and it has a right angle," even though the less sophisticated student might still visually recognize the exact same properties.

Identification of 2-D and 3-D Shapes

One way to provide experience with identifying shapes is to organize a shape hunt or a WebQuest, as described in **Activity 17.3** at the top of the next page. A shape hunt or WebQuest is a good way to connect geometry with everyday life. For example, students can observe and identify shapes in their environment, shapes in books they are reading, shapes in works of art, shapes in architectural structures, etc.

As students become more familiar with basic shape identification, they can participate in activities that focus increasingly on the geometric properties that define or classify certain shapes. For example, in **Activity 17.2**, students are working with shape classifications (quadrilaterals and non-rectangles)

ACTIVITY 17.1

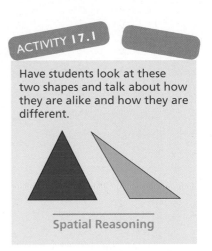

Have students look at these two shapes and talk about how they are alike and how they are different.

Spatial Reasoning

ACTIVITY 17.2

Van Hiele Level 1 students can work with shape classifications and geometric properties by creating a 2-D shape collage to fit the rules given below:

Use cutout shapes to make a collage that meets these rules:

- All the shapes are quadrilaterals.
- Two shapes have parallel sides, but are not rectangles.
- Three shapes have lines of symmetry.

Critical Thinking

that are associated with certain geometric properties (4 sides, parallel sides, and no right angles), as well as other properties such as symmetry.

ACTIVITY 17.3

Even van Hiele Level 0 students can identify 3-D shapes by taking part in a shape hunt or geometry walk in the classroom, school, or playground, or at home. Older students can identify 2-D shapes by taking part in a WebQuest on the Internet.

Shape Hunt

Shapes we looked for	Names of things we found
Cube	
Cylinder	

Spatial Reasoning

Geometric Attributes and Properties

Young students can take part in activities where they explore the attributes of shapes. For 2-D shapes, they might consider whether the sides of a shape are rounded or straight, or whether the shape is open or closed. For 3-D shapes, they might consider whether the shape can or cannot roll. The focus at this point is on exploring and comparing shapes, rather than fitting them into formal classifications.

As students become more familiar with geometric attributes, they gradually gain an awareness of the specific attributes that define each class of shape, that is, the properties of shapes. A *property* is an attribute that applies to all the shapes of a certain class. For example, the class of shapes called rectangles has these properties: 4 straight sides, 2 pairs of equal sides, and 4 right angles. Quadrilaterals (a class of shapes that includes rectangles) also have 4 straight sides but only some quadrilaterals have 4 right angles. So, having 4 right angles is a property of all rectangles, but not of all quadrilaterals, although it is an attribute of some quadrilaterals.

Comparing, sorting and patterning activities provide a context for students to explore geometric attributes and properties.

Comparing Shapes

In the Student Response at the top of the next page, the student has focused on properties of the shapes—the number and shape of the faces—in order to compare them. Other properties that differentiate these two classes of shapes could be the number of vertices or the number of edges. If asked how these shapes are the same, the student would have to refer to those properties that make these shapes part of a higher classification. The student might notice, for example, that all the faces are *polygons*, so both shapes are *polyhedrons*.

How are these prisms different?

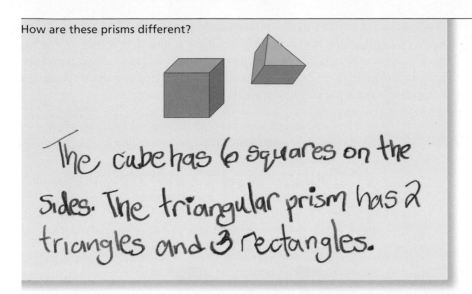

The cube has 6 squares on the sides. The triangular prism has 2 triangles and 3 rectangles.

Student Response

This student, who is likely to be at least Level I on the van Hiele scale, recognizes that cubes are different from triangle-based prisms because they have a different number of faces and different face shapes. Note that the student is still using the informal term *side* rather than the formal mathematical term *face*.

In **Activity 17.4**, students at any van Hiele level compare 2-D shapes. Suppose the student drew a rectangle. In order to differentiate it from the triangle, a student might mention the number of sides: 4 sides (a property of rectangles) versus 3 sides (a property of triangles), or he or she might draw a shape that is much bigger or a triangle that is tilted over, focusing on size or orientation. In order to find similarities, students may look for properties that the shapes share. In this case, a student might note that both have straight sides, which is a property of the class of shapes called *polygons*.

Sorting and Patterning with Shapes

Most curricula in Canada require elementary school students to sort and construct 2-D and 3-D shapes. One of the main purposes of sorting shapes and creating patterns with them is to focus students' attention on geometric attributes that they can use to classify the shapes, for example, sorting a group of 2-D shapes to separate those with 3 sides from those with 4 or more sides.

Sorting Shapes

In the sort below, a set of prisms has been sorted according to how many *faces* each has. Through a sort like this, students will begin to discover some of the geometric properties of triangle-based and rectangle-based prisms, for example, all triangle-based prisms have 5 faces and all rectangle-based prisms have 6 faces.

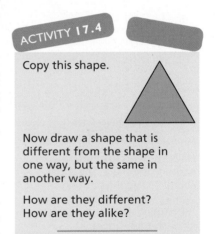

ACTIVITY 17.4

Copy this shape.

Now draw a shape that is different from the shape in one way, but the same in another way.

How are they different? How are they alike?

_____

Creative Thinking

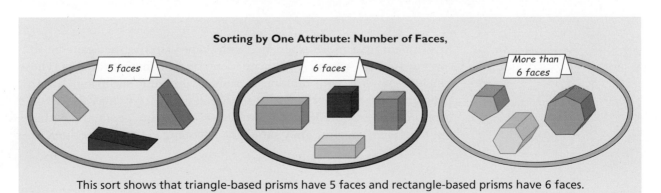

Sorting by One Attribute: Number of Faces,

5 faces

6 faces

More than 6 faces

This sort shows that triangle-based prisms have 5 faces and rectangle-based prisms have 6 faces.

Students can also use sorting to investigate properties of 2-D shapes. The Venn diagram below shows that having right angles is an *attribute* of some parallelograms, but it is not a *property* of them because some parallelograms have no right angles. Note that the orange shape is outside the circles because it is not a parallelogram and it has no right angles.

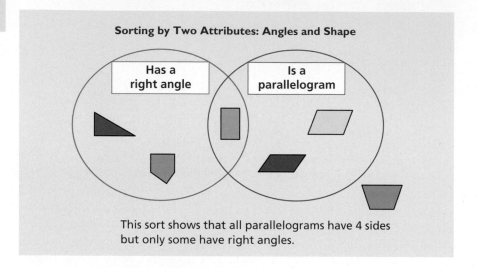

Sorting by Two Attributes: Angles and Shape

Has a right angle

Is a parallelogram

This sort shows that all parallelograms have 4 sides but only some have right angles.

Patterning to Explore Geometric Attributes and Properties

Shape patterns are founded on experience with sorting and classifying according to attributes and properties. Sorting items using attributes such as the direction in which a shape is pointing, or the properties such as number or lengths of sides (for 2-D shapes) or flat versus curved surfaces (for 3-D shapes), prepares students for patterning. It helps students focus on what makes one element in a pattern like or different from another. This then makes it possible to identify, describe, compare, and extend the pattern.

Young students usually begin with simple repeating patterns like the one shown below.

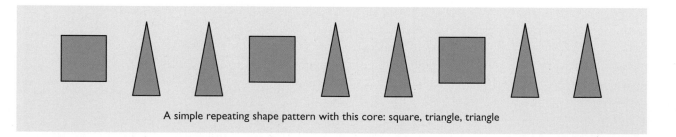

A simple repeating shape pattern with this core: square, triangle, triangle

As students gain more experience with shape patterns, they gain the ability to interpret, extend, and create increasingly complex patterns. These include patterns with multiple attributes, growing/shrinking patterns, and grid patterns that change in two directions. Patterns may also involve transformations. Students are likely to notice many geometric patterns in their environment. They should be encouraged to look for them.

More Challenging Shape Patterns

A REPEATING TWO-ATTRIBUTE PATTERN

In this pattern, not only do the shapes change, but the orientation of the shapes changes as well.

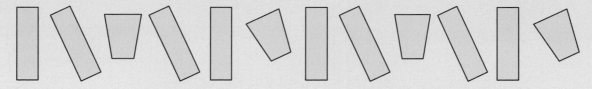

Pattern rule 1: rectangle, rectangle, trapezoid, ...

Pattern rule 2: vertical, turned, ...

A GROWING TWO-DIMENSIONAL PATTERN

In this growing pattern, both the length and the width of the square increase by 1 square each time.

 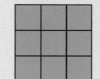

A MULTI-DIRECTIONAL PATTERN

Patterns are visible in rows, columns, and diagonals on this grid.

Types of 3-D Shapes

A number of 3-D shapes are either so familiar or of sufficient mathematical interest that they have special names.

Polyhedrons, Spheres, Cones, and Cylinders

A polyhedron is any 3-D shape whose faces are all polygons. Polyhedrons can have as few as 4 faces or they can have many more. Each face can have as few as 3 sides. All prisms and pyramids are polyhedrons (or polyhedra). Spheres, cones, and cylinders are not polyhedrons as their surfaces are not polygons, but they are shapes students are expected to become familiar with. That said, some people will reasonably classify a sphere as an infinite-sided polyhedron.

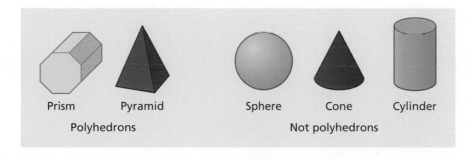

Prism   Pyramid   Sphere   Cone   Cylinder

Polyhedrons   Not polyhedrons

Components of 3-D Shapes

In order to describe the properties of 3-D shapes, and to classify them, students need to understand their components. Components are the individual parts that go together to make a shape—*faces*, *curved surfaces*, *edges*, and *vertices*.

Concrete models of 3-D shapes allow students to explore these components in a very hands-on way. For example, a student would be able to manipulate a model of a triangle-based prism to view, touch, and count all 5 faces—2 triangles and 3 rectangles. He or she would also be able to touch and count each of the 6 vertices and 9 edges.

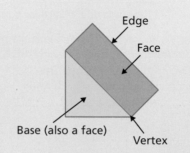

A triangle-based prism has 5 faces (including 2 bases), 9 edges, and 6 vertices.

One way to familiarize students with 3-D shapes is to provide information about the properties of a particular shape (or have students provide this information for one another), and have students figure out what the shape might be. Some students might be able to do this by visualizing; others will need concrete materials to help them.

Activities with 3-D shapes can often provide realistic and meaningful reasons for studying 2-D shapes. In fact, most teachers prefer to begin their study of shapes with 3-D shapes, which provides a natural context for studying the 2-D shapes that form their faces.

Using Properties to Classify 2-D Shapes

As with 3-D shapes, certain 2-D shapes are met regularly in elementary school curricula.

Polygons and Circles

A *polygon* is a closed 2-D shape whose sides are straight line segments that intersect only at the vertices. A circle is defined as a set of points that are the same distance from a given point, the centre.

Components of 2-D Shapes

To describe the properties of 2-D shapes, and to classify them, students can use descriptions of their components. Components are the individual parts that go together to make a shape—straight sides, curves, and angles.

Components of 2-D Shapes

COMPONENTS OF A POLYGON	COMPONENTS OF A CIRCLE
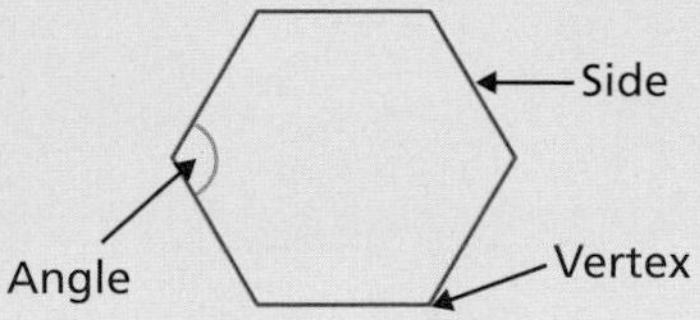 Side, Angle, Vertex	Circumference
This hexagon has 6 sides, 6 vertices, and 6 angles.	The perimeter of a circle is called its circumference.

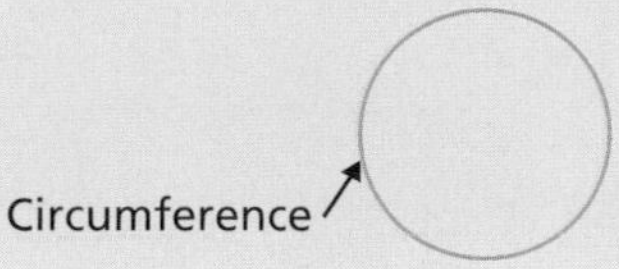

Types of Polygons

NAMING POLYGONS

Sample polygons	Number of sides	Name	Sample polygons	Number of sides	Name
	3	triangle		8	octagon
	4	quadrilateral		9	nonagon
	5	pentagon		10	decagon
	6	hexagon		11	hendecagon
	7	heptagon		12	dodecagon

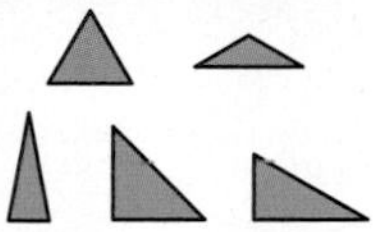

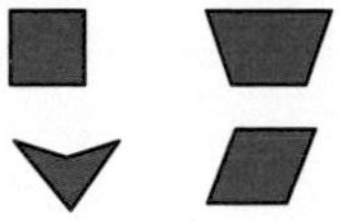

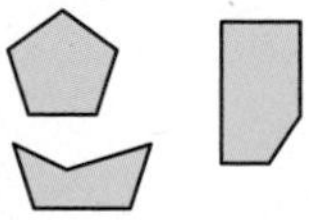

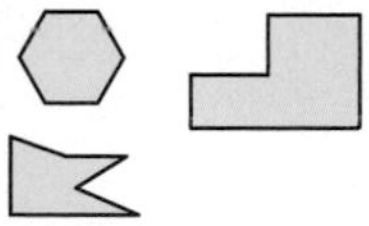

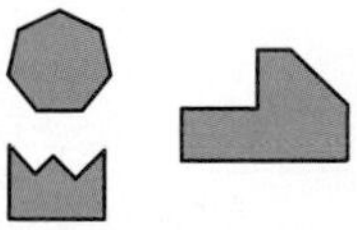

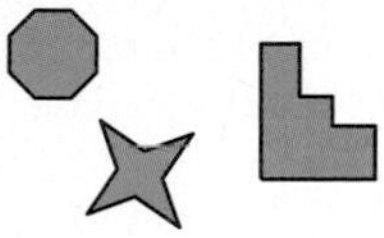

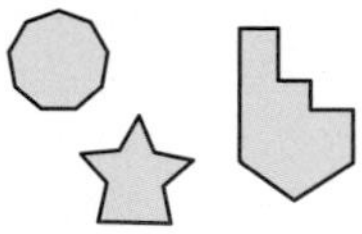

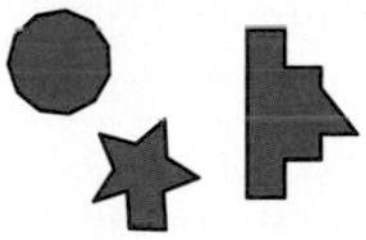

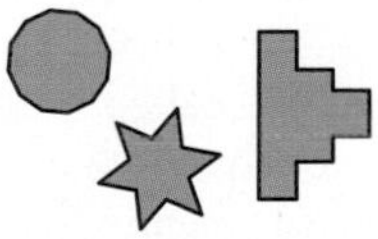

Although most polygons are called "…gons," triangles and quadrilaterals are typically not. For some students, that makes it less likely for them to include these shapes as types of polygons.

Relating Polygon Vertices and Sides

An interesting property of polygons is that the number of vertices is always equal to the number of sides. The following explains why:

In a polygon, each vertex is formed by the endpoints of 2 line segments, so the number of vertices will be equal to the total *number of separate endpoints* ÷ 2 or *n* vertices.

Each of the shapes below has 5 sides, so there are 10 endpoints altogether, which meet at 10 ÷ 2 or 5 vertices.

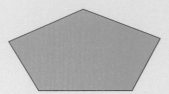
5 sides and 5 vertices

5 sides and 5 vertices

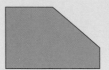
5 sides and 5 vertices

Polygons have the same number of sides as vertices.

Classifying 2-D Shapes by Properties: Polygons

CLASS OF 2-D SHAPE AND DISCUSSION

Triangles

Triangles are 3-sided polygons.

- Triangles are usually classified in terms of the relationship of their side lengths. *Equilateral triangles* have all 3 sides equal; *isosceles triangles* have 2 sides equal; and *scalene triangles* have 3 sides of different lengths.

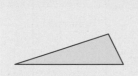

Scalene   Isosceles   Equilateral

Classifying triangles by side length

Some mathematicians say that because there are 2 equal sides in an equilateral triangle, it is a special type of isosceles triangle.

- A different way to classify triangles is in terms of their angles. If a triangle has one square corner (or right angle or 90° angle), then the triangle is called a *right triangle*. If all three angles are less than 90° (all acute angles), the triangle is called an *acute triangle*. If one angle is greater than 90° (an obtuse angle), it is called an *obtuse triangle*.

  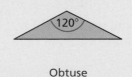

Right   Acute   Obtuse

Classifying triangles by angle measure

Since there is overlap in these two classification systems, cross-classification is possible, for example, a right isosceles triangle. See Activity 17.13 on page 413.

PROPERTIES

- All triangles are polygons with 3 straight sides and 3 vertices (3 angles).

The side and angle properties of special types of triangles are listed in the chart below.

Class of Triangle	Properties
equilateral (equiangular)	3 equal sides 3 equal angles, each 60°
isosceles	2 equal sides 2 equal angles
scalene	3 sides of different lengths 3 angles of different measures
right	1 right angle
acute	3 acute angles
obtuse	1 obtuse angle

- In order to form a triangle, the sum of the lengths of the two shorter sides must be greater than the longest side.

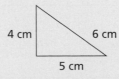 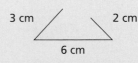

4 cm   6 cm   3 cm   2 cm

5 cm   6 cm

Can form a triangle   Cannot form a triangle

- The side opposite the greatest angle is always the longest side. Similarly, the side opposite the smallest angle is always the shortest side.

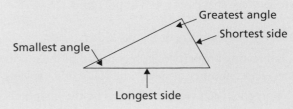

Greatest angle
Shortest side
Smallest angle
Longest side

CLASS OF 2-D SHAPE AND DISCUSSION

- Students can use dynamic geometry software to see how the side lengths, overall shape, and angle measures change when one vertex is moved.

- Students can also use concrete materials, such as geostrips, to discover that, unlike other polygons, triangles are rigid structures. This is why triangles are frequently used in construction.

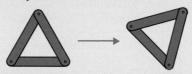

When pushed, a triangle does not change its shape because it is a rigid shape.

When pushed, a rectangle becomes a non-rectangular parallelogram.

PROPERTIES

- If two angles of a triangle have the same measure, then the sides opposite them are of equal length (and vice versa).

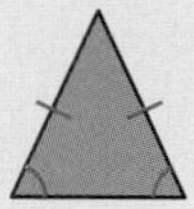

- The sum of the 3 angles is always 180°.

- A triangle can never have more than one obtuse angle (an angle greater than 90°) because the 3 angles in a triangle always add to 180°. For example, a triangle with two right angles is impossible.

A triangle can never have two 90° angles because, if it did, the sides opposite those angles would be parallel, and would not meet at a vertex.

CLASS OF 2-D SHAPE AND DISCUSSION

Quadrilaterals

Quadrilaterals are 4-sided polygons. Although rectangles are the most common quadrilateral that you see in everyday life, students will soon discover that there are many classes of quadrilaterals. The quadrilateral family includes parallelograms, kites, and trapezoids, along with other 4-sided shapes.

The diagram below shows how different classes of quadrilaterals are related. An alternative way to classify quadrilaterals is based on symmetry.

Classifying Quadrilaterals

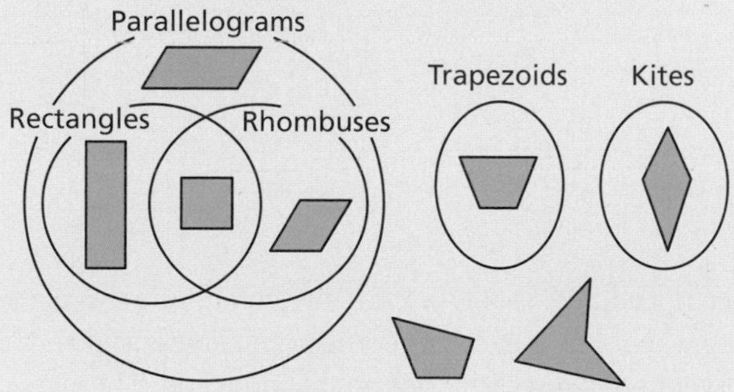

Parallelograms

Trapezoids   Kites

Rectangles   Rhombuses

Some mathematicians consider a parallelogram to be a type of trapezoid, since it has one pair of parallel sides (as well as another pair). In that case, the parallelogram circle above would be inside the trapezoid circle.

Similarly, some would consider a rhombus to be a special kind of kite, since it has 2 pairs of equal adjacent sides (even though both pairs are the same). In this case, the kite circle would need to include the rhombus circle.

PROPERTIES

- All quadrilaterals are polygons with 4 straight sides and 4 vertices (4 angles).

The side and angle properties of special types of quadrilaterals are listed in the chart below.

Quadrilateral	Properties
Parallelogram 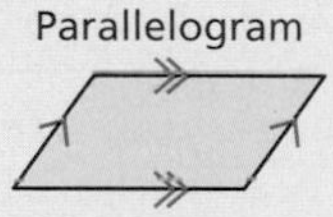	A quadrilateral with 2 pairs of parallel sides
Rhombus 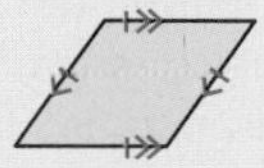	A parallelogram with all sides equal in length
Rectangle 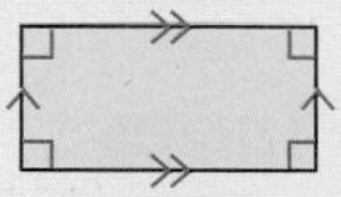	A parallelogram with 4 right angles.
Square 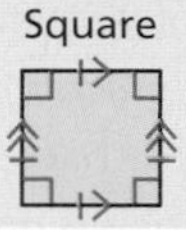	A rectangle with all sides equal in length
Trapezoid 	A quadrilateral with 1 pair of parallel sides; if 2 sides are equal, the shape is called an *isosceles trapezoid*
Kite 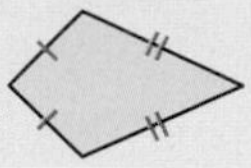	A quadrilateral with 2 pairs of equal adjacent sides

(continued)

Classifying 2-D Shapes by Properties: Polygons (Continued)

CLASS OF 2-D SHAPES AND DISCUSSION	PROPERTIES

Quadrilaterals (Continued)

Different definitions are possible for many quadrilaterals, and students at later developmental phases can explore these. For example:

- A parallelogram is typically described as a quadrilateral with 2 pairs of parallel sides. It can also be described as a quadrilateral where opposite sides are equal in length, since this is only possible where there are 2 pairs of parallel sides.

- A rectangle is typically described as a parallelogram with 4 right angles, but it can also be described as a parallelogram with at least 1 right angle, since this is only possible if the other angles are also right angles.

- Every quadrilateral has 2 diagonals.

- Typically, a diagonal divides a quadrilateral into 2 triangles, so the sum of the angles in that quadrilateral is 180° + 180° or 360°.

Angle sum = 180°   Angle sum = 180°

Angle sum = 360°

This latter property can be explored by creating the shape using dynamic geometry software, which will measure the angles for the student.

CLASS OF 2-D SHAPES AND DISCUSSION	PROPERTIES

Regular Polygons

- In a *regular* polygon, all the sides are the same length and all the angles are the same size. Equilateral triangles and squares are regular polygons.

Equilateral triangle   Square   Regular hexagon

- The word "regular" sometimes creates confusion for students, since they may think of something "regular" as something that's "ordinary." From that perspective, students may view common shapes such as circles or rectangles as "regular," but this is not the mathematical definition.

- All regular polygons are convex shapes that have all sides equal in length and all angles equal in size.

- As the number of sides on a regular polygon increases, so does the angle at each vertex. The result is a series of polygons that look more and more like circles.

3 sides	4 sides	6 sides	12 sides
60° angles	90° angles	120° angles	150° angles

When you add another side to a regular polygon, the angle at each vertex increases.

Planes

Although planes are often not addressed in K–8 formally, students discuss planes informally when working with many aspects of geometry. A plane is a 2-D or flat surface that goes on forever in two directions not on the same line. The faces of 3-D shapes are parts of planes. Planes can be *parallel* or they can *intersect*.

ACTIVITY 17.7

Students can place a regular polygon between two hinged mirrors, with the mirrors flat against adjacent sides. Counting the number of copies of the shape and dividing that number into 360° will tell the student the size of the angle at the vertex.

Spatial Reasoning

RELATING PLANES AND 3-D SHAPES

- Each face is on a different plane.
- Edges are where two planes intersect.
- Vertices are where three or more planes intersect.
- Adjacent faces of a cube are parts of intersecting planes, and opposite faces are parts of parallel planes.

For example, cubes consist of faces that are on parallel and intersecting perpendicular planes.

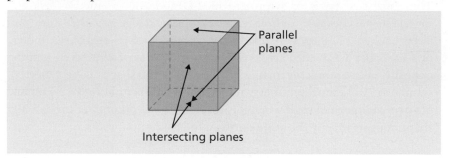

Lines, Segments, and Rays

It is normally taken for granted that students know what *lines* are, but the term is often used interchangeably with *ray* and *line segment*. The usual way of naming a line, line segment, or ray is to locate and name two points on it (usually indicated with a dot). The standard convention for showing the difference between lines, line segments, and rays is to use an arrow to indicate where a line extends indefinitely and to use a dot to indicate an endpoint.

LINE	LINE SEGMENT	RAY
A line is something straight and "infinitely thin" that extends forever in two directions.	A line segment is a "piece of a line," with two defined endpoints.	A ray has one defined endpoint and extends infinitely from it.
A　　　　　B Line ABC	A　　　　　B Line segment AB	A　　　　　B Ray AB

Lines, line segments, and rays can be *parallel* or they can *intersect*. Parallel lines, line segments, and rays never meet, as they remain a constant distance apart. Whenever two lines intersect, they meet at a single point. When lines intersect at a 90° angle, they are said to be *perpendicular*.

PARALLEL	INTERSECTING	PERPENDICULAR
Parallel lines do not meet. The distance between parallel lines remains constant.	Intersecting lines meet at a single point. The distance between the lines increases as you move from that point.	Perpendicular lines are intersecting lines that meet at a right angle.

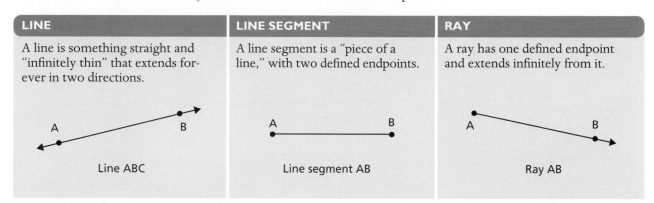

Symmetry

There are two types of symmetry in 2-D and 3-D geometry—*reflective (or reflectional) symmetry (mirror symmetry)* and *rotational symmetry (turn symmetry)*. When 2-D shapes are divided along one or more lines of symmetry, or 3-D shapes are divided across one or more planes of symmetry, and the opposite sides are mirror images, you say that the shapes have reflective symmetry. Rotational symmetry refers to the number of times a 2-D shape fits over an image of itself when it is rotated, or the number of times a 3-D shape appears exactly the same during a full rotation.

Reflective Symmetry of 2-D and 3-D Shapes

A shape has *reflective symmetry* if one half of the shape is a reflection of the other half. Both 2-D and 3-D shapes can have reflective symmetry. In a 2-D shape, the reflection is across a line. In a 3-D shape, it is across a plane.

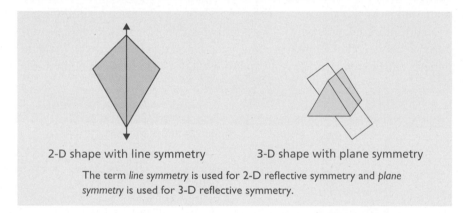

2-D shape with line symmetry   3-D shape with plane symmetry

The term *line symmetry* is used for 2-D reflective symmetry and *plane symmetry* is used for 3-D reflective symmetry.

Understanding and Determining Line Symmetry

When one half of a shape reflects onto the other half across a line, the line is called the *line of symmetry*. Shapes can have one or more lines of symmetry. In fact, a circle has an infinite number of lines of symmetry.

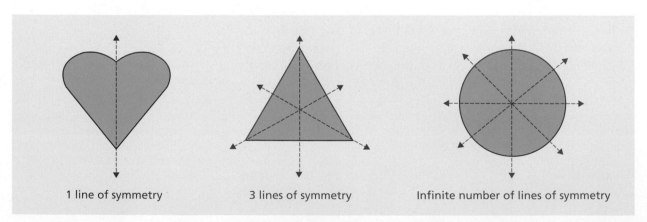

1 line of symmetry   3 lines of symmetry   Infinite number of lines of symmetry

Students are often surprised to find that a shape can have more than one line of symmetry. Note that the more sides there are on a regular polygon, the more lines of symmetry there are because the shape is getting more and more like a circle. In addition, the number of lines of symmetry in a regular polygon is always equal to the number of vertices.

Students at van Hiele Level 0 are likely to recognize symmetry without being able to articulate how they know. As students advance in their geometric thinking, they can prove symmetry. For example, they can fold the shape to see if the halves match, or use a transparent mirror (or a commercial tool called a *Mira*). In each case, if the shape is symmetrical along the fold line or where the Mira has been placed, the image of one side of the shape will fall right on top of the other side of the shape.

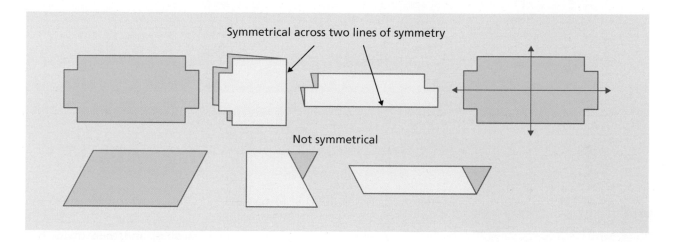

Symmetrical across two lines of symmetry

Not symmetrical

Constructing Shapes with Line Symmetry

There are a number of different ways for students to construct shapes with line symmetry. Students can build designs with square tiles or pattern blocks, use folded paper, use a Mira, use geoboards or grid paper, or use technology tools such as a drawing program or dynamic geometry software. Another approach is described in **Activity 17.8**.

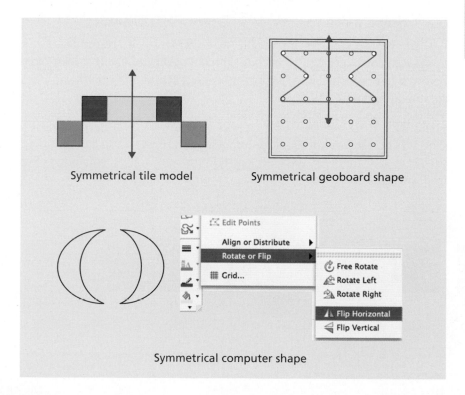

Symmetrical tile model

Symmetrical geoboard shape

Symmetrical computer shape

Understanding and Determining Plane Symmetry

When one half of a 3-D shape reflects onto the other half across a plane, the plane separating the halves is called the *plane of symmetry*. This is why reflective symmetry in 3-D shapes is called *plane symmetry*.

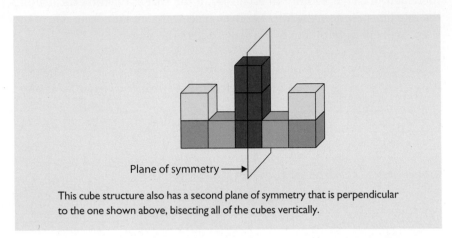

Plane of symmetry ⟶

This cube structure also has a second plane of symmetry that is perpendicular to the one shown above, bisecting all of the cubes vertically.

ACTIVITY 17.9

Have students build symmetrical castles out of building blocks. Ask students what their strategy was for making sure their castles were symmetrical.

———————

Creative Thinking

It is sometimes difficult to test 3-D shapes for symmetry, since the shapes cannot be folded and overlapped. However, they can often be represented with modelling clay or linking cubes, and then divided in half. Then students can examine and manipulate the halves to see if one half looks like the exact "reverse" of the other half.

There are a number of different ways for students to construct shapes with plane symmetry. These include building structures with linking cubes, stacking shape blocks, and using modelling clay. Block stacks can be tested for symmetry with a Mira, while modelling clay shapes can be cut through the centre with a strand of dental floss.

Rotational Symmetry of 2-D and 3-D Shapes

A shape has rotational symmetry if, when you turn it around its centre point, it fits over a tracing of itself (or into an outline of itself) at least once before it has completed a full rotation. Both 2-D and 3-D shapes can have rotational symmetry.

2-D Shapes: Rotational Symmetry

One way to test for rotational symmetry is to trace the shape, and then turn it to see whether it fits over itself. For example, a rectangle fits over itself twice—once after a half turn, and again after a full turn.

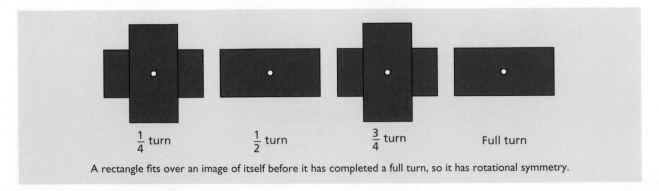

$\frac{1}{4}$ turn $\frac{1}{2}$ turn $\frac{3}{4}$ turn   Full turn

A rectangle fits over an image of itself before it has completed a full turn, so it has rotational symmetry.

Rotational symmetry is distinct from reflective symmetry. A parallelogram has rotational symmetry but no reflective symmetry. Similarly, a shape can have reflective symmetry and not rotational symmetry. For example,

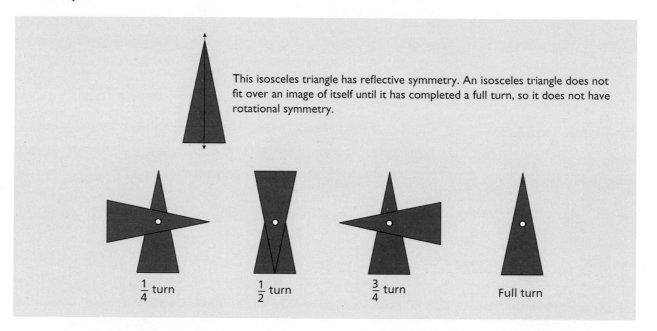

This isosceles triangle has reflective symmetry. An isosceles triangle does not fit over an image of itself until it has completed a full turn, so it does not have rotational symmetry.

$\frac{1}{4}$ turn $\frac{1}{2}$ turn $\frac{3}{4}$ turn   Full turn

Although the two types of symmetry are distinct, there are relationships. For example, if a shape has two or more lines of mirror symmetry, it also has rotational symmetry.

The number of ways that a shape fits over its outline is called its *order of rotational symmetry*. For example, for an equilateral triangle, the order of rotational symmetry is 3 because it fits over its image 3 times within a full turn. For a circle, the order of rotational symmetry is infinite, because it fits over its image an infinite number of times as it turns through 360°.

3-D Shapes: Rotational Symmetry

Rotational symmetry is also associated with 3-D shapes. For example, a cube has 13 *axes of symmetry*—lines around which the shape can be rotated to reproduce its original orientation before it has completed a full turn. In the case of a cube, there are 4 axes that connect pairs of opposite vertices, 6 that connect the midpoints of opposite edges, and 3 that connect the centres of opposite faces.

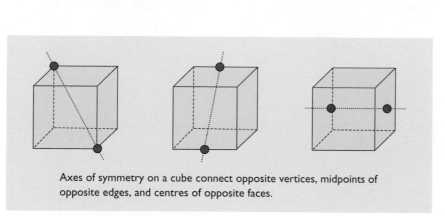

Axes of symmetry on a cube connect opposite vertices, midpoints of opposite edges, and centres of opposite faces.

ACTIVITY 17.10

Ask students who are at van Hiele Level 1 or beyond to create a shape that does not have rotational symmetry but, when turned $\frac{1}{4}$, $\frac{1}{2}$, or $\frac{3}{4}$ of a turn, it looks like a real but different object after each turn.

Creative Thinking

Representing Shapes

Creating representations of shapes is a good way for students to use their visualization skills. It is also an area of geometry that is closely linked to other curriculum areas, especially the visual arts.

Representations can take many forms, including modelling clay or linking cube models, skeletons, nets, and various types of drawings , either freehand or using technology (drawing programs). As students develop geometrically, their representations will appear more and more like the real shapes they represent. As well, they will be able to create more sophisticated representations, for example, moving from simple sketches of 3-D shapes to isometric drawings.

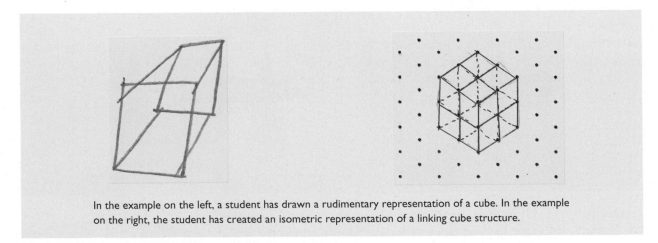

In the example on the left, a student has drawn a rudimentary representation of a cube. In the example on the right, the student has created an isometric representation of a linking cube structure.

Modelling Shapes

One way to represent shapes is to make concrete models. Making models allows students to explore shape properties in a very hands-on way.

As with any mathematics activity, students are more likely to be engaged if the activity is presented in context. For example, students could make cookies or decorations for a special occasion. Some possible contexts for modelling 3-D shapes are shown in **Activities 17.11** and **17.12**.

ACTIVITY 17.11

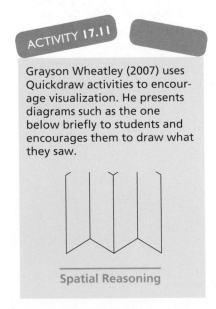

Grayson Wheatley (2007) uses Quickdraw activities to encourage visualization. He presents diagrams such as the one below briefly to students and encourages them to draw what they saw.

Spatial Reasoning

ACTIVITY 17.12

This rectangle-based prism was built from linking cubes.

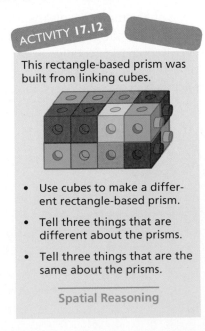

- Use cubes to make a different rectangle-based prism.

- Tell three things that are different about the prisms.

- Tell three things that are the same about the prisms.

Spatial Reasoning

Concrete Models

An appropriate activity for students at lower van Hiele levels involves using modelling clay to model shapes they can see and handle. To make the models, students can either form the clay by hand or use a mould.

For 2-D shapes, students can use cookie cutters with modelling clay or trace stencils onto paper. For 3-D shapes, students can use geometric solids or recycled materials (cans, boxes, cardboard tubes, etc.) as models, or they can work with commercial materials such as *Polydrons*.

A very concrete way for students to explore the properties of 2-D shapes is for them to form the vertices of the shapes with their own bodies. For example, provide a group of students with a large loop of yarn. Ask three of them to hold the yarn using one finger and tell you what shape they have made (a triangle). Discuss the properties of the triangle—3 sides and 3 vertices. Then ask a fourth student to join the group so the four make a rectangle. Ask how the properties of the shape have changed. Then continue to have more and more students join the group of yarn holders until they have formed a 20-sided shape. Finally, ask the students to describe the shape they have made. Most will see something very close to a circle.

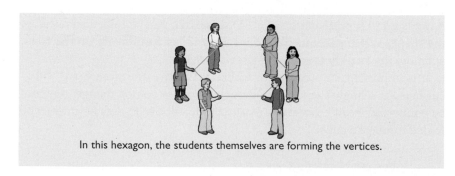

In this hexagon, the students themselves are forming the vertices.

ACTIVITY 17.13

Which types of triangle combinations are possible? Use straws for sides.

	Acute	Obtuse	Right
Equilateral			
Isosceles			
Scalene			

Critical Thinking

For students entering van Hiele level 2, teachers can use activities such as **Activity 17.13** to prompt critical thinking about shapes, in this case triangles, and their properties.

Skeletons

Another type of model is a *skeleton*—a physical representation of the edges and vertices of a 3-D shape, or the sides and vertices of a 2-D shape. Materials for constructing skeletons include toothpicks and small balls of modelling clay, wiki sticks, or straws connected with bent pipe-cleaner segments. Toothpicks are especially useful for modelling regular shapes because they have a uniform length. There are also commercial construction toys, such as *Tinkertoys*, *K'nex*, *Zoob*, *Geomag*, and *D-stix*, that are suitable for constructing skeletons.

TEACHING **TIP**

Straws and pipe cleaners can be used as an alternative to sticks and clay for building skeletons.

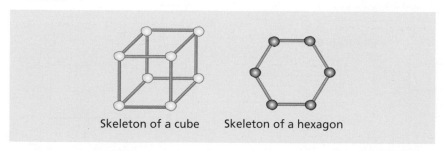

Skeleton of a cube   Skeleton of a hexagon

In order to construct the skeleton of a shape, many students need to have the shape in front of them. This way, they can look at and touch the edges, and vertices (focusing on the properties of the shape), to develop a mental picture of how many there are, and where they belong. Others are comfortable working from a picture of the shape, and still others can sometimes use just the verbal descriptions.

Skeletons help students see familiar shapes in a different way. When they are working with solid shapes, students often tend to focus more on the faces than on other components. The process of making a skeleton, where the faces are implicit, helps students become more aware of other components, such as edges, vertices, and angles. It also helps them create a mental image of the shape, which will stay with them even when they no longer have concrete models to look at. For example, when asked for the number of edges on a cube, a student might visualize the cube skeleton and mentally count the edges.

Activity 17.14 shows how a task involving skeletons can be used to help students learn more about the edge and vertex properties of 3-D shapes. For this activity, you may want to provide some samples of 3-D shapes for students' reference.

ACTIVITY 17.14

Use balls of clay for vertices and sticks for edges to build the skeleton of a 3-D shape.

- First make some skeletons that use an even number of sticks, but an odd number of balls of clay.

- Then, make some skeletons that use an odd number of sticks, but an even number of balls of clay.

Name each shape you made.

———————
Critical Thinking

Nets

A net is a 2-D representation of a 3-D shape that can be folded to re-create the shape. When students make nets, they focus particularly on the faces, and how the faces fit together to form the shape.

It is important for students to realize that there are often many different nets for a single shape. Even though the faces do not change, they can be connected in different ways. For example, all of the nets below can be folded to make a cube.

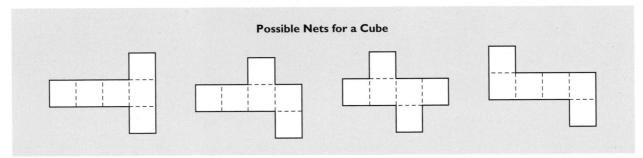

Possible Nets for a Cube

In creating the net for a cube, students work with the following properties of a cube: 6 congruent square faces, 3 pairs of opposite parallel faces, 3 faces joining at each vertex, and congruent edges that meet at right angles. However, students cannot assume that because a cube has 6 square faces, any grouping of 6 squares will create a net. The patterns below are made from 6 squares, but they are not nets because there is no way to fold them to create a top face, a bottom face, and 4 lateral faces.

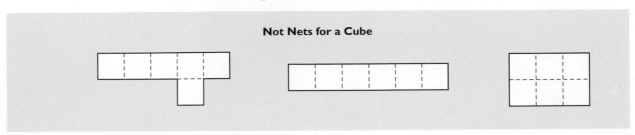

Not Nets for a Cube

Creating Nets Although nets are a focus of study mainly for students in Grade 4 or higher, they can also be introduced to younger children. Students can roll a shape and trace all the faces onto a sheet of paper, or can connect squares from a set of Polydrons. When students compare results, they will see that their nets do not all look the same, even though all the nets can be folded to produce the shape they started with.

Later, students can use more sophisticated techniques. To create a net for a pyramid, students can draw the base, and then draw congruent isosceles triangles on each side, making sure that the height of each is sufficient to reach farther than the centre of the base. Many students are surprised to find that pyramids with different heights can be created on the same base.

TEACHING **TIP**

Students can dismantle real boxes to create nets. They might also look at "folded" boxes that stores use to see how else a 3-D prism can be "flattened" out.

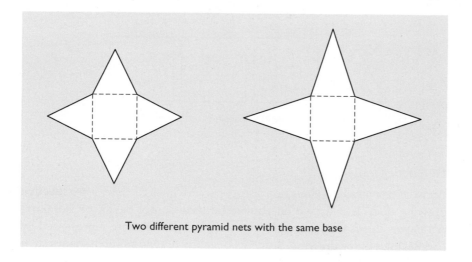

Two different pyramid nets with the same base

Nets are more difficult to make when the shape being modelled is not a polyhedron, that is, when some of the edges are curved. In the net for a cylinder below, it is important for students to ensure that the width of the rectangle representing the lateral curved surface exactly matches the circumference of the circular base (as shown in red). This concept is sophisticated and generally dealt with by older students, although younger students can cut out pre-made nets and observe this property.

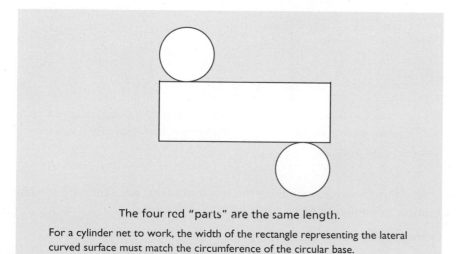

The four red "parts" are the same length.

For a cylinder net to work, the width of the rectangle representing the lateral curved surface must match the circumference of the circular base.

Drawing 3-D Shapes

Another way to represent a shape is with a picture. Before students can draw a shape, they need time to examine it. For example, to make perspective drawings of prisms, they need to focus on parallel bases and edges, as well as on face shapes.

Face Maps

In an introductory activity for students at lower van Hiele levels, a teacher might provide a set of 3-D shapes and a "map" that shows all the faces of one of the shapes. The students' task is to identify the shape represented by the map. Later, students can make their own face maps of various 3-D shapes by tracing the faces one at a time.

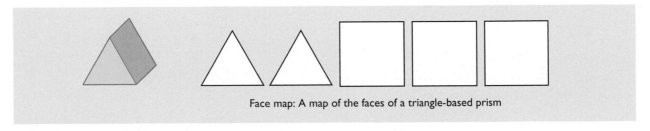

Face map: A map of the faces of a triangle-based prism

Isometric Drawings

An isometric drawing does not distort parallel lines the way a perspective drawing does. It is drawn on equilateral triangle dot paper, or isometric dot paper. Edges that are parallel on the original shape are represented by parallel lines in the drawing. Students begin by drawing simple shapes such as a cube or prism.

Isometric drawings of cube structures are the easiest composite shapes for students to draw first. However, with experience, they can learn to create isometric drawings of more complex 3-D shapes. There are digital tools to help with this as well.

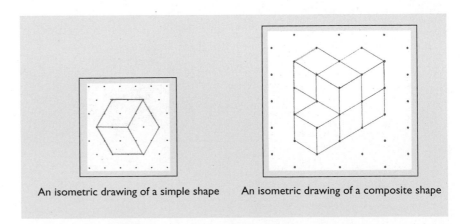

An isometric drawing of a simple shape   An isometric drawing of a composite shape

Isometric drawings may be of interest to students since they are used in a number of online games.

Orthographic Drawings of Simple 3-D Shapes

Orthographic drawings show what a shape looks like from the front, top, and sides. Draftspeople often create various views of a 3-D shape in order to help someone else build it.

When students are ready to begin drawing views of their own, they might start with a simple 3-D shape, such as a prism. View drawings can also be done for shapes with curved sides (like the cylinder shown at the top of the next page). When sides are curved, the view shows a flat representation of what the curved surface looks like.

Orthographic Drawings of 3-D Shapes

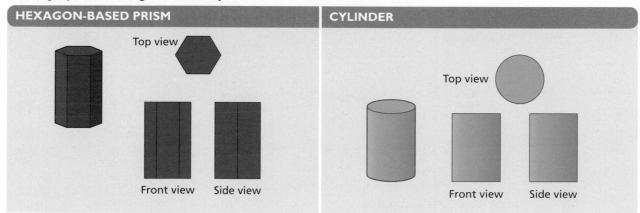

Base Plans

A base plan is another way of mapping a cube structure. The base plan is a view of the structure's base that uses numbers to indicate the height of each part of the structure. For example, the base plan below shows that the 2 rows at the back of the structure are 3 cubes high, while the front row is only 1 cube high.

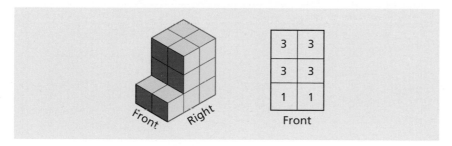

Drawing 2-D Shapes

To draw a 2-D shape on paper, students may need to apply measurement skills, such as measuring lines and angles. Luckily, there are everyday classroom tools that can help. Younger students can use tools such as fraction circles, grid paper, and pattern blocks to help them draw 2-D shapes.

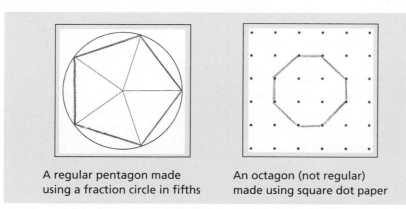

A regular pentagon made using a fraction circle in fifths

An octagon (not regular) made using square dot paper

ACTIVITY 17.15

Students at any van Hiele level might draw shapes on fabric to decorate T-shirts or on canvas to create pieces of art. For example, a student might be asked to draw a painting that includes four different shapes but looks like an object of their choice.

Other students might enjoy less realistic art and might try to create a painting in the style of Mondrian or Kandinsky.

Creative Thinking

Older students are ready to use math tools such as protractors and compasses to construct 2-D shapes. Note that the traditional view of constructions (using only a straightedge and compass) has given way to a broader view, which also includes the use of technology, protractors, rulers, paper folding, and transparent mirrors.

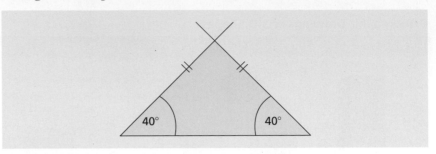

Drawing Virtual 2-D Shapes

As important as it is to have concrete experiences with shapes, there is real value for students in using virtual shapes on a computer. Not only can computer tools assist students with calculating measures which might be awkward or take a long time to do by hand, but many tools allow students to draw more exactly so that the inferences they make are well founded.

Of particular value is dynamic geometry software, such as The Geometer's Sketchpad or GeoGebra, which makes it easier for students to dissect shapes and measure side lengths and angles of shapes.

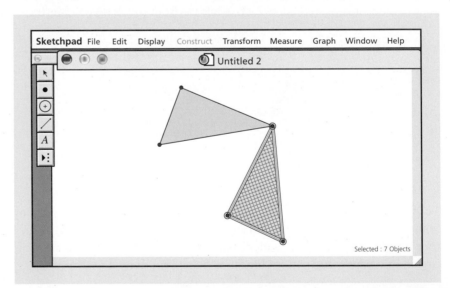

But even word processing drawing software or programs like Quickdraw allow students to translate, rotate, and reflect objects, draw a 3-D view of some simple shapes, draw parallel and perpendicular lines, build symmetric shapes, test for congruence, or draw similar shapes, as shown to the left.

For example, most drawing programs make it easy to explore similarity by drawing, copying, and stretching or reducing familiar shapes. When you enlarge a computer-made shape, it is important to stretch the shape horizontally and vertically at the same time or the resulting shape will not be similar. This can be done on some computers by holding down the shift key or by ensuring Lock Aspect Ratio is selected in the Format box.

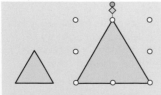

Draw programs make it easy to create similar shapes.

Dissecting and Combining Shapes

One of the key concepts in geometry is that any shape can be created by either combining or dissecting other shapes. Students are working with this concept when they are putting shapes together to make another shape, a picture, a design, or a structure, or when they are cutting a shape into pieces.

Clements (2004) has articulated the stages young children go through as they combine shapes. He talks about the stages of

- Pre-composer (usually pre-school), where children use separate shapes to denote objects, without connecting them or considering shape or size
- Piece assembler (usually pre-school or early kindergarten), where children build pictures with shapes and individual shapes represent individual parts
- Picture maker (usually kindergarten), where children build pictures by combining several pieces to represent one part of the object being pictured
- Shape composer (usually kindergarten), where children combine shapes by considering how they will fit together
- Substitution composer (usually primary years), where children form composite shapes and substitute some shapes for others
- Shape composite repeater (usually primary years), where children construct a design where a unit is intentionally repeated[*]

As students get older, dissecting and combining shapes plays a bigger role in helping them learn about properties of shapes. They can learn, for example, that diagonals cut a rectangle into four parts that have equal areas, but that are not congruent unless the rectangle is a square.

The diagonals of a rectangle dissect it into two pairs of congruent triangles.

The diagonals of a square dissect it into four congruent triangles.

The ability to combine and dissect shapes also supports the development of measurement formulas. For example, cutting a parallelogram apart and reassembling it to form a rectangle can help students see why the area of a parallelogram can be determined by multiplying its base length by its height, just like a rectangle.

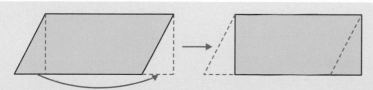
Dissecting a parallelogram to show why its area is equal to the area of a rectangle with the same base and height

---

[*]Clements (2004). Copyright © 2003, CCC Republication.

Combining Shapes

Another way to explore the properties of 3-D shapes is to combine them to build structures. Building structures can help students learn about how the properties of shapes affect the way you use them. For example, shapes with flat faces can be stacked while shapes with curved surfaces can roll. Building structures can also help students learn about symmetry.

Students can practise communicating about geometry as they describe how two structures are the same and different.

After some time for experimentation, students will be ready to build a structure to match a picture, or to fit a list of specifications. Younger students might be challenged to build a tall structure that is not wide, or a clay model with a point. They might discover, for example, that various measurements of a 3-D shape are independent of one another. Older students could complete tasks such as those in **Activity 17.16**.

Making pictures with 2-D shapes (cutouts or stickers) can also be instructive for younger students. In creating the pictures, students focus on how the shapes they learn about in school relate to shapes in their world.

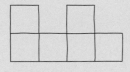

ACTIVITY 17.16

- Use toothpicks and marshmallows to build a 3-D shape with 6 vertices. What attributes does your shape have?

- Stack pattern blocks to build 3-D shapes with 8 vertices. How many different shapes can you make?

- Use 24 linking cubes to build two different symmetrical structures that look like this from the left. How are your structures the same? different?

Spatial Reasoning

Student Response

This student is beginning to recognize and name shapes, but does not yet realize that the "stick" is also a rectangle. This is a good opportunity for the teacher to focus the student's attention on geometric properties of rectangles by asking, "Which other shape in the picture is most like the stick shape? Why?"

Teacher: What can you tell me about your picture?

Student: I made a house and a tree.

Teacher: What shapes did you use?

Student: I used a rectangle and a triangle to make the house and I put a circle on top of a stick to make the tree.

Using Pattern Blocks

The pictures students create can also be made with concrete materials like pattern blocks. For example, the illustration shows 3 of the many composite 2-D shapes that students can make with 4 triangle blocks.

ACTIVITY 17.17

What shapes can you make by combining two pattern blocks?

Spatial Reasoning

ACTIVITY 17.18

Fit pattern blocks together to fill this outline.

Critical Thinking

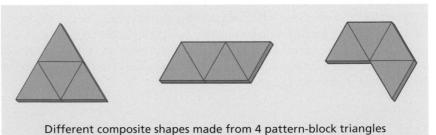

Different composite shapes made from 4 pattern-block triangles

Students also enjoy solving shape puzzles where they have to fit shapes into an outline to create a picture or cover a design.

Working on puzzles provides a context to explore many geometric concepts. For example, very young students can learn that a shape is defined by its sides and vertices, but not by its orientation. Students also have the opportunity to see what a shape looks like when it is turned, or to attend to the sharpness of the angles.

The easiest puzzles show an outline for each block, and the child simply places each block where it belongs on the picture or design. More complex puzzles have outside outlines for students to fill in, but the individual blocks are not outlined. Many students enjoy creating puzzles like these to exchange with classmates.

PATTERN BLOCK PUZZLES

With each block outlined   With only an outside outline

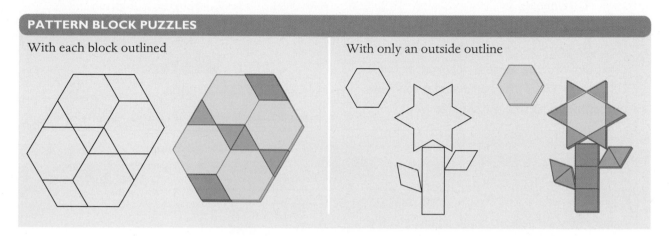

Using Tangrams

Tangram pieces (sometimes called *tans*) are formed by dissecting a square into seven smaller shapes as shown. The pieces can then be combined to reconstruct the original square (a challenge best reserved for older students), as well as to create many other shapes.

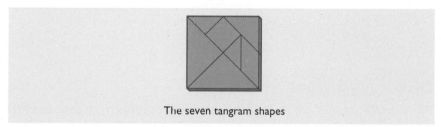

The seven tangram shapes

Like pattern blocks, tangrams can be used to illustrate both shape combinations and shape dissections. As with pattern blocks, the easiest tangram puzzles show individually outlined pieces, while the more difficult puzzles show only the outline of the shape as a whole.

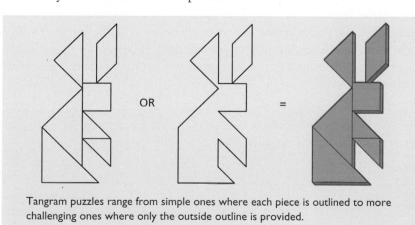

OR   =

Tangram puzzles range from simple ones where each piece is outlined to more challenging ones where only the outside outline is provided.

ACTIVITY 17.19

Use your tangram pieces to create other tangram animals.

Creative Thinking

Students can combine tangram pieces to create geometric shapes, as in **Activity 17.20**.

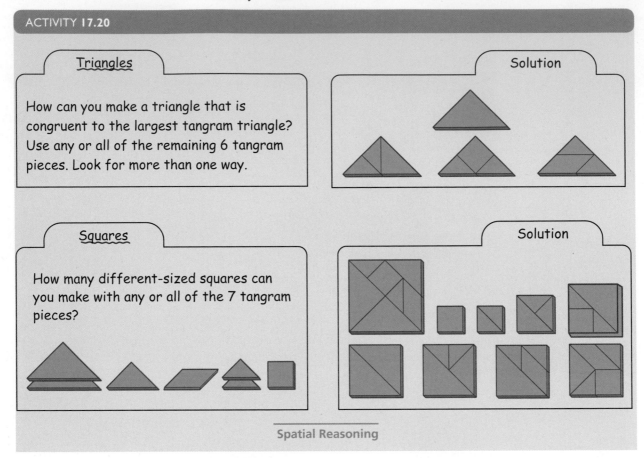

ACTIVITY 17.20

Triangles

How can you make a triangle that is congruent to the largest tangram triangle? Use any or all of the remaining 6 tangram pieces. Look for more than one way.

Solution

Squares

How many different-sized squares can you make with any or all of the 7 tangram pieces?

Solution

Spatial Reasoning

Dissecting Shapes

The idea that shapes can be dissected, or divided into parts, is fundamental to many geometry concepts that students will explore in the intermediate and senior grades, as shown in the examples that follow.

Dissecting to Create Other Shapes

Many interesting geometry problems revolve around dissecting a shape to create other shapes, and many such problems are accessible even to very young students. For example, the problem below is accessible to students at any van Hiele level, although they will not yet be able to name all the shapes that result from the cuts. The other two problems are more suitable for older students.

SAMPLE DISSECTING PROBLEMS

What shapes can you make by cutting a rectangle into 2 parts with straight cuts?

SAMPLE DISSECTING PROBLEMS

What shapes can you make by cutting a square into 4 pieces?

How can you cut a triangle into pieces so the pieces will make a square?

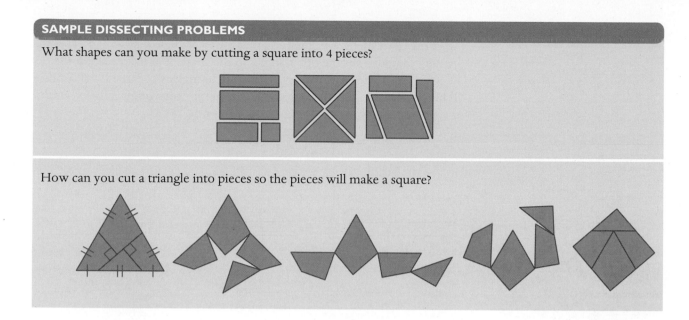

Dissecting to Calculate Angles

Students will learn that they can calculate the angle size for any regular polygon by dissecting the shape into triangles. For example, they might divide a square into four triangles and observe that each central angle is 90° since there are four equal angles filling a circle in the centre.

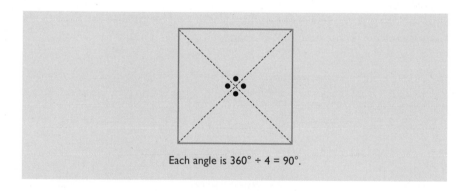

Each angle is 360° ÷ 4 = 90°.

They could do a similar dissection with a regular hexagon or octagon to figure out each of those central angles.

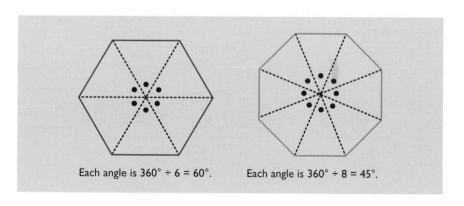

Each angle is 360° ÷ 6 = 60°.   Each angle is 360° ÷ 8 = 45°.

Once they know the size of the central angle, they can use the fact that the other two angles are equal and that the total angle measure in a triangle is 180° to figure out the other angles in the shape. For example, for the octagon, each of the other two angles in each triangle is $\frac{1}{2}$ of $(180° - 45°)$. Since it takes two of those small angles to make up the total angle at the vertex of a regular octagon, each of those angles must be 135°.

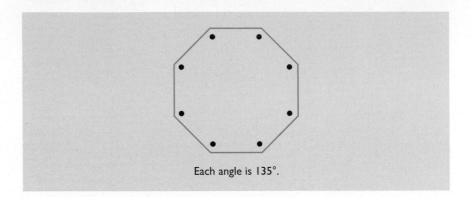

Each angle is 135°.

Congruence and Similarity

Congruence and similarity are geometric concepts that apply to both 2-D and 3-D shapes, although work with these concepts at the K–8 level is mainly limited to 2-D shapes.

Two shapes are considered to be congruent if one can be transformed into the other through a series of flips, slides, and / or turns. One fits exactly over the other (in the case of 2-D shapes).

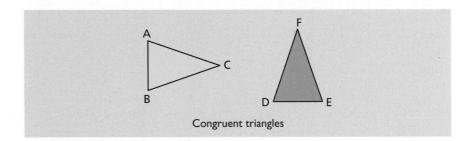

Congruent triangles

The word *congruent* is used to describe not only whole shapes, but also specific components of shapes, such as sides and angles. For example, these two triangles have a pair of congruent sides and a pair of congruent angles, but they are not congruent shapes.

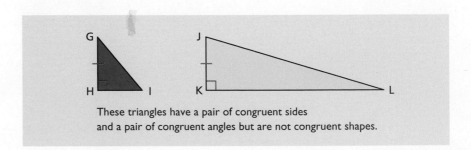

These triangles have a pair of congruent sides
and a pair of congruent angles but are not congruent shapes.

Congruence can also be found within a single shape. For example, an equilateral triangle has 3 congruent sides and angles.

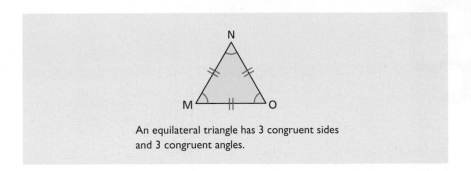

An equilateral triangle has 3 congruent sides and 3 congruent angles.

Two shapes are said to be *similar* if they have the same shape, with sides in proportion to one another. Congruent shapes are similar, but so are two shapes where one is an enlargement or reduction of the other.

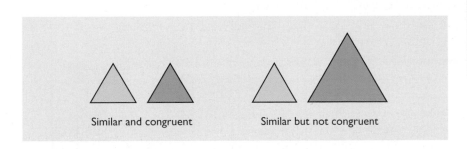

Similar and congruent   Similar but not congruent

Congruence of 2-D Shapes

Two 2-D shapes are congruent if they are identical in shape and size—that is, if one is an exact duplicate of the other. Students sometimes do not understand the difference between the math term *congruent* and the everyday term *the same*. It is important to recognize that the term *congruent* applies only to shape and size. Thus, figures can be different colours, or oriented in different ways, and they will still be congruent as long as they are the same shape and the same size.

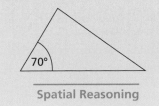
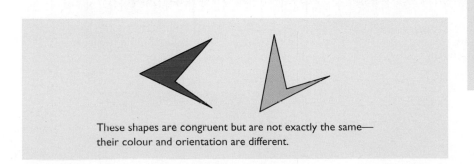

These shapes are congruent but are not exactly the same—their colour and orientation are different.

One interesting way to explore congruence is to use optical illusions, as illustrated by the examples at the top of the next page.

OPTICAL ILLUSIONS

Which picture has a larger circle in the centre?

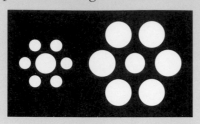

Which vertical line is longer?

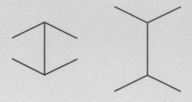

Determining Congruence of 2-D Shapes

There are many ways to test for congruence, some simpler than others.

WAYS TO TEST FOR CONGRUENCE

Superimposing

The easiest way to test 2-D shapes for congruence is simply to put one shape on top of the other to see if the outlines can be made to match exactly.

Measuring Corresponding Sides and Angles

A more sophisticated strategy (and one that works for shapes in any orientation) is to measure the sides and angles in both shapes and compare the results. With congruent shapes, all the corresponding side lengths and angle measures will match.

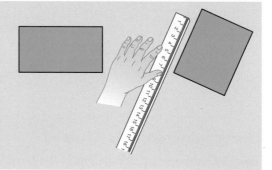

Constructing Congruent 2-D Shapes

Once students understand the nature of congruence, they can begin making congruent shapes of their own, using a wide variety of materials.

WAYS TO CONSTRUCT CONGRUENT SHAPES

Using a Geoboard

Students can use geobands to form congruent shapes. Using a geoboard helps to focus students' attention on the fact that congruent shapes have the same side lengths.

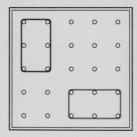

Measuring

Once students understand that congruent shapes have congruent side lengths and angle measures, they can use rulers and protractors or technology to construct congruent shapes.

Congruence of 3-D Shapes

In the case of 3-D shapes, it is much more difficult to determine congruence. If two shapes simply look the same, this may be enough for some children to assume congruence. However, testing congruence requires the ability to use measurements to compare shapes—a characteristic of more mathematically sophisticated students. Structures made of standard linking cubes might be easier to test, since the cubes can be counted in order to make comparisons.

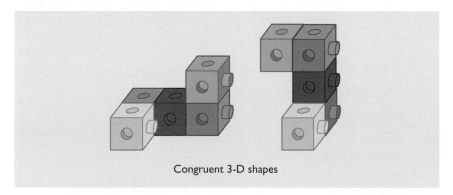

Congruent 3-D shapes

Similarity of 2-D Shapes

Figures that have the same shape, but not necessarily the same size, are said to be *similar*. Congruent shapes are similar, but so are reductions and enlargements of a shape. When shapes are similar, corresponding angles are congruent, and corresponding side lengths are all enlarged or reduced by the same factor.

In the case of the similar rectangles below, the ratio of the length to the width is the same in both rectangles. This is not true in the non-similar rectangles, where the ratio of length to width for the rectangle on the right is different from that for the rectangle on the left.

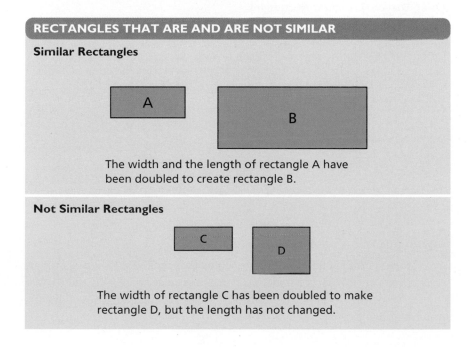

RECTANGLES THAT ARE AND ARE NOT SIMILAR

Similar Rectangles

A
B

The width and the length of rectangle A have been doubled to create rectangle B.

Not Similar Rectangles

C
D

The width of rectangle C has been doubled to make rectangle D, but the length has not changed.

Determining Similarity of 2-D Shapes

If two shapes are similar, the following statements are true:

- Corresponding angles in both shapes are congruent.
- You can multiply or divide all the side lengths in one shape by the same amount to describe the corresponding side lengths of the other shape.
- The ratio between one side length and another on one shape is the same as the ratio between the corresponding side lengths on the other shape.

Only some of these properties are typically studied at the K–8 level, with others later in secondary school.

Angle measures alone cannot be used to test two shapes for similarity. For example, a square and a long, thin rectangle both have four 90° angles, but they are not similar shapes. To determine similarity, students need to look at the side lengths of the shapes. Here are some tests for similarity.

TESTING FOR SIMILARITY

Measuring Side Lengths

To test the two rectangles below for similarity, students can measure the side lengths to see if they have been increased or decreased by the same factor.

The width and length of the second rectangle are twice the width and length of the first rectangle, so the rectangles are similar.

Another test for similarity involves comparing side lengths within each shape. For example, when you divide the length of each rectangle above by its height, the answer is 2. Both rectangles are twice as long as they are high, so the rectangles are similar.

Using Diagonals to Test Rectangles

There is a special and easy way to test rectangles for similarity. First, place the rectangles one on top of the other so the smaller one fits into the bottom left corner of the larger one. Then draw the diagonal of the larger rectangle so it passes through both shapes. If the diagonal of the large rectangle is also a diagonal of the small one, then the rectangles are similar.

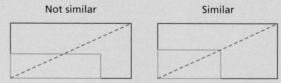

This test works because similar rectangles have the same ratio of length to height.

Constructing Similar 2-D Shapes

Once students understand the relationships that make two shapes similar, some may want to try constructing pairs of similar shapes on their own. The methods they use will depend on their mathematical knowledge, as shown on the next page.

WAYS TO CONSTRUCT SIMILAR SHAPES

Using Square Grids

Square grids are good tools for students to use when they are first learning to construct similar shapes. They can begin by constructing a shape on a square grid, and then copy the shape onto another grid with larger (or smaller) squares.

Similar shapes constructed on different-sized square grids

Measuring Sides and Angles

Older students may be ready to construct simple shapes—mainly rectangles—with rulers and protractors. Working with rectangles allows students to focus on measuring the side lengths, and then multiplying or dividing each length by the same amount. With other shapes, it will be necessary to measure and construct angles with a protractor.

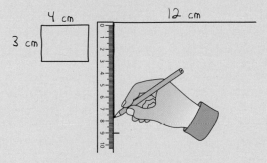

Enlarging a square by tripling the side lengths

Using Technology

Technology makes it possible for students of all ages to construct similar shapes. For example, students could use dynamic geometry software to construct a shape and then reduce it.

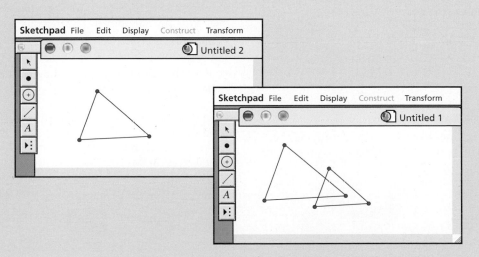

Reducing to create a similar shape

Common Errors and Misconceptions

3-D Shapes: Common Errors, Misconceptions, and Strategies

COMMON ERROR OR MISCONCEPTION	SUGGESTED STRATEGY
2-D and 3-D Vocabulary Students frequently confuse the vocabulary associated with 2-D and 3-D shapes. For example, students who have been asked to look for rectangles in the classroom might point to a tissue box. (If this happens, first ask students to elaborate in order to make sure they are not simply pointing out the rectangular faces.)  Because a rectangle-based prism has rectangular faces, students will often describe it as a rectangle.	Make sure students have opportunities to compare and contrast shapes that are likely to be confused. For example, present a square and a cube. Ask students to tell how they are different. Make sure that students attach the correct name to each shape. 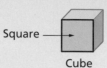 Formal names for 3-D shapes can be confusing for some young students, so teachers often introduce simple everyday names for these shapes. For example, a sphere is often called a "ball" and a rectangle-based prism is often called a "box." Most students are comfortable with the more precise language.
Components of 3-D Shapes Because students are familiar with the word *side* in the context of 2-D shapes, they may mistakenly apply the same term to the flat surfaces on 3-D shapes. 3-D shapes have faces, not sides.	Help students see that the word *side* could be confusing if it were applied to 3-D shapes. Emphasize that the flat surfaces on a 3-D shape are called *faces*, and that the places where the faces meet are called *edges*.  Correct terminology for 3-D shapes
Counting Components on 3-D Shapes Students may have trouble counting faces, edges, and vertices on 3-D shapes because they lose track of which components have already been counted. They may also not be sure whether the apex of a cone counts as a vertex (there are contrasting views on this), or whether the curved edge of a cone or cylinder counts as an edge (there are contrasting views on this).	Encourage the students to mark a starting point for counting and to count in a systematic way, perhaps from the base up. Since a cone and a cylinder are not polyhedrons, it is not usually useful to include them in component-counting activities. However, if a student is not sure about the definition of *vertex* or *edge* (even mathematicians disagree about whether these terms should be applied to non-polyhedrons), review the following definitions: • On a polyhedron, a vertex is a point common to three or more faces. • On a polyhedron, an edge is a line segment formed where two faces intersect.
Identifying the Base of a Prism Students sometimes have difficulty identifying the base of a prism, particularly when the prism is short. Students may misidentify this as a square-based prism because the lateral faces are square.	Having students build prisms from stacks of pattern blocks may help them see that the block shape they use to start and end the prism is the base, and that the lateral faces on this type of prism are always rectangles. Emphasize that there are only two bases on a prism, and they may or may not be rectangles. Prisms have two parallel bases.

COMMON ERROR OR MISCONCEPTION	SUGGESTED STRATEGY
Congruent Edges on Nets	Encourage students to measure the edges of the shape they plan to duplicate in order to ensure that the resulting net will fold properly. For example, on the net shown below, the three rectangular faces are congruent so the bases must be equilateral triangles, not isosceles.
Students who create nets simply by "eyeballing" a shape may find that their nets do not fold properly because they have not taken into account the need to match congruent edges.	

This is not a net for a triangle-based prism because the sides of the triangle are too long.	When this net is folded, the sides of the triangles will match the sides of the rectangles.

2-D Shapes: Common Errors, Misconceptions, and Strategies

COMMON ERROR OR MISCONCEPTION	SUGGESTED STRATEGY
Attributes versus Properties	Students need opportunities to explore each class of shape in many different forms. For example, when parallelograms are introduced, provide opportunities for students to examine and sort some parallelograms and non-parallelograms, and to talk about how they can tell if a shape belongs in the parallelograms group.
Students confuse attributes of shapes with their properties. An attribute applies to only some of the shapes in a group, while a property applies to all of them. For example, students may assume that since a particular rectangle has long sides and short sides, all rectangles must have long sides and short sides.	
Rectangles 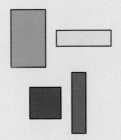	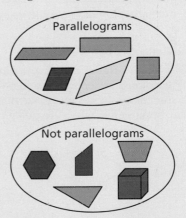
Students often assume incorrectly that rectangles have long and short sides and do not recognize a square as a rectangle.	
Changes in Orientation	Working with concrete shape models, such as pattern blocks and attribute blocks, can help students see that shapes can be oriented in different ways and still maintain their shape properties.
Students think that the way a shape is oriented is part of what defines it. For example, while younger children will usually recognize the yellow shape as a triangle, they may describe the red one as an "arrow" or a "flag," since it is oriented differently from what they think a triangle should look like. This misconception can affect an older student's ability to perceive congruence, since the student may not recognize that shapes are congruent when oriented differently.	
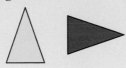	 Flipping or turning a triangle does not change its shape properties.

(continued)

2-D Shapes: Common Errors, Misconceptions, and Strategies (Continued)

COMMON ERROR OR MISCONCEPTION	SUGGESTED STRATEGY
Orientation of Perpendicular Lines Students sometimes assume that lines can only be perpendicular if one is horizontal and the other is vertical. A student with this misconception would recognize the first pair of line segments shown here as perpendicular, but not the second. 	Remind students that angles can be "tipped" or turned without changing their size. It might help to show a square, and establish that the sides are perpendicular by placing a cutout square corner in the corner. Then turn the square 45° and ask if the sides are still perpendicular; students could replace the square corner to check. Students could also look around the classroom to see if they can find any examples of perpendicular lines that are *not* vertical and horizontal.
Wrong Scale on the Protractor Students use the wrong scale on a protractor to measure an angle. For example, a student might record the size of this angle as 120°. (There is more about angle measurement in Chapter 20.) 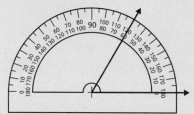 A student might misread this angle measure as 120°.	Encourage students to look at the starting arm of the angle to see which 0° mark it points to, and remind them to use that scale to make the measurement. It is also important to remind students to use estimation to check angle measures. For example, the angle shown to the left is obviously less than 90°, so a 120° measurement does not make sense. A 60° measurement, on the other hand, seems much more reasonable.
Colour and Reflective Symmetry Students mistakenly assume that shapes cannot be symmetrical if the colours or decorations do not match. For example, a student might not recognize that this shape is symmetrical, because the halves are different colours. 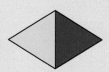	Provide students with many opportunities to test for symmetry using folding when possible and a transparent mirror when it is not possible to fold. Reinforce that matching exactly when folded along, or reflected across, the line of reflection is what defines reflective symmetry.
Parallelograms and Reflective Symmetry Students often think that a diagonal of a parallelogram is a line of symmetry. This, of course, is correct for rhombuses and squares, but not for other parallelograms, including rectangles. This common error stems from the fact that the two triangles on the sides of the diagonal are congruent.  A shape can have congruent halves and not be symmetrical.	Provide many opportunities to test for symmetry by folding and using a transparent mirror. 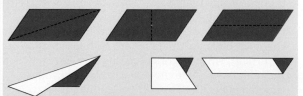 You cannot fold a non-rectangular parallelogram so that the halves match.

COMMON ERROR OR MISCONCEPTION	SUGGESTED STRATEGY
Reflective versus Rotational Symmetry Students make incorrect assumptions about reflective symmetry and rotational symmetry. For example, they think that a shape with reflective symmetry must also have rotational symmetry. This triangle has reflective symmetry, but not rotational symmetry.	Students need opportunities to work with • shapes with reflective symmetry, but not rotational symmetry • shapes with rotational symmetry, but not reflective symmetry • shapes with both types of symmetry 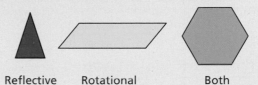 Reflective Rotational Both

Appropriate Manipulatives

2-D and 3-D Shapes: Examples of Manipulatives

MANIPULATIVE	EXAMPLE
Plastic Shapes Plastic shapes come in a wide variety of forms and from a wide range of manufacturers. They include attribute blocks (2-D shapes that vary in thickness, colour, and size) and 3-D shape models. Plastic shape blocks can be used for a number of different activities, including sorting and classifying, building structures, exploring shape properties, and patterning.	This pattern shows how the number of faces on a pyramid increases by 1 each time the number of sides on the base is increased by 1. 3 sides on base 4 sides on base 5 sides on base 4 faces 5 faces 6 faces
Blocks Wooden, plastic, or foam blocks can be used to build structures in order to explore the properties of 3-D shapes, including stability. There are also commerical boxes that can serve a similar purpose.	Building towers with cylinders, prisms, and cones provides an opportunity for students to explore the relative stability of different structures. 
Linking Cubes Linking cubes can be joined to construct simple 3-D shapes and structures. They are especially useful for exploring topics such as properties of rectangle-based prisms (see page 399), plane symmetry (see page 410), and congruence of 3-D shapes (see page 427).	Linking cube structures allow students to explore how a structure looks from different perspectives. Cube structure Front view Right view *(continued)*

2-D and 3-D Shapes: Examples of Manipulatives (Continued)

MANIPULATIVE	EXAMPLE
Toothpicks and Modelling Clay Toothpicks can be combined with small balls of modelling clay or marshmallows to make skeletons of 2-D and 3-D shapes in order to focus attention on the sides, vertices, and angles of 2-D shapes and the edges and vertices of 3-D shapes. (See page 413.)	These toothpick shapes show that each time you want to increase the number of sides on the base of a prism by 1, you need to add 3 toothpicks in all to the prism.  Pentagon-based prism with 10 vertices and 15 edges
Commercial Building Toys Building toys such as *Lego, K'nex, Tinkertoys, Frameworks, Geomag,* and *D-stix* can all be used to build and explore skeletons of 2-D and 3-D shapes. Building skeletons focuses attention on the sides, vertices, and angles of 2-D shapes and the edges and vertices of 3-D shapes. (See page 413.)	*Geomag, Tinkertoys, Frameworks, K'nex,* and *D-stix* can all be used to create skeletons of 3-D shapes. 
Pattern Blocks Pattern blocks are wooden or plastic models that young children can use to explore the properties of simple and composite 2-D shapes and prisms (see page 420), for combining and dissecting 2-D shapes, and for patterning activities.	These pattern blocks show a shape pattern. 
Geostrips Geostrips are plastic strips of different lengths that can be connected at the ends. They are useful for investigating side lengths and angles of polygons. Home-made geostrips are strips of card stock that can be attached with paper fasteners.	Making triangles with geostrips can help students discover that a triangle can be made from any set of strips in which the two shortest sides have a combined length that is greater than the longest side. 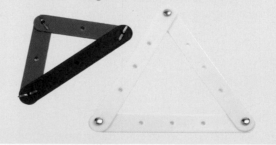
Straws and Pipe Cleaners Straws and pipe cleaners can be used to make 2-D and 3-D skeletons to explore properties of shapes related to sides, edges, and vertices. They can be cut to different lengths and connected with small pieces of pipe cleaner that are slid inside the straw ends.	This is one of many prisms students can make with straws and pipe cleaners. 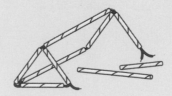

MANIPULATIVE	EXAMPLE

Polydrons

Polydrons are regular polygons that can be linked along hinged edges in order to build 3-D shapes and nets. They are particularly useful for exploring the properties of 3-D shapes.

Polydrons make it easy even for young children to make nets that they can fold into 3-D shapes.

Geoboards

On a geoboard, students use geobands to create polygons. There are many different sizes of square geoboards.

Geoboards have a wide range of uses, for example, to examine the properties of polygons, and to explore symmetry, congruence, and similarity.

Square geoboards are used most often, but triangular and circular geoboards are also available; the latter are particularly useful for exploring properties of circles and dividing circular regions into congruent parts.

Geoboards are helpful for solving problems such as the following.

I am a triangle with one square corner. Two of my sides are congruent. What could I look like?

If two triangles have the same height and base length, are they congruent?

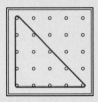

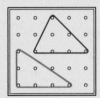

Mirrors

Both ordinary flat mirrors and transparent mirrors (Miras) are invaluable for determining symmetry, creating symmetrical shapes, creating congruent shapes, and, in some instances, determining congruency.

With a transparent mirror, students can reflect a given shape to create a symmetrical shape.

Tangrams

A tangram is a square puzzle made of 7 pieces that can be used to explore combining and dissecting shapes.

The seven tangram shapes

This illustration shows one way to combine three tangram pieces together to form a triangle. It also shows how a right isosceles triangle can be dissected into one square and two smaller congruent right isosceles triangles.

1 square and 2 right triangles combine to form a larger right triangle.

Pentominoes

Pentominoes are made of 5 congruent squares joined along full sides. Teachers can buy them or make their own.

They are often used for a geometry activity in which students look for all possible ways to combine 5 squares to make composite shapes. However, they can also be used to explore geometric properties such as symmetry and congruence (e.g., if one pentomino can be flipped or turned to fit over another, then they are congruent).

Some pentominoes have line symmetry and some do not.

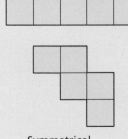

Symmetrical

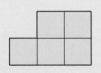

Not symmetrical

Appropriate Children's Books

The Greedy Triangle (Burns, 1994).
This amusing story focuses students on the various sorts of polygons and how they are alike and different. There is also an opportunity to see where those shapes are typically found.

So Many Circles, So Many Squares (Hoban, 1998).
Tana Hoban's beautiful photographs help students see where they can find squares and circles in the world around them.

Captain Invincible and the Space Shapes (Murphy, 2001).
This cartoon-like story built around 3-D shapes takes place in a spaceship returning to Earth. Readers focus on six 3-dimensional shapes, including a cone, a cube, and a pyramid, which the "astronauts" use to battle their way to safety.

Grandfather Tang's Story (Tompert, 1990).
This tale, which is based on the ancient Chinese tangram puzzle, revolves around the relationship between a grandfather and granddaughter. The illustrations tell the story using pictures based on tangram designs.

Appropriate Digital Resources

See the MindTap site for a selection of appropriate digital resources.

Assessing Student Understanding

- Many of the skills and concepts addressed in this chapter are best assessed through observation of students working directly with physical materials or using digital photos along with digital voice captures. In that way, it is possible to see, for example, how students cut up a shape and rearrange it into other shapes.

- Many geometric problems require a reasonable amount of precision in the placement of lines, angles, or 3-D components; often students do not have the motor ability to be that precise. It may be necessary to assist, while allowing the student to take the lead in discussing what needs to be done.

- Everyday use of geometric language sometimes interferes with student understanding. For example, it is so rare in everyday life that a student sees a square identified as a rectangle that it is reasonable that he or she would not believe it is a rectangle. Make sure to take these obstacles into account when preparing instruction and assessing student understanding.

- Students were asked to choose a shape and tell as much as they could about it. What would your feedback be?

Student Response

This Grade 2 student included attributes that a circle does not have and what real-world objects it reminded him of.

> It has no ponts. ⭕
> It has no sids.
> It has no edgs.
> It looks like a pumcin.
> It looks like a clok.

Applying What You've Learned

1. Would you assign the chapter problem to a Grade 6 student to solve without providing a mirror? Explain your position on this.

2. Read an article in a journal about the van Hiele model of geometric development. Briefly summarize the article. Why do you think it might be important, as a teacher, to know about the van Hiele model?

3. A distinction is made between properties and attributes of shapes. Why is that distinction a useful one?

4. Many primary teachers prefer to begin with 2-D geometry rather than 3-D geometry because they believe it to be simpler and more accessible. How could you convince them that starting with 3-D work in geometry might be more appropriate?

5. There is an increasing push to use technology to explore all mathematical topics, including geometry, yet many people believe that geometry needs to be hands-on. List three concepts that you think might be better explored with technology; argue as to why this would be preferable in these situations.

6. How much emphasis do you feel should be placed on geometry vocabulary? Justify your position.

7. A significant amount of time is spent on geometry learning related to symmetry. Argue as to why, or whether, this is an appropriate central topic in the study of geometry.

8. One of the key ideas in geometry is that every shape can be viewed as a part of or a combination of other shapes. Why might this be a useful unifying idea in the study of geometry?

Interact with a K–8 Student:

9. Provide a student with a set of pattern blocks.

   a) Ask the student how the different coloured shapes are alike and how they are different, other than in terms of colour.

   b) Ask the student what other shapes he or she could make by combining the provided shapes.

   c) What geometric understandings did the student display as he or she completed parts (a) and (b)?

Discuss with a K–8 Teacher:

10. Many teachers do not spend much time teaching geometry.

   a) Ask how much time this teacher spends on the topic and what his or her main emphasis is.

   b) Ask whether this teacher would like to spend more time teaching the topic or whether he or she thinks the topic does not warrant more time.

   c) Ask his/her opinion on an appropriate proportion of the year to spend on spatial work.

11. Ask whether students who have difficulty in number ever do better in geometry, or whether some with difficulty in geometry do better in number, and whether the teacher finds this to be unusual or not. Ask why they think this might occur.

Selected References

Bacon, K.A. (2010). A smorgasbord of assessment options. *Teaching Children Mathematics, 16,* 458–469.

Battista, M.T. (1999). The importance of spatial structuring in geometric reasoning. *Teaching Children Mathematics, 6,* 170–177.

Breyfogle, L.M., and Lynch, C.M. (2010). van Hiele revisited. *Mathematics Teaching in the Middle School, 16,* 232–239.

Burger, W., and Shaughnessy, J.M. (1986). Characterizing the van Hiele levels of development in geometry. *Journal for Research in Mathematics Education, 17,* 31–48.

Burns, M. (1994). *The greedy triangle.* New York: Scholastic Press.

Casey, B., Andrews, N., Schindler, H., Kersh, J.E., Samper, A., and Copley, J. (2008). The development of spatial skills through interventions involving block building activities. *Cognition and Instruction, 26(3),* 269–309.

Cheng, Y.L., and Mix, K.S. (2012). Spatial training improves children's mathematics ability. *Journal of Cognition and Development.* Advance online publication.

Clements, D.H. (2004). Major themes and recommendations. In Clements, D.H., Sarama, J., and DiBiase, A. (Eds.). *Engaging young children in mathematics: Standards for early childhood mathematics education.* Mahwah, NJ: Lawrence Erlbaum Associates, 7–72.

Clements, D.H., and Battista, M.T.(1992). Geometry and spatial reasoning. In D.A. Grouws (Ed), *Handbook of research on mathematics teaching and learning.* New York: Macmillan, 420–464.

Clements, D.H., and Sarama, J. (2000). Young children's ideas about geometric shapes. *Teaching Children Mathematics, 6,* 482–487.

Cox, D.C., and Lo, J-J (2012). Discuss similarity using visual intuition. *Mathematics Teaching in the Middle School, 18,* 30–36.

Edwards, M.T., and Harper, S.R. (2010). Paint bucket polygons. *Teaching Children Mathematics, 16,* 421–428.

Findell, C.R., Small, M., Cavanagh, M., Dacey, L., Greenes, C.E., and Sheffield, L.J. (2001). *Navigating through geometry in prekindergarten–grade 2.* Reston, VA: National Council of Teachers of Mathematics.

Fox, T.B. (2000). Implications of research on children's understanding of geometry. *Teaching Children Mathematics, 6,* 572–576.

Gavin, M.K., Belkin, L.P., Spinelli, A.M., and St. Marie, J. (2001). *Navigating through geometry in grades 3-5.* Reston, VA: National Council of Teachers of Mathematics.

Hannibal, M.A. (1999). Young children's developing understanding of geometric shapes. *Teaching Children Mathematics, 5,* 353–357.

Hoban, T. (1998). *So many circles, so many squares.* New York: Greenwillow Books.

Howse, T.D., and Howse, M.E. (2014). Linking the Van Hiele theory to instruction. *Teaching Children Mathematics, 21,* 305–313.

Jacobson, C., and Lehrer, R. (2000). Teacher appropriation and student learning of geometry through design. *Journal for Research in Mathematics Education, 31,* 71–88.

Maccarone, G., and Neuhaus, D. (1997). *Three pigs, one wolf, seven magic shapes.* New York: Cartwheel Books.

Mack, N.K. (2007). Gaining insights into children's geometric knowledge. *Teaching Children Mathematics, 14,* 238–245.

Ministry of Education, Ontario (2014). *Paying attention to spatial reasoning.* Toronto: Queen's Printer for Ontario.

Murphy, S. (2001). *Captain Invincible and the space shapes.* New York: HarperTrophy.

Newcombe, N.S. (2010). Picture this: Increasing math and science learning by improving spatial thinking. *American Educator, 34,* 29–35.

Nivens, R.A., Peters, T.C., and Nivens, J. (2012). Views of isometric geometry. *Teaching Children Mathematics, 18,* 346–353.

Piaget, J., and Inhelder, B. (1967). *The child's conception of space.* New York: W.W. Norton & Co.

Sarama, J., and Clements, D.H. (2003). Building blocks of early childhood mathematics. *Teaching Children Mathematics, 9,* 480–484.

Sinclair, M., Mamolo, A., and Whiteley, W.J. (2011). Designing spatial visual tasks for research: The case of the filling task. *Educational Studies in Mathematics, 78,* 135–163.

Sinclair, N., and Bruce, C. (2014). *Spatial reasoning for young learners.* Proceedings of the 38th Conference of the International Group for the Psychology of Mathematics Education. Vancouver, BC: PME.

Teppo, A. (1991). Van Hiele levels of geometric thought revisited. *The Mathematics Teacher, 84,* 210–221.

Tompert, A. (1990). *Grandfather Tang's story.* New York: Crown Publishers.

Wheatley, G.H., (2007). *Quick draw.* Bethany Beach, DE: Mathematics Learning.

Whiteley, W. (2004). Visualization in mathematics: Claims and questions toward a research program [Online]. Available from http://www.math.yorku.ca/Who/Faculty/Whiteley/Visualization.pdf. Cited 2007 Apr. 22.

Whitin, D.J., and Whitin, P. (2009). Why are things shaped the way they are? *Teaching Children Mathematics, 15,* 464–472.

Wilson, J.B. (2010). A foxyloxy and a lallapalagram. *Teaching Children Mathematics, 16,* 492–499.

Chapter 18

Location and Movement

IN A NUTSHELL

The main ideas in this chapter are listed below:

1. Although properties of shapes are often the focus of attention in geometry, development of skills in describing and predicting location is also an important aspect of spatial sense.

2. There is a continuum of simple to much more sophisticated systems to describe location. Even the youngest elementary school student can use a simple system.

3. The study of transformations and the use of constructions provide an excellent vehicle for exploring geometric properties of both position and shape.

CHAPTER PROBLEM

A triangle on a coordinate grid is rotated and then reflected. After the two moves, the vertices are located at $(-8, -3)$, $(-2, -3)$, and $(-2, +5)$. Describe 2 possible sets of coordinates where the triangles might have started. Explain your thinking.

Location and Movement

Geometric experiences involving location and movement support the development of spatial sense and positional vocabulary. Students should learn to

- describe the positions of objects in structures and pictures
- read and draw maps
- plot points and describe paths on coordinate grids
- transform and construct shapes

Developing Positional Vocabulary

A child's earliest spoken language might include terms such as *up*, *down*, *in*, *out*, *above*, *below*, *near*, and *far* that describe spatial relationships. As the child grows, so does his or her spatial understanding and related vocabulary.

Using Dance, Song, and Play

Many dances, songs, games, and toys for young children provide opportunities to build spatial sense and positional vocabulary, and often link well with investigations in other subject areas, such as physical education or social studies. Examples include games such as Simon Says and action songs such as "The Hokey Pokey." Dance provides an opportunity for students to think about moving forward, backward, right, and left.

Sports and imaginative play are also important vehicles for this type of development. Parents and teachers can help by modelling positional vocabulary—words that describe how one object's location relates to another's—as children play. For example, an adult observing a child who is playing with blocks and toy farm animals might ask:

- Why did you put the cow *inside* the fence?
- What animals are still *outside*?
- What block could you put *on top of* this one to make your fence higher?

Word Walls

A good way to build positional vocabulary is to record terms on a Math Word Wall as they come up in classroom activities. To help students see relationships among positional words, it may help to group words that belong together, such as *over* and *under*.

TEACHING TIP

It is important that students recognize that positional words are relative. For example,

- What one person calls "near," another might not.
- If one object is behind another and then the objects are reversed, the "behind" object is now "in front."
- If one object is "above," the other is "below." Many positional words come in pairs.

ACTIVITY 18.1

Read a story involving travelling on a path, for example, *Hansel and Gretel* or *Rosie's Walk*.

Have students draw and then describe the path they create.

Critical Thinking

Words That Tell Where Things Are

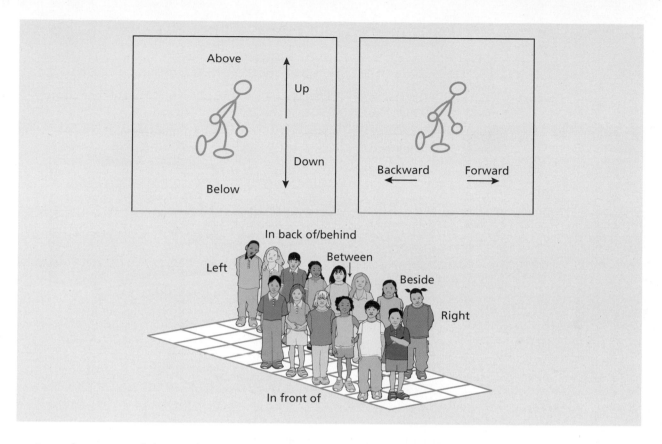

As students use and discuss these terms, they will learn that by combining terms or modifying them, they can give a more exact idea of where an object is located. For example, younger students might discuss why, although it is true to say that the Slinky on the table below is *behind* the duck, it is more useful to say that the Slinky is *behind the duck and to the right.*

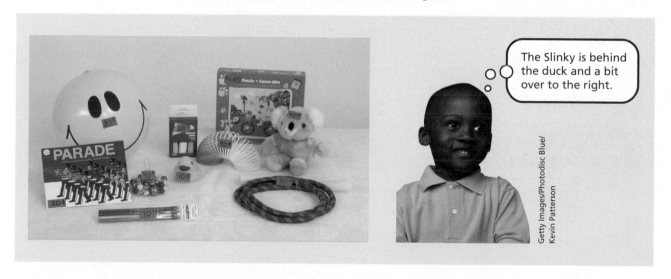

Another approach to developing positional vocabulary also supports the development of visual memory, that is, the ability of students to recall what they saw once it is out of view (see **Activities 18.2 and 18.3** on the next page). As children mature mathematically, they can be asked to recall the relative positions of more shapes in somewhat more complex spatial arrangements.

ACTIVITY 18.2

ACTIVITY 18.3

Place 3 or 4 objects under a document camera or on an interactive white board and allow students to view them for a short time.

Remove them from view and ask students to describe how the objects were arranged.

Vary the number of items and the complexity of the arrangement, as appropriate.

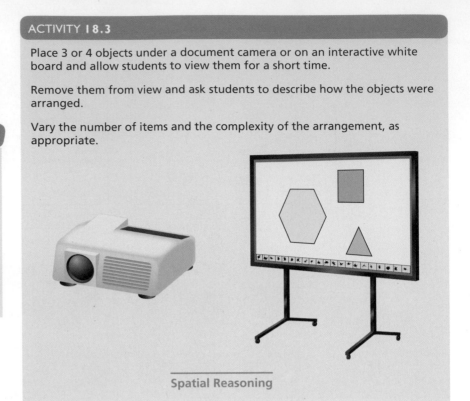

Spatial Reasoning

ACTIVITY 18.2

To develop visualization skills, have a student choose an object in the classroom and examine it. Then, the student should close his or her eyes and describe the object to a classmate. A variation of this involves using Quick Draw activities suggested by Grayson Wheatley (2007).

Spatial Reasoning

Maps and Coordinate Grids

Drawing and Interpreting Maps

Maps make it possible to record and describe how objects are located relative to one another. Even young students can make simple maps of their environment. However, as students develop better spatial sense, their maps better reflect the geometric features of objects in their surroundings, and give a more accurate impression of the proportional distances between objects. For example, a younger student might draw a classroom map similar to this one.

Student Response

This map illustrates a student's recognition of how one object should be positioned relative to others nearby.

Working with Grids

At some point, students are ready to use a grid system to identify locations on a map, or to describe how to get from one map location to another.

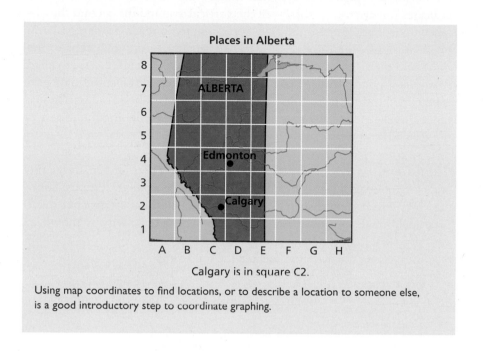

Places in Alberta

Calgary is in square C2.

Using map coordinates to find locations, or to describe a location to someone else, is a good introductory step to coordinate graphing.

Students can also create designs on grids, and then describe their designs by identifying grid squares to colour. Alternatively, students can be given grid locations and colours and asked to show the design on a grid.

Simple Four-Quadrant Grids

Although students do most of their work with coordinate grids after Grade 4, it is possible to introduce some grid-related ideas in earlier years. Younger students, for example, might simply identify the location of an object on a grid like the one shown below.

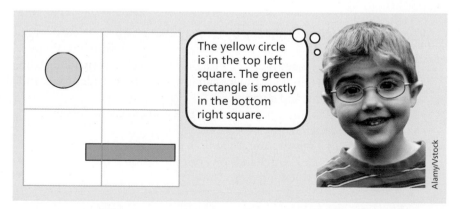

The yellow circle is in the top left square. The green rectangle is mostly in the bottom right square.

Number Coordinates

After some time working with grids like city maps where locations are designated using a letter and a number to describe a horizontal and vertical space in which they are found, students learn to use a grid on which objects are placed at lattice points and directions are given using

ACTIVITY 18.4

Ask students how many paths there are from A (1, 4) to B (4, 1) if you always have to move right or down. Ask what the paths have in common.

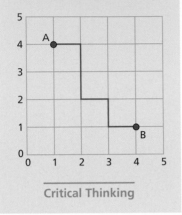

Critical Thinking

the cardinal directions north, east, south, and west. Still later, students should be introduced to the conventional number–number code for identifying locations where two grid lines intersect. At this stage, it becomes important for students to recognize that, by convention, the first number indicates the distance across from the vertical axis and the second the distance up from the horizontal axis. For example, to reach point (2, 3), you begin at (0, 0), where the two reference axes meet, move 2 steps to the right, and then 3 steps up. Designations such as (0, 0) and (2, 3) are called *ordered pairs*. Once students are familiar with integers, the coordinate grid is extended to four quadrants. The switch to using labels to describe distance travelled along the axes as opposed to simply labelling the square is not easy for some students.

Games and Activities for Coordinate Grids There are many games and activities to help students learn how to use coordinate systems. Some are commercial games, such as Battleship, while others are teacher-made or student-made. An example of one teacher-made activity is shown in **Activity 18.4**.

Other games and activities include the following:

- Plot the points (1, 1), (1, 4), (2, 4), (2, 2), (4, 2), (4, 1), and back to (1,1); connect them in that order to form a closed shape. What shape did you create?

ACTIVITY 18.5

Ask students to follow this path on a grid.

- Plot Point A at (3, 2).
- Go right 5 to plot Point B.
- Go right 2 and up 2 to plot Point C.
- Go up 2 to plot Point D.
- Go left 2 and up 2 to plot Point E.
- Go left 5 to plot Point F.
- Go left 2 and down 2 to plot Point G.
- Go down 2 to plot Point H.
- Go right 2 and down 2 to re-plot Point A.

Have students connect the points in the order they were plotted. Ask what shape was made.

Have students create directions for their own secret shape.

Spatial Reasoning

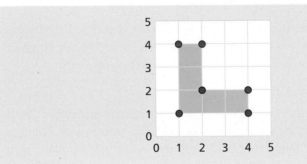

- Introduce coordinate graphing by using masking tape to make a large grid on the floor. Use cards to label the axes with coordinates. Invite a student to stand at a point on the grid: "Aaron, please come and stand on point (3, 5)." Then that student can invite another student to stand on a different point, and so on.
- Place objects at different points on the grid and have students use coordinates to describe their locations.
- In a variation of Twister, one student gives a partner directions for placing both feet and both hands on coordinates on a floor grid. Then the students trade roles and play again.

Transformations

Geometric transformations are motions that affect a shape in some specified way. K–8 students work with transformations because many mathematical concepts, such as symmetry, are described best using transformations.

Euclidean Transformations—Slides, Flips, and Turns

There are three transformations that change the location of an object in space, or the direction in which it faces, but not its size or shape. These transformations, called *Euclidean transformations,* result in images that are congruent to the original object. The three types of Euclidean transformations are *slides* (or *translations*), *flips* (or *reflections*), and *turns* (or *rotations*).

In the examples that follow, a dotted green line is used to indicate the original shape, while a solid green line is used for the transformation image, and red is used for slide arrows, flip lines, and turn centres.

Slides, Flips, and Turns

SLIDE OR TRANSLATION	FLIP OR REFLECTION	TURN OR ROTATION
A translation (or slide) to the right and down	A reflection (or flip) across a vertical reflection line (a horizontal reflection)	A rotation (or turn) around a point (the turn centre) on one of its vertices

Transformations on Simple Grids

When students first begin learning about slides, flips, and turns, they work with concrete shapes on a flat surface. Later, they might work with simple coordinate grids like the one shown below. Working with transformations, especially slides, on a simple grid helps younger students learn to describe motions with mathematical language.

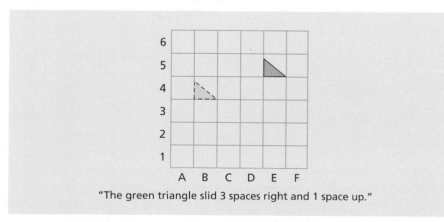

"The green triangle slid 3 spaces right and 1 space up."

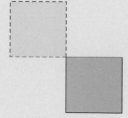
Transformations on Coordinate Grids

In later grades, students begin to explore Euclidean transformations on Cartesian coordinate grids like the one shown on the next page. Here, students can look not only at how a transformation affects the direction in which a shape is facing, but also at how it changes the coordinates of the vertices.

For example, the rectangle shown was slid right 4 units and down 1 unit. As a result, the first coordinate of each vertex increased by 4. The second coordinate decreased by 1.

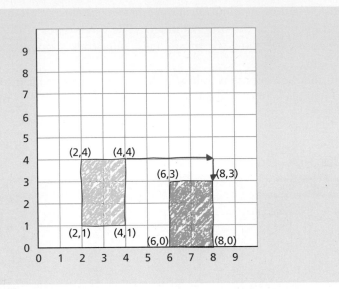

Slides

A slide (or translation) moves a shape left, right, up, down, or on a slant without changing its orientation. This type of transformation is one of the easiest for students to recognize. For example, the picture below shows 3 different slides of the same triangle. Slides can be described using words, for example, *5 units right, 2 units down*, or they can be defined by a "slide arrow" that links a point on the original shape to the matching point on the image. Slide arrows could be drawn between pairs of corresponding vertices, but one slide arrow is all that is required.

Slide Directions

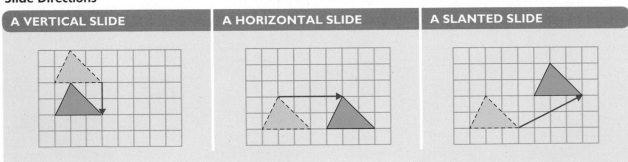

Note that students may describe a slide in a slanted direction as a *diagonal* side and this should be accepted. However, since the term *diagonal* has a special meaning in mathematics (to describe a line that connects vertices in a shape), the term *slanted* might be modelled.

Describing Slides

A slanted slide can be separated into its right–left and up–down components. This becomes useful when students are working with slides on coordinate grids. For example, the triangle at the top of the next page was translated 4 units right and 2 units up to create a slanted slide.

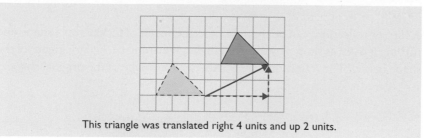

This triangle was translated right 4 units and up 2 units.

ACTIVITY 18.7

Ask students to look for examples of translations or slides in their environment.

Spatial Reasoning

Describing Slide Images

Mathematicians often use letter notation to show how each vertex on the original shape is matched to a vertex on its slide image.

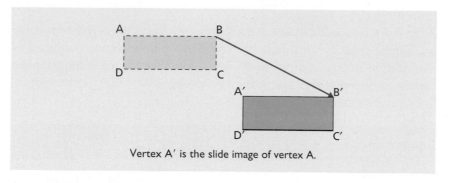

Vertex A′ is the slide image of vertex A.

Properties of Slides

SLIDE ARROWS

No matter where slide arrows are drawn to link matching points on an original shape and its image, these arrows (shown here in red) are all exactly the same length and parallel. In addition, the sides on the image are parallel to the corresponding sides on the original shape.

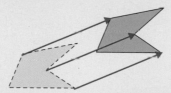

The slide arrows that define a particular translation are all the same length and parallel.

ORIENTATION

The way a shape faces does not change with a slide. If point C is below and to the right of point A on the original shape, then the image of point C is below and to the right of the image of point A on the slide shape. (A reflection, however, does change the orientation. See page 448.)

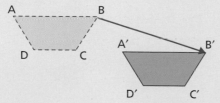

A slide does not change the orientation of a shape (like a reflection does).

Flips

A flip (or reflection) can be thought of as the result of picking up a shape and turning it over, as shown by the front (light green) and back (dark green) of the shape below. The reflection image is the mirror image of the original shape.

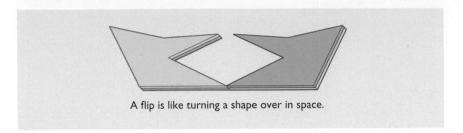

A flip is like turning a shape over in space.

Flip Lines

A flip is always made across a line called the *flip line* or *line of reflection*. A flip line can be vertical, horizontal, or slanted. A flip or reflection is defined by the location and direction of the flip line. Note that when a shape is flipped across a horizontal line, the shape moves vertically. Flips across vertical lines move shapes horizontally.

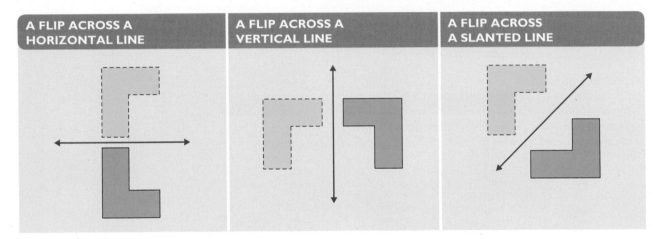

A FLIP ACROSS A HORIZONTAL LINE	A FLIP ACROSS A VERTICAL LINE	A FLIP ACROSS A SLANTED LINE

Transparent Mirrors

While students generally have little difficulty flipping a shape horizontally or vertically, flips across a slanted line can be more difficult to perform. In this situation, a transparent mirror (or Mira) can be very helpful. In a transparent mirror, students can actually see the flip image when they look through the plastic, so it becomes possible to simply trace the image onto a piece of paper.

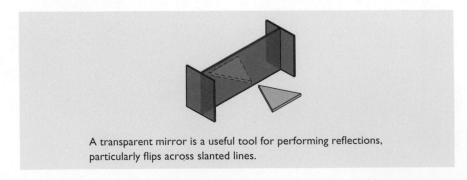

A transparent mirror is a useful tool for performing reflections, particularly flips across slanted lines.

ACTIVITY 18.8

Ask students where to put the mirror on the original shape to create the two images.

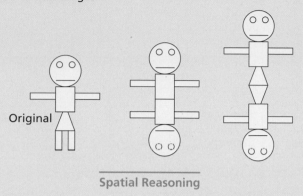

Original

Spatial Reasoning

A transparent mirror not only allows students to flip a shape across a slanted line with ease, it also makes it possible to flip across a line drawn *through* the original shape. In this case, a student actually has to perform two flips, first flipping one side of the shape, and then the other.

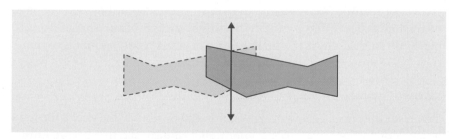

Properties of Flips

FLIPPING A SHAPE ACROSS A SIDE

If a 2-D shape is flipped across one of its own sides, the resulting combined shape is a symmetrical 2-D shape. The only points in the original shape that do not move are those that are located along the flip line.

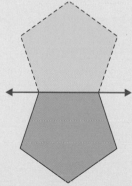

A symmetrical octagon is created by flipping a pentagon across one side.

FLIPPING A SHAPE ACROSS A LINE OF SYMMETRY

If a shape is flipped across a line of symmetry, the image will fit exactly over the original shape.

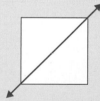

A square flipped across one of its lines of symmetry.

CHANGING ORIENTATION

When a shape is flipped, its orientation changes. In the diagram below, in the original shape, the vertices A, B, C read clockwise but the image's vertices A', B', C' read counterclockwise.

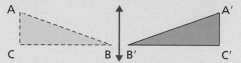

A flip changes the orientation of a shape.

(continued)

Properties of Flips (Continued)

DISTANCE FROM THE FLIP LINE	ANGLE AT THE FLIP LINE
Each point on the image is exactly the same distance from the flip line as its counterpart on the original shape.	When any point on the original is joined to its counterpart on the flip image, the connecting line is perpendicular to the flip line.

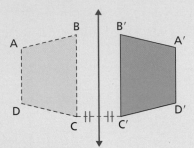

Corresponding points are the same distance from the flip line.

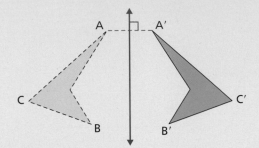

A line connecting corresponding points is perpendicular to the flip line.

Turns

A turn (or rotation) moves a shape in a circle around a turning point. Think of tracing a shape, putting the tracing right on top of the shape, using a pencil tip to hold down the tracing at a particular point, and then rotating the tracing around that point (as shown below).

Describing Turns Using Fractions of a Circle

When students first begin working with turns, they identify the size of the turn in terms of fractions of a circle: quarter turn, half turn, and three-quarter turn. In addition to describing the amount of turn, students also need to identify the turn direction (clockwise or counterclockwise). Sometimes clockwise and counterclockwise are abbreviated as "cw" and "ccw."

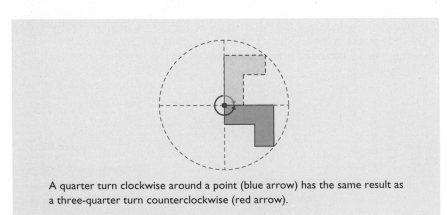

A quarter turn clockwise around a point (blue arrow) has the same result as a three-quarter turn counterclockwise (red arrow).

Describing Turns Using Angles

Later, students learn that turns can also be identified in terms of degrees. For example, the picture on page 451 shows the same shape turned 90° (a quarter turn) clockwise, and 180° (a half turn) counterclockwise.

As students turn shapes, they may find it helpful to think of hands on a clock face. This way, they can focus on the change of position for one side of the shape, as shown below. Although students can generally perform quarter and half turns without a protractor, they will need to measure angles in order to perform other turns.

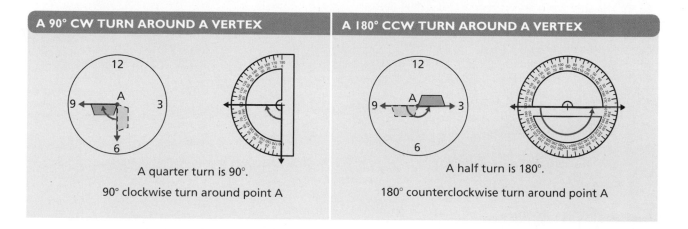

A 90° CW TURN AROUND A VERTEX

A quarter turn is 90°.

90° clockwise turn around point A

A 180° CCW TURN AROUND A VERTEX

A half turn is 180°.

180° counterclockwise turn around point A

Turn Centres

A shape can be turned around any point—not just around a vertex or its centre point. The turn centre can be inside the shape, outside the shape, or on the perimeter of the shape. When a shape is turned on a grid, its final location depends not only on the size and direction of the turn, but also on where the turn centre is located. This happens because the turn centre remains fixed, while all the other points on the shape move in a circle around that point.

The location of the turn centre, however, does not influence the direction in which the image will face. For example, each image below shows the result of turning a triangle $\frac{1}{4}$ turn clockwise around a different turn centre: the orientation of the image is the same in each case, even though its location on the grid is different.

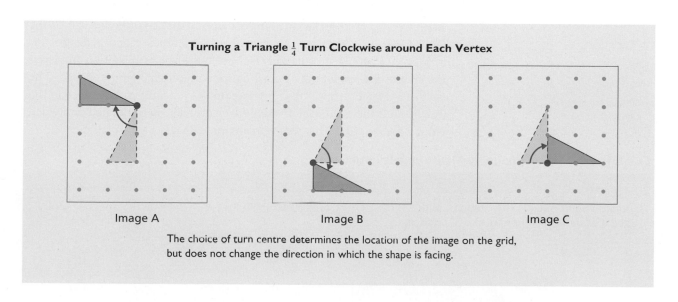

Turning a Triangle $\frac{1}{4}$ Turn Clockwise around Each Vertex

Image A

Image B

Image C

The choice of turn centre determines the location of the image on the grid, but does not change the direction in which the shape is facing.

Properties of Turns

FIXED TURN CENTRE	ORIENTATION
When a shape turns on a plane, only one point, the turn centre, stays fixed.	When a shape is turned, its orientation does not change. Notice below that the vertices A, B, C and A′, B′, C′ read clockwise in both the original shape and the turn image.
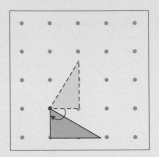	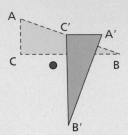
The turn centre remains fixed.	The orientation does not change.

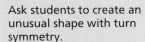

Turn or Rotational Symmetry

When a shape is turned any amount less than a full turn around its centre and "lands on" itself, it has rotational, or turn, symmetry.

For example, a square can be turned $\frac{1}{4}$ turn around its centre and set right back on its original outline, as can the shapes shown below.

These shapes have turn symmetry.

Non-Euclidean Transformations—Dilatations

There are also non-Euclidean transformations that change the size of the shape. Only one of these, the *dilatation*, sometimes called a dilation, is introduced, in some jurisdictions, at the K–8 level. A dilatation increases or decreases the size of the original figure without changing its shape. The result of a dilatation is an image whose angle measures match those in the original, and whose side or curve lengths have all been multiplied or divided by the same amount. This results in an image that is a similar shape.

Creating a Dilatation Image by Measuring–Enlargement

STEP 1	STEP 2
Choose a point outside the original shape. This is called a *dilatation point* or *centre of dilatation*.	Connect that point to each vertex on the original shape.

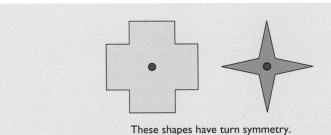

STEP 3	STEP 4
Measure the length of each connecting line.	Increase the length of each connecting line in the same proportion (called the *scale factor*). A scale factor of 2 is used here.

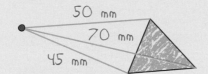

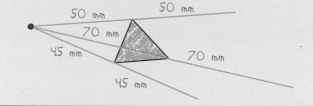

STEP 5

Join the ends of the connecting lines to form the image.

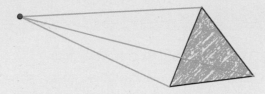

Creating a Dilatation Image by Measuring–Reduction

A dilatation can also be used to reduce a shape. For example, to create a reduction of the same triangle, you would follow Steps 1 to 3 but then, in Step 4, you would decrease the length of the connecting lines.

STEP 4	STEP 5
Decrease the length of each connecting line in the same proportion. A scale factor of 0.5 is used here.	Join the ends of the reduced connecting lines.

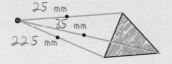

ACTIVITY 18.10

Students can explore the properties of dilatations as they experiment with this method for enlarging a shape.

1. Make a knot to tie the ends of two rubber bands together.
2. Draw a triangle on a piece of paper.
3. Hold down one end of your double rubber band near your triangle. Place a pencil inside the other end.
4. Slowly move the knot along the sides of your triangle.
5. Draw a line with your pencil as you move the knot. What happened?

Proportional Reasoning

Properties of Dilatations

SIMILARITY	INCREASE IN AREA
A dilatation image is always similar to the original. 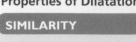	When a shape is enlarged or reduced, the area increases or decreases by the square of the scale factor. 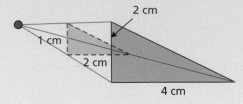 When the side lengths are multiplied by 2, the area is multiplied by 2^2 or 4.

Dilatations and Regular Polygons

Every square is a dilatation image of every other square because, by definition, the sides are all increased or decreased by the same proportion. This is true for any regular polygon.

Tessellations

Tessellations are included in many mathematics curricula because they provide an opportunity for students to focus on properties of shapes, especially side lengths and angle measures.

Relating Tessellations and Transformations

Tessellations (or *tilings*) involve translating, reflecting, and/or rotating a shape (a *tile*) or a combination of shapes in order to cover a plane surface so there are no gaps or overlaps between the tiles. One of the most famous tessellators was the artist M.C. Escher. His tessellations are often shown in museums and galleries.

2-D Shapes That Tile

Most students realize that squares or rectangles will tile a surface, and many know that regular hexagons will also work because of their experience with square counters or tiles, attribute blocks, and pattern blocks.

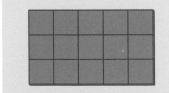 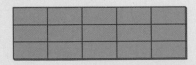 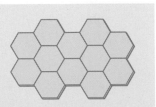

Students may be more surprised to learn that any triangle or quadrilateral can tile. This is because the sum of the measures of the interior angles is 180° in a triangle and 360° in a quadrilateral. Shapes will tessellate if the angles that meet at a central point fill a total of 360°.

In the examples below, congruent angles are colour-coded inside each shape to show how the angles combine at a centre point to fill 360°. In the first figure, each angle from the triangle occurs twice in the centre, for a total of 180° × 2, or 360°. In the second figure, all four angles from the trapezoid meet at the centre, for a total of 360°. Side lengths are also important—in a tessellation, congruent sides are matched to one another.

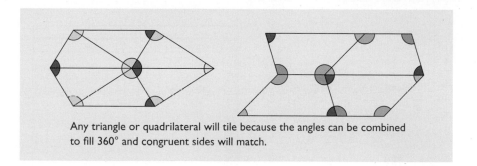

Any triangle or quadrilateral will tile because the angles can be combined to fill 360° and congruent sides will match.

In **Activity 18.11**, students explore the regular polygons to see which ones will tile a surface on their own. This activity will help them discover that the equilateral triangle, the square, and the hexagon work, because their interior angle measures can be combined to fill 360° (6 × 60°, 4 × 90°, and 3 × 120°). Since the interior angle measures of the other regular polygons are not factors of 360°, they will not tile a surface unless they are combined with other shapes.

Students might also explore what happens when they try to tile with irregular shapes, or when they combine regular and irregular shapes. For example, some irregular pentagons will tile, depending on their interior angle measures, and regular octagons will tile if they are combined with squares.

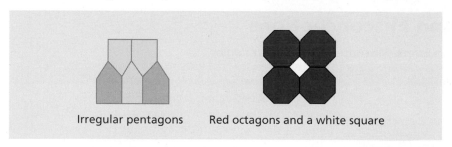

Irregular pentagons   Red octagons and a white square

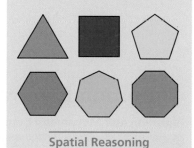
Constructions

Usually in Grade 5 or higher, students begin to perform geometric constructions. The purpose of the constructions is to allow students to apply or develop an understanding of the properties of shapes. Traditionally, construction tools were straightedge (a ruler with no numbers on it) and compass, but now constructions are also performed with other tools, such as Miras or dynamic geometry software and sometimes protractors.

Typically, students might learn to construct the following:

- the perpendicular to a line
- a line parallel to another line
- the perpendicular bisector of a line segment
- a circle with a given centre
- a circle that goes through 2 or 3 given points
- an angle bisector

By combining these ideas, students might also learn to construct angles of particular sizes, for example, a 45° or 60° angle, an equilateral triangle, a regular hexagon, and a circle touching the 3 sides of a triangle, etc.

For example, below are shown constructions of a perpendicular to a line using a straightedge and a compass, a Mira, and The Geometer's Sketchpad.

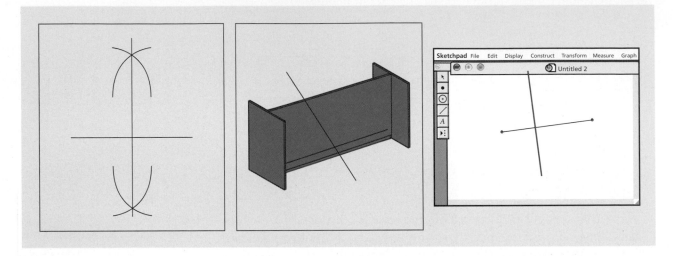

The compass and straightedge construction focuses students on recognizing that the perpendicular bisector of a segment is the set of points equidistant from both endpoints. The Mira construction focuses on the notion that the line of reflection is perpendicular to any segment joining a pre-image to its image. The computer construction is one that is automatically performed by the software, but requires students to identify a point on the line and the line to which the constructed line will be perpendicular.

Common Errors and Misconceptions

Location and Movement: Common Errors, Misconceptions, and Strategies

COMMON ERROR OR MISCONCEPTION	SUGGESTED STRATEGY
Meaning of *Above* Students sometimes misinterpret the term *above*, thinking that it must mean *directly above*. For example, they would not recognize that the cloud shown here is not just above the house, but also above the car. 	Students require opportunities to hear teachers use the term *above* in situations where one item is not directly above the other.  A teacher might ask, "Could you get me the red book from the shelf above my desk?"

COMMON ERROR OR MISCONCEPTION	SUGGESTED STRATEGY

Flips Across Slanted Lines

Students may think that flips have to be horizontal or vertical (as shown here), and may not recognize that flip lines can also be slanted.

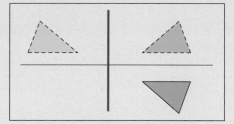

The green triangle has been flipped horizontally and then vertically.

This misconception arises because teachers often focus on horizontal and vertical flips, since these are easier to perform. In addition, most computer draw programs perform vertical and horizontal flips, but not slanted ones.

Use illustrations of other flips as the topic is being discussed. When students are performing slanted flips, they will find it helpful to use a Mira.

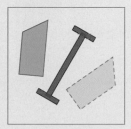

The green triangle has been flipped across a slanted line.

Confusing Quarter Turns with Half Turns

A student who has been asked to perform a half turn often performs a quarter turn. He or she is likely thinking that a full turn is only half way around.

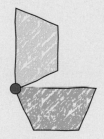

Incorrect representation of a $\frac{1}{2}$ turn

A good way to deal with this misconception is to have students use their own bodies to explore turns. A full turn is all the way around. A half turn means turning from front to back. A quarter turn means turning right or left.

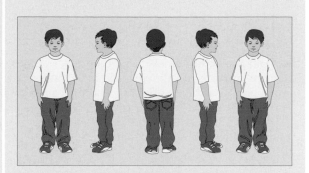

A full turn is the same as four quarter turns.

Later, students can check their turns by focusing on how one side of the shape, or even one point, moved. It also helps to draw a line to connect the turn centre to a point on the original shape and a corresponding point on the image. The angle formed will indicate the amount of turn.

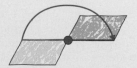

A straight angle, so a $\frac{1}{2}$ turn

(continued)

Location and Movement: Common Errors, Misconceptions, and Strategies (Continued)

COMMON ERROR OR MISCONCEPTION	SUGGESTED STRATEGY

Confusing Flips and Turns

To a student, a flip and a 180° turn can look very much the same.

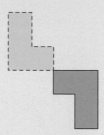

Is this a flip across a slanted line or a 180° turn?

If students match vertices on the original shape with the corresponding vertices on the image, this will help them distinguish between a flip and a turn.

As well, they could either visualize or draw a line from one of the original vertices that crosses what they think is the flip line at a right angle. They will see that the corresponding vertex is not along that line and, therefore, the transformation is not a flip.

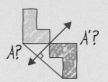

Vertex A′ is not a flip image of vertex A across the line, so the transformation is not a flip.

Students should always be encouraged to model a transformation to test their idea about what motion was performed. For example, a student who models a flip of the green shape across the slanted line will find that the image looks like this:

Locating Points on a Grid

Students may count lines rather than spaces when they are creating coordinate grids and locating points on a coordinate grid. For example, a student who wants to locate (4, 2) may count the first line as "1" (both horizontally and vertically) and, as a result, mislocate the point as shown here at (3, 1).

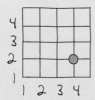

Incorrect grid and location for point (4, 2)

Encourage students to include 0 on each axis, since this will help them count correctly.

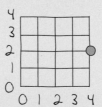

Correct grid and location for point (4, 2)

Inverting Coordinates

Students mix up the order of the Cartesian coordinates when plotting points on a Cartesian grid; for example, they plot point (3, 4) by counting up 3 and then right 4, instead of right 3 and up 4.

Encourage students to memorize the positions of (1, 0) and (0, 1) to remind them which number tells them to go right and which number tells them to go up. Since (1, 0) is 1 to the right, that means they go right first. Since (0, 1) is up, that means they go up last.

Appropriate Manipulatives

Location and Movement: Examples of Manipulatives

MANIPULATIVE	EXAMPLE
2-D Shape Models When students first begin learning about slides, flips, and turns, they work with concrete shapes, such as pattern or attribute blocks. The disadvantage of many of these shapes is that they are symmetrical, and transformations can be more difficult to identify when they are done with symmetrical shapes. Therefore, it is important to use other, less symmetrical shape pieces. Shape models can also be used for tessellations and pattern work.	2-D shape models can be used for making transformation patterns. In the pattern below, a yellow dot is used to highlight the same vertex in each triangle. Making a pattern by turning and tracing a pattern block
Geoboards Geoboards provide a hands-on model for transformations with 2-D shapes. Younger students can make a shape with an elastic, and then physically turn the geoboard (or flip it, if the geoboard is transparent). Older students can use one elastic to show the original shape and another for the transformation image. Dot paper grids (5-by-5) are useful for recording the results of geoboard activities.	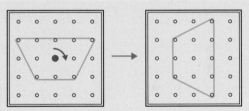 Performing a turn by rotating a geoboard
Protractors Protractors are used for measuring angles for the purpose of turning particular amounts. 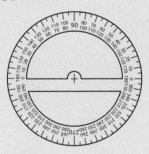 Circular protractor	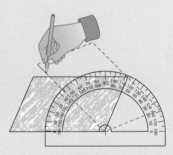 Using a regular protractor to turn a parallelogram 45° clockwise
Mirrors and Miras Either traditional mirrors or transparent ones (Miras) are invaluable for identifying and modelling flips. 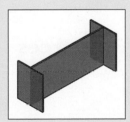 A transparent mirror	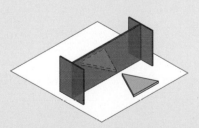 The bottom edge of the Mira represents the flip line.

Location and Movement: Examples of Manipulatives (Continued)

COMMON ERROR OR MISCONCEPTION	SUGGESTED STRATEGY
Grid Paper Grid paper is needed for work with coordinate graphing and is a useful tool for exploring slides, flips, and turns. (See page 445.) Like dot paper, it can also be used for dilatations.	When students flip a shape on a grid, they can count grid squares to locate the flip image of each vertex. They can also discover that lines drawn to link each original vertex with its flip image form a 90° angle with the flip line. 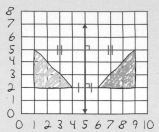 Flipping a triangle on a coordinate grid

Appropriate Children's Books

Zoom (Banyai, 1998).
This book provides a fascinating take on how things look different from different positions—*far away* and *close*, in particular.

My Map Book (Fanelli, 1995).
This book includes many opportunities for students to see their place in the world through different maps.

All About Where (Hoban, 1991).
Tana Hoban is a prolific photographer who brings the geometry in our everyday world to children's attention. In this book, students think about positional vocabulary, such as *above*, *under*, *behind*, and *between*.

Round Trip (Jonas, 1983).
This unusual black-and-white picture book is "read" through, and then turned upside down and "read" through upside down and backwards to tell its story. This book provides an opportunity to think about transformations in a unique way.

The Mirror Puzzle Book (Walter, 1985).
This book, which comes with a mirror, allows students to explore the effects of reflection. Although the book was published in the mid-1980s, the content is not at all dated. The focus is on solving puzzles by using a mirror to create particular designs.

Appropriate Digital Resources

See the MindTap site for a selection of appropriate digital resources.

Assessing Student Understanding

- It is most appropriate to assess students' knowledge of and ability to use positional vocabulary in everyday situations, not just in designated math times.

- Many of the skills and concepts addressed in this chapter are best assessed through observation of students working directly with physical materials. In that way, it is possible to see, for example, how tools like a protractor or Mira are used.

- Performing transformations on grid paper often requires less sophistication than performing those same transformations on plain paper. Decide which you think is more appropriate for students in terms of assessing them.

- Some provinces introduce transformations in a much later grade than other provinces. Where this is the case, some of the simpler ideas should be both presented and assessed in a somewhat more sophisticated way.

- A student is asked if the square was slid, flipped, or turned to move it from position A to position B.

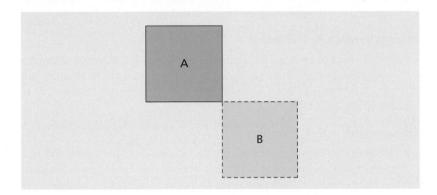

How would you respond to an answer such as this?

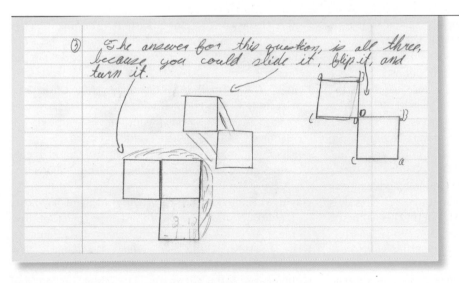

Student Response

This Grade 6 student has provided both a written answer and diagrams to show his thinking.

Applying What You've Learned

1. What information about transformations did you use to solve the chapter problem?

2. Positional vocabulary is usually introduced to young children. Which terms would you use earliest and which would you delay? Why?

3. Explain why numbering grid lines on the two axes to describe point locations is more sophisticated than using the typical city map system of letters in boxes on one axis and numbers in boxes on the other axis.

4. At what point do you think it would be appropriate to use terms like *translation*, *rotation*, and *reflection* as opposed to *slide*, *turn*, and *flip*? Explain your thinking.

5. Search the Internet for a transformation applet. Why might using that applet be better than drawing shapes on the board?

6. Search for three "fun" activities that students could do with a Mira. In each case, indicate what mathematics students are learning and discuss whether that activity is a good way to approach the math.

7. What task would you assign a Grade 6 student to find out what she or he understands about rotating shapes?

8. How could computer programming using the MIT computer program Scratch help students think about position and space?

Interact with a K–8 Student:

9. Ask a student to draw a "map" of the room where you are talking with him or her. Does he or she pay attention only to relative position of articles in the room or to relative distances between them as well? How can you tell?

Discuss with a K–8 Teacher:

10. Do some research on the game Tetris. Ask a teacher how she or he would feel about using Tetris as a vehicle for exploring transformational geometry. Describe your reaction to what you heard.

Selected References

Andrews, A.G. (**1996**). Developing spatial sense—a moving experience. *Teaching Children Mathematics, 2,* 290–293.

Banyai, I. (**1998**). *Zoom.* London: Puffin Books.

Chavez, O., Reys, R., and Jones, D. (**2005**). Spatial visualization: What happens when you turn it? *Mathematics Teaching in the Middle School, 11,* 190–195.

Clements, D.H. (**2000**). Geometric and spatial thinking in young children. In Copley, J.V. (Ed.). *The young child and mathematics.* Washington, DC: National Association for the Education of Young Children and National Council of Teachers of Mathematics.

Clements, D.H., and Battista, M.T. (**1992**). Geometry and spatial reasoning. In Grouws, D.A. (Ed.). *Handbook of research on mathematics teaching and learning.* New York: Macmillan Publishing Co., 420–464.

Clements, D.H., and Sarama, J. (**2000a**). The earliest geometry. *Teaching Children Mathematics, 7(2),* 82–86.

Clements, D.H., and Sarama, J. (**2000b**). Young children's ideas about geometric shapes. *Teaching children mathematics, 6(8),* 482–487.

Dobler, C.P., and Klein, J.M. (**2002**). First graders, flies, and a Frenchman's fascination: Introducing the Cartesian coordinate system. *Teaching Children Mathematics, 8,* 540–545.

Fanelli, S. (**1995**). *My map book.* New York: Harper Festival.

Findell, C.R., Small, M., Cavanagh, M., Dacey, L., Greenes, C.E., and Sheffield, L.J. (**2001**). *Navigating through geometry in prekindergarten–grade 2.* Reston, VA: National Council of Teachers of Mathematics.

Fonstad, C., and McGarvey, L. (**2010**). Quick images with Victoria and Joshua. *Teaching Children Mathematics, 17,* 200.

Gavin, M.K., Belkin, L.P., Spinelli, A.M., and St. Marie, J. (**2001**). *Navigating through geometry in grades 3–5.* Reston, VA: National Council of Teachers of Mathematics.

Glass, J. (**1998**). *The fly on the ceiling: A math myth.* New York: Random House.

Goldenberg, E.P., Clements, D., Zbiek, R.M., and Dougherty, B. (**2014**). *Developing essential understanding of geometry and measurement for teaching mathematics in Pre-K–Grade 2.* Reston, CA: National Council of Teachers of Mathematics.

Hoban, T. (**1991**). *All about where.* New York: Greenwillow Books.

Hutchins, P. (1971). *Rosie's walk*. New York: Aladdin Paperbacks.

Jonas, A. (1983). *Round trip*. New York: Mulberrry Books, a division of William Morrow & Co.

Logan, T., Lowrie, T., and Diezmann, C.M. (2014). Co-thought gestures: Supporting students to navigate map tasks. *Educational Studies in Mathematics, 87,* 87–102.

Pugalee, D.K., Frykholm, J., Johnson, A., Slovin, H., Malloy, C., and Preston, R. (2002). *Navigating through geometry in grades 6–8*. Reston, VA: National Council of Teachers of Mathematics.

Rollick, M.B. (2009). Toward a definition of reflection. *Mathematics Teaching in the Middle School, 14, 396–399.*

Sharman, L. (1994). *The amazing book of shapes*. New York: Dorling Kindersley Publishing.

Vasilyeva, M., and Bowers, E. (2006). Children's use of geometric information in mapping tasks. *Journal of Experimental Child Psychology, 95,* 255–277.

Walter, M. (1986). *The mirror puzzle book*. St. Albans, UK: Tarquin.

Wheatley, G. (2007). *Quick draw: Developing spatial sense in mathematics (2nd Ed.)*. Tallahassee, FL: MathematicsLearning.

Chapter 19

The Nature of Measurement, with a Focus on Length and Area

IN A NUTSHELL

The main ideas in this chapter are listed below:

1. Measurement is the process of assigning a qualitative or quantitative description of size to an object based on a particular attribute. It is always a comparison of the size of one object with another, so the same object can be described using different measurements. Therefore, knowledge of the size of certain benchmarks assists in measuring.

2. The use of standard measurement units is meant to simplify and clarify communication about the size of objects. Measurement formulas and tools are meant to simplify the determination of some measurements.

3. Measurement instruction is best approached by beginning with a definition/comparison stage, followed by a stage involving nonstandard units,

(continued)

CHAPTER PROBLEM

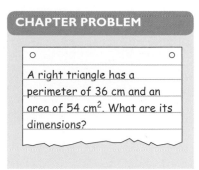

A right triangle has a perimeter of 36 cm and an area of 54 cm². What are its dimensions?

IN A NUTSHELL (*continued*)

followed by a stage involving standard units. Problem solving should be part of all stages.

4. Tools, units of measure, and degree of precision for a measurement should be appropriate to the context and purpose of that measurement.

5. Often, but not always, different measures of an object are predictable from other measures. Sometimes this involves the use of formulas and sometimes not.

The Nature of Measurement

TEACHING **TIP**

Have students consider the diversity of things we measure. Offer some less traditional starting ideas such as:

• how deep a colour is
• how funny someone is
• how talkative someone is
• how big type on a page is.

Challenge students to think of as many other things as they can that we might measure in some way.

Children are naturally curious about measurement. They are interested in how tall, how big, how heavy, how long, how hot, or how cold things are. Initially, they accept answers that describe comparisons: "An elephant is a lot taller than my teacher." Gradually, they come to understand that measurement is a tool that can help them answer questions more precisely.

Measurement is about assigning a numerical value to an attribute of an object, relative to another object called a unit. Usually, you measure to have a sense of the size of an object compared to other objects whose size you know. A greater measurement implies that one object has "more" of a particular attribute than another. In elementary and middle school, measurement is typically about length, area, capacity, mass, volume, time, temperature, and angles. Although money is sometimes treated as a measurement topic, it is often used as a context for number work. In this resource, money is included in the number chapters.

MEASUREMENT PRINCIPLES

1. Different measurement attributes of an object are not always related; it is possible for an object that is large in one way to be small in another.

2. Sometimes you measure directly; sometimes you use indirect means.

3. Most measurements can be determined in more than one way.

4. Familiarity with certain measurement referents helps you estimate.

5. There is more than one possible unit that could be used to measure an item, but the unit chosen should make sense for the object and/or the situation.

6. In order to measure, a series of uniform units must be used or a single unit must be used repeatedly.

7. The unit chosen for a measurement affects the numerical value of the measurement; a bigger unit results in a smaller number of units. This is why a measurement without a unit is meaningless.

8. No measurement of a continuous attribute can ever be exact, as there is always a smaller, more precise unit.

9. Often, an estimated measure is enough. As well, a coarse estimate can be a useful check on a more precise measurement.

10. Sometimes you want a more precise measurement; in that case, a smaller unit should be used.

There are a number of principles that underlie any type of measurement. Students will gradually come to recognize these principles as they gain experience with measurement, and it is important for teachers to recognize opportunities to bring them out through classroom discussion.

Addressing Measurement Principles in the Classroom

MEASUREMENT PRINCIPLE 1

Different measurement attributes of the same object are not always related, so it is possible for an object that is large in one way to be small in another.

"The yellow bowl is bigger, but the green one is heavier."

MEASUREMENT PRINCIPLE 2

Sometimes you measure directly and sometimes you use indirect means. For example, there are two different ways to measure the red angle.

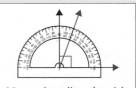 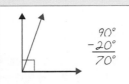

Measuring directly with a protractor

Measuring indirectly by subtracting

MEASUREMENT PRINCIPLE 3

Most measurements can be determined in more than one way.

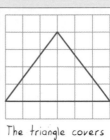 

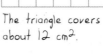 The triangle covers about 12 cm².

Area = base × height ÷ 2
= 6 × 4 ÷ 2
= 12 cm²

"I figured out the area by putting a grid over the triangle and counting squares. Sarah used a formula."

MEASUREMENT PRINCIPLE 4

Familiarity with certain measurement referents helps you estimate.

"My finger is 1 cm wide, so this string must be 1, 2, 3, 4, 5 cm long."

MEASUREMENT PRINCIPLE 5

There is more than one possible unit that could be used to measure an item, but the unit chosen should make sense for the object and the situation.

"I would use the cup to measure how much the pitcher holds because the number of units wouldn't be too big or too small."

MEASUREMENT PRINCIPLE 6

In order to measure, a series of uniform units must be used, or a single unit must be used repeatedly.

"When you measure, you have to use the same tool again and again."

(continued)

MEASUREMENT PRINCIPLE 7

The unit chosen for a measurement affects the value of the measurement; a bigger unit results in a smaller number of units. (This makes a measurement without a unit meaningless.)

"Our rope is the length of eight of John's shoes, but only seven of Ani's shoes because Ani's shoes are bigger."

MEASUREMENT PRINCIPLE 8

No measurement of a continuous attribute can ever be exact, as there is always a smaller, more precise unit.

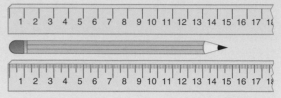

"I thought it was 15 cm long until I used millimetres. Then I saw it was a bit less."

MEASUREMENT PRINCIPLE 9

It is always useful to estimate a measurement, sometimes because an estimate is all you need, and sometimes because it is a useful check on the reasonableness of a more precise measurement.

> It's 3 km to the pool. It takes me about 10 min to walk to school and that's about 1 km. It will probably take us about half an hour to walk to the pool.

Sometimes an estimate is enough.

> The plum's mass is 135 g. That makes sense because the peach was about 300g, and the plum is about half as heavy as the peach.

Sometimes an estimate helps you decide if a measurement makes sense.

MEASUREMENT PRINCIPLE 10

Sometimes you want a more precise measurement; in that case, a smaller unit should be used.

"They're pretty close. I need to use a millimetre ruler to see how much longer."

Stages of Measurement Instruction

For most types of measurement, there are three stages that teachers typically move through with students:

- **Definition/Comparison:** Students begin to learn to define the measurement, and become aware of and apply a process for comparing items with respect to that measurement, without using units.
- **Nonstandard Units:** Students continue to define the measurement while they learn to measure with nonstandard units, such as scoops of water (for capacity) or linking cubes (for length).
- **Standard Units:** Students learn to use measurement tools to measure with standard units, such as centimetres and grams.

These three stages apply to most, but not all, types of measurement. While students generally move through all three stages in their work with length, area, capacity, volume, mass, and time, they do not typically do so in as much detail in their work with temperature and angles.

The Three Stages of Measurement Instruction

DEFINITION/COMPARISON

In this stage, students learn what a particular type of measurement is all about by using a comparison process (either direct or indirect) to determine which of two items has more of that measure. For example, to compare two vegetables directly to see which is longer, a student would line up the vegetables at one end to see which one "sticks out."

Indirect comparison is less concrete than direct comparison, but is sometimes used when direct comparison is not possible. For example, a student might cut a string to match the length of a carrot in his or her refrigerator at home, and bring it to school to compare with carrot strings cut by other students. In this case, carrot lengths are being compared indirectly because students are using representations of carrots, rather than the carrots themselves. Whether the comparison is direct or indirect, the process for comparing is the same.

While the same thinking applies to other types of measurement besides length, the processes used to compare the items are different. Students' understanding of each type of measurement develops implicitly as they discuss how to decide which of two items has more of that measure.

"I know the carrot is longer because it sticks out more."

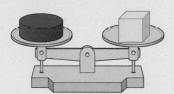

"I know the blocks have the same mass because the pans balance."

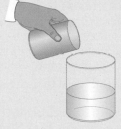

"I know the clear container holds more than the blue container because there's still space after you pour everything from the blue container into it."

NONSTANDARD UNITS

When familiar objects are used as units for measuring, these are typically referred to as nonstandard units since there is no universal meaning that can be attached; there is, for example, no single standard length of a block, capacity of a can, or mass of a cube. Although there are some researchers who have found evidence that it is appropriate to use standard tools and standard units right away, as long as meaning is emphasized over procedure (Stephan and Clements, 2003), most experts continue to believe that students need time to work with nonstandard units before they will be ready for standard units and tools.

Using nonstandard units helps to reinforce important measurement concepts. For example, with length, the use of nonstandard units reinforces the notion that measuring is about determining the distance between two points and not just about identifying the point on a ruler where the length ends.

In the nonstandard unit stage, it is important for students to choose a unit that is appropriate for the type of measurement and the object being measured. For example, if the student is measuring length, the units should

• be uniform (all the same size and shape)

• be smaller than the object being measured (so a reasonable degree of precision is possible)

• combine to create something long and thin that fits along the distance to be measured

(continued)

The Three Stages of Measurement Instruction (Continued)

NONSTANDARD UNITS (CONTINUED)

Small cubes make an excellent nonstandard length unit.

"The carrot is 16 cubes long."

The nonstandard unit stage is also relevant for other types of measurement. Whether students are learning to measure capacity, mass, area, volume, or even time, they need time to work with various nonstandard units before standard units are introduced in order to understand what each measurement type is all about.

STANDARD UNITS

In the standard unit stage, students are ready to use a standard unit, and eventually a variety of standard units, to measure. They soon learn that this makes it easier to compare and communicate about measurements. For example, if someone says that a carrot is 22 cm long, everyone knows exactly how long that is. A description with nonstandard units, such as "16 cubes long," would be more difficult to interpret.

At this stage, students learn to use standard tools for measuring. These include such things as rulers, measuring tapes, and trundle wheels (circles with a fixed circumference, usually 1 m, on a stick to allow rolling) for measuring length, measuring cups and spoons for measuring capacity, and gram and kilogram masses for measuring mass. This is more sophisticated than working with direct or indirect comparison or with nonstandard units because it requires students to have an abstract understanding of what is represented by the marks on a ruler or measuring cup, or the size of a standard mass.

"I know the carrot is 22 cm long because it fills up the space from 0 to 22 along the ruler."

The Metric System of Measurement

TEACHING TIP

Because of Canadian use of the metric system and U.S. use of the Imperial system, teachers need to be cautious about sending students to the Internet for measurement activities; some may be difficult for them to interpret.

About 40 years ago, Canada adopted the International System of Units (called SI, for Système International) as its official measurement system. The rationale for adopting the metric system included the fact that this system is already used by most countries around the world, and especially in the scientific community, because of its ease of use.

Clearly, one of the attractions of the metric system is its consistency with the place value system. This is particularly valuable when units are renamed, or converted. For example, 3.56 m can easily be renamed as 356 cm without any complicated calculations.

SI Base Units

While the old Imperial system of measurement required Canadians to memorize a wide range of unrelated numbers—12 inches in a foot, 3 feet in a yard, 1760 yards in a mile, etc.—the adoption of the metric system meant that people would simply need to learn a few base units and a series of prefixes that could be applied to these base units.

At the K–8 level, students are introduced to three of the seven SI base units—the metre, the kilogram, and the second. It may seem odd that the kilogram is called the base unit when the metric prefixes are attached to the word "gram," not "kilogram." In fact, the gram was actually a base unit in the older CGS system of measurement, but was superseded by the kilogram, which was considered more convenient for practical purposes.

SI Base Units Introduced in Elementary School

Unit	Attribute Measured	Symbol	Definition
metre	length	m	One metre is the length of the path travelled by laser-generated light in a vacuum during the time interval of $\frac{1}{299792458}$ a light-second.
kilogram	mass	kg	One kilogram is a mass equal to the international prototype of the kilogram (about the mass of 1 dm^3 of water at 4°C).
second	time	s	One second is the duration of 9 192 631 770 periods of radiation corresponding to the transition between the two hyperfine levels of the ground state of the cesium-133 atom at 0 kelvin.

Each of the three base units is based on a precise measurement associated with a science-related situation. While these situations may be of interest to teachers, it is not necessary to teach them, or the term "base unit," to students.

SI Derived and Customary Units

The International System of Units also uses a number of *derived units*—units that were created by applying arithmetic operations to the SI base units. Derived-unit measures used in elementary school mathematics include square metres for area, cubic metres for volume, metres per second for speed or velocity, and *degrees Celsius* for temperature. There are also other derived-unit measures that are not typically dealt with in elementary school. One example is the kilogram per cubic metre, which is used to describe density.

In addition, there are a number of widely used *customary units* that are considered to be outside the International System of Units, but are accepted for use with SI. These include the *litre* to describe capacity, the *tonne* (metric ton) to describe mass, *minute, hour*, and *day* to describe time, and the *degree* to describe angle arc.

Metric Prefixes

Metric prefixes allow the user to begin with a unit and create larger and smaller units. There are actually 20 prefixes—10 to create larger units, and 10 to create smaller units—but we commonly use only about half of these.

The charts at the top of the next page show the 10 prefixes and the more commonly used ones.

> ### ACTIVITY 19.1
>
> A day is defined as 24 hours. How long should a deciday be? How long should a centiday be?
>
> _____
>
> **Critical Thinking**

Metric Prefixes in Common Use

giga-	mega-	kilo-	hecto-	deca-	unit	deci-	centi-	milli-	micro-	nano-
1 billion units	1 million units	1000 units	100 units	10 units	1 unit	0.1 units	0.01 units	0.001 units	0.000001 units	0.000000001 units

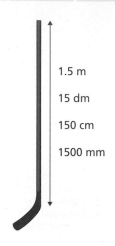

1.5 m

15 dm

150 cm

1500 mm

Common Metric Prefixes for Length

kilo-	unit	deci-	centi-	milli-
1000 m	1 m	0.1 m	0.01 m	0.001 m

Note that the smaller units in the tables above are described with decimals rather than fractions. Decimals are used in the International System of Units because of the relationship of the metric prefixes to the place value system. Using decimals makes it particularly easy to rename a recorded measurement in terms of another unit. For example, to change centimetres to millimetres, you simply need to multiply by 10, which moves each digit one place to the left: 2.4 cm = 24 mm.

Measuring Length

We use the term *length*, or *linear measure*, to describe measurements in one dimension. Linear measurements include height, width, length, depth, distance, and perimeter. Ideas about length are introduced even in preschool, probably since estimating and measuring length is something people do often in everyday life. For example, a student might want to know if a pair of pants is long enough, if a distance is too far to walk, or how the heights of family members compare.

Introducing Length Concepts

Ideas about length can be introduced through the same three stages as many other measurement concepts—definition/comparison, nonstandard units, standard units. An alternative very specific trajectory for measuring length is offered in Szilágyi, Clements, and Sarama (2013).

How Concepts of Length Can Be Introduced

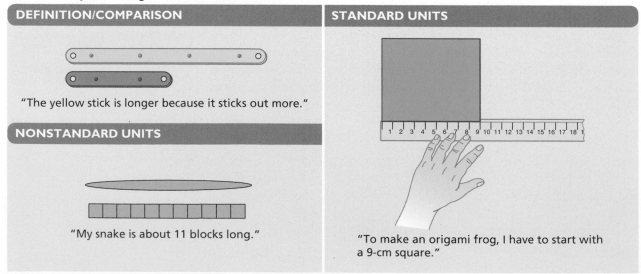

DEFINITION/COMPARISON

"The yellow stick is longer because it sticks out more."

NONSTANDARD UNITS

"My snake is about 11 blocks long."

STANDARD UNITS

"To make an origami frog, I have to start with a 9-cm square."

Length: The Definition/Comparison Stage

At this stage, students explore the notion that one item is longer than another if, when the items are lined up to start at a common base line, one sticks out (or up) farther than the other. In the process, students begin to develop vocabulary for comparing lengths—terms such as "longer than" and "shorter than," or, if they are comparing more than two items, terms such as "longest," "second-longest," and "shortest."

Direct and Indirect Comparison

Sometimes, lengths are compared directly by placing the items to be compared side by side. For example, students might use *direct comparison* to compare the lengths of snakes they have made from modelling clay to see whose is longest. At other times, they will need to use *indirect comparison*. With indirect comparison, students compare actual-size representations of objects, rather than the objects themselves. Indirect comparison is usually used when direct comparison would be difficult. For example, students might cut strings to represent the length of their hand-spans and compare the strings with other body lengths, such as their foot lengths or their elbow-to-wrist distances. Comfort with this sort of indirect method is predicated on a student's understanding of *transitivity of measure*; that is, if measure A = measure B and measure B = measure C, then measure A = measure C. Students usually need lots of experience with direct comparison before indirect comparison situations are presented.

Comparison activities, whether direct or indirect, can also be part of larger investigations, such as finding out whether people with longer feet also tend to have wider hand-spans. **Activity 19.2** suggests examples of direct and indirect comparison activities for young students.

Length: The Nonstandard Unit Stage

Teachers can introduce work with nonstandard units when students realize that, rather than aligning objects directly or indirectly to compare their lengths, they can use uniform units to assign a numerical value to the length of each object. This makes it possible to compare lengths simply by comparing these values.

Appropriate Nonstandard Units for Length

Nonstandard units are handy everyday items of uniform length, such as unsharpened pencils, new crayons, new erasers, toothpicks, craft sticks (Popsicle sticks), plastic links, paper clips, Cuisenaire rods, and straws. Students can also use body measurements, such as hand-spans, foot lengths, and paces. Students might want to use items such as sharpened pencils or used erasers, but these are not ideal since they are not uniform.

For length, it helps students to use items that are long and thin, so there will be no ambiguity about which attribute is being measured. Therefore, items like recipe cards are not ideal, even though one of their dimensions could be used as a unit.

Initially, you want students to use units that are meaningful to them. If, for example, they hear that something is 5 new pencils long, this gives them a sense of its length because they have a mental image of a pencil's length.

ACTIVITY 19.2

Ask three students to come to the front and line them up from shortest to tallest. Ask other students to come up one at a time, figure out where they belong in the sequence, and join the line. When everyone is in line, take a picture. Ask questions such as

- Who is the tallest student in our class? the shortest?

- Who is right in the middle?

- Who is shorter than Ishan but taller than Eric?

Show students a string that matches the height of one of the students in the class. Challenge the class to find out whose height the string represents.

Spatial Reasoning

As they work with nonstandard units, students can discover these important notions:

- Any measurement can be determined with a variety of different units.
- When you use the same unit to measure different lengths, the results are easy to compare.
- Measurements can be determined either by laying out multiple uniform units end to end, or by repeatedly using and moving a single unit along the length to be measured.

Measuring the Same Length with Different Units

It is important for students to have opportunities to measure the same length with different units. This will help them discover that the same item can be described in different ways. It will also help them discover that, as the size of the unit increases, the number of units decreases. For example, the same item might be 56 paper clips long but only 8 straws long. Experiences like the ones represented in **Activity 19.3** and in the teacher–student interview that follows not only help students learn about using different units to measure the same length, but also help them discover that it is more efficient to use longer units to measure longer lengths and shorter units to measure shorter lengths.

ACTIVITY 19.3

Ask students to have partners help them cut strings that match their heights. They can then look for some different kinds of units to use to measure their heights by measuring the strings.

- What are some different ways to tell someone how tall you are?

- Which unit was easiest for you to use? Why?

***

Spatial Reasoning

Student Response

This student is learning that the number of units required to measure a length can be different if a different unit is used.

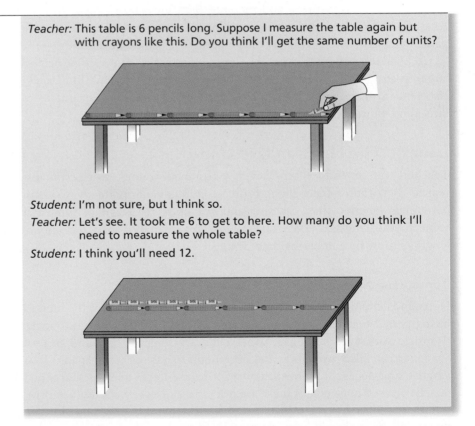

Teacher: This table is 6 pencils long. Suppose I measure the table again but with crayons like this. Do you think I'll get the same number of units?

Student: I'm not sure, but I think so.

Teacher: Let's see. It took me 6 to get to here. How many do you think I'll need to measure the whole table?

Student: I think you'll need 12.

Measuring Different Lengths with a Constant Unit

Just as it is important for students to have opportunities to measure a constant length with different units, it is also important for them to measure different lengths with the same unit. This will help them build their estimation skills.

Learning to Iterate

One of the first things students learn about measuring length in nonstandard units is that the units are uniform objects that are used repeatedly. Initially, students measure by lining up the required number of units along the object to be measured. For example, they might observe that a table is about 8 craft sticks long. Later, they learn to use a single item to *iterate*; that is, they move the unit from one position to another along the length of the object and count the number of times it fits along the length. Through experience, students will learn that some units lend themselves to iteration more easily than others. A new pencil, a paper clip, or a foot length will iterate easily, for example, while an arm length might not.

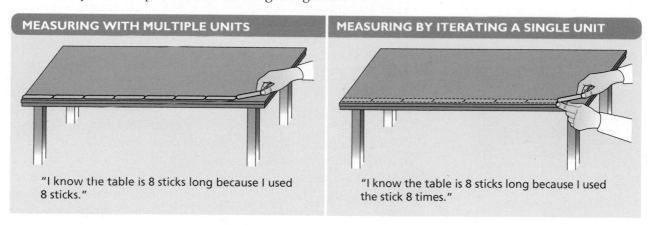

MEASURING WITH MULTIPLE UNITS

"I know the table is 8 sticks long because I used 8 sticks."

MEASURING BY ITERATING A SINGLE UNIT

"I know the table is 8 sticks long because I used the stick 8 times."

To help students make the transition from using multiple uniform items to using iteration, a teacher might place a strip of modelling clay along the length to be measured so students can make end-to-end imprints of the unit until the entire distance is covered. Students need to practise this in order to ensure that each imprint starts exactly where the old one left off, with no space left out and no overlap. With this form of iteration, the imprints give the impression that multiple units were used when, really, the length was measured with a single unit. Later, students will not need to do this. Instead, they will learn to use a finger as a marker to show where to start each new iteration of the unit.

Another way to help with the transition from multiple units to iteration is to let students use two units, for example, two craft sticks, to measure. This way, there is always a unit in place, making it easy to locate where the next unit should be placed.

Estimating Lengths in Nonstandard Units

Once students have learned how to measure with nonstandard units, whether using multiple units or iteration, it becomes possible for them to estimate how many units long a particular item will be. To help students learn to estimate, a teacher could provide situations in which an item is partially measured; the student's task is to estimate how many units it will take to measure the full length. Eventually, students will adopt a similar strategy themselves, using partial measurements as an aid to making reasonable estimates.

Another opportunity for estimation is to have students use a measurement for one object to estimate the length of another object. For example, a student who knows that a doorway is 15 erasers wide can use this information to estimate the widths, in erasers, of other objects that are wider or narrower.

Using the measurement of one object to estimate another

Photos.com (Jupiter Images)

> The classroom door was 15 erasers wide. My backpack is about half as wide as the door, so it's probably about 7 or 8 erasers wide.

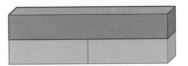

I dark green rod = 2 light green rods

Students can also measure in one unit, and then use the measurement to make an estimate involving another unit. For example, a student could use dark green Cuisenaire rods to measure a length, and then predict how many of the light green rods (which are half the length of the dark green rods) it would take to measure the same length. Initially, it is best to work with units that are simple multiples of each other, for example, units in a 1:2 or 1:3 or 1:4 ratio. These sorts of tasks help students see that as the unit size decreases, the number of units required to measure a length increases.

Nonstandard Unit Rulers

To help students make the transition to using a standard ruler, teachers can have them make their own nonstandard "rulers" by connecting uniform units, such as plastic links, linking cubes, paper clips, or foot tracings.

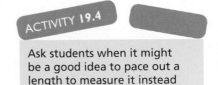

ACTIVITY 19.4

Ask students when it might be a good idea to pace out a length to measure it instead of using a "ruler."

_____

Critical Thinking

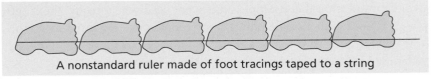

A nonstandard ruler made of foot tracings taped to a string

These "rulers" help students learn that the same tool can be used to measure many different things without having to actively iterate.

Nonstandard Units and Scale Drawings

The topic of scale drawings bridges the geometry and measurement strands because it deals with shapes as well as with measuring lengths (and sometimes angles). Although students do most of their work with scale drawings in Grades 6 or 7 and beyond, younger students work with maps (which are fundamentally scale drawings), and may also explore enlargements and reductions in the context of geometry activities or in art.

Although, typically, scale drawings are introduced once students use standard units—for example, letting 1 cm represent 1 m—the notion of scale can be very effectively introduced using nonstandard units. You can invite young students to choose two nonstandard units—one small and one large. Students could use the larger unit to measure the dimensions of a fairly large object or space, and then make a scale drawing by using one small unit to represent each large unit in the measurement.

Length: The Standard Unit Stage

Students can be introduced to standard units when they realize that, rather than measuring lengths in nonstandard units, which can mean different things to different people, they can use standard units that everyone will understand.

Introducing Standard Units of Length

Standard units are best introduced in a context that helps students see their value and efficiency. For example, a teacher might

- read a story such as *How Big Is a Foot?* by Rolf Myller (1991), which describes the confusion that ensues when a king uses his own foot to measure the dimensions for the queen's new bed
- use an everyday classroom measurement situation to illustrate how confusion can result from using nonstandard units to describe lengths, for example, by asking each of two students to cut a piece of string that is 5 shoes long, and then comparing the results

Learning about Metric Units of Length

CENTIMETRES (cm)

Introducing the Centimetre

Measuring with centimetre cubes provides a bridge from non-standard units to standard units. These "act like" nonstandard units because students can physically line up cubes along the distance to be measured, or perhaps even link them, but the measurement can be reported in a standard unit—centimetres. Whether metres or centimetres are introduced first, students should have the experience of seeing 100 centimetre cubes lined up along a metre stick.

Introducing Centimetre Rulers

It is important to begin with a ruler that will not confuse students. Primary rulers with alternating coloured stripes work well, or students can use rulers that show only numbered centimetres, and not inches or millimetres. Some primary rulers have both (as shown below).

Lining up centimetre cubes along the ruler helps students see that the stripes or numbers correspond to the number of centimetre cubes that can fit along the same distance.

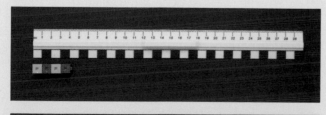

A length of 4 cm is the distance between 0 cm and 4 cm on the ruler. It is not just about the 4 cm mark on the ruler where the length ends.

METRES (m)

Introducing the Metre

Many students are already familiar with the metre stick and will quickly be able to develop a personal sense of the length of a metre. Some teachers find that this personal sense develops more quickly if students make their own tools for measuring 1 m. These might include lengths of string or strips of Bristol board. They can use these "tools" to find objects in their environment that are about a metre long, less than a metre long, and longer than a metre. These tools let them focus on the metre as a unit instead of being distracted by the centimetre or millimetre markings that are usually found on metre sticks.

Tools for Measuring in Metres

To measure lengths in metres, students can use multiple metre sticks (or measuring tapes), or they can iterate the metre stick (or tape). Measuring tapes are particularly handy for measuring lengths that are not straight lines.

Trundle wheels are good for measuring longer distances in metres. A trundle wheel has a wheel circumference of 1 m, usually marked off in centimetres. As the wheel turns, it makes a click for each metre travelled. Because metre sticks, measuring tapes, and trundle wheels usually have centimetre markings, they can also be used to measure somewhat more precisely; for example, the room is 10 m and 17 cm long.

(continued)

CENTIMETRES (CONTINUED)

When students begin using rulers with numbers, they need to be taught to line up the 0 mark with one end of the object. This can be difficult if the 0 mark is implicit (as on the ruler shown on page 477), or if the label is not right at the edge of the ruler.

Once students are comfortable using a ruler, the following situations can be introduced gradually:

- the length of an object falls between two centimetre markings (Students initially round to the nearest centimetre. Later, they use millimetres to measure more precisely.)

- the length is greater than 30 cm (The ruler is used more than once—or multiple rulers are used—and the results are added.)

- the distance to be measured is not a straight line (Students measure indirectly with string, or they use a measuring tape or add the lengths of pieces.)

- the ruler is "broken" and doesn't start at 0 (Students determine the difference between two lengths by measuring from one number on the ruler to another, for example, measuring from 3 cm to 8 cm.)

KILOMETRES (km)

Introducing the Kilometre

Measuring with a trundle wheel is a good way to introduce the concept of the kilometre. Too often, students are introduced to kilometres in a fairly abstract way—the distance you can walk in 12 minutes, or the distance between the school and the park. Students can gain a more concrete and personal understanding of the size of a kilometre if they actually use a trundle wheel and go for a 1-km walk, counting out 1000 turns of the wheel.

Another option is to measure a 100-m running track with a 10-m piece of rope, and then run the track 10 times.

DECIMETRE (dm)

Introducing the Decimetre

Because a decimetre is in between a centimetre (1 dm = 10 cm) and a metre (1 dm = 0.1 m), it is a handy unit for measuring objects when the centimetre might be too small and the metre too big. As well, the base ten rod, used for place value work, is exactly 1 dm long and can serve as a referent for developing a sense of the length of a decimetre and for estimation. (The rod can also be used to measure objects in decimetres in the same way that centimetre cubes can be used to measure objects in centimetres.) However, the decimetre has never caught on and many teachers choose not to introduce it.

Another reason for introducing the decimetre is the place value aspect of measurement—it sets up a pattern students will later see extended when they learn about millimetres.

Metre	Decimetre	Centimetre	Millimetre
1 m	0.1 m	0.01 m	0.001 m

Tools for Measuring in Decimetres

Decimetre rods are good tools to use to show the relationship between decimetres and centimetres.

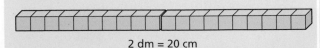

2 dm = 20 cm

Another useful tool is a metre stick with 10-cm increments marked off in alternating colours to show their relationship to the metre.

MILLIMETRES (mm)

Introducing the Millimetre

The time to introduce millimetres is after students have had a lot of experience using centimetres and when a particular measurement falls between two numbers on the centimetre ruler.

Millimetres become necessary when a measurement falls between two numbers on a centimetre ruler.

Introducing Rulers Marked with Millimetres

Introduce rulers marked with millimetres when students are ready to deal with the abstraction of working with tick marks on a ruler, rather than needing the numbers on the ruler to define each mark. Students can look at the millimetre markings to see that there are 10 millimetres in 1 centimetre.

A ruler marked in millimetres

Some students may be able to measure in millimetres, if properly instructed, before they actually realize that the purpose of using millimetres is to gain required precision in a measurement situation. At some point, students should have an opportunity to think about how many millimetres make up a metre. To do this, they will need to visualize (or see on a metre stick) 100 cm, with 10 mm making up each centimetre, so there are 1000 mm in all.

There are differing perspectives about which metric unit, centimetres or metres, to introduce first. Some believe that the metre should come first, not only because it is a base unit, but also because measuring in metres results in fewer errors due to problems with fine motor coordination. On the other hand, it may be more convenient for the teacher if all students in a class can work on measurement activities at the same time, and this usually necessitates measuring smaller items using the smaller centimetre unit.

Referents for Estimating Standard Units

Referents are familiar objects of particular lengths that students can use to help them estimate. For example, a centimetre is about the width of a baby finger, a decimetre is a bit shorter than a craft stick, and a metre is about the height from the floor to a doorknob. Eventually, many of these referents are internalized so that students can call upon visual images of them when estimating.

Many educators advocate the use of referents that are personally meaningful, since these are easier for students to remember and eventually internalize or visualize. For example, the student who wrote the response below has used the familiar height of a 3-m diving board to visualize a length of 4 m and compare it to 1 km.

To encourage students to develop referents, teachers can use activities such as the one in **Activity 19.5**.

> **ACTIVITY 19.5**
>
> Ask students to find something that is about 1 dm long. Then, cover it up.
>
> • Have them use a mental picture of the object to cut a length of yarn that is as close to 4 dm long as possible by imagining four of those lengths.
>
> • Have them compare the length of yarn to the object to see how close they were.
>
> ───────────
>
> **Spatial Reasoning**

Chris told Ben he walked 4 kilometres to school. Suppose Chris had told Ben the distance using metres instead of kilometres.

a) Which of these statements is true?

Circle one: ⟨The distance would be more than 4 metres.⟩
The distance would be less than 4 metres.

b) Explain your thinking.

> Because a diving board at the pool is 3 metres high but a kilometre would be way higher than the roof.

Student Response

This student has used a personal referent—the height of a familiar diving board—to estimate how long 4 metres would be in comparison to 1 kilometre.

Renaming Measurements

Part of learning about metric units is learning about the relationships between one unit and another. For example, students need to know that there are 100 centimetres or 10 decimetres in a metre, and 1000 metres in a kilometre. Once students have learned these relationships, they will be able to express a measurement in more than one way. For example, they will understand that 300 cm is another name for 3 m, or that 21.6 cm could also be written as 216 mm.

The ability to rename measurements is useful for
• expressing units in a form that is easier to visualize; for example, a measure of 1.1 m is easier to visualize than 110 cm because it is readily apparent that it is just a little longer than 1 m

- comparing measurements; for example, if two heights are reported in centimetres and metres, respectively, it is easier to compare them if one is renamed
- calculating with measurement formulas; for example, if a rectangle's dimensions are reported in decimetres and centimetres, one of the dimensions has to be renamed to use the area formula
- working with scale; for example, if a map uses 1 cm to represent 1 km, the student needs to rename 1 km as 100 000 cm in order to understand that the map scale is actually 100 000:1

Measuring with More Precision

Once students have a range of standard units at their disposal, they need to learn how to choose an appropriate unit (or combination of units) for the task at hand. This choice depends on

- the magnitude of the length to be measured
- the level of precision required by the task

Some students believe that you use very small units only when you want to measure very small things. It is important for students to understand that you can also use small units to help you measure large things if you want the measurement to be more precise.

Students who are measuring in metres will soon find that by combining metres with centimetres, they can measure more precisely. For example, young students who are not yet renaming units can use a combined measurement such as 5 m and 10 cm to give a more precise record of the length of a piece of playground equipment than a rounded measurement of 5 m. (Note that combining measurements also helps people get a better idea of a length. The measurement 510 cm may be equivalent to 5 m and 10 cm, but it is easier to visualize the combined measurement of "5 m and 10 cm more" than it is to visualize "510 cm.")

The need for precision has a bearing on when new units are introduced. For example, if metres are introduced first to students, centimetres can be introduced by setting up a situation where a measurement falls between metres and a more precise measurement is required. The requirement should be such that simply rounding to the nearest metre or using estimation language, for example, "between 2 m and 3 m," will not be sufficient.

There is a mathematical convention associated with precision that older students will eventually need to understand. The way a measurement is recorded indicates the level of precision that was used in measuring. For example, if you record a measurement of 3 cm, this indicates that the measurement has been measured and rounded to the nearest centimetre, and could be anywhere between 2.5 cm and 3.5 cm. However, if you record 3.0 cm, then the distance has been measured and rounded to the nearest millimetre, and could be anywhere between 2.95 and 3.05 cm. As a result, a recorded measurement of 3.0 cm is considered to be more precise than a recorded measurement of 3 cm.

To understand the importance of precision, students need to encounter situations where it is important to measure very accurately. There are opportunities in many subject areas, such as art and science, where students need to measure carefully and precisely with small units. Hobbies such as sewing and woodworking can also provide such contexts.

> **TEACHING TIP**
>
> As students become more sophisticated with length measurement, they might use dynamic geometry software such as The Geometer's Sketchpad to help them discover length relationships. The software will automatically measure highlighted lengths.

Measuring Perimeter

Although measuring perimeter is often perceived to be distinct from linear measurement, it is really only a variation in which students measure a linear distance that is not a straight line. The perimeter of an object can be reported using either nonstandard or standard units, depending on how the side lengths are reported. It also can be determined in different ways.

Ways to Measure Perimeter

PERIMETER: MEASURING INDIRECTLY

Initially, students will learn to measure the perimeter of a shape by fitting a string around the shape, cutting it to that length, and then measuring the length of the string. Initially, students may find it more comfortable to refer to the perimeter as the "distance around" the shape, rather than using the more formal term. Measuring perimeter indirectly with a string helps students see that perimeter.

PERIMETER: MEASURING AND ADDING SIDE LENGTHS

Later, students will measure each side of a shape individually and add the side lengths to calculate the perimeter.

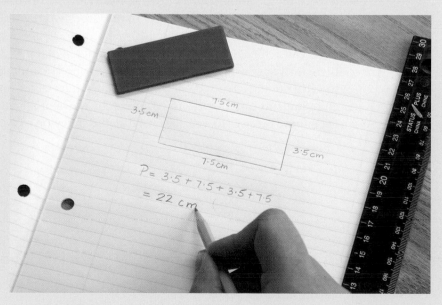

(*continued*)

Ways to Measure Perimeter (Continued)

PERIMETER: MEASURING AND USING A FORMULA

Using addition to calculate perimeters will inevitably lead to the discovery that there are "shortcuts" for calculating the perimeter of shapes with some equal sides, such as rectangles, squares, equilateral triangles, and parallelograms. These shortcuts lead to formulas. One of the key concepts in measurement is the notion that formulas simplify the determination of some measures.

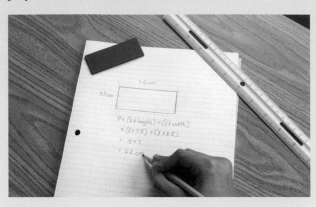

Perimeter of a Circle (Circumference)

The perimeter of a circle is called its *circumference*. The topic of circumference is usually dealt with in Grade 6 and up, although younger students are certainly capable of understanding the notion of measuring around curves.

When the concept of circumference is first introduced, students generally experiment with string or measuring tapes and a variety of circle sizes to discover that the distance around any circle is always about triple the distance across the circle through its centre (the *diameter*). This presents an opportunity to introduce the concept of π (pi). The circumference is actually π, or $3.1415926\ldots$ times the length of the diameter. (If students use a circle with a diameter of 10 cm, they can derive π by dividing the circumference by 10.) Some sources say that this value is named π because, in the Greek alphabet, π is the first letter of the Greek word for perimeter.

It is difficult to be accurate when measuring around a circle unless the circle can actually be cut and straightened out. Therefore, it is helpful that there is a relationship between the diameter and circumference to allow us to calculate the circumference of a circle from its easier-to-measure diameter. Students can multiply the diameter by the approximation 3.14. Or, to get a more precise answer, they can use the π key on a calculator.

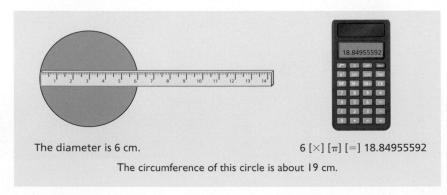

The diameter is 6 cm.   6 [×] [π] [=] 18.84955592

The circumference of this circle is about 19 cm.

Common Errors and Misconceptions

Length and Perimeter: Common Errors, Misconceptions, and Strategies

COMMON ERROR OR MISCONCEPTION	SUGGESTED STRATEGY
Not Allowing for Hidden Parts Some students at the definition/comparison stage may think that when one length is partly hidden and another is not, the item they can see more of must be longer. For example, some students may think the first stick shown here is longer because they can see all of it. In fact, both lengths are the same.  "The top stick is the longest."	Show two objects that are the same length, and allow students to see that they are equal. Then hide part of one object behind a container and ask which is longer now. Move the container and ask again. Talk about whether students think the length of the object has changed while it was behind the container. (The belief that the length of the object has somehow changed indicates that students cannot yet conserve length.)
Comparing Lengths That Do Not Align Some students at the definition/comparison stage may try to compare lengths without aligning the objects first. These students will often think that length is determined by where an object ends, rather than by the distance from start to end. For example, a student may believe that the lower stick shown here is longer because it sticks out farther.  "The bottom stick is the longest."	Show two sticks so they are not aligned at one end. Ask which stick is longer. Then move the bottom stick to the left to line up with the top stick and ask again. Talk about whether the student thinks the length of the stick changed when it was moved.
Measuring Curved and Zigzag Lengths Some students at the definition/comparison stage may not take curves or zigzags into account when deciding which of two lengths is longer. For example, a student may believe the green piece of yarn is longer because it extends farther from left to right.  "The green yarn must be longer. It sticks out more."	Show a curved piece of yarn and a straight piece that is shorter, but that extends farther. Ask which piece of yarn is longer. Then straighten the curved piece and ask again. Ask whether the student thinks the amount of yarn has changed, and discuss why the piece that looked shorter before looks longer now. *(continued)*

Length and Perimeter: Common Errors, Misconceptions, and Strategies (Continued)

COMMON ERROR OR MISCONCEPTION	SUGGESTED STRATEGY
Problems with Iteration When students first begin to measure lengths by moving a single nonstandard unit along the distance, they may find it difficult to keep track of where one iteration of a unit ends and the next one begins. This results in gaps or overlap between units and, therefore, incorrect measurement.	Teachers should model how to iterate correctly by using a finger or thin stick to mark the end of each unit to help position the next unit. Students also need opportunities to see that, if they do not begin each new unit where the old one ended, they might get a different measurement each time they measure the same object. This will become evident if the teacher asks them to measure the same object twice and the results are different. A strategy for helping students learn to iterate correctly is imprinting the units in a strip of modelling clay or letting them use two units initially (see *Learning to Iterate* on page 475).
Ruler Placement When students first learn to use a centimetre ruler, some will mistakenly begin measuring from points other than the 0-cm mark without subtracting the initial value. Beginning partway along the ruler can indicate that the student has not yet learned that the measurement represents the whole length of the object, from where it begins to where it ends, rather than just the endpoint. Beginning from the 1-cm mark may indicate that the student does not realize that the scale on the ruler actually begins at 0 cm, or simply that the student assumes you always start at 1. This problem often occurs if the 0-cm end is not labelled. As well, students sometimes begin from the opposite end of the ruler, rather than from 0. 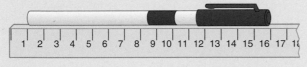 "The pen is 16 cm long."	To help students who begin measuring from the wrong location along the ruler, a teacher might move the item to a new position along the ruler and ask if the student believes that the item actually got shorter (or longer) now that the end-point is a lesser (or greater) number. If the problem is that the student is unaware of the 0-cm mark, it is useful to line up centimetre cubes along the ruler to show that one cube reaches from 0 cm to 1 cm, two cubes stretch from 0 cm to 2 cm, etc.  "Four cubes reach from 0 cm to 4 cm." (Note that some students intentionally measure from points other than 0 cm, but know to subtract the initial value. This shows a real comfort with using a ruler.)
Renaming Units A common misconception about metric units is that all smaller units relate to larger ones in the same way. It is especially common for students to believe that there are always 100 smaller units in a larger unit, possibly because the first relationship they learn is that 1 m = 100 cm, and this idea stays with them. For example, a student might say that there must be 100 mm in a metre, 100 g in a kilogram, or 100 mL in a litre.	The time to dispel this misconception is when new units are being introduced. For example, when students are ready to begin using millimetres, the teacher can use a metre stick with millimetre markings to point out that there are far more millimetres in a metre than there are centimetres. It would also be helpful to post a chart so students can check relationships they are not sure of.
Using Small Units Some students think that you use small units only to measure small items. This is not surprising since it is efficient to use a larger unit to measure a longer item. However, if you want to be more precise, you need to supplement your use of a large unit with the use of a small unit.	Ask students to use metre-long sticks or lengths of string to compare two lengths that cannot be compared directly and that are both between, for example, 3 m and 4 m. Students will see that just using metres does not allow them to make the comparison. Encourage them to finish the task by using a ruler or metre stick to measure the part of the distance that exceeds the last whole metre.

COMMON ERROR OR MISCONCEPTION	SUGGESTED STRATEGY
Distinguishing between Units	If a student reports that an item is, for example, 5 cm long rather than 3 cm and 2 mm, provide a centimetre ruler and ask the student to point to the 5-cm mark on the ruler. Then have the student re-measure the length of the object to see that it is not 5 cm.
When students begin to measure with precision, for example, measuring a distance in centimetres and then combining it with millimetres (see *Measuring with More Precision* on page 480), they sometimes do not distinguish the units when reporting the measurement. For example, a student might measure a distance of 3 cm and 2 mm and report it as 5 cm because he or she counted on from 3 cm: "1, 2, 3, ..., 4, 5."	Discuss a parallel situation with larger units. For example, an item that is 3 m and 2 cm long is just barely over 3 m long, while an item that is 5 m long is quite a bit longer than 3 m.

Describing Any Part of a Unit as a Half

Some students have trouble reporting measurements that fall between two units on a ruler. For example, they might report both measurements below as "7 and a half centimetres" because they use the term "half" in an informal way to include anything that is not whole.

Ensure students understand that the term "half" has a unique meaning and is the point halfway between two points on a ruler. Have students mark the halfway point between pairs of centimetre markings on a ruler or metre stick. When they measure, encourage them to discuss whether the partial unit at the end of a measurement represents more or less than half of the unit.

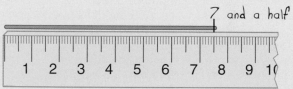

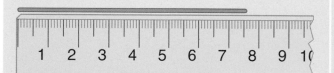

A student might say that both lines are 7 and a half centimetres long.

"Neither line is 7 and a half centimetres long—one's a bit less and the other's a bit more than 7 and a half centimetres."

Implicit Information in a Diagram

When some of the measurements in a diagram are labelled and others are not, students sometimes forget to include the measures of the unlabelled sides in calculating the perimeter.

Before students begin to calculate the perimeter, encourage them to label any side lengths that do not already have labels. Discuss why these labels were not originally provided on the diagram (you can tell what the lengths are just by looking, because they are equal to other lengths in the shape). Emphasize that the perimeter is the entire distance around the shape.

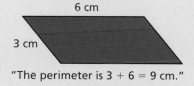

"The perimeter is 3 + 6 = 9 cm."

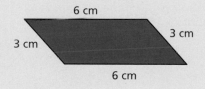

Appropriate Manipulatives

Length and Perimeter: Examples of Manipulatives

STRING, YARN, OR ROPE	EXAMPLE

String, yarn, and rope are handy tools for many measurement purposes. Students can simply measure pieces that have been cut to different lengths, or they can use these as tools for measuring other lengths. For example, a string that is exactly 1 m long can be used to measure distances in metres. String, yarn, and rope are also useful for measuring distances that are not straight lines, such as curved lines or perimeters, and for comparing lengths in-directly. (See *Direct and Indirect Comparison* on page 473.)

A string is useful for comparing lengths or for measuring distances that cannot easily be measured directly with a ruler or metre stick.

Students can create their own 1-m tool from string to find objects that are less than a metre, about a metre, and greater than a metre around.

NONSTANDARD UNITS	EXAMPLE

Nonstandard units are everyday objects that can be used to measure lengths. These should come in uniform sets, and, ideally, should have or combine to have a long, thin shape. Students will need some longer and shorter units, since different units are suitable for measuring different distances. Good items to have on hand include toothpicks, straws, paper clips, unsharpened pencils, crayons, markers, plastic links, craft sticks (Popsicle sticks), and linking cubes.

A child might connect plastic links or paper clips to create a nonstandard unit measuring tool (see *Nonstandard Unit Rulers* on page 476). Students should be aware that using links and paper clips in this way, as opposed to lining them up end to end, may result in slightly different measurements because of the overlap between units.

CENTIMETRE CUBES OR SQUARES	EXAMPLE

Centimetre cubes are not easy for young students to work with because they are so small. However, centimetre cubes that link together are useful for helping students make the transition between measuring with nonstandard units and measuring with a centimetre ruler (see *Centimetres* on page 477). An alternative is to use a strip of centimetre squares cut from a centimetre grid.

Centimetre cubes or squares can be used to create early centimetre "rulers" to introduce the centimetre as a standard unit and introduce the standard centimetre ruler. Students can place their rulers beside standard rulers to see that each marking on the ruler represents 1 cm.

A centimetre cube ruler helps with the transition from nonstandard units to standard units.

CUISENAIRE RODS

Cuisenaire rods (sometimes called "counting rods") come in lengths ranging from 1 cm to 10 cm. Each length is colour-coded. They can be used as nonstandard units or to measure in centimetres.

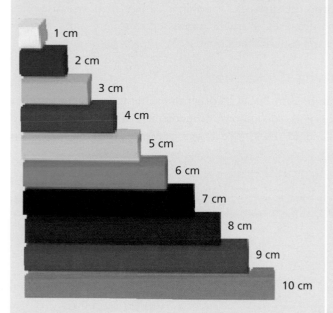

1 cm
2 cm
3 cm
4 cm
5 cm
6 cm
7 cm
8 cm
9 cm
10 cm

EXAMPLE

"This toy fire truck ladder is 4 yellow rods long."

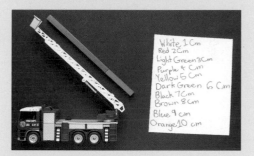

White 1 Cm
Red 2 Cm
Light Green 3 Cm
Purple 4 Cm
Yellow 5 Cm
Dark Green 6 Cm
Black 7 Cm
Brown 8 Cm
Blue 9 cm
Orange 10 cm

"Pink is 4 cm, orange is 10 cm, and green is 6 cm, so the fire truck ladder is 20 cm long."

BASE TEN BLOCKS

Unit cubes from a set of base ten blocks are exactly 1 cm long, and 10-rods are exactly 10 cm long. Because the rods have unit markings along their length, they can be used to measure lengths in centimetres as well as in decimetres.

EXAMPLE

By combining 10-rods and unit cubes, students can measure lengths to the nearest centimetre.

"My footstep is 1 dm and 6 cm long. That's 16 cm."

STANDARD UNIT MEASURING TOOLS

After students are introduced to standard units, they are ready to begin measuring with standard measurement tools, such as rulers, metre sticks, measuring tapes, and trundle wheels. Initially, students should use tools without millimetre markings. Tools with millimetre markings are introduced when students are ready to measure more precisely. (See *Learning about Metric Units of Length* on pages 477.)

EXAMPLE

Measuring tapes are useful tools for measuring distances that do not follow a straight line. Trundle wheels are useful for measuring long distances.

Measuring Area

While length describes a one-dimensional attribute of a shape, *area* describes a two-dimensional attribute—the amount of two-dimensional (flat) space that a shape covers or, in the case of a 3-D shape, the amount of flat space that forms the surface of the shape (*surface area*). Because of its two-dimensional nature, area is usually expressed in square units, such as square centimetres and square metres.

Introducing Area Concepts

Ideas about area can be introduced through the same three stages as other measurement concepts—definition/comparison, using nonstandard units, and using standard units. (See *Stages of Measurement Instruction* on pages 468–470.)

How Concepts of Area Can Be Introduced

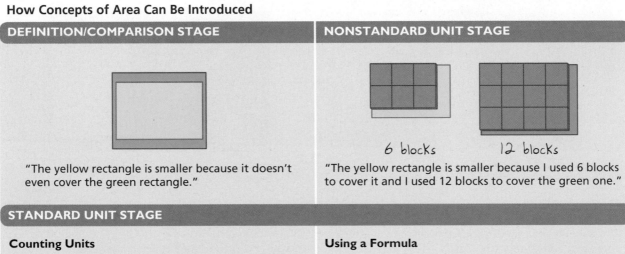

DEFINITION/COMPARISON STAGE

"The yellow rectangle is smaller because it doesn't even cover the green rectangle."

NONSTANDARD UNIT STAGE

6 blocks   12 blocks

"The yellow rectangle is smaller because I used 6 blocks to cover it and I used 12 blocks to cover the green one."

STANDARD UNIT STAGE

Counting Units

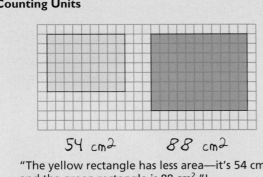

54 cm²   88 cm²

"The yellow rectangle has less area—it's 54 cm² and the green rectangle is 88 cm²."I

Using a Formula

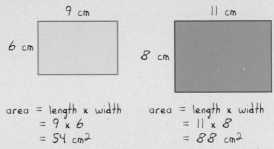

9 cm   6 cm   11 cm   8 cm

area = length × width
     = 9 × 6
     = 54 cm²

area = length × width
     = 11 × 8
     = 88 cm²

"The yellow rectangle has less area—it's 54 cm² and the green rectangle is 88 cm²."

Area: The Definition/Comparison Stage

At this stage, students explore the notion that one item has more area than another if you can cover one shape with the other and there is still some part that is uncovered.

Sometimes, one shape does not fit completely on top of the other. When this happens, students may find they need to dissect one of the shapes in order to make a direct comparison. In the example shown at the top of the next page, a student tried unsuccessfully to fit the orange rectangle over the blue one, and eventually discovered that cutting the orange rectangle in half made it easier to see that the blue rectangle was larger.

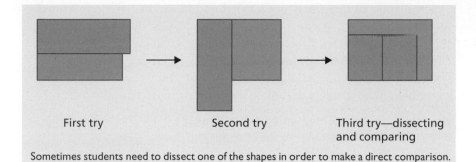

First try   Second try   Third try—dissecting
and comparing

Sometimes students need to dissect one of the shapes in order to make a direct comparison.

In order for students to use this dissection method, they need to understand that the area of a shape does not change when it is dissected, as long as no parts are removed. This understanding is called *conservation of area*, and develops at different times in different students.

One possible activity for students at the Definition/Comparison stage is described in **Activity 19.6**. Others might include

- tracing their shoeprints and comparing areas with other students
- tracing faces of different-sized boxes and ordering the tracings
- using a computer drawing program to create two different rectangles that look similar in size, and then printing the rectangles and comparing to see which one is larger

Area: The Nonstandard Unit Stage

Because it is often quite difficult to compare the areas of two shapes unless one fits completely on top of the other, students move quickly to the notion of covering each shape with the same nonstandard units to decide which of two shapes covers more area.

Appropriate Nonstandard Units for Area

Nonstandard area units are simply handy everyday items of uniform size that can be used to tile a surface. These include sheets of paper or newsprint (to cover big areas), pattern blocks, square tiles, attribute blocks, and ink stamps.

One possible activity for students at the nonstandard unit stage is described in **Activity 19.7**.

Other activities might include

- using sheets of newspaper to compare the areas of two bulletin boards or windows
- using nonstandard units to determine the areas of different shapes that can be outlined with the same piece of yarn
- cutting a piece of wrapping paper that is the right size to wrap a gift, and then measuring the area of the paper with nonstandard units
- using a box to make a house for a mouse, and then writing a description of the house that includes the floor area, along with features of the home that a mouse might like
- making a paper shape that can be covered by exactly 100 items (100 pennies, 100 cubes, 100 seeds, 100 craft sticks, etc.)
- determining the area of a shape (in nonstandard units) in order to share it equally in two parts
- determining the greatest possible area that can be covered with a rolled-out piece of modelling clay

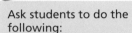

ACTIVITY 19.6

Ask students to do the following:

- Cut five pictures out of a magazine.
- Which picture covers the biggest area? How do you know?
- Put your five pictures in order from smallest area to largest area.

Spatial Reasoning

ACTIVITY 19.7

- Ask students to find an envelope that is big enough to hold a folded piece of letter-sized paper. (It does not matter how the paper is folded.)
- Have them take the envelope apart, flatten it, and use square tiles to measure the amount of paper that was used to make it.
- Ask them: Can you design a different envelope big enough to hold the folded pieces of paper that uses less paper to make?

Spatial Reasoning

From time to time, it is important for students to have opportunities to make choices about which unit to use to measure an area. These situations help students build their understanding of area concepts and provide concrete experience that will support them later when they move on to work with standard units. The examples that follow illustrate some of the area concepts that can be developed through work with various types of units.

Nonstandard Units: Developing Area Concepts

MEASURING WITH UNITS THAT DO NOT TILE

Students should measure area with units that do not tile—that is, that do not fit tightly together—only during introductory work with area, when they are exploring why some units work well for measuring area and others do not. When students use units that do not tile, they learn that much of the area is not counted in the measurement, and that different students can get different results for the same area, depending on how they arrange the units.

The area is about 10 pennies.

The area is about 9 pennies.

Remind students that they should not see any of the surface they are measuring if they have covered the whole area.

ESTIMATING

Even when units do tile, there are sometimes parts of a shape that cannot be covered with those units. Situations like these help students learn to combine estimating with measuring to get a better approximation of the area. Students need to estimate to add on parts of an area that cannot be covered with units.

"That's 24 whole squares and about $1\frac{1}{2}$ more, so the area is about $25\frac{1}{2}$ squares."

At other times, students subtract to compensate for units that extend beyond the shape being measured.

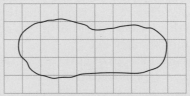

"There are 50 squares with about 29 not covered, so my shoe covers about 21 squares."

USING UNITS THAT TILE, BUT ARE NOT SQUARES

When students use units that tile, they learn that it is important to fit the units together with no spaces between them. Otherwise, there are large amounts of area that are not counted in the measurement.

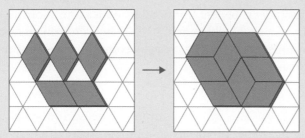

Working with non-square units helps students learn that squares are not the only shapes you can use to measure area.

Teacher: Here are some circles, some triangles, some squares, and some trapezoids. I want you to pick whichever shape you want and tell me how many shapes like that it takes to cover the envelope.

Student: I think I'll pick the circles. *(Covers the envelope.)* It took 18 circles to cover the envelope.

Teacher: Why did you pick the circles?

Student: Because I like circles.

Teacher: Did you cover the whole envelope or is part of it still showing?

Student: There's just a little showing—not very much.

Teacher: So is the area of the envelope 18 circles?

Student: Sort of, I guess.

Teacher: Do you think some of the envelope would still show if you covered it with squares?

Student: I'm not sure—I have to try.

Student Response

This student was not initially sensitive to the fact that circles do not fit together to cover an area completely; however, when presented with the issue of whether the whole envelope was covered, the student realized the problem.

Strategies for Measuring with Nonstandard Units

Students need to recognize that there is never just one way to measure an area. For example, to determine the area of an equilateral triangle, students at the nonstandard unit stage could do any of the following:

- cover the triangle with concrete units, such as triangle pattern blocks, and count how many units it takes to cover the triangle, estimating as necessary to account for regions not covered by the blocks
- place a transparent grid over the triangle and count how many full and how many partial grid squares fit within the shape
- place a transparent grid over the triangle, determine the area of a rectangle that encloses the triangle, and subtract any full or partial grid squares that are inside the rectangle but outside the triangle

Measuring the Same Area with Different Units

Students need to have opportunities to measure the same area with different units to help them discover that the area can be described in different ways. It will also help them discover that as the size of the unit increases, the number of units decreases. For example, an area that covers 49 squares on a centimetre grid could also be covered with only 8 square pattern blocks.

Experiences like this also help students discover that it is more efficient to use larger units to measure larger areas and smaller units to measure smaller areas.

Measuring Different Areas with the Same Unit

Not only do students benefit from opportunities to explore area by covering the same shape with different units, but they also benefit from using the same unit to measure different areas. A common unit is especially useful when the areas are to be compared, as illustrated in **Activity 19.8**.

Iteration and Area

As with length, students who are learning to measure areas with nonstandard units are most comfortable using multiple copies of a unit, such as a set of square tiles. However, there may be times when it is necessary or simply convenient to iterate by moving a single unit from one location to another. This may occur, for example, if there are not enough units to cover the entire space.

In order to measure area by iterating, students need to move the single unit both horizontally and vertically to cover a 2-D space. This task takes both physical and visual coordination, since students need to keep careful track of where one iteration of the unit ends and the next one starts, in two directions.

Initially, a student might use a transition such as the one suggested for length on page 475—leaving impressions of single units as they are iterated. For example, a student might use impressions from a cookie cutter to measure the area of a flat piece of modelling clay that has been placed over the area to be measured, or use an ink stamp, stickers, or stamps to measure an area outlined on paper. The advantage is that this will make it easier to see where to place the unit for each new iteration, and easier to keep track of the total number of units.

Covering an area with stickers prepares students for iterating with a unit.

Iterating a large area with a single area unit is more complicated than iterating to measure length because of the second dimension. Eventually, students will learn to use their knowledge of multiplication to simplify the task of iterating, as illustrated at the top of the next page.

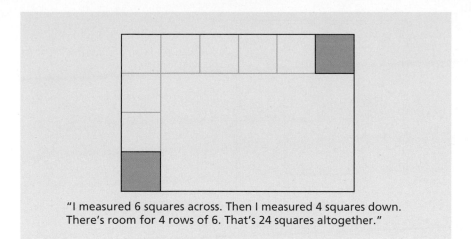

"I measured 6 squares across. Then I measured 4 squares down. There's room for 4 rows of 6. That's 24 squares altogether."

Measuring Area with a Transparent Grid

Just as a ruler provides a pictorial model for measuring length, a transparent grid provides a pictorial model for measuring area. The grid removes the need for students either to use many individual units or to face the daunting task of iterating the entire space.

A transparent grid can be placed on top of a shape, making it possible to count the number of grid units that are filled or partially filled by the shape. Like the ruler, the grid allows students to measure different shapes with the same tool. Although a transparent grid usually has square units, there are times when a triangular grid might also be used.

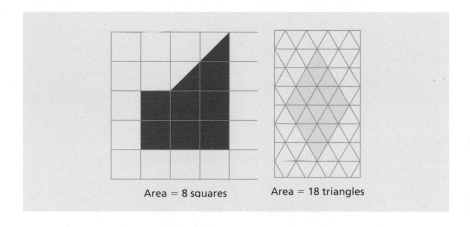

Area = 8 squares Area = 18 triangles

Measuring Area on a Geoboard

Geoboards, which are also grids, are useful for exploring areas measured in nonstandard units, as shown below and in **Activity 19.9**.

An interesting approach to calculating the areas of shapes on geoboards is to view the shapes as combinations of rectangles and "half-rectangles." For example, to calculate the area of the irregular trapezoid at the top of the next page, a student would

- look for the biggest rectangle they can inside the trapezoid
- calculate the area of this rectangle
- imagine a rectangle that encloses the rest of the trapezoid
- use this rectangle to determine the area of the rest of the trapezoid
- add these two areas

ACTIVITY 19.9

Ask students to use an elastic on a geoboard to create each shape described below. They can record their work on dot paper.

- a shape that touches 10 pins and has room for exactly 4 full squares of area inside

- a shape that touches 8 pins and has room for exactly 6 full squares of area inside

Write a description of a different shape someone could make following the same rules.

Spatial Reasoning

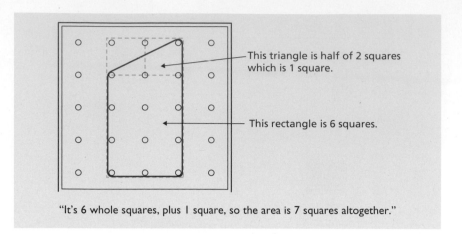

"It's 6 whole squares, plus I square, so the area is 7 squares altogether."

Estimating Areas in Nonstandard Units

Students must learn to estimate area measurements, as well as to measure them. To help students learn to estimate, teachers might provide situations in which a surface is partially measured; the student's task is to estimate how many units it will take to measure the full area. Eventually, students will adopt a similar strategy themselves, using partial measurements as an aid to making reasonable estimates.

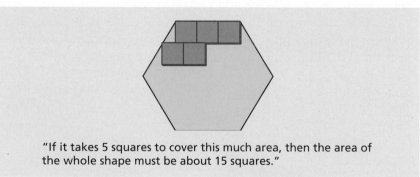

"If it takes 5 squares to cover this much area, then the area of the whole shape must be about 15 squares."

To help students build their understanding of units, it is important for them to have opportunities to measure in one unit, and then use that measurement to make an estimate involving another unit. An example activity is described in **Activity 19.10**.

Area: The Standard Unit Stage

Students can be introduced to standard units when they realize that, rather than measuring areas with nonstandard units, which can mean different things to different people, they can use units that everyone will understand.

Introducing Standard Units of Area

The first standard unit of area that students encounter is usually the square centimetre. They then move on to working with square metres, and finally square kilometres. There are also other standard units of area measure, such as the square millimetre and the square decimetre, but these are rarely used.

Although the standard units of area measure are often described in terms of squares with that area, students need to understand that these squares can be dissected and rearranged to form many different shapes, all representing the same area.

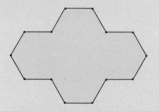

For example, a shape with an area of 1 square metre could be a square, but it could also be a triangle, a rectangle, or any other shape that covers the same area. A square metre (or centimetre or kilometre) has no defined shape—it is a measure of area and, as a result, is a somewhat abstract notion.

Standard Units of Area

SQUARE CENTIMETRE (cm²)

Defining a Square Centimetre

A square centimetre is an area equivalent to the area of a square with a side length of 1 cm.

Introducing the Square Centimetre

Initially square centimetres are introduced in a concrete way, using materials such as centimetre cubes (base ten units), and then pictorially, using centimetre grid paper and transparent centimetre grids. The cubes and grids provide a good transition from nonstandard units because students can simply cover a shape with cubes and count to measure the area without focusing on the fact that it is a standard unit. Larger areas can be measured using base ten flats, which cover 100 cm², or by combining flats, rods (10 cm²), and cubes.

Square Centimetre Referents

Students should develop personal referents for square centimetres to help develop a sense of the unit and also to help with estimating. For example, a fingernail or the tip of a baby finger might be a good referent for 1 cm². The palm of a child's hand might serve as a referent for 100 cm².

SQUARE KILOMETRE (km²)

Defining a Square Kilometre

A square kilometre is an area equivalent to the area of a square with a side length of 1 km.

Introducing the Square Kilometre

This unit is harder for students to get a sense of because of its size. It may be useful for them to associate it with a familiar place.

A square kilometre is about the size of Lakeview Park.

Getty Images/Leland Bobbe

SQUARE METRE (m²)

Defining a Square Metre

A square metre is an area equivalent to the area of a square with a side length of 1 m.

Introducing the Square Metre

The square metre can be modelled by arranging four metre sticks so that they form the side lengths of a square. The square metre is the area inside. A piece of newspaper or wrapping paper can be assembled to fit the space inside, and then can be used as a transportable square metre unit to locate objects in the room that are smaller than, about the same size as, or larger than 1 m².

Once students have had time to work with the model square metre, it is important for them to realize that the area can be rearranged into different shapes. Small groups can dissect and rearrange part of a square metre made out of paper to create different shapes, each with an area of 1 m². This will help students understand that a square metre has no defined shape—it is a measure of area and, as result, is a somewhat abstract notion.

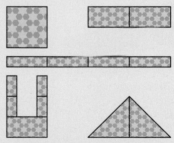

Shapes with an area of 1 m²

Square Metre Referents

Students might look for an object in their classroom that covers about 1 m² using any or all of the square metre shapes shown above, for example, about half of a small rug, or they might visualize a square metre as an area in which a certain number of students can comfortably stand.

ACTIVITY 19.11

Have students create designs with pattern blocks and measure the areas first in green pattern blocks, but then in square centimetres.

___

Proportional Reasoning

ACTIVITY 19.12

Ask students to create as many different shapes as they can on a grid with an area of 12 cm².

___

Spatial Reasoning

ACTIVITY 19.13

Ask students to determine the amount of gift wrap they use to cover a box.

___

Spatial Reasoning

ACTIVITY 19.14

Ask students to trace their handprints (with fingers held tightly together) onto a centimetre grid and then,

• use the grid to estimate the area of the handprint.

• compare their own area with other students' handprint areas.

Ask:

• *How would you describe a typical handprint area?*

• *What can you find that covers about the same area as your handprint?*

___

Proportional Reasoning

Recording Area Measures in Standard Units

It is important for students to realize that, when they begin to measure with standard units, they need to report measurements in *square units*. This is different from measuring in nonstandard units, where an area might be reported, for example, as 10 blue pattern blocks. Initially, the units should be spelled out, for example, "12 square metres."

Eventually, students will be ready to write the units in an abbreviated form using exponents. With standard units, the exponent 2 is used to indicate that the units have two dimensions. For example, if an area is 12 square centimetres, we write "12 cm²."

Using a Centimetre Grid

Centimetre grid paper and transparent centimetre grids are useful when students are first beginning to measure areas in square centimetres. For example, they might complete any of **Activities 19.11 to 19.14**.

Like geoboards, centimetre grids are especially useful for dealing with areas of irregular shapes. For example, to estimate the area of the irregular shape below, students might overlay a transparent centimetre grid, and then count the number of squares that are completely covered and the number of squares that are mostly covered. They add these together, and check to see if the squares with only a little covered seem to balance the missing parts in the squares that are mostly covered. They can then either increase or decrease their estimate appropriately.

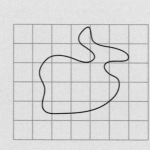

	5 squares are completely covered.
	5 squares are mostly covered.
	The extra little bits would fill up the missing bits in the 5 squares.
	The shape covers about 10 cm².

The area of an irregular shape is estimated by counting full and mostly full squares, and by making any necessary adjustments.

Formulas for Calculating Areas of Shapes

During K–8 instruction in math, students normally have an opportunity to develop and use formulas for determining the areas of rectangles, parallelograms, triangles, circles, and sometimes trapezoids.

All too often, formulas are seen as rote procedures for calculating a measurement such as volume. A formula actually describes the shape in terms of relationships among its component measurement attributes. The formula for calculating the area of a rectangle, for example, describes the area in terms of an array of squares:

Area = number of rows × number in each row, or
Area = length × width, or
Area = width × length.

Students who do not understand the nature of a formula may apply it to the wrong shape or measurement attribute without knowing why this is incorrect, for example, applying the rectangle formula to the side lengths of a parallelogram or confusing area with perimeter. As well, students who do not understand will have difficulty rearranging the formula to find something other than area, for example, using the area and length of a rectangle to calculate its width. The best way to help students understand and make sense of each formula is to let them play a role in developing the formula for themselves.

Area of a Rectangle

The first area formula introduced at the elementary level is usually the formula for calculating the area of a rectangle:

$$\textit{Area of a rectangle} = \textit{length} \times \textit{width, or } A = l \times w, \textit{ or } A = w \times l$$

Using an Array Model A good way to introduce the formula is to have students work with rectangles created with square tiles, so that the rectangles are basically arrays of squares. From earlier work with multiplication and the array meaning or model of multiplication, students will know that, to determine the total number of squares, you multiply the number of rows of squares by the number of squares in each row. In the consolidation discussion, the teacher might ask:

- What does the length of this rectangle tell you about the number of squares in the rectangle? (the number of rows of squares)
- What does the width tell you? (the number of squares in each row)
- What does the area tell you? (the number of squares altogether)
- If you could not see each square, how could you use just the length and width of a rectangle to figure out its area?

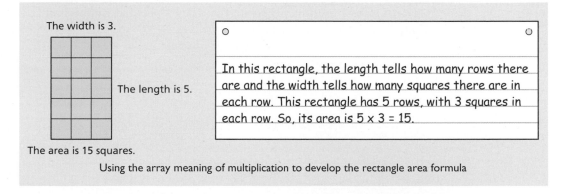

The width is 3.

The length is 5.

The area is 15 squares.

In this rectangle, the length tells how many rows there are and the width tells how many squares there are in each row. This rectangle has 5 rows, with 3 squares in each row. So, its area is 5 x 3 = 15.

Using the array meaning of multiplication to develop the rectangle area formula

Using Relationships Another way to introduce the formula is to have students create some different-sized rectangles on grid paper and determine the length, width, and area of each rectangle by counting grid spaces and grid square side lengths, recording the data in a table.

Rectangle	Length (cm)	Width (cm)	Area (cm²)
A	8	2	16
B	5	3	15
C	7	4	28

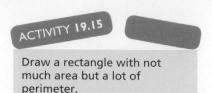

ACTIVITY 19.15

Draw a rectangle with not much area but a lot of perimeter.

Spatial Reasoning

Students can then look for relationships in the table among the length, width, and area, which will lead to the formula, *Area = length × width*. They might also notice that they can determine the length by dividing the area by the width, or the width by dividing the area by the length.

Because the formula for determining the area of a rectangle is usually introduced before any other area formulas, it is a common misconception that the formula *Area = length × width* can be applied to determine the area of shapes other than rectangles. When students develop the formula in a concrete way using arrays and using relationships, they are less likely to have this misconception.

Area of a Square

The formula for calculating the area of a square,

$$Area = side\ length \times side\ length\ (A = s \times s)$$

is a special case of the rectangle formula since *length × width* in this case is the same as *side length × side length*. Students can create different squares on grid paper and record data about the squares in a table such as that shown. They will soon realize that the area of a square is its side length multiplied by itself.

Area of a Parallelogram

Once students have a solid understanding of the rectangle formula, they are ready to learn that a related formula,

$$Area = base\ length \times height$$

can be used to calculate the area of a parallelogram. To explore this idea, the teacher can demonstrate that it is possible to transform a parallelogram into a rectangle with the same base length and height as the parallelogram by cutting a triangle from one side of the parallelogram and moving it to the opposite side, or by cutting to create two trapezoids that can be similarly rearranged.

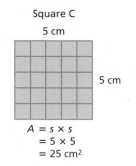

Square C

5 cm

5 cm

$$A = s \times s$$
$$= 5 \times 5$$
$$= 25\ cm^2$$

Square	Side length (cm)	Area (cm²)
A	8	64
B	7	49
C	5	25

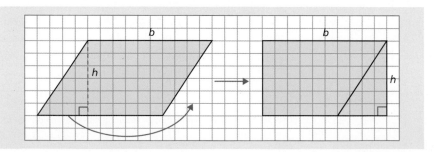

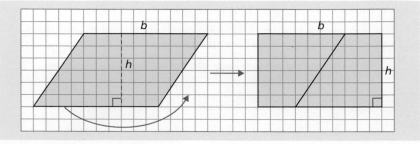

Students can then construct and cut out some other parallelograms and test them to see if they can all be transformed the same way. They may notice that the fact that the opposite sides of a parallelogram are equal is the reason why the triangle that is cut off on one side can be moved to the other side or the two trapezoids fit to make a rectangle. It is also important for students to recognize that

- the base that is cut remains the same length because the part removed from one end is added to the other end
- the height is measured at right angles to the base

For these reasons, the parts of a parallelogram can always be reassembled to form a rectangle with the same base length and height.

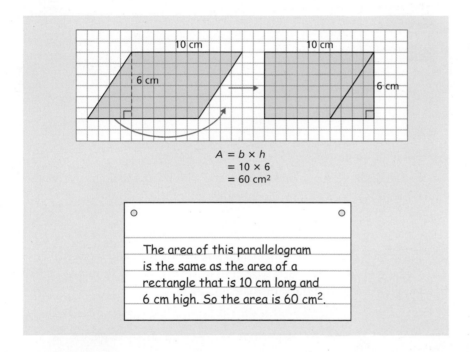

$A = b \times h$
$= 10 \times 6$
$= 60$ cm²

The area of this parallelogram
is the same as the area of a
rectangle that is 10 cm long and
6 cm high. So the area is 60 cm².

Some students will be interested to note that either side length of the parallelogram can be used as the base, and that they can measure the height from either inside or outside the boundaries of the parallelogram. As long as they measure the height from the side they are using as the base length, the formula will produce the correct area.

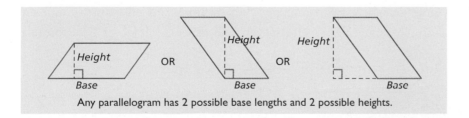

Any parallelogram has 2 possible base lengths and 2 possible heights.

An activity that will help students understand how the base length and height of a parallelogram relate to its area is described in **Activity 19.16**. This activity indirectly demonstrates the independence of perimeter and area—the perimeter remains the same as the area decreases.

ACTIVITY 19.16

Have students form a rectangle out of Geostrips or cardboard strips hinged together at the four vertices with butterfly clips or pipe cleaners. Each side should be a whole number of centimetres long. Ask them to place the rectangle on grid paper and record a sketch of the shape, the base length, the height, and the area.

Then have students adjust the rectangle to change the height several times to form a series of other parallelograms (with the base anchored on the same location on the grid paper each time). They can record the information about each shape in a table like the one shown here.

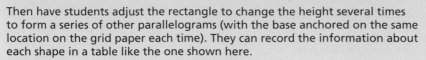

Sketch of shape	Base (cm)	Height (cm)	Area (cm²)
	8	5	40
	8	3	24

Algebraic Reasoning

Area of a Triangle

Once students have developed and worked with the parallelogram area formula, the next step is usually the introduction of the formula for determining the area of a triangle:

$$Area = base \times height \div 2$$

This formula is derived from the parallelogram formula and works because every triangle, no matter what type of triangle it is, can be shown to be half of a parallelogram with the same base and height.

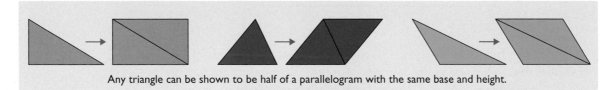

Any triangle can be shown to be half of a parallelogram with the same base and height.

The triangle formula can also be written as $Area = \frac{1}{2} \times base \times height$ or $Area = \frac{base \times height}{2}$, but it makes sense to use $Area = base \times height \div 2$ until students learn to multiply with fractions. Students can try different examples of specific triangles to eventually generalize to develop the formula.

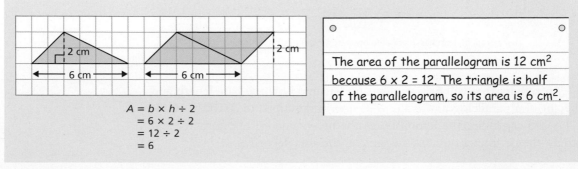

$$A = b \times h \div 2$$
$$= 6 \times 2 \div 2$$
$$= 12 \div 2$$
$$= 6$$

The area of the parallelogram is 12 cm² because 6 x 2 = 12. The triangle is half of the parallelogram, so its area is 6 cm².

The idea that two triangles with the same base and height must have the same area, even if they look different, is very difficult for some students to understand. This can be modelled on a geoboard, where base lengths and heights can be determined by counting horizontal and vertical units. For example, all three of the triangles below have the same base (3 units) and the same height (4 units), so they must also have the same area.

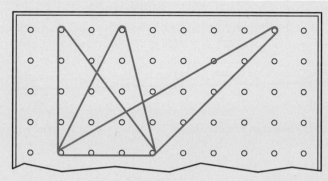

Each triangle has a base length of 3 units and a height of 4 units, so the area of each triangle is 3 × 4 ÷ 2 or 6 square units.

Areas of Other 2-D Shapes

AREA OF A TRAPEZOID

A trapezoid can always be viewed as half of a parallelogram. The height of the parallelogram is the same as the height of the trapezoid, and the base length of the parallelogram is equal to the sum of the two bases of the trapezoid. (On a trapezoid, the bases are considered to be the two parallel sides.)

 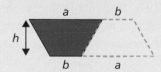

The area of the parallelogram is *base × height* or $(b + a) × h$, so the area of the trapezoid (which is half the parallelogram) is $(b + a) × h ÷ 2$.

The area of any trapezoid can be calculated using the formula

$$A = h × (a + b) ÷ 2$$

where h is the height of the trapezoid, and a and b are the lengths of the bases.

AREA OF A CIRCLE

A circle can be divided up into many sectors (pie slices) to help students see that these pieces can be formed into an "almost" parallelogram, where the height is the radius of the circle and the base is half the circumference of the circle. It is when the number of pieces is much greater that the top and bottom sides come much closer to being straight.

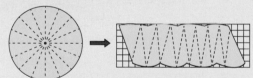

Sectors of a circle can be reformed into an "almost" parallelogram.

The area of the "almost" parallelogram is approximately *base × height* or, in this case, (*circumference ÷ 2*) × *radius*. If the students already know that the circumference is equal to 2 × π × *radius*, then they can simplify the formula to

$$A = π × radius × radius = πr^2.$$

Of course, this formula is based on ideas about limits which are generally only informally presented at this level.

Area of Irregular Shapes

To calculate areas of irregular shapes, students can apply area formulas for more familiar shapes drawn inside or outside the shape in question. For example, the student at the top of the next page recognized that square and triangle areas could be used to calculate the area of an irregular hexagon.

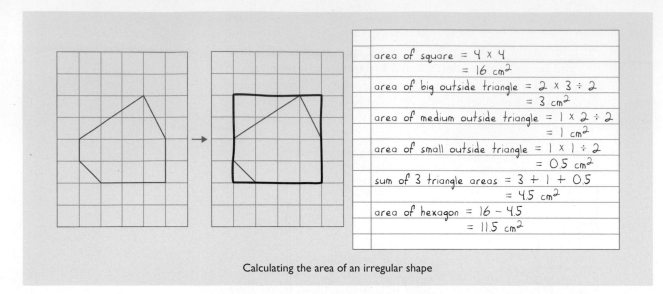

Calculating the area of an irregular shape

Area and Perimeter

Students are often surprised to find that shapes with the same area can have different perimeters, and that shapes with the same perimeter can have different areas.

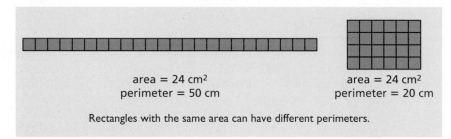

| area = 24 cm² | area = 24 cm² |
| perimeter = 50 cm | perimeter = 20 cm |

Rectangles with the same area can have different perimeters.

Exploring the perimeters of rectangles with the same area, as illustrated in **Activity 19.17**, can help students make an important discovery—the perimeter of a shape increases as the area is "stretched out" and decreases as the parts are "pushed together" or become more like a circle. The rectangle with the least perimeter for a given area is a square; the *shape* with the least possible perimeter for any given area is always a circle.

ACTIVITY 19.17

Students use 36 square tiles to make as many rectangles as they can. They work systematically, starting with a rectangle with a width of 1 unit, and record the data in a table such as that shown here:

Width (cm)	Length (cm)	Area (cm²)	Perimeter (cm)
1	36	36	74
2	18	36	40
3	12	36	30
4	9	36	26
6	6	36	24
9	4	36	26

Spatial Reasoning

Surface Area

Students in Grades 6 or 7 and up work with the surface areas of 3-D shapes, usually beginning with prisms, and then pyramids and other shapes. The surface area of a 3-D shape is the sum of the areas of all the faces.

Prisms with bases that are rectangles and triangles are introduced first, since students know how to calculate the areas of these shapes.

Surface Areas of Prisms

RECTANGLE-BASED PRISM

The rectangle-based prism below has 3 pairs of faces that are congruent rectangles. Nets provide an excellent model to work with when calculating the surface area of a 3-D shape.

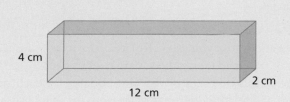

Area of rectangle A   = 12 × 2
                       = 24 cm²
Area of rectangle B   = 12 × 4
                       = 48 cm²
Area of rectangle C = 2 × 4
                       = 8 cm²
Total surface area   = (2 × A) + (2 × B) + (2 × C)
                       = (2 × 24) + (2 × 48) + (2 × 8)
                       = 48 + 96 + 16
                       = 160 cm²
The surface area is 160 cm².

The surface area of a square-based prism would be simpler to calculate as it is covered by 4 congruent lateral rectangle faces and 2 congruent square bases. A cube has the easiest surface area to calculate because it has 6 congruent square faces.

TRIANGLE-BASED PRISM

The triangle-based prism below has 2 faces that are congruent triangles and 3 faces that are rectangles. The net makes this easier to see.

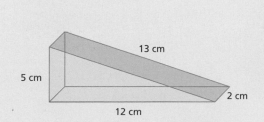

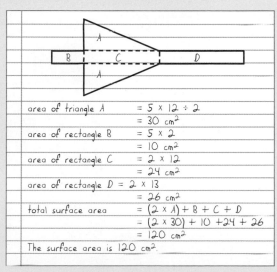

area of triangle A   = 5 × 12 ÷ 2
                       = 30 cm²
area of rectangle B   = 5 × 2
                       = 10 cm²
area of rectangle C   = 2 × 12
                       = 24 cm²
area of rectangle D = 2 × 13
                       = 26 cm²
total surface area   = (2 × A) + B + C + D
                       = (2 × 30) + 10 + 24 + 26
                       = 120 cm²
The surface area is 120 cm².

The surface area of an equilateral-triangle–based prism would be simpler to calculate as it is covered by 3 congruent lateral rectangle faces and 2 congruent equilateral triangle bases.

Pythagorean Theorem

Another formula that students meet in the middle or junior high grades is the Pythagorean theorem. It is interesting in that it involves both length and area.

Length

If the sides of a right triangle are a, b, and c, as below, the lengths of the sides have a certain relationship, specifically that $a^2 + b^2 = c^2$.

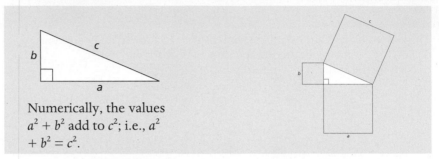

Numerically, the values $a^2 + b^2$ add to c^2; i.e., $a^2 + b^2 = c^2$.

For example, if $a = 3$ and $b = 4$, you can calculate c, the hypotenuse, or longest side, by adding $3^2 + 4^2$ and taking the square root to get 5.

Students make sense of this theorem by drawing squares on each side of various right triangles and relating the areas of the squares. But "proofs" of the theorem need to be more general and are based on decomposition of shapes. These proofs are accessible to many students (MARS, 2012).

Area

If you draw any group of 3 similar shapes on the sides of the triangles, not just squares, the green area + the blue area (the sum of the areas of the shapes on the legs) = the yellow area (the area of the shape on the hypotenuse).

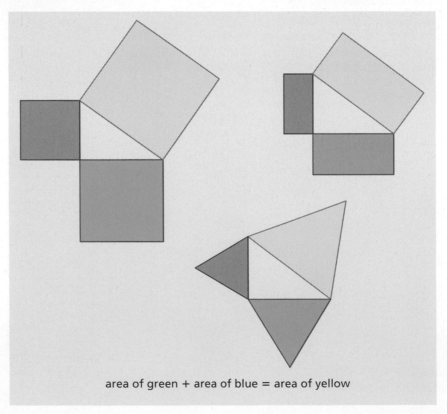

area of green + area of blue = area of yellow

Common Errors and Misconceptions

Area: Common Errors, Misconceptions, and Strategies

COMMON ERROR OR MISCONCEPTION	SUGGESTED STRATEGY
Confusing Length with Area Some students continue to focus on linear dimensions of an object to decide which has a greater area.  "I think the green rectangle is bigger."	Remind students that area tells how much flat space objects take up or how many units can cover the object. In the example shown to the left, students at the definition/comparison stage could compare by dissecting one of the shapes and rearranging the parts on top of the other shape. Students at the nonstandard unit stage could cover each shape with square tiles to see which shape has the greater area. 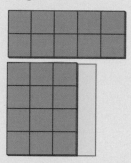 "It only takes 10 squares to cover the green rectangle but it takes more than 12 of the same size squares to cover the yellow shape."
Comparing with Different Units When students are using nonstandard units to compare areas, some may rely on number alone, without considering the size of the units. In the example below, the blue rectangle has a greater area but is covered by fewer but larger area units. 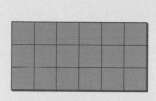 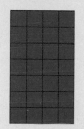 "The red one is bigger because it has 28 squares and the blue one only has 18 squares."	Make a rectangle that can be covered by two large squares. Cover it and ask students what the area is. After students indicate the area is 2 squares, cover the same space with 8 small squares (each one-fourth of the size of the large square). Ask for the area again. Discuss how the amount of space did not change, but the units did. The same space can be covered by many little squares or by fewer big ones. Now tell students that another shape is covered by 6 squares. Ask if it is bigger or smaller than the rectangle they just looked at. Help students to see that they can only tell which is larger if they know whether big squares or small squares were used. The shape is bigger if the area was 6 bigger squares, but smaller if it was 6 smaller squares.
Disregarding Spaces Many students place area units on a surface in a disorganized way, ignoring the fact that some parts of the surface are left uncovered. "I think the area is 3 squares."	To determine area, you need to figure out how many units it takes to cover a surface without any gaps. If there are parts that cannot be covered, you need to estimate those areas as well. For example, the uncovered area on the rectangle above is about $1\frac{1}{2}$ squares, bringing the total area to about $7\frac{1}{2}$ squares.

(continued)

Area: Common Errors, Misconceptions, and Strategies (Continued)

COMMON ERROR OR MISCONCEPTION	SUGGESTED STRATEGY

Dealing with Partial Grid Squares

Some students ignore partial squares altogether, while others describe the area of any partial square as one half. As a result, they consider the sum of the areas of any 2 partial squares to be 1 whole square.

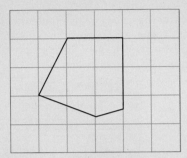

"There are 4 whole squares and 2 halves and 3 more halves. That's $6\frac{1}{2}$ altogether."

If students ignore partial squares, remind them that these are also part of the area and must be counted. If they count all partial squares as half squares, have them compare the areas of 2 rectangles like the ones below. They should recognize that the areas are different, so they can't both be $1\frac{1}{2}$ squares.

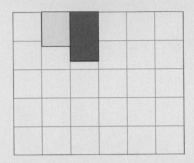

"The yellow shape is about $1\frac{1}{4}$ squares and the blue shape is more like $1\frac{3}{4}$ squares."

While combining parts to make whole squares is one counting strategy, there are also others. For example, students can visualize the partial squares inside rectangles. Below, the partial squares in the blue rectangle cover about half of 2 squares, or 1 full square. The parts in the red rectangle cover less than half of 3 squares, or about 1 square.

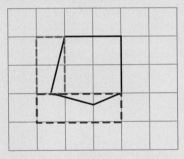

"There are 4 whole squares plus 1 whole square plus 1 more. That's about 6 squares."

Shape of a Square Metre or Square Centimetre

Many students assume that a square centimetre or a square metre has to be square-shaped. In fact, it simply has to cover the same area as the square.

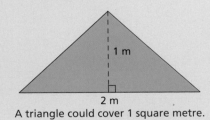

A triangle could cover 1 square metre.

A good way to introduce this idea is to use a tangram square. Have students cut out the pieces and rearrange them to form different shapes that use all 7 pieces. Ask, "Whose arrangement covers the most area?" Students should realize that the arrangements all cover the same area because they are all made from pieces of the same original square.

Point out that the same is true for a square metre (or square centimetre). Even if you cut the square into parts and rearrange the parts, they will still cover the same area as the original square.

COMMON ERROR OR MISCONCEPTION	SUGGESTED STRATEGY
Converting Square Metres to Square Centimetres Students, and even many adults, are surprised when they realize that 1 m² is not the same amount of space as 100 cm². People tend to assume that since there are 100 cm in 1 m, there must also be 100 cm² in 1 m².	To determine the number of square centimetres in a square metre, ask students to begin covering the square metre with centimetre cubes. They can start at the bottom and begin to cover the bottom row. They probably will not complete the row since it would take 100 cubes, but they can fill in enough to get an idea that 100 cm² is nowhere near enough to cover the whole square. This is because the sides of the square are 100 cm long, so the square is actually made up of 100 rows of 100 cm², or 10 000 cm² altogether.

Multiplying Length × Width for a Non-Rectangle Students might mistakenly apply the *length × width* formula to calculate the area of a shape that is not a rectangle. This error often occurs with parallelograms, especially when adjacent side lengths are labelled. 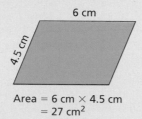 Area = 6 cm × 4.5 cm = 27 cm² This area has been calculated incorrectly.	Students need to understand that the *length × width* formula works for a rectangle because it describes how square units can be arranged in rows to cover it. 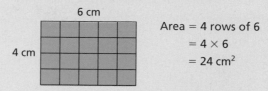 In the case of the parallelogram, students should be able to see that an array of squares will not match the shape of the area to be covered. However, if the parallelogram is changed by cutting a right triangle from one side and moving it to the other side, then the resulting rectangle *can* be covered with rows of squares. 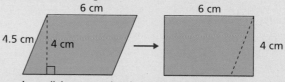 A parallelogram with side lengths 4.5 cm and 6 cm might have an area of 6 cm × 4 cm = 24 cm².

Not Recognizing the Need for Common Units Some students will calculate the area of the blue rectangle below as 70 cm² or as 70 m².  Errors often occur when different units are used.	Many times, students simply do not pay attention to the units, and need to be reminded about what the measurements mean. For example, you might ask, "How much area of the blue rectangle would 1 centimetre square cover? If I had 70 centimetre squares, would they be enough to cover the whole shape?" Students will soon realize that 70 centimetre squares would only be enough to make one column of 70 squares down the side of the rectangle, while there's actually room for 100 columns this size.

Confusing Area with Perimeter Sometimes students do not make the distinction between perimeter and area, and calculate the area instead of the perimeter (or vice versa), often using whichever formula they know best.	It might help students to think of a garden (the area) surrounded by a fence (the perimeter). It may also help to remind them of the definition when posing a problem, for example, "What is the area of this shape? Remember—area is about how many units it would take to cover it."

Appropriate Manipulatives

Area: Examples of Manipulatives

MANIPULATIVE	EXAMPLE
Square Tiles Square tiles make good nonstandard units for measuring area, since they fit together (tile) to cover shapes. Square tiles are also available in square-centimetre size and can be used to introduce students to the square centimetre as a standard unit. However, young children may have difficulty manipulating them.	 This rectangle has an area of 10 square units.
Geoboards Geoboards, which are available in various sizes, can be used to make shapes whose areas can then be described in square geoboard units.	Geoboards provide an opportunity for students to explore partial as well as whole square units. For example, students could create different shapes with an area of 6 square units. 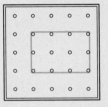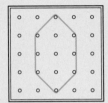 Both of these shapes have an area of 6 square units.
Sheets of Paper Sheets of construction paper or newsprint can be used to determine the area of larger spaces.	The bulletin board has an area of about 9 sheets of paper.  Measuring an area with sheets of paper
Ink Stamps and Ink A variety of interesting stamp shapes can be used to allow students to measure areas by iterating—stamping multiple copies of a single unit. As with cookie cutters, it is important to choose stamps with shapes that will tile when the goal is measurement.	Students can determine the area of a piece of paper by counting the number of stamps they can fit on it.  "I think it will take about 25 stamps to cover the paper."

MANIPULATIVE	EXAMPLE
Cookie Cutters Cookie cutters not only provide an interesting way to measure area, but also allow students to iterate with a single unit. Note that shapes that do not tile are fine for introducing the concept of area, but students should soon realize that they are not very useful for measuring because of the spaces between them. On the other hand, irregular shapes can provide a basis for making estimates.	Working with modelling clay or even real cookie dough gives students an opportunity to use a cookie cutter to determine area. Afterwards, the cutout "cookies" can be placed side by side to estimate the area of a cookie tray.  Students use a single unit over and over when they use a cookie cutter to measure rolled-out modelling clay.
Pattern Blocks Because pattern blocks fit together to tile a surface, and they come in uniform sets, they make good units for measuring area. 	Students can use one type of pattern block to measure a surface, and then use the results to estimate the number of blocks of a different type that it would take to cover the same surface.  "It's a bit more than 10 blocks. I can put 3 greens on every red one, so I think I can fit 30 and a few more, maybe 32 greens altogether."
Tangram Pieces Plastic or wooden tangram pieces can be used as non-standard units for measuring area. (Students can trace a single piece over and over to measure a paper shape.) Students can also use tangram pieces to create two or more shapes with the same area, or they can compare the area of one piece with the area of another.	Students can explore area relationships as they build shapes with pieces from multiple tangram sets. 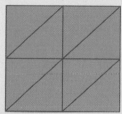 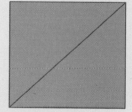 "I can build the same square with 8 small tangram triangles or 2 big ones. That means each big triangle must have the same area as 4 small ones."

(continued)

Area: Examples of Manipulatives (Continued)

MANIPULATIVE	EXAMPLE
Grid Paper and Transparent Grids Grid paper, and especially a transparent grid photocopied onto acetate, is useful for determining the areas of shapes by counting grid squares. For example, students can trace their footprints onto grids, or place a transparent grid over an area to be measured. Grids come in a variety of sizes, some of which are measured in square centimetres, so they can be used for work with either nonstandard or standard units.	Transparent grids are especially useful for estimating the areas of irregular shapes. 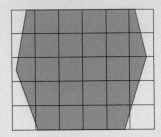 "This hexagon covers about 25 square centimetres. There are 20 whole squares inside, and the part squares are about another 5 square centimetres."
Base Ten Blocks Base ten blocks make it easy to measure areas quickly and accurately in square centimetres. 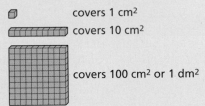	A student could use base ten blocks to measure the area of an envelope. 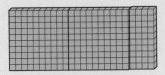 "I used 2 hundreds and 4 tens to cover almost all of the envelope, so the area is about 240 square centimetres."
Rulers, Metre Sticks, and Measuring Tapes Once students have learned formulas for calculating the areas of polygons, they can use rulers, metre sticks, and tape measures to measure the lengths they need to know in order to apply the appropriate area formula.	A student could measure the base and height of a parallelogram with a ruler and multiply *base* × *height* to determine its area.

Within the Base Ten Blocks cell:

covers 1 cm²

covers 10 cm²

covers 100 cm² or 1 dm²

Appropriate Children's Books

How Tall, How Short, How Far Away? (Adler, 1999).
This book focuses on the history of measurement and talks about many different units of measure, from measurements in ancient Egypt to the metric system.

Counting on Frank (Clement, 1991).
This amusing story about a boy who asks lots of hypothetical questions about measurement and his very unusual dog presents very interesting measurement comparisons.

How Big Is a Foot? (Myller, 1991).
This funny story shows the need for a standard unit of length measure. The story appeals to many age levels.

Sir Cumference and the Isle of Immeter (Neuschwander, 1997).
This book in the Sir Cumference series focuses students on perimeter and area in order to solve a mystery.

If You Hopped Like a Frog (Schwartz, 1999).
This story compares human and animal behaviours, and focuses on the use of scale or proportion to consider measurement situations.

Appropriate Digital Resources

See the MindTap site for a selection of appropriate digital resources.

Assessing Student Understanding

- When assessing student understanding of measurement ideas, it is important that teachers attend to both skill and concept understanding, as well as to problem solving. For instance, to determine if a student understands perimeter, you might

  - provide a shape and ask students to measure to determine the perimeter
  - provide a shape with measures given and ask students to calculate to determine the perimeter
  - ask how perimeter would change in particular situations, for example, if the lengths were all doubled
  - ask students to construct a shape with a particular perimeter
  - ask students to determine the cost of a material required to "fence" in a shape

  Similarly, assessment of student knowledge related to measurement formulas should revolve around application of the formula as well as its development.

- Assessment opportunities should include those where only one measurement is the focus, but also those where multiple measurements are involved, for example, determining areas for different shapes with the same perimeter.

- Students should, in many circumstances, be given a choice of what tool to use to accomplish a measurement.

A girl has really long hair. How many centimetres long do you think it would be? How do you know?

I think it is at least 35 cm because 30 cm is normal girl hair

Student Responses

This student has used personal experience to help her answer this question.

- Students should have opportunities to exhibit their understanding of when particular types of measurements are appropriate to use, for example, responding to a question such as, "You are getting a new rug for your bedroom. Why might you want to know its area? Why might you want to know its perimeter?"
- What feedback would you give the response?

Applying What You've Learned

1. What problem-solving strategy did you use to solve the chapter problem? How can you be sure there are no other solutions?

2. a) Describe three interesting activities not already listed in the chapter that are appropriate for students at each of the three stages of teaching length.

   b) Repeat part a) for the three stages of teaching area.

3. It is important for students to develop strategies for estimating length and area. What are some of the things you can do to help them develop those strategies?

4. Describe some everyday situations where nonstandard units are just as appropriate as standard units.

5. Some educators argue that the importance of measurement in the mathematics curriculum is that it is the content that brings together the two main branches of math—number and geometry. How central a role do you think measurement should play in the curriculum? Explain your answer.

6. a) Make a list of each step that you would need to use to measure the length of the edge of a table that is longer than your ruler.

   b) Why might it be advisable to delay the introduction of ruler use?

   c) How can you help students make the link between measuring with units and using a ruler?

7. Some teachers argue that you cannot teach about area until students know about length. Why might that not be true?

8. Many students believe that you cannot measure the areas of any shapes other than squares using the unit square centimetres. How would you convince them that this is not true?

9. Locate a current Canadian textbook.

   a) Describe a lesson on measuring area that you think is particularly strong. Indicate its strengths.

   b) Describe a lesson on measuring length that you think is weak. Indicate its deficits.

Interact with a K–8 Student:

10. Ask a student to tell you as many items as he or she can that might be a certain measurement, for example, about 50 cm long or about 100 cm^2 in area. What measurement understanding did he or she display?

Discuss with a K–8 Teacher:

11. Ask a teacher to share with you a lesson he or she has taught for measuring length that has been particularly successful and engaging. Ask him or her to explain what made the lesson work so well.

Selected References

Adler, D. (1999). *How tall, how short, how far away?* New York: Holiday House.

Barrett, J.E., Jones, G., Thornton, C., and Dickson, S. (2003). Understanding children's developing strategies about concepts for length. In Clement, D.H., and Bright, G. (Eds.). *Learning and teaching measurement.* Reston, VA: National Council of Teachers of Mathematics, 17–30.

Battista, M. (2006). Understanding the development of students' thinking about length. *Teaching Children Mathematics, 13,* 140–146.

Battista, M.T., Clements, D.H., Arnoff, J., Battista, K., and Van Auken Borrow, C. (1998). Students' spatial structuring of 2D arrays of squares. *Journal for Research in Mathematics Education, 29,* 503–532.

Clement, R. (1991). *Counting on Frank.* Milwaukee: Gareth Stevens Publishing.

Clements, D.H., Battista, M.T., and Sarama, J. (1998). Development of geometric and measurement ideas. In Lehrer, R., and Chazan, D. (Eds.). *Designing learning environments for developing understanding of geometry and space.* Mahwah, NJ: Erlbaum, 201–225.

Clements, D.H., and Bright, G. (2003). *Learning and teaching measurement.* Reston, VA: National Council of Teachers of Mathematics.

Copley, J.V., Glass, K., Nix, L., Faseler, A., De Jesus, M., and Tanksley, S. (2004). Measuring experiences for young children. *Teaching Children Mathematics, 10,* 314–319.

Dacey, L., Cavanagh, M., Findell, C., Greenes, C., Sheffield, L.J., and Small, M. (2003). *Navigating through measurement, prekindergarten–grade 2.* Reston, VA: National Council of Teachers of Mathematics.

Hiebert, J. (1981). Cognitive development and learning linear measurement. *Journal for Research in Mathematics Education, 12,* 197–211.

Joram, E., Hartman, C., and Trafton, P.R. (2004). "As people get older, they get taller": An integrated unit on measurement, linear relationships and data analysis. *Teaching Children Mathematics, 10,* 344–351.

Kaami, C. (2006). Measurement of length: How can we teach it better? *Teaching Children Mathematics, 13,* 154–158.

Lee, M., and Miller, M. (2000). *50 fabulous measurement activities.* New York: Scholastic.

Lehrer, R. (2003). Developing understanding of measurement. In Kilpatrick, J., Martin, W.G., and Schifter, D. (Eds.). *A research companion to principles and standards for school mathematics.* Reston, VA: National Council of Teachers of Mathematics, 179–192.

MARS (Mathematics Assessment Resource Service, University of Nottingham & US Berkeley) (2012). *Proofs of the Pythagorean theorem.* Retrieved on February 15, 2015, at http://map.mathshell.org/materials/download.php?fileid=1231.

Moyer, P.S. (2001). Using representations to explore perimeter and area. *Teaching Children Mathematics, 8,* 52–59.

Murphy, E. (2004). A mathematical measurement mystery. *Teaching Children Mathematics, 11,* 54–64.

Murphy, S. (2002). *Bigger, better, best!* New York: HarperFestival.

Myller, R. (1991). *How big is a foot?* New York: Yearling.

Neuschwander, C. (2006). *Sir Cumference and the Isle of Immeter.* Watertown, MA: Charlesbridge Publishing.

Outhred, L.N., and Mitchelmore, M. (2000). Young children's intuitive understanding of rectangular measurement. *Journal for Research in Mathematics Education, 31,* 144–167.

Schwartz, D. (1999). *If you hopped like a frog.* New York: Scholastic Press.

Small, M. (2010). *Professional resources and instruction for mathematics educators: Measurement.* Toronto, ON: Nelson Education Ltd.

Smith, J.P. III, Males, L.M., Dietiker, L.C., Lee, K., and Mosier, A. (2013). Curricular treatments of length measurement in the United States: Do they address known learning challenges? *Cognition and Instruction, 31,* 388–433.

Sophian, C. (2002). Learning about what fits: Preschool children's reasoning about effects of object size. *Journal of Research in Mathematics Education, 33,* 290–302.

Stephan, M., Bowers, J., Cobb, P., with Gravemeijer, K. (2003). *Supporting students' development of measuring conceptions: Analyzing students' learning in social context.* Reston, VA: National Council of Teachers of Mathematics.

Stephan, M., and Clements, D.H. (2003). Linear and area measurement in prekindergarten to grade 2. In Clements, D.H., and Bright, G. (Eds.). *Learning and teaching measurement.* Reston, VA: National Council of Teachers of Mathematics, 3–16.

Szilágyi, J., Clements, D.H., and Sarama, J. (2013). Young children's understanding of length measurement: Evaluating a learning trajectory. *Journal for Research in Mathematics Education, 44* 581–620.

Tyminski, A.M., Weilbacher, M., Lenburg, N., and Brown, C. (2008). Ladybug lengths: Beginning measurement. *Teaching Children Mathematics, 15,* 34–37.

Wright, T., Mokros, J., and Russell, S. J. (1997). *Bigger, taller, heavier, smaller. A grade 1 unit in investigations in number, data, and space.* Palo Alto, CA: Dale Seymour Publications.

Chapter 20

Capacity, Volume, Mass, Time, Temperature, and Angles

IN A NUTSHELL

The main ideas in this chapter are listed below:

1. The stages for measuring capacity, volume, time, and angles are the same as those for length and area.

2. Capacity and volume are related concepts, but not identical.

3. The attributes of mass and volume or capacity are independent.

4. Use of actual 3-D objects, and not just pictures, is important for student understanding of capacity, volume, and mass.

5. Measuring time and telling time are different processes. Measuring time is a lot like measuring length.

CHAPTER PROBLEM

Use centimetre grid paper. Cut out a 10 cm × 6 cm rectangle. Then cut a 1 by 1 square out of each corner and fold to make an open box.
• How many centimetre cubes will it hold?
• How does your answer change if you cut a 2 × 2 square out of each corner? Why might you expect this?
• What size square would you need to cut out of each corner for the greatest possible volume?

Measuring Capacity, Volume, and Mass

Capacity, volume, and mass are all measures that are attached to 3-D objects. The examples that follow show how students might conceptualize each measure at the nonstandard unit stage.

Capacity is the amount that a container can hold.

"My cupped hands can hold a lot of sand."

Volume is the amount of space occupied by an object.

"It takes 48 linking cubes to match the amount of space my box takes up."

Mass is the amount of matter in an object. It is what causes the object to feel light or heavy.

"It takes 15 pennies to balance my bear."

Introducing Capacity Concepts

You use capacity to describe how much of a pourable substance, such as water or sand, would fit inside a container such as a cup, a pail, a swimming pool, or even a room.

Ideas about capacity can be introduced through the same three stages as other measurement concepts—definition/comparison, nonstandard units, and standard units. As with length, the second stage is usually introduced fairly soon after the first stage.

How Concepts of Capacity Can Be Introduced

DEFINITION/COMPARISON

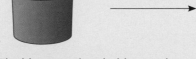

"The blue container holds more because there's still room in it after pouring in the sand from the red container."

NONSTANDARD UNITS

"The blue container holds more because it holds 5 scoops of sand and the red one only holds 3 scoops."

STANDARD UNITS

"The blue container has a greater capacity because it holds 500 mL of sand and the red one only holds 300 mL."

Capacity: The Definition/Comparison Stage

At this stage, students explore the idea that you can compare the capacity of two containers by filling one of the containers with a pourable material, such as water, sand, rice, or small peas, and then pouring the contents into the other container. Through comparing, students can discover that the capacity of a container is determined not only by its height, but also by the area of its base and the configuration of its sides. To this end, students should have opportunities to compare containers that differ in only one dimension, and also to compare containers that differ in more than one way.

When only one dimension of the containers differs ...	When the dimensions differ in more than one way ...

"The red container holds more."	"One is wide but the other one is tall."
... it is easy to compare visually to see at a glance which holds more, as long as the containers are of similar width and thickness.	... students can compare visually to estimate which container holds more, but unless the differences are very obvious, they will need to pour the contents of one into the other to be certain.

In the course of measuring capacity, students will use a variety of measurement terms such as *holds more*, *holds less*, *full*, and *empty*.

Appropriate activities for students at the definition/comparison stage might include comparing the capacities of empty drink containers (perhaps collected from students' lunches), comparing the capacities of cooking pots, or deciding what bag sizes to use for a class popcorn sale. Students should begin by comparing only two containers, but will soon be ready for the greater challenge of putting three, or perhaps even more than three, containers in order. Although the activity described in **Activity 20.1** involves several containers, it is simpler than an ordering activity because students need to compare only two containers at a time. With younger students, a sand or water table is a good place for comparing capacities.

ACTIVITY 20.1

- Provide a container and mark it with an "X."

- Provide several other containers of varying capacities and shapes, including some that hold about the same amount as the container marked "X."

- Ask students to predict how each container might compare with the marked one, measure to check, and then record the results with words or pictures on a chart like the one shown here.

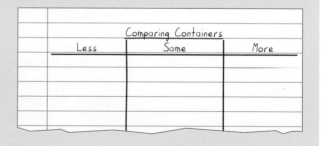

Spatial Reasoning

TEACHING TIP

Be careful to use the term *capacity* only to refer to the amount it takes to fill an object (by thinking of the object as a container), that is, the amount of space inside. Use the term *volume* to refer to a "solid" amount, that is, how much space an object occupies.

Capacity: The Nonstandard Unit Stage

At this stage, students learn to measure capacity with nonstandard units such as cups or spoons. Nonstandard units make it possible to assign a number to a container's capacity, allowing students to record the capacities of many containers so they can be compared without having to refill them repeatedly.

Nonstandard units also help students develop referents they can use for estimating. For this reason, students need many opportunities to measure with familiar units such as water bottles, yogurt cups, cereal bowls, and teaspoons. A student who knows, for example, that a container holds 4 teaspoons of sand has a good feel for the capacity of this container.

At this stage, students can use multiple units to measure capacity, or they can use the same unit over and over. It may be more practical, though, to use one unit repeatedly.

Appropriate Nonstandard Units for Capacity

Tools for measuring capacity are handy everyday items of uniform size, such as spoons, cups, and small containers. These are generally filled with water, or with a pourable solid such as sand or rice; these amounts serve as the nonstandard units.

If students are measuring boxes, cubes make good nonstandard units because they pack. (The term *pack* used with 3-D shapes is equivalent to the term *tile* for 2-D shapes. It means the shapes fit together within a space with no overlap or gaps.) In the early stages of work with definition/comparison, teachers may want to let students experiment with units that suit a particular context, but do not pack. For example, students could figure out how many apples will fit in a basket, or how many pennies or jelly beans will fit in a jar. However, whenever these materials are used, the discussion that follows the activity should bring out the idea that some of the space in the container was not measured because the units did not fit tightly together. As a result, these units might not be good ones to use if the purpose of the activity is to compare the capacities of two containers that are similar in size.

Discuss the limitations of using a unit such as a jelly bean to measure capacity.

Estimating Capacity with Nonstandard Units

In the definition/comparison stage, estimating was simply used to determine which of two containers would hold more. Now students are able to estimate how many units a container might hold. As with other types of measurement, it helps students to compare unknown amounts with amounts they know. For example, a student at this stage might determine that it takes 5 big spoons to fill a container, and then estimate how many little spoons it would take to fill the same container by comparing the capacities of the two different size spoons. It is also appropriate at this stage to partially fill a container, for example, to approximately $\frac{1}{4}$, $\frac{1}{3}$, or $\frac{1}{2}$ of its capacity, and then ask students, "There are x units in the container so far. About how many units would it take to fill the container?" (See the example at the top of the next page.) These are practical examples of proportional reasoning.

About how many apples will it take to fill this pail?

In order to use a partial measurement to make an estimate, students need to think, "How many times will this quantity fit into the whole amount I have to measure?"

ACTIVITY 20.2

Students at the nonstandard unit stage can practise estimating capacity as they complete this task.

- Show a large pail and a small mixing bowl. Ask each student to estimate how many bowls of sand or water it would take to fill the pail.

- Have individual students record their estimates by attaching name cards to the appropriate categories in the graph.

- Give students a chance to change their estimates after they have seen all the estimates.

- Pour one bowl of sand into the pail, and then give students another chance to change their estimates.

- Fill the rest of the pail and count the number of bowls needed.

Proportional Reasoning

How many bowls will fill the pail?

1 to 3	4 to 6	7 to 9	more than 9
	Mahmoud		
	Lachlan		
	Nadia		
	Jordan	Ravi	
Dale	Liz	Billy	
Devica	Sayada	Julie	
Estela	Carmen	Gord	

Number of bowls

Making Nonstandard Measuring Tools

A good way to help students understand the importance of uniformity in nonstandard units is to let them measure out equal amounts in order to make their own measuring tools. For example, a student can make a measuring cup from a large transparent cup or glass (preferably cylindrical rather than tapered) by filling it repeatedly from a smaller container and marking the side of the cup to show the level after each new measure is added. The student can then use the cup to measure the capacity of various bowls.

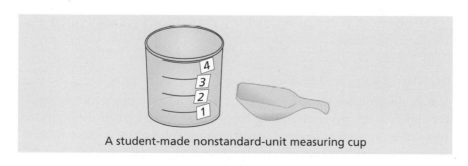

A student-made nonstandard-unit measuring cup

Capacity: The Standard Unit Stage

Students can be introduced to standard units when they realize that, rather than measuring capacity in nonstandard units, which can mean different things to different people, they can use units that everyone will understand.

Introducing Standard Units of Capacity

The litre tends to be introduced early in work with capacity. This is, in part, because litre containers are such a familiar part of everyday life. Products such as milk and ice cream often come in litre containers. This familiarity also helps students understand that litre containers can look different; after all, a milk carton looks quite different from an ice cream tub.

Standard Units of Capacity

LITRES (L)

Defining a Litre

A *litre* is the amount of liquid it would take to fill a cubic container that is 10 cm by 10 cm by 10 cm.

Litre Referents

Aside from familiar referents such as 1-L milk cartons and water bottles, students can also refer to a thousand cube from a base ten block set.

If a 10-cm thousand cube (a 1000 base ten block) were hollowed out, its capacity would be 1 L.

MILLILITRES (mL)

Defining a Millilitre

A *millilitre* is $\frac{1}{1000}$ or 0.001 of a litre.

Millilitre Referents

For a millilitre referent, students can refer to the amount of liquid it would take to fill a hollow unit cube from a base ten block set.

Because a millilitre is so small, students should also have millilitre referents that represent multiple units, such as teaspoons (5 mL) and tablespoons (15 mL). Graduated medicine cups also make good referents for amounts measured in millilitres.

If a unit cube were a container, its capacity would be 1 mL.

There are, of course, other metric units of capacity, such as decilitres, kilolitres, and centilitres, but these are rarely used in everyday life.

Standard Tools for Measuring Capacity

Just as a ruler helps students learn that they can use a single tool to measure different lengths, a measuring cup illustrates that a single tool can also be used to measure different capacities. A measuring cup is like a ruler in other ways, too. For example, students need to estimate amounts that fall between the marks on the cup, such as 130 mL. They also need to learn to combine full cups with partial ones to measure quantities greater than the capacity of the measuring cup.

A measuring cup shares many characteristics with a ruler.

Other standard tools for measuring capacity include measuring spoons, measuring scoops, and graduated cylinders.

Activities for Measuring Capacity

There are many activities teachers can use to provide practice with measuring in millilitres and litres. For example, students could

- estimate the capacities of a variety of containers, and then check by measuring
- prepare recipes that require quantities in millilitres and litres
- compare several cereal bowls to see how much a typical bowl holds
- estimate the number of pieces of popcorn it would take to fill a litre container

There are also a number of environmental issues that provide contexts for measuring capacity at home.

Introducing Volume Concepts

The volume of a shape is a measure that describes how much space the shape occupies. Many students and adults interchange the terms *volume* and *capacity*. This is not surprising since people sometimes measure capacities, such as how much a moving truck holds, in units of volume (cubic metres).

In order to understand volume, a student benefits from a clear understanding of the measurement process, as well as considerable experience with measuring length, area, and capacity.

ACTIVITY 20.3

Ask students to explore these environmental issues:

- Estimate how many litres of water you could save by having a shower instead of a bath. Describe how you found out.

- Place a container under a dripping tap for 1 hour and estimate how much water is wasted in one day, one week, and one month.

Proportional Reasoning

Ideas about volume can be introduced through the same three stages as other measurement concepts—definition/comparison, using nonstandard units, and using standard units.

How Concepts of Volume Can Be Introduced

DEFINITION/COMPARISON

"The blue box is bigger than the red box since it takes up less space."

NONSTANDARD UNITS

"The blue box is bigger—it took 3 layers of 12 to build it. That's 36 cubes. The red box is 2 layers of 9. That's 18 cubes."

STANDARD UNITS

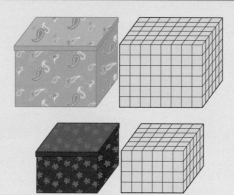

"The blue box is bigger—it took 288 cm³ to build a model of it and the red box only took 144 cm³."

Volume = Area of base × height	
Blue box	Red box
V = 8 × 6 × 6	V = 6 × 6 × 4
= 48 × 6	= 36 × 4
= 288 cm³	= 144 cm³

"The blue box is bigger—it's 288 cm³ and the red one is only 144 cm³."

Volume: The Definition/Comparison Stage

At this stage, students explore the notion that one item has more volume than another if the object is "bigger" (occupies more space) than another object. Initially, comparisons should be made with items that are easy to compare visually (as shown above). However, when the difference in volume is not obvious—for example, one prism might be taller and wider than another but not as deep—this visual direct comparison method is limited. This situation facilitates the progression to the nonstandard unit stage. A rapid transition to nonstandard units is possible for most students because, by the time volume is introduced, students will have had considerable experience with measurement in general.

Volume: The Nonstandard Unit Stage

Nonstandard units make it possible to assign a number to an object's volume, allowing students to record the volumes of many objects so they can be compared numerically rather than spatially.

Generally, students initially work with objects made by putting together rectangular prisms for measuring volume. To measure the volume of a small box, students would measure (count) the number of blocks it takes to build a full-size model of the box. Students generally need to use multiple copies of a unit since it is very difficult to measure volume by iteration (using a single unit over and over).

Appropriate Nonstandard Units for Volume

Students generally measure volume using uniform units that pack (that is, fit together with no overlap or spaces). The size of the blocks does not matter as long as they are uniform. Examples include centimetre cubes, linking cubes, and building blocks. (Even though centimetre cubes are a standard unit (1 cm^3), this has no significance for students at the nonstandard unit stage, so these students are able to use centimetre cubes as nonstandard units.)

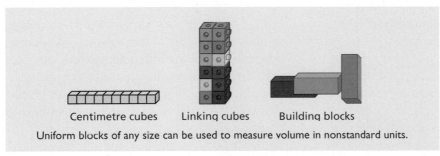

Centimetre cubes   Linking cubes   Building blocks

Uniform blocks of any size can be used to measure volume in nonstandard units.

Rectangular blocks are often used for volume, but other shape units can work just as well, depending on the shape of the object to be measured.

"The jar is just a bit smaller than 11 yellow blocks."

Volume and Shape

Students at the nonstandard unit stage are often surprised to find that shapes that look very different can have the same volume.

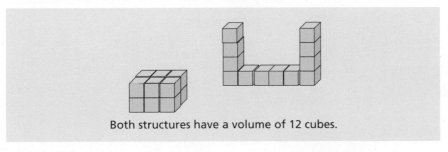

Both structures have a volume of 12 cubes.

To help students explore this concept, a teacher can pose problems that involve making different shapes with the same number of blocks or cubes, or ask questions such as the one illustrated below.

Student Response

This student recognizes that the volume of a structure depends on the number of cubes that were used to build it, and is not influenced by how the cubes are arranged.

Use 11 linking cubes to build a cube structure like the one shown here.

A different cube structure has the same volume but it's taller than this one.

How can that be possible?
Use words and a picture to explain.

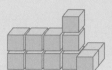

The volume of this structure is 11 cubes.

The picture of the structure has the same volume as the one above.
I know because I have counted. It does not matter about the shape and size of the structure, but that it has the same volume.

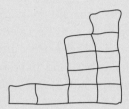

Estimating Volume with Nonstandard Units

In the definition/comparison stage, estimating was simply used to determine which of two objects took up more space. Now students are able to estimate how many units of space an object might fill. As with other types of measurement, it helps students to compare unknown amounts with amounts they know. For example, a student at this stage might determine that it takes 15 linking cubes to match the size of a small box, and then estimate how many linking cubes it would take to match the size of a larger box. It is also appropriate at this stage to use cubes to model the base of a box, and then ask students, "About how many cubes do you think it would take to match the size of the whole box?"

How many cubes would it take to build a box this size?

"It looks like it will take 3 layers this size to build the box, so I think the volume is about 36 cubes."

ACTIVITY 20.5

Have students build a box with green Cuisenaire rods. Ask,

- How many rods did you use?
- How many yellow rods would you need to build the same-size box?

Have students build a box with linking cubes. Ask,

- How many cubes did you use?
- How many cubes would you need to build the same-size box with Centicubes?

Proportional Reasoning

Volume: The Standard Unit Stage

Standard units of volume are related to standard units of length. However, while length is measured in units that are straight lines, volume is measured in cubic units. This is because cubic units represent a space that has three dimensions.

Introducing Standard Units of Volume

Generally, the cubic centimetre is introduced first. This is partly because centimetres are familiar to students, and partly because cubic centimetres are a suitable size for measuring many shapes that are easy for students to handle. In addition, concrete models in the form of Centicubes or unit cubes from a set of base ten blocks are readily accessible in many classrooms.

Standard Units of Volume

CUBIC CENTIMETRES (cm³)	CUBIC METRES (m³)

Defining a Cubic Centimetre

A cubic centimetre is a volume equivalent to the space occupied by a cube with a side length of 1 cm. It is important for students to realize that an object with a volume of 1 cm³ is not necessarily cube-shaped, as illustrated by the prisms below.

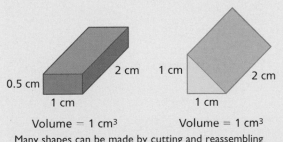

Volume = 1 cm³   Volume = 1 cm³

Many shapes can be made by cutting and reassembling a centimetre cube.

Cubic Centimetre Referents

Students can refer to Centicubes or base ten block unit cubes. A base ten rod serves as a referent for 10 cm³, a flat for 100 cm³, and a thousand cube for 1000 cm³.

Defining a Cubic Metre

A cubic metre is a volume equivalent to the space occupied by a cube with a side length of 1 m. Students should realize that an object with a volume of 1 m³ does not have to be cube-shaped. It simply has to occupy the same amount of space as the cube.

Cubic Metre Referents

A good way to model a cubic metre and provide a referent is to make 12 rolls of newspaper, each 1 m long, and tape them together to form the edges of a cube. If the cube were solid, it would have a volume of 1 m³.

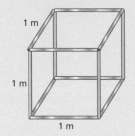

If this were a closed box, its volume would be 1 m³.

Students can use this model to find objects in the classroom and outside that have a greater volume, about the same volume, or a lesser volume. They might also use the model to estimate the volumes of familiar objects, such as a shed or a garbage dumpster.

CUBIC DECIMETRES (dm³)	

The cubic decimetre is another unit of volume that is useful for students in the elementary grades. Its size is suitable for measuring classroom objects, and it can readily be modelled using a thousand cube from a set of base ten blocks.

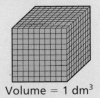

Volume = 1 dm³

Other standard units of volume include cubic millimetres and cubic kilometres, but these are rarely used in everyday life.

Recording Standard Units of Volume It is important for students to realize that, when they begin to measure volume with standard units, they need to report measurements in *cubic units*. (This is different from measuring in nonstandard units, where a volume might be reported, for example, as 20 blocks or 17 linking cubes.)

Initially, the units should be spelled out, for example, "12 cubic metres." Spelling the units out helps students build an understanding of the unit. Eventually, students will be ready to write the units in an abbreviated form using exponents, for example, 12 cm³. With standard units, the exponent 3 is used to indicate that the units have three dimensions.

Relating Units of Volume Students need opportunities to discuss how one cubic unit relates to another. Just as students may be surprised to discover that 1 m² = 10 000 cm² (and not 100 cm²), students may be even more surprised to find that 1 m³ = 1 000 000 cm³.

Relating Units: Linear, Area, and Volume

Linear	1 m	$\overline{}$ 100 cm	100 cm
Area	1 m²	100 cm × 100 cm (square)	100 cm × 100 cm = 10 000 cm²
Volume	1 m³	100 cm × 100 cm × 100 cm (cube)	100 cm × 100 cm × 100 cm = 1 000 000 cm³

Formulas for Measuring Volume

In K–6, students deal with formulas, if at all, mainly in the context of working with prisms, and especially rectangular prisms. In Grades 7 to 9, they learn formulas for calculating the volumes of other shapes, usually more general prisms, pyramids, cones, cylinders, and spheres. Although volume formulas are officially introduced at the standard unit stage, the notion of a formula or shortcut can be introduced at the nonstandard unit stage.

Students are not simply told the formulas; they develop them. For example, to develop the formula for rectangular prisms, students create a rectangular base and build layers of that base to make the prism.

They soon notice that the volume of the prism depends on both how high it is and the area of the base. In fact, the number of cubes is based on multiplying the area of the base by the height.

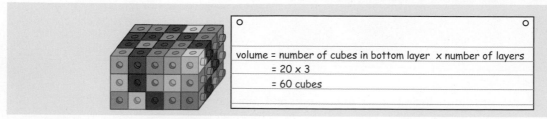

volume = number of cubes in bottom layer x number of layers
= 20 x 3
= 60 cubes

Volume Formulas for Prisms and Cylinders

TRIANGLE-BASED PRISM

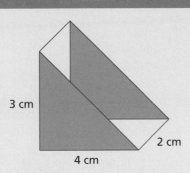

3 cm

3 cm

2 cm

4 cm

The triangular prism on the left is made up of layers of the base. It makes sense that its volume is the product of the height and the area of the base.

The triangular prism on the right is half of a rectangular prism which would be 3 layers of a 4×2 rectangle.

Therefore, the volume is $4 \times 2 \times 3 \div 2$.

That is, in fact, the area of the triangular base $(4 \times 3 \div 2)$ multiplied by the height.

$$Area\ of\ base\ = (3 \times 4) \div 2$$
$$= 6\ cm^2$$
$$Volume\ of\ prism\ = Area\ of\ polygon\ base \times height$$
$$= 6 \times 2$$
$$= 12\ cm^3$$

CYLINDER

2 cm

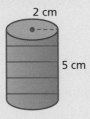

5 cm

A cylinder is much like a prism, although rounded. Just as a prism is made by building layers of a base, one can think of a cylinder as layers of a circular base.

The volume is affected by the area of the base as well as the cylinder's height. In fact, as with polygonal prisms, the volume is the product of the area of the base and the height.

$$Area\ of\ base\ = \pi \times radius^2$$
$$= \pi \times 2^2$$
$$\approx 12.6\ cm^2$$
$$Volume\ of\ cylinder\ = Area\ of\ base \times height$$
$$\approx 12.6 \times 5$$
$$\approx 63\ cm^3 D$$

Volume of Other Shapes Later on, students will learn that they can use the formulas for the volumes of prisms and cylinders to calculate the volumes of related shapes, such as pyramids, cones, and spheres. This leads to the development of formulas for the volumes of those shapes.

Relating Volume Formulas

VOLUME OF A PYRAMID

The volume of a pyramid is $\frac{1}{3}$ of the volume of the prism with the same base and height. Students generally learn this by using visualization or by filling a non-solid pyramid and pouring the contents into a prism with the same base and height, noticing it takes three pours to fill the prism.

$V = \frac{1}{3} \times$ *base area* $\times$ *height*

VOLUME OF A CONE

The volume of a cone is $\frac{1}{3}$ of the volume of the cylinder with the same base and height. Students generally learn this by using visualization or by filling a non-solid cone and pouring the contents into a cylinder with the same base and height, noticing it takes three pours to fill the cylinder.

$V = \frac{4}{3} \times$ *base area* $\times$ *height*

VOLUME OF A SPHERE

The volume of a sphere turns out to be $\frac{2}{3}$ of the volume of the cylinder that fits exactly around it. The height of the cylinder is double the radius, r, so the volume of the cylinder is $(\pi \times r^2) \times 2r$ or, in simplified form, $2 \times \pi \times r^3$. The volume of the sphere is $\frac{2}{3}$ as large, so it is $\frac{4}{3} \times \pi \times r^3$. (This formula is generally introduced later than the other volume formulas.) The 2/3 is discovered by filling the non-solid sphere and filling the non-solid cylinder that fits exactly around it. Three fills of the sphere would result in two fills of the cylinder.

$V = \frac{4}{3} \times \pi \times$ radius^3

ACTIVITY 20.7

Have students use centimetre grid paper to make nets for two prisms with the same volume, but different surface areas.

_____

Spatial Reasoning

Volume and Surface Area At the nonstandard unit stage, students learned that objects with the same volume can have different shapes. Now they can explore the idea that objects with the same volume can also have different surface areas. They might also discover that, as the shape becomes more like a cube, the surface area decreases.

The activities described in **Activity 20.7** and **Activity 20.8** can help students see that a short, wide shape has more surface area than a more compact, but taller, shape with the same volume.

Volume = 12 cubes
Surface area = 50 squares

Volume = 12 cubes
Surface area = 40 squares

Volume = 12 cubes
Surface area = 32 squares

Relating Volume to Capacity through Displacement

When an object is completely immersed in water, it displaces an amount of water that is equal to its own volume. At the definition/comparison stage, students

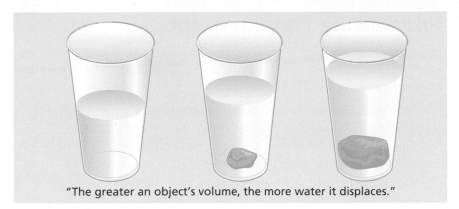

"The greater an object's volume, the more water it displaces."

can compare the volumes of two objects simply by immersing each object in the same amount of water and checking to compare the changes in the water level. The more the water level rises, the greater the volume of the object.

Although displacement is a fairly simple concept, it is usually not introduced until after students have had some experience with measuring length, area, and capacity. Students require a fairly sophisticated understanding of measurement in order to understand the indirect relationship between the object and the displaced water.

Students often expect a heavier object to displace more water than a light one. For example, a student might be surprised to find that a large plastic bottle displaces more water than a smaller stone. To help students see that volume depends on size, not mass, teachers need to set up displacement experiments with objects that are made of different materials. They might, for example, compare the volumes of a variety of balls.

At the standard units stage, students are ready to learn that metric units of volume are related not only to one another, but also to standard units of capacity. This is why familiarity with units of capacity is a helpful prerequisite for work with volume displacement. When students immerse 1 cm^3 of material in water, it displaces exactly 1 mL of liquid. When they immerse 1000 cm^3 (1 dm^3), this displaces exactly 1 L. As a result, students can use displacement not only to compare volumes, but also to calculate the volumes of irregularly shaped objects in standard units.

The water level went from 100 mL to 135 mL, so the volume must be 35 cm^3.

The same relationship ($1 \text{ cm}^3 = 1 \text{ mL}$) can be used to estimate the capacity of a container with a known volume (assuming the sides of the container are not too thick). For example, if the volume of a box is 560 cm^3, then the box has a capacity of about 560 mL.

Introducing Mass Concepts

In Canada, we generally teach children to use the term *mass*, rather than *weight*, to describe the heaviness or lightness of an object. The differences between mass and weight are listed below:

- Mass measures the amount of matter in an object, while weight is a measure of force—the combined effect of mass and gravity.
- The mass of an object is measured by using a balance to compare it to a known amount of matter, but weight is measured on a scale.
- The mass of an object does not change when location changes, but the weight can change with a change in location.

In everyday use, the terms *mass* and *weight* are interchangeable; in fact, we often tell a student to weigh an object to determine its mass, although some more advanced scientific and technological applications require that the distinction between the two terms be carefully made.

How Concepts of Mass Can Be Introduced

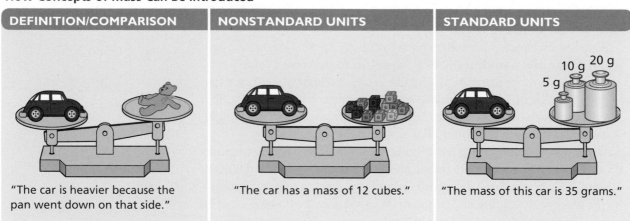

DEFINITION/COMPARISON	NONSTANDARD UNITS	STANDARD UNITS
"The car is heavier because the pan went down on that side."	"The car has a mass of 12 cubes."	"The mass of this car is 35 grams."

Mass: The Definition/Comparison Stage

At this stage, students use a pan balance to compare the masses of two objects. The balance then acts like a teeter-totter, with the object whose mass is greater pulling its side of the balance down (as shown above for Definition/Comparison).

Activities for students in the definition/comparison stage might include comparing the masses of different types of fruit, or hunting for objects that have less mass (or more mass) than a given object.

Students at this stage sometimes find it difficult to estimate which of two objects has more mass, since they cannot rely on size. Sometimes a smaller object has a greater mass than a large one. Therefore, students need to be able to physically handle the materials they are comparing. As students are developing their ability to estimate in order to make mass comparisons, they will benefit from opportunities to handle and compare a wide range of materials.

Another way to help students learn to estimate masses is to encourage them to use their own bodies like pan balances. To do this, students take an item in each hand, stretch out their arms, and try to feel which item is heavier. Then they move their arms to show how a pan balance would look if the items in their hands were on the balance.

TEACHING TIP

We often focus on the term *heavier,* asking which item is heavier than another. It is equally important to use the term *lighter* to focus on which item is lighter than another.

Using Pan Balances to Compare Mass Directly

While students can make their own pan balances, for example, by using string and paper clips to connect paper cups to both ends of a coat hanger, it is also practical to have some commercial models on hand.

Before using a pan balance, it is important to level the balance, that is, to make sure the empty pans balance exactly. Pan balances tend to slip out of balance when they are not levelled regularly. An unlevelled balance will result in inaccurate measurements and may foster misconceptions about mass. Most classroom pan balances are suited for a fairly limited range of masses, usually up to 1 kg or 2 kg.

A STUDENT-MADE PAN BALANCE

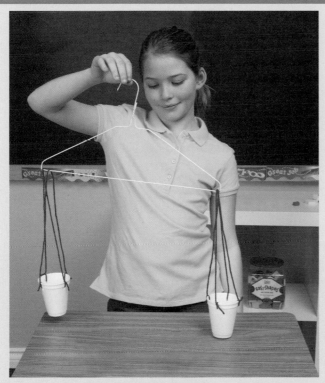

COMMERCIAL PAN BALANCES

Some commercial balances have a flat plate on each side, making it easy to see the objects being measured. Others have a removable container, often clear, on each side, making it possible to balance liquids, or small items that might otherwise roll away.

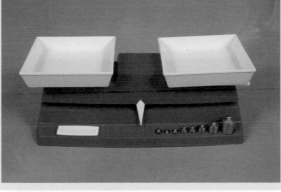

Dennis MacDonald/PhotoEdit

Mass: The Nonstandard Unit Stage

Nonstandard units make it possible to assign a number to an object's mass, allowing students to record the masses of many objects so they can be compared without having to be measured over and over.

To measure an object's mass with nonstandard units, a student places the object on one side of a pan balance, and then counts how many uniform units must be placed on the other side to make the pans balance. For example, it might take 12 blocks to balance the mass of a pet rock.

My pet rock's mass is 12 cubes.

Appropriate Nonstandard Units for Mass

Students can measure mass with nonstandard units such as marbles, coins, linking cubes, base ten blocks, ball bearings, unused erasers, or other small counters. For practical reasons, the unit should have a reasonable amount of mass—not too much or too little. For example, if ping pong balls were used, you would need a significant number of them to measure the mass of even a light object, such as an apple, making them an impractical unit. A unit with too much mass, such as a book, would not allow for much precision in measuring mass.

I think I would need about 10 square blocks to balance this apple.

Measuring Mass with Different Units

Work with nonstandard units provides an opportunity for students to explore the concept that using a bigger unit to measure mass results in a smaller number of units. It is important for students to have opportunities to balance a particular object with several different types of units and to record the results each time. Work with different units also helps students develop personal referents that they can use to estimate masses.

I measured the tennis ball

What I Used	My Guess	How Many?
pennies	15	21

ACTIVITY 20.10

Provide various small units for measuring mass, such as square pattern blocks, pennies, linking cubes, and marbles. Have students use some different units to estimate and measure the mass of a small ball. They can record the results on a chart like the one to the left.

Proportional Reasoning

Measuring Different Items with the Same Unit

It is also important for students to have opportunities to balance different items against a common unit. For example, students could use linking cubes to balance a series of small toys. Using the same nonstandard unit for each item allows students to compare masses to see which item has a greater mass, and also to determine the amount of difference.

Activities that provide a context for measuring different items with the same unit might include hunting for items with a particular mass, such as "10 marbles," or putting a series of objects in order according to mass.

Estimating Mass with Nonstandard Units

In the definition/comparison stage, estimating was simply used to determine which of two objects had more mass. Now students are able to estimate how many units it might take to balance a particular object. As with other types of measurement, it helps students to compare unknown amounts with amounts they know. For example, a student at this stage might determine that it takes 10 linking cubes to balance a small object, and then estimate how many linking cubes it would take to balance a larger one.

Estimating the mass of an object is more difficult than estimating other measures because there is no direct relationship between the object's size and its mass. To estimate length, area, capacity, or volume, students simply need to visualize how many units will fit along or inside what is being measured. With mass, students need to think about how the unit feels. It is not an easy task to feel one unit and imagine what two units, or ten units, might feel like.

Mass: The Standard Unit Stage

Introducing Standard Units of Mass

The first standard unit of mass that students usually encounter is the kilogram. Students should be given the opportunity to make a kilogram mass of their own. Students might, for example, fill a plastic container with sand until it exactly balances a 1 kg mass on a pan balance.

Metric Units of Mass

KILOGRAMS (kg)	GRAMS (g)

Defining a Kilogram

One *kilogram* is a mass equal to the mass of 1 dm³ of water at 4°C.

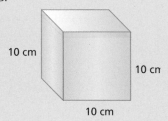

10 cm
10 cm
10 cm

Defining a Gram

A *gram* is $\frac{1}{1000}$ or 0.001 of a kilogram.

Kilogram Referents

A kilogram is the mass of 1 L of water or milk.

MILK
1 L

Gram Referents

A *gram* is the mass of 1 mL of water, or about the mass of a Centicube (or a unit cube). A raisin or paper clip is another useful referent for 1 g.

Some unit cubes have a mass of 1 g.

Because a gram is so small, students should also have referents that represent multiple units, such as a wooden pattern-block square for 5 g and a wooden base-10 rod for 10 g.

Measuring with Kilograms

A pan balance is the preferred tool for measuring mass. However, since classroom pan balances seldom have the capacity to measure beyond 1 or 2 kg, it is sometimes necessary to use a scale. Scale measures may differ slightly from mass measure depending on where, in relation to sea level, the scale is being used. (At sea level, weight and mass are about the same.) Many scales have a feature that allows users to adjust for differences in altitude.

"The scale went from 41 kg to 44 kg, so the box I'm holding must be 3 kg."

Measuring with Grams

Due to the small size of a gram, students typically work with pan balances that have masses of 5 g, 10 g, 20 g, 50 g, and 100 g. However, there are some sets that include 1 g, 2 g, 100 g, 200 g, and 500 g masses.

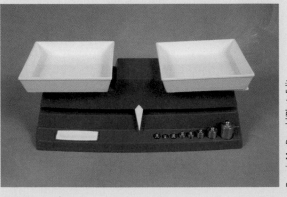

Dennis MacDonald/PhotoEdit

There are other units of mass that students eventually need to understand, but that cannot be measured with a classroom pan balance. *Milligrams* are thousandths of a gram, and are used to measure objects with very little mass. *Tonnes*, on the other hand, are used to measure objects with a lot of mass. One tonne is 1000 kg. While students need not measure with these units, they should be able to say whether milligrams, grams, kilograms, or tonnes would be appropriate in a particular situation. Grams, for example, would be good units to use to measure the mass of raisins in a package, while tonnes would be better for measuring the mass of a truck.

There are, of course, other metric units of mass, such as centigrams, decigrams, and hectograms, but these are rarely used in everyday life.

Tools for Measuring Mass in Standard Units

While a pan balance is the tool students might use most often to measure mass, a bathroom scale is also useful, especially when the object's mass exceeds what the pan balance can accommodate. For example, a student could determine the mass of a book by reading his own mass on a scale, first without the book, and then again while holding it. The mass of the book represents the difference between the two readings.

Note that, for younger students, a bathroom scale is a less appropriate tool because it simply involves reading a number, while the pan balance makes it possible to actually see the mass that balances a particular object.

ACTIVITY 20.11

Ask students to try one of these activities:

- Compare the masses of different types of balls, such as baseballs and ping pong balls. Are balls that are bigger usually heavier?

- What is the mass of your backpack? Is it safe for you to carry that much?

- Check 3 products on your pantry shelf. Are the masses reported on the packages accurate?

- How much would 1 kg of pennies be worth? What about 1 kg of quarters?

- If you had to pay for a meal based on your mass, would a fee of 10¢ per kilogram be a good deal?

Critical Thinking

Common Errors and Misconceptions

Capacity, Volume, and Mass: Common Errors, Misconceptions, and Strategies

COMMON ERROR OR MISCONCEPTION	SUGGESTED STRATEGY
Judging Capacity by Height Alone Many children at the definition/comparison stage believe that a container that is taller will also have a greater **capacity**, or that if two containers are the same height, they must hold the same amount.	Students need opportunities to compare objects of varying heights and widths in order to learn that a container that is large in one way can be small in another. A good time to do this is when students are comparing two containers, or putting several containers in order according to their capacity. For example, students could be asked to compare a shorter object that holds more (e.g., a wide bowl) with a taller object that holds less (e.g., a plastic glass), or to compare several containers that are about the same height, but that vary in terms of base shape or width.
Measuring Capacity Inconsistently When measuring **capacity**, some students do not fill the measuring tool in a consistent way. As well, they sometimes switch to partial units when a container is nearly full.  Measurement units are meaningful only when they are uniform.	Students may need to be reminded that units are useful only if they are uniform. If you know a bottle holds 6 spoonfuls of sand, you can compare this bottle with another only if you know how full they were. To demonstrate, use two transparent containers. Show what happens when you pour 5 full scoops of water into one, and 5 partial scoops of water into the other. To help students learn to measure with uniform units, encourage them to fill spoons or scoops to the top, and to level them off if necessary.

(continued)

Capacity, Volume, and Mass: Common Errors, Misconceptions, and Strategies (Continued)

COMMON ERROR OR MISCONCEPTION	SUGGESTED STRATEGY
Assuming a Longer Object Has More Volume Some students will use the length of an object as the only basis for extrapolating other measures. For example, a student might decide that the green prism shown here has more **volume** than the red one because the green prism is longer. 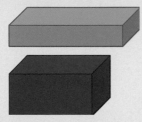 Length is only one of the factors that determine the volume of a shape.	Emphasize that volume tells how much space an object takes up, or how many units it would take to create a model of the object. In this case, students might reconstruct each prism with centimetre cubes, making it readily apparent that it takes more cubes to build the red prism than the green one. 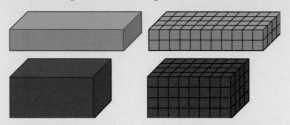 Reconstructing these prisms with cubes shows that the red prism has the greater volume.
Learning to Conserve Volume Some younger students believe that if you move cubes around in a cube structure, the volume of the structure will change. This misconception becomes apparent when the same blocks are used to build a second structure and the student recounts the cubes.	Students develop their ability to conserve volume through experience. To move beyond this misconception, they will need to do some activities that involve building a cube structure, counting the cubes to determine its volume, and then rearranging the cubes and counting them again. Through discussion, the teacher can help students recognize that the number of cubes does not change unless cubes are added or removed.
Converting Cubic Metres to Cubic Centimetres Students, and even many adults, are surprised when they realize that 1 m^3 is not the same **volume** as 100 cm^3. People tend to assume that since there are 100 cm in 1 m, there must also be 100 cm^3 in 1 m^3.	To determine the number of cubic centimetres in a cubic metre, model a cubic metre with edges made of newspaper rolls and ask students to begin covering the bottom of the metre cube with centimetre cubes. They should realize quite quickly that 100 cm^3 is nowhere near enough to fill the whole cube. This is because each edge of the cube is 100 cm, so there are actually 100 layers with 100 rows of 100 in each layer, or 1 million cubes altogether.
Using Inconsistent Units in Volume Calculations Some students will not attend to the fact that one side of this prism is measured in metres, while the other two sides are measured in centimetres. These students are likely to calculate the **volume** of the prism by multiplying $1 \times 30 \times 50$ and reporting the result as 1500 cm^3 or 1500 m^3. 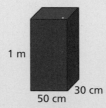 1 m 30 cm 50 cm The volume can be calculated in cubic metres or cubic centimetres, but the units cannot be combined.	To remind students what they are calculating, a teacher might ask, • How many centimetre cubes will it take to model the bottom layer of the prism? (1500) • How many layers this size would it take to fill in the entire prism? (100) • How many cubes is that altogether? ($1500 \times 100 = 150\,000$ cubes in all)

COMMON ERROR OR MISCONCEPTION	SUGGESTED STRATEGY

Assuming a Larger Object Has More Mass

Many students believe that if one object is larger (or longer) than another, then it must also have more **mass**.

To help a child learn that it is possible for an object that is large in one way to be small in another, provide opportunities to compare a small heavy object (e.g., a stone) with a larger object that is lighter (e.g., an empty can).

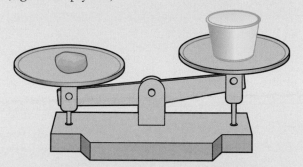

Sometimes the small object is heavier than the large one.

Learning to Conserve Mass

Some younger students believe that if you break an object into parts, its **mass** will change.

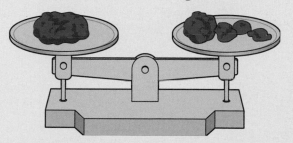

Breaking an object into parts does not change its mass.

An interesting experiment to do with younger students involves two identical balls of modelling clay. Show students that the balls balance each other, and then break one ball up into several smaller balls. Ask, "If I put this ball on one side of the pan balance and these smaller balls on the other side, what do you think will happen?"

Use the pan balance to demonstrate that breaking the ball into parts did not change its mass.

Experiments like this can help students develop the ability to conserve mass.

Misinterpreting Standard Masses

Students who are just beginning to use standard masses may not realize that each **mass** represents a different amount. For example, a student may balance an object with a 20 g mass and a 10 g mass, and then record the mass as 2 g because 2 masses were used.

Initially, students could use a consistent unit, such as the 5 g mass, for determining mass. Later, when they are more comfortable with standard masses, they can add more sizes.

Using a set of masses with a different colour for each size may help students keep track of the values. Different colours will also make it easier for students to record and label the masses they used to solve a particular problem.

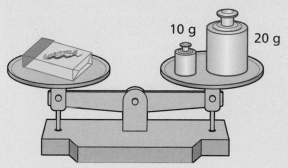

The crayons have a mass of 30 g, not 2 g.

Appropriate Manipulatives

Capacity, Volume, and Mass: Examples of Manipulatives

MEASURING TOOLS

When students ares learning to measure **capacity**, it is useful to have on hand some transparent and opaque measuring cups, scoops, and spoons. These can be used to measure in nonstandard units until students are ready to measure in litres and millilitres. Students will also need some pourable material, such as sand or coloured water, to use with these measuring tools. (See *How Concepts of Capacity Can Be Introduced* on page 516.)

EXAMPLES

Cups, spoons, and scoops can be used as tools for measuring with nonstandard units.

"If half of it is 6 scoops, then it must hold 12 scoops."

Standard measuring tools can be used for classroom cooking activities. Commercial sets of containers are also useful for older students.

Play Dough
500 mL flour
125 mL salt
250 mL water
60 mL cream of tartar

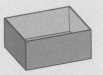

"I'll need a 250-mL measuring cup and a 15-mL measuring spoon."

VARIOUS CONTAINERS

Containers and boxes of varying sizes and shapes are versatile materials for measuring. Students can measure their **capacity**, **mass**, **and/or volume**, and can also use smaller containers as units for measuring larger ones.

EXAMPLES

Students can measure the capacity of containers with different sizes and shapes.

"This bowl holds 10 yogurt cups of popcorn."

A small box can be used as a unit for measuring the volume of a larger box.

"I wonder how many small boxes I would need to make this big box."

LINKING CUBES

Linking cubes can be used as units for measuring **capacity or mass**, or students can use them to explore the **volumes** of rectangular prisms. (See *Volume: The Nonstandard Unit Stage* on page 523.)

EXAMPLE

Students could use cubes to build different rectangular prisms with a given volume.

"Both prisms have a volume of 10 cubes."

BLOCKS

Although we most often use rectangular prisms for measuring **volume**, any uniform blocks that pack (combine to fill space without gaps or overlap) work just as well. Examples include building blocks and pattern blocks.

EXAMPLE

Students can stack pattern blocks to build prisms, and then count blocks to determine their volume. For example, the triangle-based prism shown here has a volume of 6 triangle blocks. This experience will help them later when they are introduced to the formula for calculating the volume of a prism or cylinder: *Volume = Area of base × height.*

GEOMETRIC SOLIDS

Commercial geometric solids can be measured in order to determine their **volume** and **mass**.

EXAMPLE

Sets of solids contain several different types of prisms. Students can calculate their volumes by measuring the dimensions, and then multiplying the base area by the height. Students can also use nonstandard or standard units to determine and compare the masses of solids in nonstandard units or in grams.

"This pyramid has a mass of 15 pennies."

CENTICUBES

Centicubes are a commercial brand of linking cubes with a side length of 1 cm and a **volume** of 1 cm³. These cubes have a **mass** of 1 g and, if they were empty, would have a **capacity** of 1 mL. Thus, Centicubes can be excellent referents for **volume**, **mass**, and **capacity**.

There are also other centimetre cubes available, including base ten unit cubes, but they do not always link and their mass is not always 1 g.

EXAMPLE

A student who has built a prism out of Centicubes can simply count the cubes to determine its volume or mass. Thus, working with Centicubes can help students move from the nonstandard unit stage to the standard unit stage with regard to these measures.

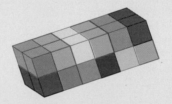

"This prism has a volume of 24 cm³ and a mass of 24 g."

BASE TEN BLOCKS

The basic unit in a set of base ten blocks is a cubic centimetre, so these blocks are good tools for measuring **volume** and **capacity**. Some sets can also be used to measure **mass** (if the unit cube has a mass of 1 g).

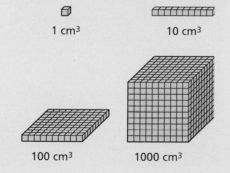

1 cm³   10 cm³

100 cm³   1000 cm³

EXAMPLE

A student could measure the **volume** of a box by making a model with base ten blocks.

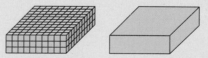

"It took 3 flats and 3 rods to build the model of the box, so it has a volume of 330 cm³."

(continued)

Capacity, Volume, and Mass: Examples of Manipulatives (Continued)

RULERS, METRE STICKS, AND TAPE MEASURES	EXAMPLE
Rulers, metre sticks, and tape measures can be used to measure lengths in order to make **volume** calculations with formulas. (See *Formulas for Measuring Volume* on page 526.)	A student can use a ruler to measure the edges of a rectangular prism, and then apply the formula *Volume = Area of base × height*. 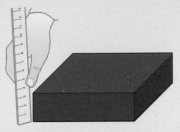 "Once I know the height, I can multiply it by the area of the bottom of the box to figure out the volume."

PAN BALANCES	EXAMPLE
Student-made or commercial pan balances can be used to compare **masses** or to measure masses with nonstandard or standard masses. (See *How Concepts of Mass Can Be Introduced* on page 530.)	Students could use standard masses on a pan balance to find something that has a mass of about 120 g. 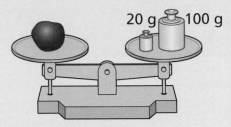 20 g 100 g "The plum has a mass of 120 g."

BATHROOM SCALES	EXAMPLE
Scales with kilogram measures can be used to determine the weight of objects that are too large to fit on a pan balance. As noted earlier, weight diverges from mass as the scale's location diverges from sea level. (Many scales have a feature that compensates for this.)	To calculate the weight of a heavy box, a student can use a bathroom scale to determine his or her own weight, with and without the box, and subtract to find the difference.  "The scale went from 41 kg to 44 kg, so the box I'm holding must be 3 kg."

Measuring Time and Temperature

Time and temperature are measurement topics that play important roles in students' everyday lives. From very early on, children are aware that the temperature influences what they wear, that there are things they do at certain times of the day, week, and year, and that some events take longer than others.

Introducing Time Concepts

Time can be represented using a linear model. For example, a student can sequence pictures of events by arranging them in a line and, to calculate elapsed time, he or she can visualize a timeline (see *Measuring and Calculating Elapsed Time* on page 548). Although time is often referred to as cyclical and can be modelled that way, time itself is actually linear. It is simply our descriptions of time—names of the hours in a day, names of the days of the weeks, names of the months and seasons, etc.—that cycle.

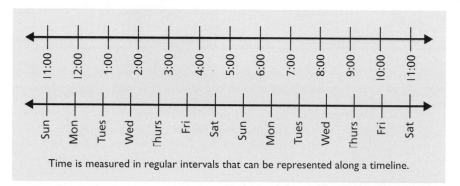

Time is measured in regular intervals that can be represented along a timeline.

Although timelines are linear, they can be cut out of paper and folded into a circle to show the cyclical nature of the names we use for hours and days. A "time circle" is a good tool to use for calculating elapsed time.

A time circle represents the cyclical nature of time.

Time, as a measurement, is about duration, or how long an event takes from beginning to end. To measure duration, students not only need to develop a personal understanding of how long time units last; they also need to learn to use time measurement tools such as clocks and calendars. Note that reading clocks or telling time has little to do with actually measuring time, except in circumstances where you must read a clock at the beginning and end of an event to figure out its duration.

Ideas about time can be introduced through the same three stages as other measurement concepts—definition/comparison, nonstandard unit, and standard unit.

How Concepts of Time Can Be Introduced

DEFINITION/COMPARISON

Students focus on sequencing familiar events and on comparing durations by starting two events simultaneously and comparing the end times.

Sequencing Events

"After I wake up, I eat breakfast, and then I walk to school."

Comparing Durations

Getty Images/Jayme Thornton

"My sister and I woke up at the same time. I know it took her longer to get ready and walk to school because she got to school after I did."

NONSTANDARD UNITS

Students use tools such as hourglasses or pendulums to measure time in nonstandard units.

"My mom timed me while I got dressed. She turned the egg timer over 4 times from when I started till when I was done."

STANDARD UNITS

Students learn to measure time in minutes, hours, and seconds.

Reading a Stopwatch

"It took me 1 hour and 13 minutes to get ready and walk to school."

Calculating Elapsed Time

Woke up   Arrived at school

"It took me 1 hour and 13 minutes to get ready and walk to school."

Time: The Definition/Comparison Stage

At the definition/comparison stage, students focus on the sequencing of events. These students often enjoy activities where they draw or organize a sequence of pictures to tell a story. The story might be about what happens before and after school, or after school and before supper. Students might also tell oral stories about what happened first, then next, then next, etc.

At this stage, students also compare the durations of two events to see which takes longer. Without units, the only way to compare durations is to start both events simultaneously and wait to see which one keeps going when the other is over. Many students will see the parallel to the measurement of length; the longer event extends farther than the shorter one.

Students in the definition/comparison stage are building vocabulary they can use to talk about time. They might tell what happened *first*, *last*, *next*, *before*, or *after*, or they might identify one event as *longer*, *shorter*, *faster*, or *slower* than another.

Time: The Nonstandard Unit Stage

Although students in the early grades are introduced to standard units such as hours and minutes, because these are used in everyday life, it still benefits them to work with nonstandard units to measure time duration before they begin using standard units to measure time. A broad experience with measuring in different ways will encourage students to build a better understanding of what it really means to measure time.

There are many nonstandard tools that students can use to measure duration, or elapsed time, including sand timers of various sizes, pendulums, and metronomes. For example, a student could use the number of pendulum swings to measure how long it takes someone to walk down the hall and back.

An advantage of many of the tools used for measuring time in nonstandard units is that they can be adjusted to measure time in a wide variety of unit sizes. Traditional metronomes, for example, can be reset for different speeds by adjusting the position of the weight. Pendulums can be adjusted by using longer or shorter strings, and sand clocks can be made with varying amounts of sand and different dimensions. Making adjustments like these helps students build a better understanding of the factors that influence how the size of the unit affects the resulting measurement.

Appropriate Nonstandard Units for Time

As with all other types of measurement, the key notion behind nonstandard units for measuring time is that the units must be uniform and appropriate. When using tools for measuring in nonstandard units, it is important for students to know that the tools must be used consistently to ensure uniformity. Very young children can use units such as claps or counting to measure time; however, students will eventually realize that it is not possible to ensure uniformity with units that vary from person to person. Tools such as metronomes, sand timers, and pendulums provide these uniform units. Shorter units are used to measure short durations or to increase precision, while longer units are used to measure longer durations.

Estimating Time with Nonstandard Units

It is valuable for students to learn to estimate time measurements, as well as to measure them. In order to learn to estimate, students require many opportunities to predict and check how many time units are necessary to accomplish a variety of tasks. As with other measurements, they can use activities with known durations as referents for estimating. For example, students might learn that a pendulum swings 7 times while they write their first name. Students could then use this information to estimate how many times the pendulum will swing as they write their full name or as they copy a sentence from the board.

A possible estimation activity is described in **Activity 20.12**.

Time: The Standard Unit Stage

The Système International (SI) standard unit of time is the second, but minutes and hours are usually introduced first because students use them more often in everyday life. Standard units of time should always be introduced in a way that relates them to students' own experiences, since personal experiences will give students a sense of what the units mean and help them establish referents they can use to estimate duration.

Standard Units of Time

MINUTES (min)

Defining a Minute

A *minute* is equal to 60 seconds. It is also $\frac{1}{60}$ of an hour.

Minute Referents

To help students get a feel for 1 minute, a teacher might use an estimating activity. First, students watch as the teacher times 1 minute. Then they put their heads down, and they raise their hands when they think 1 minute is over.

Other activities that will help students establish personal referents include problems such as the following:

- How many times can you write your name in 1 minute?
- How many times can you clap your hands in 1 minute?
- How high can you count in 1 minute?
- How far can you go saying the letters of the alphabet in 1 minute?

HOURS (h)

Defining an Hour

An *hour* is equal to 60 minutes.

Hour Referents

To help students establish personal referents for 1 hour, a teacher might pose problems such as the following:

- What takes you about 1 hour to do?
- How far could you walk in 1 hour?

Familiar referents for 1 hour might include the amount of time students spend in math class, the length of a favourite TV show, or how long they have for lunch and recess.

SECONDS (s)

Defining a Second

A *second* is the basic SI unit of time (see page 471).

Second Referents

To help students establish personal referents for seconds, a teacher might pose problems such as the following:

- What is something that takes about 1 second to do?
- What is something that takes about 10 seconds to do?
- How many seconds does it take you to walk 100 m? to run 100 m?

There are also other standard units that are used to measure longer spans of time. These include days, weeks, months, years, decades (10 years), centuries (100 years), and millennia (1000 years).

Standard Tools for Measuring Time

Students need to learn to tell time on both analog and digital clocks. The world is increasingly digital, but there are still many analog clocks in use. In addition, understanding analog time helps students make sense of common time-related terms. The analog clock makes it apparent why 9:15 can also be read as "a quarter past 9," as the minute hand has literally moved a quarter of the way around the clock. For a student to relate to 9:15 on a digital clock as a quarter past the hour, he or she would have to employ a considerable amount of number sense, realizing that 15 minutes is $\frac{1}{4}$ of 60 minutes.

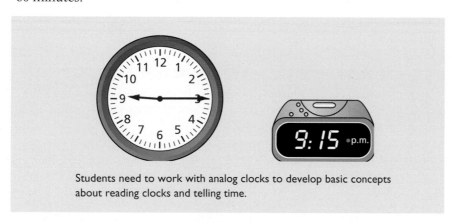

Students need to work with analog clocks to develop basic concepts about reading clocks and telling time.

Most students are readily able to read the time on a digital clock, but teachers need to be aware that, without an understanding of clock time, the times may not have much meaning for students. For example, a student might see 7:54 and read "seven fifty-four" without recognizing that this means it is almost 8:00.

For students to make sense of digital times, they need to understand

- there are 24 hours in a day and they are numbered from 1 a.m. to 12 noon, and again from 1 p.m. to 12 midnight (24-hour time is introduced later)
- there are 60 minutes in 1 hour

Initially students learn that there are two hands on an analog clock—the minute hand and the hour hand—and that the minute hand is longer. Some teachers have students make their own paper-plate clocks with the hands labelled. (For teacher modelling, a geared clock is more suitable because it shows the movement of the hour hand as well as the movement of the minute hand.) Students usually have little difficulty telling time to the hour with an analog clock. Times that fall between the hours are more challenging until students know more about how these clocks work.

ACTIVITY 20.13

Ask students to talk about their favourite times in the day and what an analog clock would look like at each of those times.

_____

Spatial Reasoning

The chart on the next page outlines some of the typical challenges that analog clocks pose and that cause difficulties for students.

What Students Need to Know about Analog Clocks

MOVEMENT OF THE HANDS

As the minute hand travels around the clock during each hour, the hour hand moves much more slowly from one number to the next. For "in-between" times, the hour hand does not point directly at the number you need to say.

At 6:25, the hour hand does not point to the 6.

CLOCK NUMBERS AND MINUTES

The numbers on a clock (1, 2, ..., 12) correspond to the hours, not to the minutes. For example, when the minute hand points to the 1, you say the time is "5 after" not "1 after."

The ability to interpret the number of minutes after the hour can depend on students' comfort with counting by 5s.

DIFFERENT MEANINGS FOR DIFFERENT HANDS

We say different words when different hands point to the same number on the clock. For example, if the hour hand points to the 6, we say *six*, but if the minute hand points to the 6, we say *thirty*. As a result, students need to be very attentive to the hand lengths as well as the numbers.

6:00

12:30

TIMES WITH MORE THAN ONE NAME

If the time falls more than halfway through the hour, we can read it as a number of minutes after one hour, or as a number of minutes before the next.

We can read this time as "3:40" or as "20 to 4."

ACTIVITY 20.14

Ask students what time it might be if

- the minute hand is pointed to a spot between 3 and 4
- the hour hand is pointed to a spot between 1 and 2
- the hour hand and minute hand are both pointed directly at numbers

Spatial Reasoning

Because of these difficulties, teachers usually sequence work with analog time so students learn to tell time to the hour, then to the half hour, to the quarter hour, to the nearest 5 minutes, and finally to the nearest minute. If a clock also has a second hand, telling time to the minute can be especially challenging because students need to observe the position of the second hand as well as the minute and hour hands.

Teachers should be aware that setting the time on a digital or analog clock is a different skill from simply reading the time. Most curriculum expectations/outcomes are about reading clocks, so this should be the focus of classroom activities. However, it is a useful life skill to be able to set a watch or clock. For some students, this will come later. Many interesting problems can be set related to the position of hands on a clock (see **Activity 20.14**).

A.M. and P.M.

Time is usually described in ordinary speech using the 12-hour clock, in which the hours cycle from 1:00 in the morning until 12:00 noon, and then repeat the cycle from 1:00 in the afternoon until midnight. Since having two times with the same name in a single day has the potential to be confusing, you can specify whether you mean morning or evening by using the acronyms "a.m." and "p.m." These stand for the Latin words *ante meridiem* and *post meridiem*, which mean "before noon" and "after noon," respectively. A good way to introduce the concept of a.m. and p.m. is to use a full-day timeline.

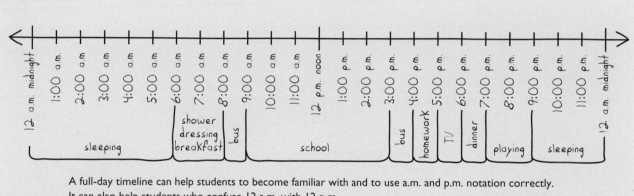

A full-day timeline can help students to become familiar with and to use a.m. and p.m. notation correctly. It can also help students who confuse 12 a.m. with 12 p.m.

24-Hour Time

Eventually, it is important for students to learn about the 24-hour time system, since they will encounter it in everyday life, particularly when they travel. Airports often post times using the 24-hour clock, and students may find that their own watches or computer clocks offer them the option of using 24-hour time. The convention for reporting times in the 24-hour system is to use 4 digits, so times that occur before noon are usually reported with a 0, for example, 04:35 for 4:35 a.m.

The 24-hour clock is used because it eliminates ambiguity—there is only one 11:23 in the day, not two. This can help to ensure that passengers arrive for a plane at the right time, but people often find it convenient to convert 24-hour times that occur after noon to more familiar 12-hour times. The conversion process is simple once students understand that they can simply subtract 12 hours—16:20 is the same as 4:20 p.m.

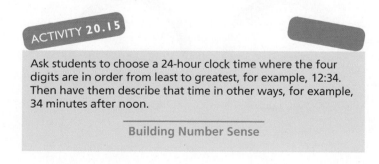

ACTIVITY 20.15

Ask students to choose a 24-hour clock time where the four digits are in order from least to greatest, for example, 12:34. Then have them describe that time in other ways, for example, 34 minutes after noon.

Building Number Sense

It is interesting to measure elapsed time when time zones are crossed. For example, you might ask what time a plane will land if a 1.5-hour flight from Toronto to Winnipeg leaves at 8:10 a.m.

Building Number Sense

Measuring and Calculating Elapsed Time

Sometimes students measure elapsed time using tools such as stopwatches. This is usually when the duration is short. For longer durations, it is often necessary to determine the duration of an event from two reported times. For example, a student who arrived at a game at 6:45 and left at 8:25 might want to find out how much time he or she spent at the game. There are a number of approaches for calculating elapsed time.

Ways to Calculate Elapsed Time—from 6:45 to 8:25

USING A TIMELINE

Students could sketch or visualize a timeline as an aid in helping them "count up" (or back) from one time to the other.

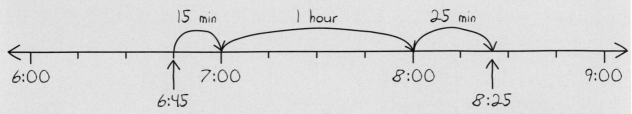

"1 hour + 15 minutes + 25 minutes = 1 hour 40 minutes"

USING A CLOCK FACE

Students could refer to or visualize the clock face to help them "count up" (or back) from one time to the other.

Counting Up

"6:45 to 7:45 is 1 h. 7:45 to 8:15 is 30 min. 8:15 to 8:25 is 10 min. That's 1 h and 30, ..., 40 min."

Counting Back

"6:45 to 8:45 is 2 h. 8:45 back to 8:25 is 20 min. 2 h subtract 20 min is 1 h and 40 min."

Introducing Temperature Concepts

Temperature is usually considered linear because of the tool used most often to measure it—the linear analog thermometer.

Temperature measurement is usually taught quite differently from other types of measurement. Rather than introducing work with temperature through the three stages that have been discussed for each of the other measurements, teachers usually only work through the definition/comparison stage and the standard unit stage (because it would be difficult to create nonstandard units). Those stages can be handled quite efficiently in the context of work students do in other subject areas, especially science. It can be included in work with the calendar and the seasons as well.

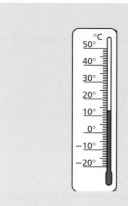

Most analog thermometers use a linear scale to measure temperature.

How Concepts of Temperature Can Be Introduced

DEFINITION/COMPARISON

Students talk about how hot (or cold) something feels by making reference to personal experiences such as outdoor temperatures or familiar foods.

"The water in the red glass is warm, like bathwater. The other water is cold, like juice out of the fridge."

USING STANDARD UNITS

Students learn to use a typical thermometer and are introduced to degrees Celsius, although they rarely have a sense of what a degree is. However, they do come to recognize that one item is warmer than another if the line of colour inside the thermometer reaches farther along the number line.

"The water in the red glass is 40°C. The other water is much colder—it's 15°C."

Interpreting Negative Temperatures

When students are measuring the daily temperature throughout the year, they may sometimes encounter temperatures that are less than 0°C. Because these temperatures are meaningful for them, and because the thermometer provides a concrete model for comparing these with warmer temperatures, young children are often ready to read and compare negative numbers on a thermometer long before integers have been formally introduced. The children might begin by referring to these temperatures in terms of the number of degrees below zero. For example, a winter day might have a temperature of "5 degrees below 0." This is a good time for the teacher to point out the negative signs on the thermometer and introduce the idea that another way to say this is "negative 5°C."

Estimating Temperatures

To estimate temperatures in degrees Celsius, students need to develop personal referents for certain benchmark temperatures. They should know that

- it is cold enough to freeze water when the temperature reaches 0°C
- it is a nice spring day if the temperature is 20°C
- a person's body temperature is about 37°C
- water boils at 100°C

These referents can then be used as points of comparison for other temperatures. For example:

- "The hot water from the tap feels warmer than my body temperature but it's certainly not hot enough to boil, so it must be between 37°C and 100°C."
- "There was ice on the puddle in the morning so the temperature must have dropped below 0°C last night."

Measuring and Calculating Temperature Change

Students might use a vertical number line, which relates directly to a thermometer scale, to measure temperature change. Many students find changes in temperature particularly difficult to interpret when the change is from a negative temperature to a positive one. For example, you can use a vertical number line to show that if the temperature is $-3°C$ in the morning and $+7°C$ in the afternoon, the temperature has increased by $3 + 7 = 10$ degrees.

Common Errors and Misconceptions

Time and Temperature: Common Errors, Misconceptions, and Strategies

COMMON ERROR OR MISCONCEPTION	SUGGESTED STRATEGY
Comparing Durations by End Time Some young children look at end times to compare the duration of events, but do not consider the start times. For example, they say that something took more time because it ended at 8:30 instead of 8:00.	To help students recognize that elapsed time measures the length of time from start to end, a teacher might show two wind-up toys and ask students to predict which will run longer. The teacher could then start one toy, wait for a noticeable amount of time, and then start the other. Many students will recognize that this is not a fair test unless the toys are started at the same time. The teacher could then ask a student to help by winding one of the toys so both can be started at the same time.

COMMON ERROR OR MISCONCEPTION	SUGGESTED STRATEGY

Misusing a Sand Timer

When students measure time with a sand timer, some do not wait for the timer to empty completely before turning it over, while others wait too long.

A sand timer being turned too early

Ask students to watch a sand timer as you time an event and to raise their hands when it is time to turn it over. Afterwards, discuss what would have happened if you had turned the timer too soon (the event would have been measured with a greater number of units), or if you had forgotten to turn the timer when the sand stopped (the event would have been measured with a lesser number of units). Remind students that whenever they measure, it is important to use units that are all the same size. Turning a sand timer at the moment when the sand runs out ensures that the time units will all be the same.

Locating the Hour Hand

Students do not position the hour hand on a clock to reflect the number of minutes after the hour.

Incorrect hour-hand position for 7:45

Students need to discuss how the hour hand moves over the course of each hour. Some teachers use a clock with only an hour hand, showing students how it is possible to estimate the amount of the hour that has passed by looking at just the hour hand.

| about 4:00 | about 4:30 | about 4:55 |

Misinterpreting Minutes on a Clock Face

Students who are learning to tell time on an analog clock may have trouble reading the number of minutes before or after the hour.

1:15

"It's 3 after 1."

This happens because the numbers on a clock directly identify the hour, but the minutes have to be determined by counting by 5s.

Students need to know that there are 60 minutes in one hour, and they need lots of practice reading clocks in the context of everyday classroom activities, not just during math class. For example, a teacher might ask, "What time is it now? How many minutes do we have for tidying up before recess starts?" Teachers must explicitly model how they tell time by talking out loud and pointing to the clock. For example, a teacher might say, "The hour hand is pointing to just past the 1—that means it's just after 1 o'clock. The minute hand is pointing here—that's 5, 10, 15 minutes after the hour. It's 15 minutes after 1."

Some analog clocks and watches have small minute numbers around the edge of the clock face. If the classroom clock does not have these numbers, a teacher could attach sticky notes (5, 10, 15, etc.) around the circumference of the clock face.

(continued)

Time and Temperature: Common Errors, Misconceptions, and Strategies (Continued)

COMMON ERROR OR MISCONCEPTION	SUGGESTED STRATEGY
Number of Seconds in an Hour Students think that there are 60 seconds in an hour.	This may happen because there are 60 seconds in 1 minute and 60 minutes in 1 hour, so students mistakenly assume that there are always 60 smaller time units in a larger one. If a student responds this way, ask the student to suggest an event that might take about an hour, such as a TV program. Then, with the student, watch a second hand on a clock complete 60 seconds. Ask, • That was 60 s. Was that the same as an hour? • If it wasn't an hour, then what was it? (minute) Through discussion, help the student see that there are 60 seconds in 1 minute, and 60 groups of 60 seconds, or 3600 seconds, in 1 hour.
Confusing 12 a.m. and 12 p.m. Many people confuse 12 a.m. and 12 p.m., thinking that because a.m. means morning, 12 a.m. must be noon.	A timeline is a good tool for helping students remember that, by convention, 12 a.m. represents midnight and 12 p.m. represents noon. (See *A.M. and P.M.* on page 547.)
Interpreting a 24-Hour Clock To convert a 24-hour clock time such as 16:20 to a 12-hour equivalent, students will often subtract 10 hours rather than 12 hours because of their familiarity with the place value system for numbers.  16:20 "16:20 must mean 6:20 p.m."	Make a timeline that shows the 24-hour times aligned with their 12-hour equivalents. Then have students align equivalent times to see that, beginning after noon, there is always a difference of 12 hours between 24-hour times and their 12-hour equivalents. 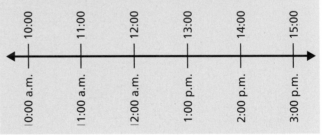
Misinterpreting Times Shown with Decimals Although people usually do not use decimals with times, students might encounter times written this way, for example, 7.5 hours. A student might think that this means 7 hours and 5 minutes.	Use a clock face to show the decimal part of the hour. Remind students that 0.5 means 5 tenths, or half, so 7.5 hours means 7 hours and another half hour, or 7 hours and 30 minutes.
Calculating Elapsed Time across the Hour Students sometimes have difficulty calculating elapsed times that bridge from one hour to the next. For example, one student might mistakenly determine that an event lasting from 7:25 p.m. until 8:15 p.m. lasts 1 hour and 10 minutes (since $8 \text{ h} - 7 \text{ h} = 1 \text{ h}$, and $25 \text{ min} - 15 \text{ min} = 10 \text{ min}$), while another student might say it lasts 1 hour and 50 minutes (because there are 50 minutes from 25 after until a quarter after, and 1 hour from 7 till 8).	Teachers can use a geared clock or a timeline to help students visualize how much time actually passes.  "35 minutes to 8 o'clock and another 15 minutes to 8:15 is 50 minutes."

COMMON ERROR OR MISCONCEPTION	SUGGESTED STRATEGY
Reading Temperatures between Scale Numbers Most students find it easier to read temperatures that are labelled on the scale, such as 10°C or 20°C, than temperatures that fall between scale numbers, such as 37°C.  "The temperature is 30.7°C."	Provide blackline master thermometers with every 10°C labelled, and with space for students to label smaller scale marks in between in 1° increments. Discuss what the unlabelled scale marks mean and have the students label them. Then ask students to point to where given temperatures would be on the thermometer. For example, 35°C would be halfway between 30°C and 40°C, but 30.5°C would be halfway between 30°C and 31°C.
Misreading Negative Temperatures When reading negative temperatures, students may incorrectly interpret temperatures that fall between the labelled increments. 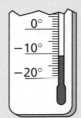 "It's right below −10°C, so it's −9°C."	In the early grades (before integer number lines have been introduced), any work with negative temperatures should be very informal, and should be directly related to a meaningful context, such as the outdoor temperature. At this stage, students may find it useful to refer to negative temperatures in terms of the number of degrees "below 0." If they count down from 0, they will see that the temperature shown at left is actually 11 degrees below 0, not 9.

Appropriate Manipulatives

Time: Examples of Manipulatives

NONSTANDARD TIMERS	EXAMPLE
Tools such as sand timers, pendulums, and metronomes are useful for measuring time in uniform nonstandard units. These tools can be adjusted so the units are longer or shorter, depending on what is being measured.	The weight on a metronome can be adjusted to create a variety of different units for measuring duration. For example, students might use a longer unit to measure how long it takes to eat a snack. A shorter unit could be used to measure how long it takes to walk from the front of the room to the back. 

A metronome

Josep M. Penalver Rufas/Shutterstock

(*continued*)

Time: Examples of Manipulatives (Continued)

KITCHEN TIMERS	EXAMPLE
Kitchen timers are useful for working with minutes because they can be set to go off at the end of a given time period.	Kitchen timers are especially useful for estimating activities and for developing personal referents for short periods of time. (See *Minute Referents* on page 544.) For example, students can establish personal referents for 1 minute by finding out how many steps they can take in 1 minute, or how many times they can repeat the alphabet in 1 minute.

A kitchen timer

DIGITAL AND ANALOG CLOCKS	EXAMPLE
Digital and analog clocks, including an alarm clock, can be used to provide contexts for solving problems, to provide practice with telling time, and to give students a sense of the duration of various lengths of time.	Clocks can be used to introduce the standard units of time. A teacher might set an alarm clock to go off every hour, or invite students to sit still as one minute passes on a digital or analog clock.

STOPWATCHES	EXAMPLE
Stopwatches can be used to determine the duration of various events.	Students can work in pairs to time each other as they complete activities, such as printing their full names. Then they can compare the results to see who took less time.

LEARNING CLOCKS	EXAMPLE
Learning clocks, made by attaching card-stock hands to a paper plate with a metal fastener, can be used to provide practice with reading and setting analog times. The process of making the clock ensures that each student will recognize the parts of an analog clock. Commercial learning clocks are available as well, some with gears that move the hour hand with the minute hand. Demonstration learning clocks are handy for both the teacher and students to show a large group a specific time.	Students can be asked to set their clocks to times they have drawn out of a hat.

Temperature: Examples of Manipulatives

THERMOMETERS	EXAMPLE
Students will need easy-to-read linear analog thermometers to practise reading temperatures. There are also large demonstration thermometers and overhead thermometers that teachers and students could use to, for example, show the temperature outside. It is also useful to provide blackline master versions of thermometers that students can colour to show different temperatures.	Students might use a thermometer to measure and keep a record of the outside temperature at the same time every day.  "It's a bit more than 10°C—maybe about 12°C."
STUDENT-MADE THERMOMETERS	**EXAMPLE**
Student-made thermometers, made by inserting a ribbon that is coloured part white and part red into a cardboard thermometer outline, can be used to provide practice with showing different temperatures.	Students can be asked to set their thermometers to benchmark temperatures, such as the temperature at which water freezes (0°C) or standard body temperature (37°C). 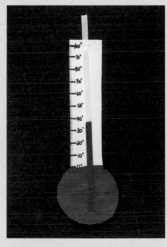 This student recognized that, to show 37°C, he had to move the string so the red ended just below the 40°C mark.

Measuring Angles

Like volume, angle measurement is generally introduced later than some other types of measurement.

The measurement of angles is considered to be a geometry topic in some curriculums and a measurement topic in others. In some curriculums, certain aspects of the topic of angles are found in both strands.

One important reason for learning how to measure angles is that angle comparisons are integral to many geometry concepts. For example, students might measure angles in order to determine whether a triangle is *acute* or *obtuse*, whether two shapes are *congruent* or *similar*, or whether a four-sided shape has four right angles, making it a rectangle.

An angle is formed by two line segments or rays with a common endpoint, which is referred to as the *vertex* of the angle. The line segments or rays are called the *arms* of the angle.

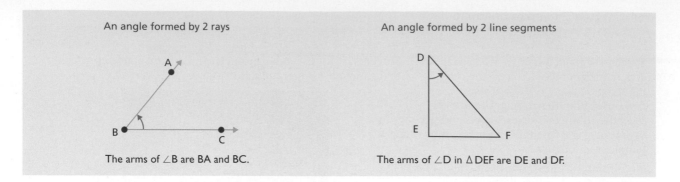

An angle formed by 2 rays

An angle formed by 2 line segments

The arms of ∠B are BA and BC.

The arms of ∠D in △DEF are DE and DF.

Because angles in 2-D are defined as two rays with a common endpoint, the question is, How can you measure them? You do not want to use the area inside the angle as a measure, since you want angles to have the same measure whether their arms are long or short.

Two approaches avoid this problem. One approach is to think of the measure of an angle in terms of what fraction of a circle it is.

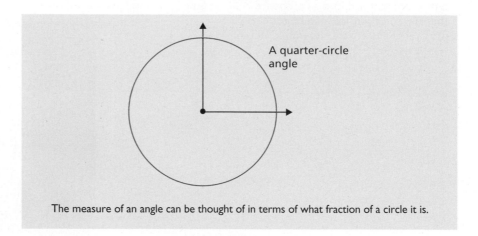

A quarter-circle angle

The measure of an angle can be thought of in terms of what fraction of a circle it is.

The other approach is to think of the measurement this way: Imagine attaching two thin strips of card stock with a paper fastener and positioning them so one is exactly on top of the other. Then imagine rotating the top arm counterclockwise around the joint (called the vertex) until it reaches the correct position; what you measure is the amount of rotation.

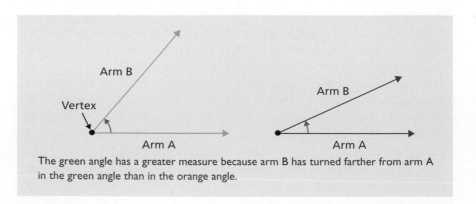

Arm B

Vertex

Arm A

Arm B

Arm A

The green angle has a greater measure because arm B has turned farther from arm A in the green angle than in the orange angle.

To build an understanding of the connection between angles and turns, students benefit from opportunities to model angles by physically turning arms made from cardboard strips or commercial Geostrips (see page 565) fastened together at one end or by physically all moving in unison in response to teacher directions.

Introducing Angle Concepts

Ideas about angles can be introduced through the same three stages as other measurement concepts—definition/comparison, nonstandard unit, and standard unit. Since angles are introduced later than some other types of measurement, students can move fairly quickly through the first two stages. Many teachers bypass the first two stages, but each stage provides students with experiences that will help them develop a better understanding of angle measure.

How Concepts of Angles Can Be Introduced

DEFINITION/COMPARISON

Students compare angles by aligning one arm of one angle with the corresponding arm of the other. The angle that "sticks out" is larger. They can do this directly, by superimposing one angle on top of the other, or indirectly, by creating a model of one angle and comparing it to the other angle.

Direct Comparison

"The blue angle is bigger because the red one fits inside it and there's still room left over."

Indirect Comparison

"The blue angle is bigger because the model of the red angle fits inside it and there's still room left over."

NONSTANDARD UNITS

Students compare angles by measuring both angles with nonstandard units and comparing the measurements to determine how much larger one angle is than the other.

"The blue angle is bigger because it has room for 2 pattern block corners, and the red angle only has room for 1 of the same block."

(continued)

How Concepts of Angles Can Be Introduced (Continued)

Students compare angles by measuring both angles in degrees with a protractor and comparing the measurements to determine how much larger one angle is than the other.

"The blue angle is 60° and the red angle is only 35°, so the blue angle is greater."

Angles: The Definition/Comparison Stage

To determine which of two angles is greater, students at the definition/comparison stage can compare angles directly or indirectly. If the angles are "concrete" angles in, for example, pattern block shapes, a direct comparison is simple. If the angles are pictorial, students can either compare directly by cutting out one angle and placing it on top of the other, or compare a model of one of the angles (made using cardboard arms fastened with a paper fastener at one end) with the other angle.

Comparing angles indirectly by using a concrete model

Using concrete materials to model angles is important at this stage, since it helps students develop a definition of what an angle is, and how it is created by rotating one arm away from the other. This is also the stage at which students learn to use the vocabulary terms *vertex* and *arm* to refer to the parts of the angle.

Angles: The Nonstandard Unit Stage

Nonstandard units make it possible to assign a number to an angle measurement, allowing students to record the measurements of many angles so they can be compared without having to be tested repeatedly.

Students can use a paper angle model of any size as a nonstandard unit for measuring. For example, if the unit selected were the red model shown below at the left, the measures of the angles on the right would be 2 reds, 3 reds, and $1\frac{1}{2}$ reds, respectively.

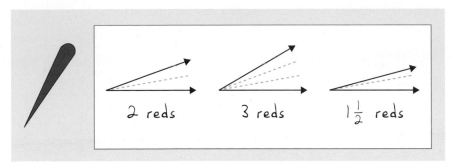

Although nonstandard units for measuring angles are easy to cut out of card stock or waxed paper, it also makes sense to use readily accessible angles such as the vertices of commercial geometric shapes. Pattern blocks, green and tan blocks in particular, make excellent nonstandard units and are readily available in many classrooms. The smaller angle of the tan block is 30°, so this block can be used to measure with a reasonable amount of precision. The relationship between the angles in the green and tan blocks makes them good tools for measuring the same angle with different units.

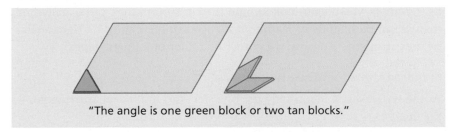

"The angle is one green block or two tan blocks."

A Nonstandard Unit Protractor

Students can create their own nonstandard unit protractors out of transparent paper, such as waxed or parchment paper. They simply cut out a large circle, perhaps about 12 cm in diameter, and then fold it in half and in half again until they have folded four times. When they unfold the paper, students have a transparent circular protractor that can be used to measure angles in nonstandard units.

Start with a large circle.   Fold four times.   Use the "protractor" to measure angles in nonstandard units.

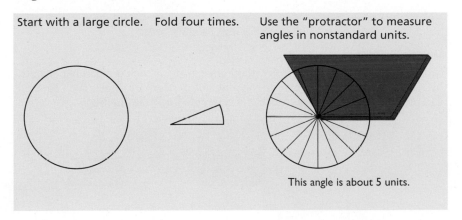

This angle is about 5 units.

Using a Full Turn as a Nonstandard Unit

Students at the nonstandard unit stage can interpret angles as fractions of a full turn. In essence, the full turn is being used as the nonstandard unit. Thinking of angles this way provides a good foundation for the later introduction of degrees, and for the use of a circular protractor.

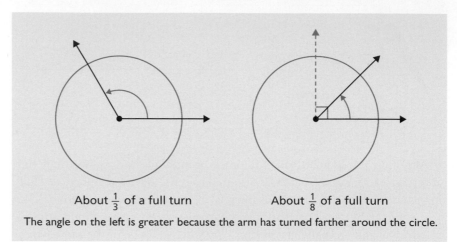

About $\frac{1}{3}$ of a full turn   About $\frac{1}{8}$ of a full turn

The angle on the left is greater because the arm has turned farther around the circle.

Angles: The Standard Unit Stage

The first standard unit angle students usually encounter is the *right angle*, or 90° angle. If students look around the classroom, they can usually find many examples. Students learn to test angles to see if they are right angles by measuring them against the corner of a ruler or a square block.

Standard Units for Measuring Angles

At the K–8 level, students only use one standard unit to measure angles—the degree.

DEGREES (°)

Defining a Degree

A degree is $\frac{1}{360}$ of the amount of turn needed to complete a full circle.

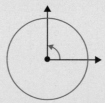

This turn measures $\frac{1}{4}$ of 360° or 90°.

Degree Referents

Most students do not have a very good sense of 1°, which is a barely perceptible angle, but they often develop referents for benchmark angles such as 90°, 45°, and 60°. Pattern blocks are useful referents for these angles.

90°   45°   60°

DEGREES (°)

Degree Referents

An analog clock face is another useful aid for establishing angle referents:

- 30° is the size of an angle formed between adjacent numbers.
- 60° is the size of an angle formed between numbers that are 2 apart.
- 90° is the size of an angle formed between numbers that are 3 apart.

A 30° angle

Classifying Angles

Angles can be classified by how they relate to a 90° angle, a 180° angle, or a 360° angle. Note that, while an angle is usually marked with an arc (to indicate its relationship to a turn), a special notation (a small square) is used to indicate a 90° angle.

Classifying Angles

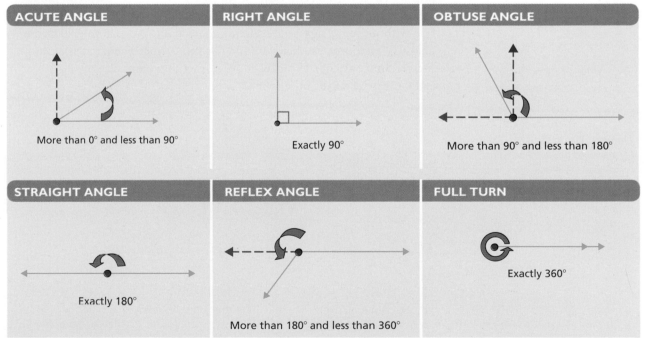

ACUTE ANGLE	RIGHT ANGLE	OBTUSE ANGLE
More than 0° and less than 90°	Exactly 90°	More than 90° and less than 180°

STRAIGHT ANGLE	REFLEX ANGLE	FULL TURN
Exactly 180°	More than 180° and less than 360°	Exactly 360°

Tools for Measuring Angles in Standard Units

Because 1° represents $\frac{1}{360}$ of the amount of turn needed to complete a full circle, you use a circular or semicircular device called a protractor to measure angles.

Ask students to draw two shapes with three of the angles less than 45°. One shape should have a lot more sides than the other. Have them describe the sizes of any other angles in the shape.

Critical Thinking

There are two scales on most protractors because the amount of turn can be measured in either a clockwise or a counterclockwise direction. This can, however, be confusing for students if they always choose to measure from a particular side; therefore, it may be easier for students to begin with single-scale protractors. (Note that either arm of the angle can be used as a base for measuring.) The circular protractor will help students see angles as parts of a full turn, but if they are measuring only angles less than 180°, then a semicircular protractor would be just as convenient.

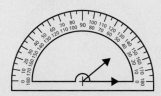

To measure an angle, place one arm of the angle on the 0° line, and use the scale to determine the number of degrees that fall between the two arms.

Later, students will be able to use the more common protractor, with two sets of numbers around the edge. To choose the correct scale, students should use estimation skills to compare the angle with a benchmark angle such as 180°, 90°, or 45°, and then look at the scale to see which measurement makes more sense. It also helps if students think about what they are measuring—the number of degrees between the starting arm, which is positioned at 0°, and the other arm. (If they recognize the 10° intervals on the protractor, then they can make a reasonable estimate of an angle's size without referring to the scale numbers at all. For example, each angle below is obviously less than 90°, and fills six 10° increments on the protractor, so a measure of 60° makes more sense than a measure of 120° (which is the measure on the other scale).

Using a Double-Scale Protractor

USING THE INNER SCALE	USING THE OUTER SCALE
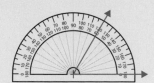	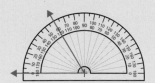
The blue angle is 60°.	The blue angle is 60°.
The starting arm of the angle points to 0° on the inner scale, so the inner scale is used to measure the angle.	The starting arm of the angle points to 0° on the outer scale, so the outer scale is used to measure the angle.

ACTIVITY 20.19

- Ask students to cut out the shapes shown.

- Have them put the shapes in order according to how many sides they have.

- Then ask them to measure the angles at the vertices of each shape. Ask what they notice.

Looking for angle patterns in regular polygons

Spatial Reasoning

Students can also relate angles to images of familiar turns, such as quarter turns and half turns, in order to get a better sense of benchmark angles such as 90°, 180°, 270°, and 360°. For example, once students learn that there are 360° in a full turn, it becomes clearer to them why a quarter turn is sometimes called a 90° turn.

ACTIVITY 20.20

An interesting activity for students is to place a set of hinged flat mirrors along two adjacent sides of a polygon. They will see reflections of the polygon along with the actual polygon. By dividing 360° by the sum of the number of reflection images plus the actual polygon, students can calculate the size of the polygon's angle.

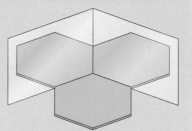

Since 3 hexagons fit in 360°, each angle must be 120°.

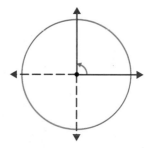

A 90° angle can be thought of as $\frac{1}{4}$ of a full turn.

Spatial Reasoning

Common Errors and Misconceptions

Angles: Common Errors, Misconceptions, and Strategies

COMMON ERROR OR MISCONCEPTION	SUGGESTED STRATEGY
Confusing Angle Measure with Arm Length Some students may think that arm length has something to do with the size of an angle.  "The red angle is bigger." This misconception can be particularly problematic when students are working with geometric shapes. For example, a student might think that one angle is bigger than another simply because it is located inside a triangle with a larger area.	Through working with angles of different arm lengths, students learn that it is the amount of turn and not the length of the arm that is important in describing the measurement of the angle. It may help to demonstrate with two pairs of Geo-strips—one short pair and one long pair, each attached at one end. Fit the pairs one over the other, and then turn both the same amount at the same time. 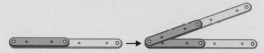 Even though the yellow and green angles have arms of different lengths, the amount of turn is the same. *(continued)*

Angles: Common Errors, Misconceptions, and Strategies (Continued)

COMMON ERROR OR MISCONCEPTION	SUGGESTED STRATEGY

Wrong Scale on the Protractor

Students use the wrong scale on a protractor to measure an angle. For example, a student might record the size of this angle as 120°.

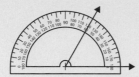

"It says this angle is 120°."

The ability to choose the correct scale depends on the student's conceptual understanding of what is being measured. If a student realizes that the measurement represents a turn through part of a 360° circle, and if the student thinks about known benchmark angles such as 90° and 180°, then it is easy to tell which scale to use. For example, the angle at left is obviously less than 90°, so a 60° measure makes sense but a 120° measure does not.

If students are having difficulty with standard protractors, it may be preferable to offer them a circular protractor, ideally one with a single scale. However, it is even more important to make sure that students understand what the degree markings on the protractor really mean.

Misaligning the Protractor

Sometimes a student measures an angle incorrectly by lining up the base of the angle along the edge of the protractor rather than the 0° line.

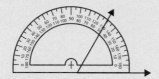

"It says this angle is 50°."

If students are misaligning the protractor, remind them that the crosshairs on the protractor represent the centre of a full turn, and that this is where they should place the vertex of the angle to measure the turn of the angle in degrees. Point to the 0° mark and emphasize that it is useful to align one arm with 0° in order to find out how far it would have to turn to reach the other arm.

It may also help to ask a student to compare his or her measurement of an angle with one obtained by another student, and to talk about why the two measurements are different.

Misinterpreting "Right" Angles

A student who usually sees right angles presented in the same orientation may think that the term "right" has something to do with the direction in which the arms are pointing. This student might not recognize a differently oriented angle as a right angle, and might even refer to it as a "left" angle.

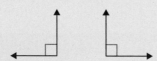

For some students, it may be preferable to use the term "square corner," rather than right angle. Students also need to see right angles (and non–right angles) in many different positions before they will fully grasp the concept.

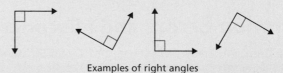

Examples of right angles

Not Recognizing 180° Angles as Angles

Many students cannot accept that the picture below shows an angle and not just a line.

Connect two Geostrips so they form an angle of 0°. Start turning one of the two strips as students observe. They will see that, as the strip turns, the size of the angle moves from 0° through a series of other angles, including 90°, until it finally reaches 180° (halfway around a full circle). Discuss how it makes sense that if 90° represents a quarter turn, then 180° represents a half turn. Let a student check with a protractor to see that the straight angle measures 180°.

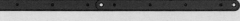

A straight angle represents a half turn.

COMMON ERROR OR MISCONCEPTION	SUGGESTED STRATEGY
Angles That Do Not Reach the Protractor Scale Sometimes students have difficulty measuring an angle whose arms are too short to reach the protractor scale. 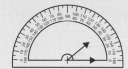 "I can't tell how big it is."	Students will often encounter situations like this one, especially if they are measuring angles in a textbook or angles inside geometric shapes. It is important to talk about these situations, and to discuss possible strategies. For example, if the angle is on paper, students may be able to extend the arms with a ruler and pencil. If it is in a textbook, they can trace the angle on paper and then extend the arms. If the angle cannot be extended directly, a student could position one arm along the baseline, and then align a ruler with the other arm so the ruler meets the scale. If the angle does not need to be measured precisely, then the student may simply be able to "eyeball" the measurement.

Appropriate Manipulatives

Angles: Examples of Manipulatives

GEOSTRIPS	EXAMPLE
Geostrips are strips that can be connected to form angles and/or polygons. Similar tools can be created from strips of card stock connected with paper fasteners, or students can simply use a bent pipe cleaner. When students are using these tools to measure angles, emphasize that it is important to measure against the angle formed inside the two strips, rather than the one formed outside, because the inside angle has a more obvious vertex.	Students can use Geostrips to practise their angle estimation skills. For example, when a teacher calls out a measure such as 45°, students try to create that angle with Geostrips, and then check by measuring the results.  "45° is half as big as a right angle, so I think it looks like this."

PATTERN BLOCKS	EXAMPLE
A variety of pattern blocks and other polygons should be on hand so students can compare their interior angles or use them as nonstandard units for measuring angles.	Students at the standard unit stage could measure all the different angles they can make by putting two pattern-block corners together. 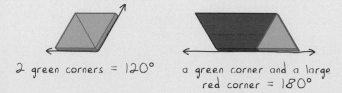 Combining pattern blocks to make angles *(continued)*

Angles: Examples of Manipulatives (Continued)

FRACTION CIRCLES

Fraction circles are circles that are divided into equal parts through the centre. Students can cut out sectors from different circles and compare the angles by superimposing or measuring. These sectors could also be used as nonstandard units for measuring other angles.

EXAMPLE

Students might also use fraction circles to explore what happens to the central angles as a pizza is sliced into more and more pieces.

As the number of slices increases, the central angle gets smaller.

PROTRACTORS

Protractors are used to measure and construct angles and polygons. (See page 403.) They come in semicircular and circular forms, and some are available with a single scale.

The circular form reinforces the concept that angles are parts of a circle and allows students to get a better feel for what angles look like when they are greater than 180°.

Although you generally think of protractors as tools for measuring in standard units, it is also possible for students to make nonstandard-unit protractors.

EXAMPLE

Either type of protractor could be used to measure angles less than 180°, but only the circular protractor could be used to directly measure angles greater than 180°.

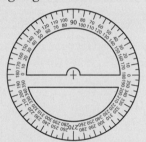

Circular protractor

GEOBOARDS AND SQUARE DOT PAPER

On a geoboard, students use elastics to create angles and polygons. They can keep a record of their work by drawing shapes they have created on square dot paper.

There are many different sizes of square geoboards. Their "dimensions" are determined by the number of pins.

Geoboards have a wide range of uses, for example, to create and measure angles, to examine the angle properties of polygons, and to explore similarity and congruence. (See pages 424–429.)

Square geoboards are used most often, but triangular and circular geoboards are also available. The latter are particularly useful for dividing circular regions into congruent parts in order to explore the angles at the centre of shapes to the vertices.

EXAMPLE

Students who are using standard units might want to see how many different angles (less than 180°) they can create on a square geoboard of a given size. They can draw pictures of the angles on dot paper and record the measure of each angle, identifying it as acute, right, or obtuse.

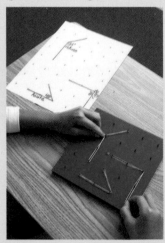

Geoboards are good tools for exploring angles.

ANGLE RULER	EXAMPLE
The angle ruler can be bent to measure angles or straightened to measure straight lines. It includes markings for measuring length as well as a protractor for measuring angles.	An angle ruler is a handy tool for measuring side lengths and angles in triangles. 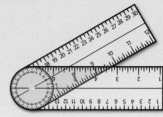

Appropriate Children's Books

The Dragon's Scales (Albee, 1998).
A young girl challenges a dragon by asking questions about comparing weights. She wins the challenge.

Mr. Archimedes' Bath (Allen, 1980).
This picture book tells the story of Archimedes, who figured out the relationship between volume and capacity using water displacement. The story is told by using animals who get in and out of a bathtub and cause the water to spill over.

How Big Is It? (Hillman, 2007).
This resource for older students provides lots of interesting information that relates to measurements of large objects.

Measuring Penny (Leedy, 2000).
A child measures her dog in a variety of ways, including measurements involving capacity and time, and standard and nonstandard units.

Pastry School in Paris: An Adventure in Capacity (Neuschwander, 2009).
This prolific children's math author sets the stage for the importance of care in capacity measurement through a story about baking. Many issues related to capacity are raised.

Appropriate Digital Resources

See the MindTap site for a selection of appropriate digital resources.

Assessing Student Understanding

- Part of the assessment of capacity, volume, mass, and angle should involve estimation. Students might be asked to estimate the measure of one object if they are given the measure of another object that they can use as a benchmark. For example, if students are shown an object with a volume reported as 20 cm^3, they might estimate the volume of another object that is larger or smaller. This supports proportional reasoning.

An object holds 1000 mL. What might it be?

An object that holds 1000 mL might be a car or truck.

Student Response

How would you respond to what this student has suggested?

- Students should be asked to relate measurements to their everyday world. For example, you might ask, What object might have a mass of about 5 kg? What kind of container or object might have a capacity of 1000 mL?

- Because size is not a good visual cue for mass, it is important that most assessments involving mass be performance tasks and not paper-and-pencil tasks.

- Part of assessment of capacity, volume, mass, time, temperature, or angle measurement should involve observing students' use of tools. Do they use the tools correctly? Do they use them comfortably?

- Make sure to appropriately balance attention to analog and digital clocks in assessment situations. Also distinguish between tasks that require students to read time and those that require them to set a clock to show a time; these are different skills.

- Once students have met angles greater than 90°, it is important that assessments provide the opportunity for students to show that they can distinguish between angles more and less than 90°, and use their protractors accordingly.

Applying What You've Learned

1. The problem at the start of the chapter is one of a class of problems called optimizing problems. Others are, for example, "What is the greatest area for a given perimeter? What is the greatest volume for a given surface area?" etc. Why might these problems be important for students to meet?

2. Describe an interesting activity not already listed in the chapter that is appropriate for students at each of the three stages of teaching one of these measurements: capacity, volume, mass, time, or angle.

3. Create a lesson plan that would be of use in teaching students how the volume of a pyramid relates to the volume of an associated prism.

4. Study the curriculum documents for your region. At what grade level is each of these introduced?
   – standard units for capacity, volume, and mass
   – measurement of angle
   – relating volume and capacity units
   – volume and area formulas
   Do these particular grade levels seem reasonable to you? Explain.

5. Do you think it might be useful to teach volume and mass together, or do you think they should be taught separately? Explain.

6. The mass of 1 L of water is 1 kg. Create three problems that might be of interest to a student to solve using that information.

7. Both time and angle measures are based more on the Imperial system of measurement than on the metric system. What numbers skills are supported by work with each set of measurements (Imperial and metric)? Explain.

8. The clock is sometimes used as a "compass." For example, you might say that someone is at 2 o'clock. Do you think this use of the clock enhances or detracts from students' understanding of telling time? Explain.

Interact with a K–8 Student:

9. Observe as a student solves one of these problems:

   Older student: What is the mass of a single sheet of paper?

   Younger student: How many paper clips would balance your eraser?

   What measurement understandings do you observe?

10. Create a game that you think would be useful for practising angle measurement. Try out the game with some students. What aspects of it would you change? Why?

Discuss with a K–8 Teacher:

11. Ask a teacher to share a successful activity for measuring volume or capacity, and what she or he thinks made it successful.

Selected References

Albee, S. (1998). *The dragon's scales.* New York: Random House Books for Young Readers.

Allen, P. (1980). *Mr. Archimedes' bath.* New York: HarperCollins.

Assuah, C.K., and Wiest, L.R. (2010). Comparing the volumes of rectangular prisms. *Mathematics Teaching in the Middle School, 15,* 502–504.

Battista, M.T. (2003). Understanding students' thinking about area and volume measurement. In Clement, D., and Bright, G. (Eds.). *Learning and teaching measurement.* Reston, VA: National Council of Teachers of Mathematics, 122–142.

Battista, M.T., and Clements, D.H. (1998). Students' understanding of three-dimensional cube arrays. Findings from a research and curriculum development project. In Lehrer, R., and Chazan, D. (Eds.) *Designing learning environments for developing understanding of geometry and space.* Mahwah, NJ: Erlbaum, 227–248.

Browning, C.A., Garza-King, G., and Sundling, E.H. (2007). What's your angle on angles? *Teaching Children Mathematics, 14,* 283–287.

Carmody, H.G. (2010). Water bottle designs and measures. *Mathematics Teaching in the Middle School, 16,* 272–279.

Clarke, D., Cheeseman, J., McDonough, A., and Clark, B. (2003). Assessing and developing measurement with young children. In Clement, D., and Bright, G. (Eds.). *Learning and teaching measurement.* Reston, VA: National Council of Teachers of Mathematics, 68–80.

Clement, R. (1994). *Counting on Frank.* Boston: Houghton Mifflin School.

Dacey, L., Cavanagh, M., Findell, C., Greenes, C., Sheffield, L.J., and Small, M. (2003). *Navigating through measurement, prekindergarten–grade 2.* Reston, VA: National Council of Teachers of Mathematics.

Friederwitzer, F.J., and Berman, B. (1999). The language of time. *Teaching Children Mathematics, 6,* 254–259.

Hillman, B. (2007). *How big is it?* New York: Scholastic Reference.

Hutchins, H. (2004). *A second is a hiccup: A child's book of time.* Toronto, ON: North Winds Press.

Irving, D. (2010). *Measuring time at a race.* Mankato, MN: Capstone Press.

Kamii, C., and Russell, K.A. (2010). The older of two trees: Young children's development of operational time. *Journal for Research in Mathematics Education, 41,* 6–13.

Kamii, C.K., and Long, K. (2003). The measurement of time: Transitivity, unit iteration, and conservation of speed. In Clement, D., and Bright, G. (Eds.). *Learning and teaching measurement.* Reston, VA: National Council of Teachers of Mathematics, 169–180.

Leedy, L. (2000). *Measuring Penny.* New York: Henry Holt and Company, Inc.

Lehrer, R. (2003). Developing understanding of measurement. In Kilpatrick, J., Martin, W.G., and Schilfter, D. (Eds.). *A research companion to principles and standards for school mathematics.* Reston, VA: National Council of Teachers of Mathematics, 179–192.

Maida, P., and Maida, M. (2006). How does your doughnut measure up? *Mathematics Teaching in the Middle School, 11,* 212–219.

Merz, A.H., and Belzer, S. (2003). Hurry up and weight. *Teaching Children Mathematics, 10,* 8–15.

Millsaps, G. M. (2012). How wedge you teach the unit-angle concept? *Teaching Children Mathematics, 18,* 362–369.

Moone, G., and de Groot, C. (2005). Investigations: Time is of the essence. *Teaching Children Mathematics, 12,* 90–98.

Neuschwander, C. (2009). *Pastry school in Paris: An adventure in capacity.* New York: Henry Holt.

Pagni, D.L. (2005). Angles, time and proportion. *Mathematics Teaching in the Middle School, 10,* 436–441.

Sophian, C. (2002). Learning about what fits: Preschool children's reasoning about effects of object size. *Journal of Research in Mathematics Education, 33,* 290–302.

Chapter 21

Data

IN A NUTSHELL

The main ideas in this chapter are listed below:

1. Most data collection activities are based on the prior sorting of information into categories.

2. To collect data, you must create appropriate questions and think about how best to gather the data.

3. It is often useful to "summarize" data by using one or two statistics that, in some way, reflect the whole data set.

4. Different types of data displays are appropriate for different situations. The choice of organization and display should reflect the purpose for collecting the data. As with other mathematical situations, concrete data displays should precede semi-concrete or symbolic ones.

(continued)

CHAPTER PROBLEM

In a big city, there are 100 schools. The graph below shows the enrolments in those 100 schools, but the vertical scale is missing. About how many schools have fewer than 200 students?

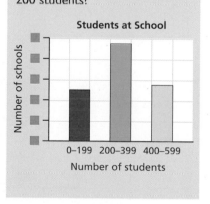

Students at School

(bar graph with y-axis labelled "Number of schools" and x-axis labelled "Number of students" with categories 0–199, 200–399, 400–599)

> **IN A NUTSHELL (*continued*)**
>
> 5. When data are displayed, either visually or in a table or chart, they can be analyzed to look for patterns, make predictions, make comparisons, draw inferences, and make decisions.
>
> 6. Graphs are powerful data displays since visual displays quickly reveal information about data.

Data Organization

Sorting and Classifying

Students' early work in data includes sorting and classifying objects. *Sorting* is the physical act of grouping objects according to shared characteristics. *Classifying* is the process of differentiating among the groups by giving each group a category name.

Many of the basic concepts and skills involved in sorting and classifying objects are also fundamental to the organization of data. Students must be able to sort and classify, or organize and categorize data, in order to record the results of data collection in an effective way.

Students need frequent practice with sorting and classifying objects, especially, although not exclusively, in the early grades. Sorting and classifying activities can be done with everyday materials, or with materials created specifically for the purpose.

Recognizing Attributes

Before sorting and classifying objects, it is important that students understand that any object has many *attributes*. An *attribute* is a way we compare objects, whether by colour or size, and so on. This can be contrasted with the term *characteristic*, which tells how the attribute is reflected in a particular situation. For example, an attribute of an object might be *colour*, but the characteristic

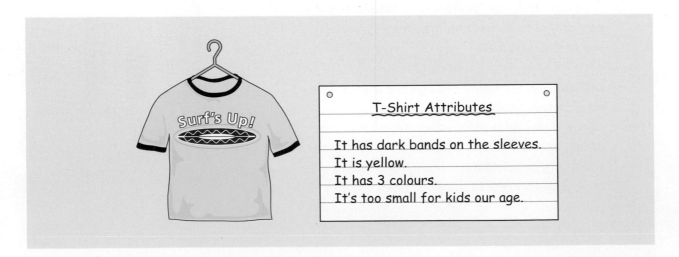

might be *red*. Usually, activities that build this understanding are exploratory in nature—an object is displayed and students are asked to describe it. For example, students are shown a T-shirt and asked to describe it.

Some students respond with more ideas if they have two objects to compare and contrast. For example, show a pencil and a ruler and ask for ways in which the objects are the same and ways they are different.

Describing a Sorting Rule

Students also need practice in recognizing and verbalizing a *sorting rule* for a pre-sorted set of objects. This task is often appealing to students because it involves solving a "mystery." One possible activity is outlined in **Activity 21.1** and illustrated below. You can re-sort using other characteristics.

ACTIVITY 21.1

Choose five students to come to the front of the room, so there will be a characteristic that applies to some, but not all, of them. Organize students into two groups, those with the characteristic and those without it. Ask the rest of the students to identify the rule you used to sort.

_____

Critical Thinking

Sorting by hair colour: blond and not blond

You can also engage students in activities where they decide where an object belongs when there are pre-sorted sets (**Activity 21.2**), or what object does not belong in a sorted set.

Sorting by One Attribute

When sorting by one attribute, students sometimes apply a sorting rule simply by moving items together or grouping them if they are alike. For example:

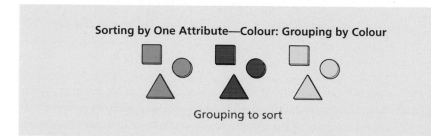

Sorting by One Attribute—Colour: Grouping by Colour

Grouping to sort

ACTIVITY 21.2

Where Does It Belong?

Show two containers with wooden shapes in one and plastic shapes in the other. Do not describe the contents of the containers. Hold up a shape, for example, a wooden one, and ask which pail it belongs in and why. Drop the shape in the appropriate container, but do not ask for or reveal the sorting rule yet. Continue with more objects until it appears that most students have figured out the rule.

_____

Critical Thinking

If they are asked simply to sort in order to find all the red shapes, objects that are not red are simply put outside of a sorting circle labelled "Red" (as shown at the top of the next page).

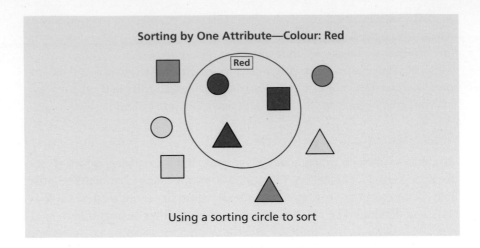

Sorting by One Attribute—Colour: Red

Red

Using a sorting circle to sort

It is sometimes helpful to use concrete organizational tools to assist students in sorting. For example, the teacher might provide two (preferably transparent) containers labelled "Red" and "Not Red" into which students can place shapes as they are sorted. Alternatively, they could use sorting "mats," plates, or yarn or hula hoops to enclose items.

Some students have difficulty dealing with objects that do not have the characteristic that is the focus of the sort. In the example above, they find it easy to put the red objects together, but may be uncomfortable without a name for the other objects. Rather than using the phrase "not red," they may come up with another term, such as "blue or yellow."

Sorting by Multiple Attributes

In a number of situations, students may need to sort in terms of two attributes, for example, by colour and size. A two-way sorting table is helpful.

Sorting by Two Attributes—Colour and Size

	Red	Blue
Big	●● ●	● ●
Small	● ●	● ● ●

Later, students can use more sophisticated sorting tools such as Venn diagrams, which are particularly useful when *cross-classification* is involved. Cross-classification occurs when a single item has multiple attributes that must be considered in the same sorting situation. For example, if a student sorted foods using the categories "Hot Foods" and "Healthy Foods," then a food such as corn would cross-classify because it has both characteristics.

Venn Diagrams

Venn diagrams are a commonly used sorting tool. Each circle is used to contain all the objects with a particular characteristic. The name of the sorting rule is shown as a label for each circle. The number of circles depends on the number of characteristics being used to sort the items. In each case, the circle or circles are included in a large rectangle that represents the "universe," or the whole set of objects being sorted. Every object being sorted has to have a place in the diagram, even if it is outside the circles but inside the rectangle.

When introducing students to Venn diagrams, hula hoops or large rings of string or yarn can serve as concrete Venn diagram circles. Initially, students can sort actual objects into these hoops. Later, they can draw the circles and objects. Later still, students can sort more symbolic items like numerals.

Venn Diagrams for One-Attribute Sorting

This one-circle Venn diagram shows a set of hexagon and rectangle attribute blocks being sorted according to whether they are hexagons. The rectangle blocks are outside the circle but still inside the rectangle, as they are not hexagons but they are still part of the universal set being sorted.

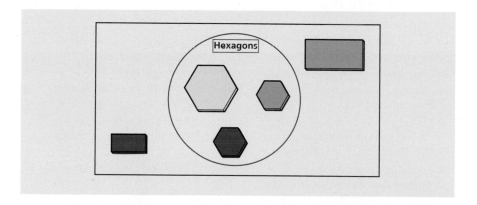

Venn Diagrams for Two-Attribute Sorting

Venn diagrams are excellent tools for sorting by multiple attributes because they make it easy to see when there are items that cross-classify. For example, the buttons in this Venn diagram are being sorted according to two attributes—colour and number of holes. The buttons in the middle where the circles overlap have both characteristics (two holes and blue). The button outside the circles does not have either characteristic.

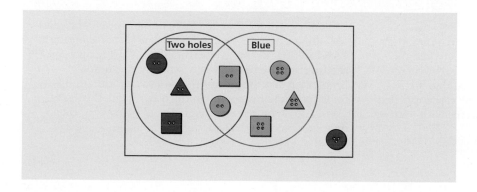

ACTIVITY 21.3

Students can use Venn diagrams to solve problems like these:

In a class of 22 students, 10 play hockey and 15 play basketball.

a) Is it possible that there are some students who play neither sport? What is the greatest possible number of students who do not play either sport? Explain your answer. Show your work.

b) Is it possible that all 22 students are involved in one sport or the other or both? Explain your answer. Show your work.

Critical Thinking

To introduce the notion of how cross-classification is shown in Venn diagrams, set out two hoops, side by side, and label each one with a sorting rule. Ensure the sorting rules and objects to be sorted lend themselves to cross-classification, for example, triangles and square corners (not triangles and quadrilaterals). Have students sort objects into the hoops until they come to an object that cross-classifies. Discuss where the object belongs and elicit the idea of crossing the hoops to form an overlap.

Note that the circles of a Venn diagram do not have to overlap. They can be two discrete circles if the attributes are exclusive, for example, if one were used to contain girls and one contained boys. They could also be separate circles if the items involved in the sort do not exhibit the same characteristics, even if they have the potential to do so. For example, if a group of shapes were sorted using the characteristics red and striped, the Venn diagram circles could remain as separate circles if there were no shapes that were both red and striped. As soon as a striped red shape was included in the set, the circles would have to overlap to accommodate that shape in the intersection of the two circles.

IMPORTANT POINTS ABOUT DATA ORGANIZATION

- Sorting and classifying objects will help students with organizing and categorizing data.
- Sorting is the action of grouping (or organizing) objects (or data); classification (or categorization) is the naming of the groups of objects (or data).
- Students need opportunities to explore attributes and characteristics of objects that can be used for sorting.
- When students sort by two or more attributes, there is potential for overlap or cross-classification.
- A Venn diagram is not only an organizational tool for sorting, but is sometimes a form of data display that can be used to display an object or data when the categories overlap.

Common Errors and Misconceptions

Data Organization: Common Errors, Misconceptions, and Strategies

COMMON ERROR OR MISCONCEPTION	SUGGESTED STRATEGY
Using "and" and "or" When students engage in sorting activities, they often have trouble distinguishing between the words "and" and "or." For example, the category "Red or Pink" would include items that are red as well as items that are pink. The category "Red and Pink" would only include items with both red and pink parts.	Explicitly consider situations where the words "and" and "or" are used, and discuss with students what is meant in each case. For example, you might say, "Bring up your report if you are presenting it Monday or Tuesday." Emphasize that this means that you want both groups to bring up their reports. On the other hand, if you say, "Stand up if you have brown hair and blue eyes," then only students who have both brown hair and blue eyes should stand.

(continued)

COMMON ERROR OR MISCONCEPTION	SUGGESTED STRATEGY
Using Venn Diagrams When students use Venn diagrams to show a sorting, they ignore the items that do not belong inside the circles.	Whenever students create a Venn diagram, ensure that they show the universe as a rectangle around the circle(s). Regularly ask them to think about what kind of items belong in the circles, and also what kind of items belong in the rectangle, but not inside a circle. For example, the blue square and green circle may not belong inside the sorting circle, but they do have a place outside the circle and inside the rectangle. 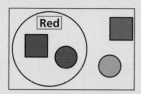 As often as possible, ensure there are objects that will not fit in a circle so students have opportunities to place objects in the region outside the circles. Another strategy is to list the places where objects can go. For example, in the case of a two-attribute sort, objects can go • inside the left circle • inside the right circle • in the intersecting region • outside the circles but inside the rectangle 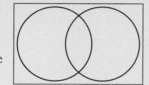

Appropriate Manipulatives

Data Organization: Examples of Manipulatives

ATTRIBUTE BLOCKS	EXAMPLE
Attribute, or logic, blocks are ideal for sorting because of their many attributes: size, colour, shape, and thickness.	Students can use attribute blocks to practise sorting with a Venn diagram. 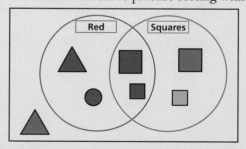

GEOMETRIC SHAPES	EXAMPLE
Shapes of different sizes are useful for sorting. Geometric shapes, both 2-D and 3-D, can be teacher-made or commercial. Attributes such as number of sides, concavity or convexity, and symmetry can be included.	These shapes can be sorted according to a variety of attributes: • symmetry • equal sides • parallel sides • number of sides  

Data Collection

Why People Collect Data

People collect data in order to solve problems. Children do this naturally even before they come to school. For example, suppose a child is given a new and unfamiliar toy. The child now has a problem to solve: how does the toy work? The child may conduct a variety of "experiments" to collect data—trying many different things and often repeating actions—in order to figure out what the toy can do. The child may also ask questions about the toy, with the intention of gathering further data from caregivers or other children.

School activities should support this idea that data collection is a tool that can help solve problems, rather than an end in itself. There should always be a purpose for collecting data, and the method of data collection should suit that purpose.

Asking Good Survey Questions

Children constantly ask questions to gather data. They know intuitively that questions can help them gather data, but activities at school can help them learn to ask the right questions in the right way. For example, a student might conduct a survey to find out what books his or her classmates like to read. If the student asks a group of people an open-ended question such as "What is your favourite book?", there might be eight or more different answers—too much data to draw any useful conclusions about reading preferences. If, on the other hand, the child asks, "Do you like detective stories? Yes or no.", the data will be easier to use—the child will learn whether more students do or do not like these books and how the proportions compare.

If the student were to ask, "Which is your favourite type of book to read?", and then provide several categories of books to choose from, such as stories about the past, fantasy, detective stories, or nonfiction, he or she would get data that could be organized in a form that is useful. One suggestion is for a student to conduct a small "pilot" asking a more open-ended question to see what answers are given and use what she or he learned to refine the survey.

Initially, students should be encouraged to ask yes/no questions because it is much easier to collect and organize data when only two responses are possible. Later, students can ask questions with more than two possible answers, but where choices are still limited. In the multiple-choice example, notice the category labelled "Other." This is a handy category for the odd, unexpected answer. However, if students get a lot of data in this category, it is an indication that their categories need to be revised.

Asking questions with multiple possible answers can sometimes lead students to the discovery that questions involving levels or ratings can produce useful information. For example, students might ask the yes/no question "Can you swim?" Students who respond to the question may have difficulty answering with a simple yes or no since some are able to swim short distances, and others are strong swimmers. The student can then go back and refine the question to include levels of swimming ability.

Audience

To make sure a question is clear enough to elicit meaningful data, students have to think about who will be reading or using the data they plan to collect and put themselves in that person's shoes. For example, Grade 4 students might want to find out, through a survey, which night of the week should be homework-free for their class. They might develop a survey such as the following, and distribute it to each classmate:

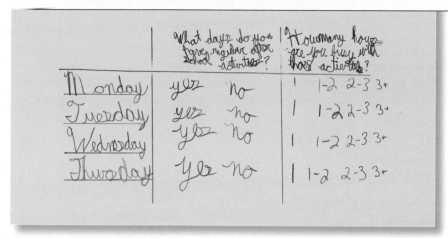

Student Response

By asking clear questions about their classmates' after-school activities, students are likely to get specific and useful data that they can present to their audience (the teacher) for consideration.

Note that once all these individual survey sheets are collected, the pieces of data will have to be combined and organized in such a way that they can be analyzed to determine which is the busiest night. Students could also display this combined data using, for example, a table or graph to provide their audience with supporting evidence for their recommendation.

Choosing Data Collection Topics

Primary students are interested mostly in issues related directly to their own lives, such as activities they like to do, or their measurements, toys, hobbies, family's clothing, or pets.

Later on, students become increasingly interested in the broader world, whether it is geography, sports, politics, the environment, or other cultures, although, not surprisingly, they remain interested in topics related to their own lives.

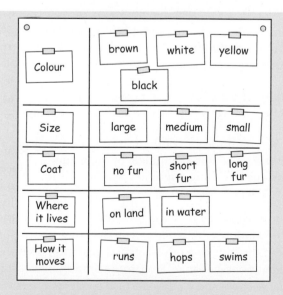

Collecting and organizing data on pets

Olympic Medals Won by Canadian Figure Skaters

	Men	Women	Dance	Pairs
2010		Bronze		Gold
2006	Bronze			
2002				Gold
1998	Silver			
1994	Silver			Bronze
1992				Bronze
1988	Silver	Silver	Bronze	

Collecting and organizing data on figure skating results

Data Sources

Data sources are directly related to the topics under investigation.

Primary or Firsthand Data

Primary data is firsthand data that students collect themselves or with their classmates or teacher. Using primary data makes sense when students are looking for answers to questions about objects and people in their own environment. It also makes sense when students are just beginning to learn about data, or when the amount of data is limited, for example, a survey of only 10 or 20 people rather than hundreds.

Secondary or Secondhand Data

Later, students collect and analyze *secondary data* from secondary sources such as atlases, almanacs, other reference books, and the Internet. Browsers make it easier than ever for students to access secondhand data. The difficulty lies in deciding what data is really useful and what data is reliable or accurate.

Factors Influencing Data Collection

Older students are more likely than younger ones to begin to think about how the methods they use to collect data can affect their results. They will be ready to consider issues such as the potential for *bias* or how many people they should include in their survey.

Sometimes, students will be able to conduct a *census*, that is, survey everyone from a given population. For example, suppose students want to conduct a survey to find out where to go on a school trip. It would be easy to ask everyone in the class. With a larger population, it is impractical to survey everyone, so students need to use a *sample group*. Suppose they want to conduct a survey to find out whether people in their community support year-round schooling. In this case, they will have to carefully consider whom to ask (the make-up of the sample), how many people to ask (the sample size), and when to gather the data. For example:

- If they ask only students, the results will not reflect the concerns of other segments of the community, including parents, teachers, or people who operate summer businesses such as camps or resorts.
- If they ask mainly adults who do not have school-age children, the results will not reflect the views of those who are concerned—students and parents.
- If they conduct their survey at the end of the summer, they may get a different answer than if they do it in the middle of the winter.
- If they ask only a dozen people, they might get significantly different results than if they ask 100 people.

Students need to begin to think about ways to gather data so that the results will be both reliable and useful. This means that they should be able to use the results from the sample to make generalizations about the population. These considerations become even more important as students move on to secondary school and study statistical concepts at a more sophisticated level, for example, random sampling techniques, or ways to select samples to ensure they are appropriate.

TEACHING TIP

These are some of the excellent resources that provide secondary data for students:

- *World Almanac for Kids*
- *Scholastic Book of Lists*
- *Time for Kids Almanac*
- *The World Almanac and Book of Facts*
- *The Top 10 of Everything: Canadian Edition*
- *Guinness World Records*

TEACHING TIP

Older elementary students might be particularly interested in the Canada Census at School website to participate in joint data collection projects with other students around the country.

IMPORTANT POINTS ABOUT DATA COLLECTION

- Data should be collected to solve relevant problems.
- A good survey question has a limited number of answer choices, yet enough to accommodate everyone (one of the answer choices may be "Other"). The choices or categories should generally be discrete, that is, they should not overlap.
- When designing a survey, students must consider the audience—who will use the information and how they will use it.
- Data can be primary (collected directly by students) or secondary (collected by others and used by students). Younger students work with primary data; older students work with both primary and secondary data.
- There are many data collection factors that have the potential to influence the results, such as bias and sample size.

Common Errors and Misconceptions

Data Collection: Common Errors, Misconceptions, and Strategies

COMMON ERROR OR MISCONCEPTION	SUGGESTED STRATEGY
Unclear or Vague Survey Questions When students develop survey questions, they do not consider the clarity of the wording or the vagueness of the question. For example, if students want to know whether children are likely to be the ones who care for their pets or whether they leave it to their parents, they might simply ask, "How much do you look after your pet?" This can mean very different things to different respondents. Some might tell how many times they feed the pet, others might just say "a lot."	Have students try out their questions on a variety of different audiences to see the kinds of responses they get. For example, by asking the pet question of an older sibling or parent who might respond with "What do you mean?", it becomes clearer that the question needs refinement. Encourage students to ask questions that will result in responses that are unambiguous because they ask for specific information. For example, asking "How many times a week do you feed your dog?" will usually prompt specific responses.
COMMON ERROR OR MISCONCEPTION	SUGGESTED STRATEGY
Non-Discrete Categories When students create survey questions, they include choices that are not exclusive or discrete. For example: What is your favourite type of game? - *Monopoly* - *Sorry* - Board games - Games of chance	It is important to remind students that, if they want to compare the sizes of the groups who chose each answer, or determine the total number of people who were surveyed, then they cannot ask questions where the same person chooses more than one answer. In the case of the survey question shown here, you might ask why someone who likes *Sorry* might have trouble deciding whether to choose *Sorry*, board games, or games of chance. Encourage students to review the list of categories to see how they can refine it so that categories do not overlap.

Appropriate Manipulatives

Data Collection: Examples of Manipulatives

CONCRETE GRAPHING MATERIALS	EXAMPLE
Younger students may prefer to use concrete materials to keep track of survey results. Note that, in many cases, the results of the data collection also serve as a data display.	Students can use concrete materials for surveying in a variety of ways, including • hanging clothespins on a string • linking cubes to make a "tower" for each response • making rows of stickers • stacking paper cups • using magnetic pictures or name tags • placing craft sticks in labelled cups 

CLIPBOARDS	EXAMPLE
Many students enjoy using clipboards when they are surveying others.	Clipboards make it easy for students to conduct surveys anywhere.

Statistics

The study of data inevitably leads to the study of *statistics*. Statistics involves using numerical values to describe a set of data. For example, a number of 10-year-olds might be measured and have their individual heights recorded. The average height is then calculated in order to describe the group of students with a single value that will give someone a good idea of how tall a typical student from the group might be. Most statistical study is undertaken at the secondary school level, but the calculation of averages is a topic that students learn about prior to that.

Measures of Central Tendency

There are three *measures of central tendency* that students encounter: *mean*, *median*, and *mode*. Each one is a way to describe a set of data with a single meaningful number. In some situations, only one of these descriptions makes sense, but in other situations, two or three are meaningful, even if they are different.

The Mean

The *mean* is the number that people are usually referring to when they talk about "the average." A mean describes a set of data by indicating the value that would result from putting all the values together and distributing them evenly. It is calculated by adding up all the data values and dividing by the number of values.

ACTIVITY 21.4

Ask students to create three data sets that they think are quite different, but still have the same mean.

Building Number Sense

For example, suppose there are the following numbers of students in six different groups. To calculate the mean group size, you add all six numbers for a total of 30, and then divide by 6 to get 5. The mean indicates that, if all students were redistributed into six equal groups, there would be 5 students in each group.

Group A	Group B	Group C	Group D	Group E	Group F
3	5	4	7	5	6

The mean is $\frac{3+5+4+7+5+6}{2} = \frac{30}{6} = 5$.

When the Mean Is Meaningful A mean of 5 is an appropriate representation of the data above because there are a few groups that have slightly fewer than 5, a few that have slightly more than 5, and two groups that have exactly 5. However, when there are one or two extremely high or extremely low values, the mean is not the best indicator of the "average" group size. For example, the data below shows the test scores of six students. Because there is one extremely low score, the mean gives the false impression that the students, as a group, did not do well.

Student A	Student B	Student C	Student D	Student E	Student F
90	90	90	90	90	30.

The mean is $\frac{90+90+90+90+90+30}{6} = 60$. However, this number does not appropriately represent this set of data.

Working Concretely to Establish the Notion of Mean

ACTING IT OUT

When students are first introduced to the concept of mean, they should have opportunities to act it out and explore it concretely.

To model the first grouping situation above, students could arrange themselves into one group of 3, one group of 4, two groups of 5, one group of 6, and one group of 7, and then redistribute themselves into six equal groups to find out how many students would be in each new group.

Students might use trial and error to form equal groups. Or, they might form one large group, and then break off into six smaller groups by moving people one at a time to each group, always keeping them equal.

> When we made the groups equal, we ended up with 5 in each group, so 5 is the mean.

ACTIVITY 21.5

Provide students with an incomplete list of data and the mean of the data, and ask them to identify the missing data. For example, tell them that the mean of 7, 9, 10, 15, and x is 11, and ask them to figure out the value of x.

Building Number Sense

(continued)

USING LINKING CUBES

Another way to model the same grouping situation is to use linking cubes, with a different colour for each original group. The mean number of cubes could be found in two ways:

- combining all the cubes into one larger group, and then sharing them equally among 6 groups
- making a cube train for each group, as shown here, and redistributing the cubes until all of the trains are of equal length

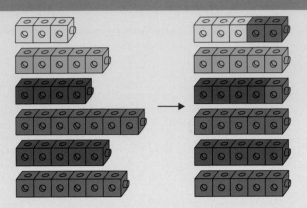

Redistributing cubes to find the mean

USING A STRAIGHT LINE

Another way to find the mean is to move a ruler or taut string along the cube trains representing the groups until the number of cubes above the mean (to the right of the string) exactly balances the number of empty spaces below the mean (to the left of the string). The placement of the vertical line highlights the mean, which is 5. The total length of the arrows on the left of the vertical line, or mean, is 2 + 1 = 3. The total on the right of the mean is 2 + 1 = 3.

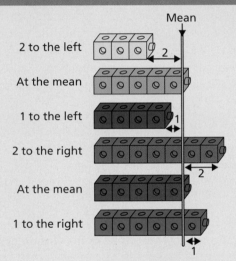

"Balancing" cubes above and below the mean

ACTIVITY 21.6

Ask students to record a set of 8 numbers and calculate the mean. Now have them do the following:

- Add 10 to each value and recalculate the mean. Ask what they notice.

- Multiply each value by 10 and recalculate the mean. Ask what they notice.

Building Number Sense

Exploring Properties of the Mean There are many properties of the mean that older students can explore, as described in **Activity 21.6**.

The Median

The *median* is another measure of central tendency used to describe a set of data with a single value. It is the middle value when the data is in order. To find the median group size of the six school populations below, the values are first put in order from least to greatest. The number in the middle is the median. In this case, there are two middle numbers, so the median is 295, halfway between 289 and 301. Notice that half of the numbers are above the median and half are below. Also, note that the median and mean of this set of data (327.8) are not equal, but in other cases, they might be.

School A	School B	School C	School D	School E	School F
187	225	289	301	320	645

The median is the mean of 289 and 301, or 295.

When the Median Is Meaningful A median of 295 is an appropriate representation of the data above. The median is particularly valuable if there are just one or two very extreme pieces of data as is the case above. The 645 skews the mean but does not affect the median.

The Mode

The *mode* is another measure of central tendency used to describe a set of data. It is the most frequent value in the data set.

ACTIVITY 21.7

Ask students to consider whether it is possible for a set of data to have a mean that is exactly 1 greater than the median.

Critical Thinking

Group A	Group B	Group C	Group D	Group E	Group F
3	5	4	7	5	6

The mode is 5.

A set of data can have one mode, multiple modes, or no mode at all. (If each number in a set of data values occurs as frequently as the rest, there is no mode, for example, the set 2, 3, 4, 5 has no mode; there are multiple modes for 2, 2, 3, 3, 4, 4, 5, 5.)

If there are many pieces of data, the best way to determine the mode might be to write all the values in order and look for the longest set of matching numbers.

It is easy to determine the mode from a bar graph, a line graph, or a stem-and-leaf plot. [NOTE: See descriptions of these graphs in subsequent sections.] The mode is the value described by the highest bar, the highest point, or the longest set of leaves.

When the Mode Is Meaningful A mode of 5 is an appropriate representation of the data above. However, if the other data values were all quite different from the mode, as in the situation below, using the mode to describe the average group size might be misleading. In this case, the mean might be a more appropriate description of the data.

Group A	Group B	Group C	Group D	Group E	Group F
12	12	1	2	3	4

The mode is 12. However, this number does not appropriately represent this particular set of data.

There are certain real-life situations where the mode is the only appropriate measure. For example, a shoe store might keep a record of the shoe sizes it sells most often (the mode) to help with making orders for new stock. A mean or median shoe size of, for example, 4.2, is not useful information, nor does it make sense, because there is no such thing as a 4.2 shoe size.

Measures of Data Spread

Range

There are many sophisticated measures of the spread of data. Although mathematicians most frequently use a statistic called a standard deviation, its calculation is difficult. One statistic that is accessible to K–8 students is the *range*. The range is the difference between the least value and the greatest value, so it shows the spread of the data. For example, in the set of values below, the range is the difference between the age of the youngest member of the family, which is 3, and the age of the oldest, which is 62.

Person A	Person B	Person C	Person D	Person E	Person F
3	7	15	28	40	62

The range of this set of data is 62 − 3 = 59.

What the range does not show is whether the values are distributed evenly or whether there are gaps or clusters. The set of data below has the same range as the set above, but the data distribution is different.

Person A	Person B	Person C	Person D	Person E	Person F
5	5	5	5	5	64

The range of this set of data is also 59.

ACTIVITY 21.8

Ask students to create sets of data to meet various statistical criteria. For example, they might be asked to create a set of data with a mean of 10, a median of 5, and a range of 33.

Building Number Sense

IMPORTANT POINTS ABOUT MEASURES OF CENTRAL TENDENCY AND DATA SPREAD

- The purpose of a measure of central tendency is to assign a value, usually a single value, to a set of data that is a good representation of the data.
- Three measures of central tendency are mean, median, and mode.
- The mean indicates the value that would result from putting all the values together and distributing them evenly.
- The median is the middle value when pieces of data are listed in order. If there are two middle values, the median is the mean of these values.
- The mode is the most frequent value(s) in a data set.

Common Errors and Misconceptions

Statistics: Common Errors, Misconceptions, and Strategies

COMMON ERROR OR MISCONCEPTION	SUGGESTED STRATEGY
Incorrectly Calculating the Median Students have a number of difficulties in calculating the median: • They sometimes forget to put the numbers in order and simply write down the middle number in the unordered list. For example, they might write 8 if the data were: 7, 8, 1. • Students might take half of the number of values and use that value to incorrectly identify the median. For example, if the data were: 2, 3, 5, 9, they would say there are 4 pieces of data, half of 4 is 2, and use the second number (3), rather than the mean of 3 and 5.	Remind students often that once the median is located, there should be just as many numbers in the data set above that median as below it. If this does not occur, the median was incorrectly identified. What is more important is that students check that there are as many pieces of data greater than the median as less than it. *(continued)*

Statistics: Common Errors, Misconceptions, and Strategies (Continued)

COMMON ERROR OR MISCONCEPTION	SUGGESTED STRATEGY
Incorrectly Reporting the Range Students describe the range using the minimum and maximum data values rather than calculating the single-value difference. For example, a student might describe the range of the set of data below as "from 4 to 9" rather than "5." 4, 4, 5, 7, 7, 7, 8, 9	Tell students that, like the mean or median, the range is a single value. While measures of central tendency are single values used to identify a typical data value, the range is a single value used to describe the spread of the data.

Appropriate Manipulatives

Statistics: Example of Manipulatives

LINKING CUBES AND GRID PAPER	EXAMPLE
Linking cubes and grid paper are good tools to use when you first introduce the concepts of mean, mode, and median.	Students can create cube trains to represent values in a set of data. To determine the mean, they adjust the trains until they are all the same length, as was shown on page 584. To determine the median, students line up the trains in order, from least to greatest, and identify the middle train. (If there are 2 middle trains of a different value, they might be able to move cubes from one of these trains to the other until the trains are equal.) To determine the mode, students line up the trains in order and identify the most frequent length. In this example, the mode is the same as the median and the mean. (Usually, these are different.)

Data Display

Sometimes a *data display*, such as a graph, is used to solve a problem. For example, if a city is planning to adjust a set of traffic lights, and the planners need to know if there is a relationship between the frequency of cars on the road and the time of day, they could collect the data by counting cars over a period of time. They could then graph the data in a scatter plot, and then look for a pattern.

In other cases, a data display is used to communicate information. Most people find that information presented graphically is more accessible and easier to read at a glance, as long as it is presented effectively and accurately.

Some display formats require a particular kind of organization. For example, to create a stem-and-leaf plot (see page 599), you must order the data from least to greatest within each data interval. Other formats allow for some variation in how the data are organized.

Data Display Formats

Students need to consider both the audience and the nature of the data to decide about the type of data display they plan to construct. It is important to choose a format that suits the data, and to include clear titles and labels to guide the audience, or reader, in interpreting it.

The first data displays children usually create are tally charts and concrete graphs made from real objects. They then move on to recording numerals in frequency tables or charts. As students begin to recognize that

> **TEACHING TIP**
>
> In all grades, but especially in the early years, it is important that students choose the topics about which they collect and display data.

the number of objects in each category can be represented in other ways, they progress to graph types characterized by increasing levels of complexity and abstraction—from graphs made with pictures of real objects (picture graphs), to graphs that use symbols (pictographs), and, finally, to more abstract graphs (bar graphs, broken-line graphs, and stem-and-leaf plots).

Tally Charts

One of the simplest types of data display is the *tally chart*. Students use tally marks to count the frequency of responses or items in different categories. Using tally marks grouped in 5s makes it easier for students to quickly count the number in each category. Notice how the tallies are aligned across the columns for easy comparison. From this tally chart, it is easy to see at a glance that more people chose the first story than the second one. Note that, with a tally chart, as with any data display, it is important to include a title that clearly explains the meaning of the data.

> Which story should we read today?
>
> | I Want a Dog | If You Give a Mouse a Cookie |
> | --- | --- |
> | ⌊⌍⌍⌍ | ⌊⌍⌍⌍ |
> | ⌊⌍⌍⌍ | ‖‖‖ |
> | ⎮ | |

ACTIVITY 21.9

Ask students to do a survey of 10 people on the playground to see whether they prefer crunchy cookies or chewy cookies. They can make a tally chart and then a picture graph, using cookie pictures.

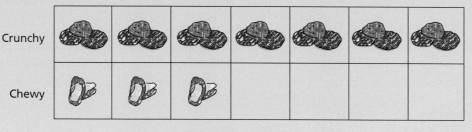

Spatial Reasoning

Frequency Tables

Eventually, tally charts can be replaced by *frequency tables*, in which the number of responses or items in each category is recorded in the form of a numeral instead of tally marks. A tally chart is easier to use while a set of data is being collected. However, a frequency table is more useful as a summary table after all the data have been collected and counted.

Colours of Cars in the Parking Lot		
Colour	Tally	Number of Cars
Blue	⌊⌍⌍⌍ ⌊⌍⌍⌍	10
Green	‖‖‖‖	4
Black	⌊⌍⌍⌍ ⎮	6
White	⌊⌍⌍⌍ ‖‖	7
Silver	⌊⌍⌍⌍	5
Gold	‖‖‖	3

Colours of Cars in the Parking Lot	
Colour	Number of Cars
Blue	10
Green	4
Black	6
White	7
Silver	5
Gold	3

A frequency table can be an extension of a tally chart, or students can record the numerical data directly in a frequency table.

Concrete Graphs

Initially, students use real objects to display the results of a sorting in a graph. Graphs made with real objects are called *concrete graphs*. At first, the graphs are arrangements of the actual objects being sorted. Later, other concrete materials are used to model, or represent, the real objects.

A people graph is a concrete graph that uses actual people as objects in the graph. These types of graphs suit contexts where students are graphing personal data, such as data about choices or opinions.

Notice that students in the concrete graph below are lined up on a large floor graphing mat, which is a large square grid. This aligns students so that comparisons are easy to make.

ACTIVITY 21.10

Ask students to arrange themselves into a concrete "people graph" to compare the number of students wearing long sleeves with those wearing short sleeves. Ask why it is easy to tell which group is greater once students are lined up in the graph.

Spatial Reasoning

It's easy to see that there are 4 more students with long sleeves than short sleeves.

A concrete "people graph" can be used by students to answer a simple question about themselves.

"People graphs" are usually formed in a way that parallels a pictograph or bar graph with one-to-one correspondence across the categories. However, a concrete "people graph" can also take the form of a circle graph. (See *Ways to Make Circle Graphs* on page 603.)

Concrete Graphs Using Models After students have gained some experience with concrete graphs made with real objects, they will be ready to begin making graphs from concrete models that represent the real objects. This adds a level of abstraction because the model is one step removed from the object it represents.

For example, to represent the information from the sleeve-length concrete "people graph," students could move away from the floor graphing mat, leaving items such as clothespins or linking cubes to hold their place. They could then put the clothespins (as shown in the margin) or cubes together to create a concrete graph. When the students sit down, the model will help them recall the information from their concrete "people graph."

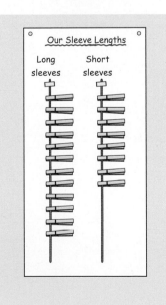

As models of concrete graphs are introduced, teachers have an opportunity to talk about why it helps if each object is the same size or if the objects are placed on a grid. Doing so ensures that the objects are equally spaced within each row or column and aligned across the categories, allowing for easy counting and comparisons. Providing cubes of different sizes can help make this point. For example, if students were to place different-sized cubes in categories on a concrete representational graph to show whether they have cats, they would discover that quick visual comparisons are impossible. (See Important Points About Concrete Graphs below.)

When objects are used to create a concrete graph, and there is no grid, it is important that the objects be the same size and shape.

IMPORTANT POINTS ABOUT CONCRETE GRAPHS

- The first person or concrete object in each category is at the same level or baseline.
- The people or objects in each category are equally spaced.
- The people or objects in each of the categories are spaced the same way or are the same size so that each person or object is aligned with its counterpart in the other categories.
- Concrete graphs can be vertical or horizontal.
- It is important to include labels and a concise but meaningful title to help the reader understand the graph.

Picture Graphs

Before long, students learn that concrete graphs can be unwieldy and difficult to keep intact, and discover that it is more convenient to use pictures to represent data in a *picture graph*. As well, using pictures also allows a display to be more permanent. The same basic principle of concrete graphs applies: the reader should be able to make comparisons at a glance.

In a picture graph, each picture is unique to the object or person it represents. Picture graphs form a bridge between concrete graphs and the more abstract pictographs and bar graphs.

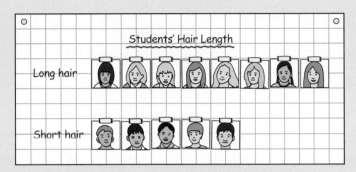

When the pieces of data (represented by pictures) in a picture graph are lined up one to one across the categories, it is easy to read the graph.

Because it is important that the corresponding items in the picture graph be aligned, grid paper is often used to help place the pictures. If the pictures are all the same size, the grid paper is not as important. For example, the use of grid paper for the pictograph above was optional.

IMPORTANT POINTS ABOUT PICTURE GRAPHS

- Each picture is unique to the individual object or person it represents.
- The first picture in each category is at the same level or baseline.
- The pictures in each category are equally spaced.
- The pictures in each of the categories are spaced the same way or are the same size so that each picture is aligned with its counterpart in the other categories.
- Picture graphs can be vertical or horizontal.
- It is important to include labels and a concise and meaningful title to help the reader understand the graph.

Pictographs

A *pictograph* is one step farther than a picture graph along the continuum from concrete to symbolic. Symbols are used to represent data, and sometimes these symbols are picture-like representations. The same symbol is used throughout the pictograph (or, for "early" pictographs, the same symbol is used for each category), making it different from a picture graph, which uses different pictures throughout. The same basic principles of concrete and picture graphs apply: the reader should be able to interpret the graph at a glance by comparing rows or columns.

The following pictograph shows that 10 children were surveyed about their favourite fruits, and 6 children chose strawberries. The same symbol, a happy face, is used to represent each of the 10 children, although a different colour has been used for each category.

TEACHING **TIP**

As with concrete graphs, it is important to provide a grid background for students to use for their pictographs to ensure that items are properly lined up.

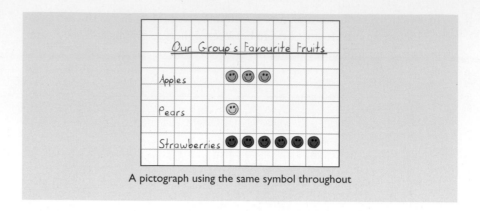

A pictograph using the same symbol throughout

Choosing Symbols Students enjoy choosing symbols for their pictographs, but there is a challenge involved in choosing something that is representative of all the categories. The symbol used to make a pictograph does not have to reflect the context, but choosing a meaningful symbol makes a graph more interesting, and also provides some immediate information about the data. In the pictograph above, a symbol of a particular type of fruit would not be suitable; in fact, it might be misleading. A symbol such as an empty circle would be acceptable, but would not provide as much information as the happy face. With the happy face, it is obvious that each symbol represents a child. Another possibility might be a stick figure.

Choosing an appropriate symbol can be achieved through group discussion and trial and error. The teacher can present some data to students to graph and invite suggestions for possible symbols. Small groups can discuss some possibilities and then present their ideas and justifications to the larger group. The class can then talk about why one symbol would be more appropriate than another, or why a certain symbol would be inappropriate.

One important thing to consider in choosing a symbol for a pictograph is the ease with which the symbol can be drawn and copied. Materials such as stamps, stickers, and stencils can help students create pictographs quickly and efficiently.

Scale or Many-to-One Correspondence As students begin to work with greater amounts of data, it becomes inconvenient to draw a symbol to represent every piece of data. Using a scale allows a single symbol to represent a number of items, a situation referred to as many-to-one correspondence. In the example below, it is easier to draw a graph with 10 comic book symbols than with 50.

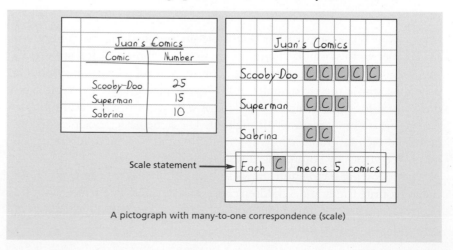

A pictograph with many-to-one correspondence (scale)

Once students are introduced to the concept of scale, they need to learn how to choose one that is appropriate for a given situation. In the example above, students with knowledge of multiplication facts might immediately notice that each number is a multiple of 5 and realize that having each symbol represent 5 comics would make the graph easy to create and interpret. However, a scale of 1 to 5 is not the only possibility.

Scale and Partial Symbols If, in the comic book example above, each symbol represented 2 comics, it would mean using partial symbols for two of the categories. If each symbol represented 4 comics, partial symbols would have to be used for all three categories. Obviously, once scale is introduced, choosing the right symbol becomes more complicated, as the symbol must allow for partial symbols that are easy to read. Thus, a circle or square shape is often the easiest to use.

Partial symbols are introduced when students are confronted with data where there is no obvious common factor other than 1. The best time to introduce this idea is when most of the pieces of data are even, but there is one odd number. Then each symbol represents 2 items, and students will need a half-symbol to represent the odd number of items.

In the following example, partial symbols are unavoidable because there is no common factor for 8, 2, and 5 (other than 1) that can be used as a scale for this data. In this pictograph, the choice of a rectangle as a symbol is appropriate because it is easy to represent 1 game using half of a rectangle.

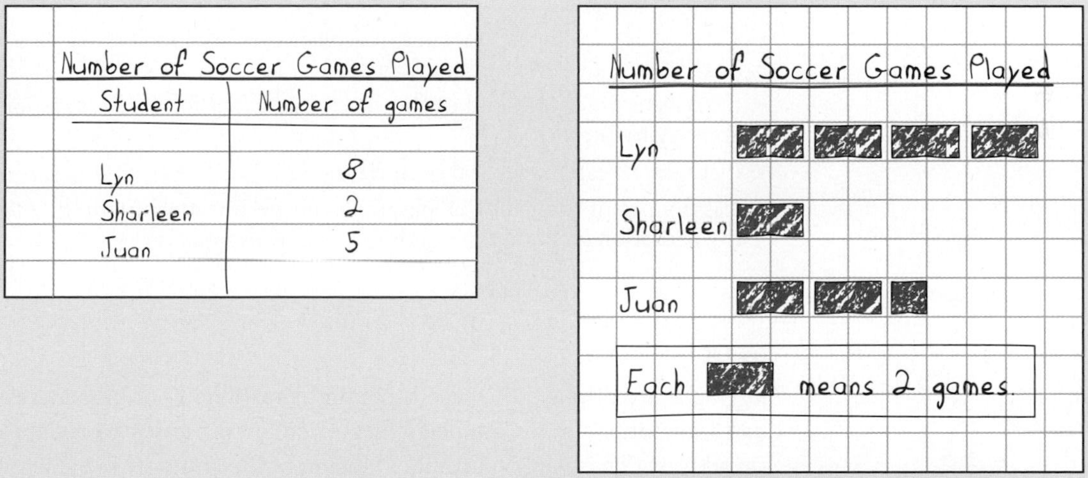

Number of Soccer Games Played	
Student	Number of games
Lyn	8
Sharleen	2
Juan	5

Number of Soccer Games Played

Lyn   ▨ ▨ ▨ ▨

Sharleen   ▨

Juan   ▨ ▨ ▨

Each   ▨   means 2 games.

A symbol shape such as a rectangle is a good one to use for a scale of 1 to 2 as it can easily be divided into half symbols.

If the pieces of data are greater numbers, for example, mostly beyond 20, it is more efficient to use symbols that represent more than 2 items. For example, for the hockey card data shown below, students might use a scale of 1 symbol to 4 cards since it would be relatively easy to show 38 as $9\frac{1}{2}$ symbols, 22 as $5\frac{1}{2}$ symbols, and 17 as $4\frac{1}{4}$ symbols. Once a scale of 4 has been chosen to suit the numbers in the set of data, the next task is to choose a symbol that can easily be partitioned into halves and fourths. In this case, a circle works better than a rectangle since the quarter and half symbols are more obvious.

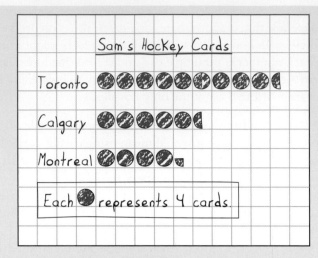

Sam's Hockey Cards	
Team	Number
Toronto	38
Calgary	22
Montreal	17

A circle is the ideal symbol, as it can easily be divided into quarter and half symbols that are easy to interpret.

IMPORTANT POINTS ABOUT PICTOGRAPHS

- The same symbol is usually used throughout the graph (although some "early" pictographs use the same symbol for each category). This symbol may or may not reflect the context of the data.
- The first symbol in each category is at the same level or baseline.
- The symbols in each category are equally spaced.
- If many-to-one correspondence or scale is used, the scale must be clearly stated in a scale statement, or legend.
- If a scale is used, the symbol chosen should allow for partial symbols that are easy to interpret.
- Pictographs can be vertical or horizontal.
- It is important to include labels and a concise but meaningful title to help the reader understand the graph.

Bar Graphs

Bar graphs are displays that use the lengths or heights of bars to represent quantities, often the frequencies of particular responses to a data collection activity. These are a natural extension of the concrete representational graphs made with linking cubes and the use of square pictures and symbols in pictographs. Normally, students should work on grid paper to draw bar graphs, thereby ensuring that all the squares are the same size.

Scale With bar graphs, as with pictographs, students begin with situations in which each square represents a frequency or quantity of one. Later, when they begin working with greater data values, students learn to use a scale along the axis, as shown in the graph on the next page. (See page 592 for a discussion of the use of many-to-one correspondence with pictographs.) Initially, students tend to choose scales of 2, 5, and 10. This is likely because they feel comfortable skip counting with these numbers. As with pictographs, it is important for students to think about which scale would be best suited to the data, and how they will show amounts that fall between two numbers in the scale.

ACTIVITY 21.11

Provide data about the number of visitors to various museum exhibits. Make sure the data involves a variety of 3-digit numbers, not all multiples of 100. Ask students to choose an appropriate scale for the data.

Building Number Sense

The bar graphs shown below display the same data, vertically and horizontally. Both use a scale of 10 (as indicated on each numbered axis). Dividing squares horizontally or vertically shows partial amounts. The number of roller coaster riders, 45, is easy to interpret because it is halfway between 40 and 50. The number of merry-go-round riders, about 12 or 13, is more difficult to identify. However, you do not need to know the exact number of riders to make general comparisons with other bars.

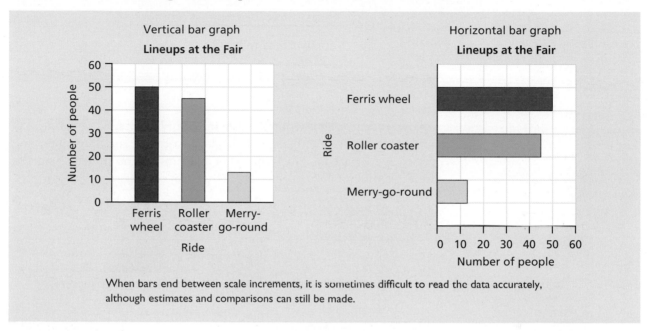

When bars end between scale increments, it is sometimes difficult to read the data accurately, although estimates and comparisons can still be made.

Notice that the bars are spaced an equal distance apart and not connected, making it easier to read each graph. The separation of the bars also shows that each bar represents a separate or discrete category. (See page 597 for a discussion of histograms—graphs where the bars touch because they represent intervals in a continuous number sequence.) Notice also that the horizontal axis of the graph on the left has both labels (one per bar) and an axis heading, "Ride." For many graphs, including both labels is necessary for clarity. In the case of this graph, the axis heading "Ride" is optional as the labels are self-explanatory.

Intervals For some types of data, such as data about fair rides, birthday months, or pets, the categories are discrete, and a bar graph is fairly easy to make and interpret. One axis shows the category names and the other shows a numbered scale. However, when the pieces of data themselves are numerical, things become more complex, and two numbered axes are needed. In this case, it is often useful to group the data into *intervals* before making the display. For example, suppose 27 students in a Grade 4 class conducted an experiment to determine how many paper clips each student can link in two minutes.

> ### ACTIVITY 21.12
>
> To connect data work to probability work, ask students to roll a pair of dice and keep track of the values of the differences of the numbers rolled. Students then display the data in a bar graph.
>
> ___
>
> **Spatial Reasoning**

Step 1 Collect the data.

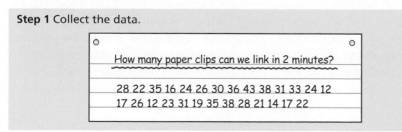

How many paper clips can we link in 2 minutes?

28 22 35 16 24 26 30 36 43 38 31 33 24 12
17 26 12 23 31 19 35 38 28 21 14 17 22

The next step is to organize the data in order from least to greatest to highlight any patterns. Students can readily find the least and greatest numbers, along with any results that occurred more than once.

Step 2 Organize the data from least to greatest.

How many paper clips can we link in 2 minutes?

12 12 14 16 17 17 19 21 22 22 23 24 24 26
26 28 28 28 30 31 31 33 35 35 36 38 43

Now students might group the data into number-interval categories, as shown in the table, and then graph the data. Note that some students may opt to leave a space for 0 to 9 paper clips, even though no students actually connected this number of paper clips. This is not necessary, but it is correct.

Step 3 Group into intervals.

How many paper clips can we link in 2 minutes?

Number of paper clips	Number of people
10–19	7
20–29	11
30–39	8
40–49	1

Step 4 Graph the data.

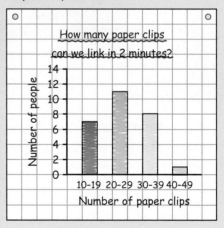

Imagine what the bar graph would look like if intervals were not used. There would have been 18 bars or more—one for each number of paper clips linked in 2 minutes. This would not be a practical or useful way to display the data.

Note that the bars are separated because the data can still be described as discrete. For example, there is no bar to represent quantities between 19 and 20 because you cannot link $19\frac{1}{2}$ clips.

Choosing Intervals The choice of interval categories will depend on the data. For example, if the pieces of data are quite spread out and there are to be only four categories or bars, each interval in the group will include a greater range of numbers. The graphs below show how using different intervals affects the appearance of the paper clip data. The smaller the intervals, the more you can learn about the detail of the data from the graph. However, there is a point where the number of bars becomes excessive.

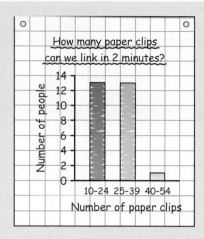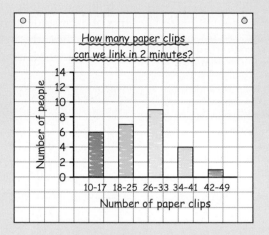

Changing the way data values are grouped in intervals can make the same data look very different.

IMPORTANT POINTS ABOUT BAR GRAPHS

- A grid square is used to represent the same quantity throughout.
- If a many-to-one correspondence is used, the scale must be clearly shown along a numbered vertical or horizontal axis.
- Bars should be separated to indicate that they represent discrete data, although it is not incorrect if there are no spaces between the bars.
- If there are no pieces of data for a category or interval, a space can be left where the bar would be, although it is not required.
- Bar graphs can be vertical or horizontal.
- Both axes should be labelled. Each bar should have a category label, which might be a discrete topic name or a numerical interval. The other axis, the scale axis, is labelled numerically.
- Axis headings should be used, as necessary, for clarity.
- It is important to include a concise but meaningful title to help the reader understand the graph.

Variations of Bar Graphs

Double-Bar Graphs Sometimes it is useful to look at two sets of data simultaneously, for example, to compare the number of sisters that class-mates have with the number of brothers. To show how two different sets of data are alike or different, it would be appropriate to create a *double-bar graph*.

Histograms A *histogram* is basically a bar graph that has been adapted to continuous data. The categories along the horizontal axis are always continuous number intervals (intervals with no gaps between them), and the bars touch to show the continuity. The heights of the bars show how many pieces of data are in each interval (the frequency).

ACTIVITY 21.13

Students might conduct a traffic survey and record the number of vehicles that pass a particular busy intersection during each hour during the school day. The data would be displayed in a histogram since time is continuous.

———————————

Spatial Reasoning

Suppose the following data were collected about the height in centimetres of each student in a math class. The data could be displayed in a bar graph to show the height of each student. In this case, the categories are discrete and the bars would not touch.

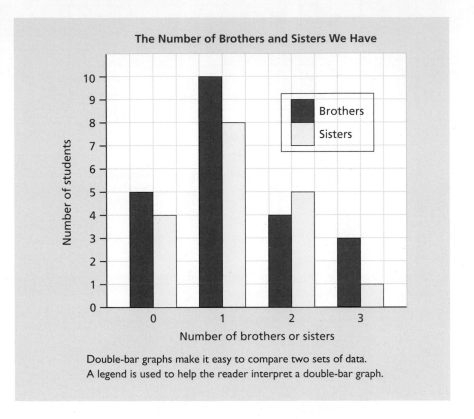

Double-bar graphs make it easy to compare two sets of data.
A legend is used to help the reader interpret a double-bar graph.

Heights of Students in Our Class

Allison	143	Karin	157
Keiko	143	Evan	167
Shawn	153	Victoria	145
Jessie	168	Rashid	152
Christie	141	Lucie	149
Ahmed	150	Cam	147
Sam	157	Peter	151
Julie	148	Lois	143
Jose	156	Nicole	154
Luigi	155	Sheldon	158

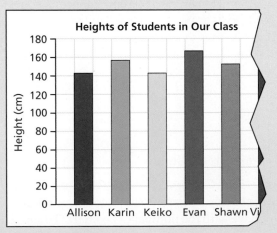

In a bar graph, the spaces between the bars indicate that the data categories are discrete.

To make the graph more concise, the data could be organized into intervals as shown in the frequency table below, and then displayed in a histogram.

Heights of Students in Our Class

Height (cm)	Number of students
140–145	4
145–150	4
150–155	5
155–160	5
160–165	0
165–170	2

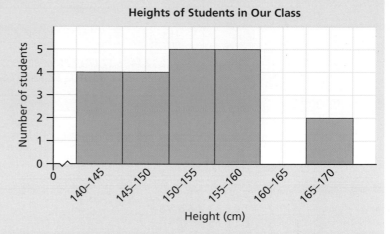

Heights of Students in Our Class

In a histogram, the bars touch to indicate that the data intervals are continuous.

Note that the intervals in the table (and on the graph) appear to overlap; for example, it appears as if 145 cm belongs in both the first and second intervals. By convention, pieces of data that arc "on the border" between two intervals are counted in the higher interval. A 145-cm height, for example, is included in the 145- to 150-cm interval.

IMPORTANT POINTS ABOUT HISTOGRAMS

- Histograms are used to show data in continuous number intervals.
- Histograms always describe frequencies or show how many are in each interval.
- The bars should touch to show the continuity of the data.
- If there are no pieces of data for an interval, a space is left where the bar would be.
- Histograms are usually oriented vertically.
- Each bar should have a label, which will be a numerical interval.
- Both axes should have headings.
- It is important to include a concise but meaningful title to help the reader understand the graph.

Stem-and-Leaf Plots A *stem-and-leaf plot* is a way of both organizing and displaying numerical data. It is similar to a horizontal bar graph, except that each piece of data is displayed in its original form. Numbers are grouped together by place value: the "stem" is determined by the digit(s) of greater place value when the number is written in standard form; the "leaves" are determined by the digit(s) of lesser place value. For example, using the data about paper clips, students begin by ordering the pieces of data they collected, and then they group the numbers to make the stem-and-leaf plot as shown below.

The stem-and-leaf plot on the next page allows students to compare frequencies for different numbers of tens. For example, it is easy to see that the greatest number of students had results in the twenties, but only one student had a result in the forties.

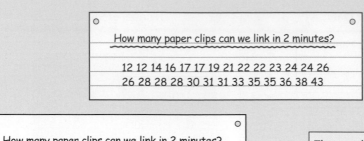

How many paper clips can we link in 2 minutes?

12 12 14 16 17 17 19 21 22 22 23 24 24 26
26 28 28 28 30 31 31 33 35 35 36 38 43

How many paper clips can we link in 2 minutes?

Stem	Leaves
1	2 2 4 6 7 7 9
2	1 2 2 3 4 4 6 6 8 8 8
3	0 1 1 3 5 5 6 8
4	3

The number 12 is shown as the leaf of 2 in the row with the stem of 1 (which includes all values from 10 to 19). Since 12 is repeated twice in the data, it is also represented twice in the stem-and-leaf plot.

A stem-and-leaf plot is like a horizontal bar graph where the data values themselves create the shape of the graph.

ACTIVITY 21.14

Invite students to perform long jumps and record the distances jumped in a stem-and-leaf plot. Notice that the data below shows jump distances between 172 cm and 230 cm.

Long-Jump Distances (cm)	
Stem	Leaf
17	2 3 5
18	5 6 6 7 8 9
19	3 3 6 8
20	0 2 5 5 6 7 8
21	2 2 2 4 5 5 8
22	0 1 1 2 3 7 8 9
23	0

Spatial Reasoning

If the stem-and-leaf plot above were recorded on grid paper, it would look like a horizontal bar graph that shows the frequency of the data in each of the intervals 10–19, 20–29, 30–39, and 40–49. The advantage of the stem-and-leaf plot, though, is that you can see each individual data value. Without going back to the original list of data values, students can determine the following directly from the stem-and-leaf plot:

- the range (from 12 to 43, so the range is 31)
- the mean (add the values and divide by 27 to get 25.6)
- the median (the 14th value from either end, which is 26)
- the mode (28)

In the stem-and-leaf plot shown, the stems are the tens digits and the leaves are the ones digits. In other stem-and-leaf plots, the stems might be the hundreds and tens digits together and the leaves would be the ones digits (as shown in the margin); or the stems might be ones and tenths (e.g., 1.2 for 1.23), and the leaves the hundredths (0.03 for 1.23). The choice of stem depends on the nature of the data and the purpose for which it is being organized.

It is easy to determine the mean, median, mode, and range from a stem-and-leaf plot. For example, for the set of test score data in the stem-and-leaf plot on the next page:

- The median test score is 89. This is the middle data value in the set of 29 data values (counting to the halfway point, the 15th number (out of 29) from either end). There are as many pieces of data below it (14) as above it (14).
- The mean is 86.3. This is calculated by finding the sum of all 29 data values and then dividing by 29.
- The mode is 29, the most frequently appearing data value.
- The range is 98 – 71 = 27 (the difference between the highest and lowest data values).

TEST SCORES

7	1 2 2 7 8 9
8	0 0 3 4 4 5 8 9 9
9	0 0 0 0 1 1 2 2 3 3 3 5 5 8

> **IMPORTANT POINTS ABOUT STEM-AND-LEAF PLOTS**
>
> - Each number in the data set is represented by a leaf placed in a row beside a stem.
> - The stems are determined by the greater place value(s).
> - The data values by stem are in order vertically, usually from least to greatest.
> - The data values in each stem (the leaves) are in order horizontally, from least to greatest, and are aligned from stem to stem.
> - If there are no data for a stem, the stem is still included with no data values (leaves) recorded beside it.
> - It is important to include a concise but meaningful title to help the reader understand the graph.

Line Graphs

Line graphs are used to show trends in data, usually over time. They are sometimes called *broken-line graphs* since they appear jagged or crooked, consisting of connected plotted points that are not in a straight line. The points are plotted to show *relationships* between two *variables*—one of which is often time but can be another continuous variable—and the points are joined with a line to make it easier to see trends. Like bar graphs, line graphs have a title, labelled categories, axis headings, and a clear scale.

ACTIVITY 21.15

Students enjoy interpreting line graphs that tell a story.

Ask students to describe this graph showing Marc's hike.

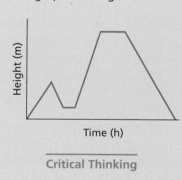

Critical Thinking

Scatter Plots

A *scatter plot* is also designed to show trends and to indicate whether there is a relationship between two variables. Often the data are first recorded in a T-chart or a table of values, and then the points are plotted on a coordinate grid. The points tend to be scattered on the graph, which is why the graph

ACTIVITY 21.16

Students might create a scatter plot to relate the cost of a phone call to different numbers of minutes the call might take.

Algebraic Reasoning

is called a scatter plot. However, if there is a relationship between the variables, the scattering will actually form a pattern. If there is no relationship, the points will form a random scattering.

For example, the table and scatter plot below show a pattern in the test scores of students who studied for different lengths of time.

Are Study Hours Related to Test Scores?

Hours of study	Test score
2	70
5	90
3	80
6	85
7	90
1	60
7	85
6	80
1	50

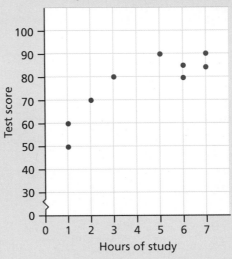

Are Study Hours Related to Test Scores?

Scatter plots are used to look for trends and to determine if there is a relationship between two variables. The scattering of plotted points can be random or it can form a pattern indicating a trend or relationship.

From the data points, it is easy to see that there is a trend or relationship: more study generally led to higher grades. However, if you continue to examine the graph, you will notice that students who study the same amount, for example, 7 hours, can still get quite different scores.

Dependent and Independent Variables Broken-line graphs and scatter plots are examples of graphs that show *relationships* between two variables. In a relationship, changing one variable can result in a change to the other. For example, as growth time increases, so does the height of a bean plant. (See the *Height of a Bean Plant* graph on page 607.) In mathematics, the variable that changes "independently" (in this case, the plant's growth time) is called the *independent variable*. The variable that is affected by or "depends" on this change (in this case, the height of a plant) is called the *dependent variable*.

By mathematical convention, the independent variable is usually plotted along the horizontal axis, and the dependent variable along the vertical axis. Another example is the scatter plot above, where the amount of study time might influence test scores, so the horizontal axis is labelled "Hours of study" (the independent variable) and the vertical axis is labelled "Test score" (the dependent variable). (See the example in *Common Errors, Misconceptions, and Strategies* on page 612, *Numbering the Wrong Axis.*)

Circle Graphs

Another familiar type of graph is a *circle graph*. Like other types of graphs, a circle graph is based on categorizing data, but its function is primarily to show relationships among the parts of a whole and, at the same time, show relationships between each part and the whole. This type of graph makes the most sense when it is important to see how a total amount is distributed.

For example, a circle graph might show the proportions of

- a budget spent on different categories
- books in a library of different genres or for different age groups
- a day spent on different activities
- a class of students who chose each type of hot lunch, as shown in the graph below

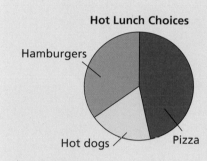

Hot Lunch Choices

Hamburgers

- Almost half the class chose pizza. (This is a part–whole relationship.)
- More students chose pizza than hamburgers. (This is a part–part relationship.)

Hot dogs   Pizza

A circle graph allows you to see at a glance the relationships between each of the parts and the whole (part–whole relationships). It also shows relationships among the parts (part–part relationships).

Creating Circle Graphs With a circle graph, it is especially important that no piece of data belong to more than one category, since the sum of the data pieces must be equal to the whole.

Ways to Make Circle Graphs

MAKE A CONCRETE CIRCLE GRAPH WITH PEOPLE

Ask students a question, for example, you might ask, "Do you own a dog?"

- Have them stand in lines that represent their answers.
- Give a label to the first student in each line.
- Bring the ends of the lines together so the children are standing in a circle, but are still in their places in the sequence.
- To create the circle graph, stretch a string from the centre of the circle to each student who is holding a label.
- Then move the labels into the sectors you have marked off with the strings.

Dogs

No Dogs

A concrete circle "people graph"

(continued)

USE FRACTION CIRCLES

Fraction circles are useful tools for creating circle graphs. Initially, students can use fraction circles that match their data (e.g., a circle divided in tenths to represent 10 people), and simply colour the appropriate fractions on the circle.

How Many Siblings We Have

Fraction circles can be used to create circle graphs for data representing groups of certain sizes.

Once students understand the concept of percent, they can graph data for groups of 100 or percent data using a percent circle (a fraction circle whose circumference is divided into hundredths). For example, if 7 out of 33 students wear glasses, students would calculate that 7 out of 33 is about 21%, so they would colour $\frac{21}{1000}$ of the circle to represent these students. (When students round percents, they may sometimes need to adjust the rounding to make sure the results add to exactly 100%.)

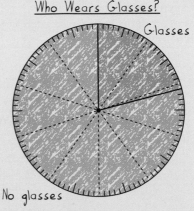

Who Wears Glasses?

Percent circles can be used to create circle graphs for groups of 100 or when data are in percent form.

USE ANGLES

Older students can use the fact that there are 360° in a circle to create sectors of a circle that accurately represent groups of data as described below.

Step 1 Draw a circle using a compass or template.

Step 2 Calculate the percent of the whole group represented by each category.

Step 3 Calculate the angle that represents the corresponding percent or fraction of 360°.

Step 4 Use a protractor and a ruler to draw the angle and sector to the nearest degree.

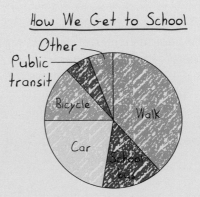

How We Get to School

A VARIATION OF A CIRCLE GRAPH

A variation of the circle graph is a hundredths grid. Students count the squares on a grid to construct or read the graph. A hundredths grid is similar to a circle graph because, like a circle graph, it shows the relationships of the parts to the whole, as well as the relationships among the parts.

The grid here, for example, shows that 50% of the members of the team were on the team last year, 33% were on a different team last year, and 17% are new to the sport.

Where Our Team Members Played Last Year

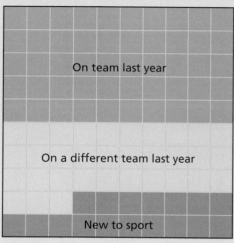

On team last year

On a different team last year

New to sport

In a hundredths grid, it is easy to count to find the percent for each part.

A hundredths grid is a simple, suitable alternative to a circle graph for showing percent data.

Box Plots

A box plot is used, usually in Grade 8 or up, to show how a set of data is distributed. The data are divided into four quartiles, each containing 25% of the data. For example, the data below about student scores (out of 100) on a quiz was collected and displayed in a box plot. The box plot shows that

- 25% of the students scored between 30 and 60
- 25% between 60 and 70
- 25% between 70 and 85 and
- 25% between 85 and 100

The middle 50% of the data are included in a box divided at the median, and the upper and lower 25% of the data are described by "whiskers," which is why this is often also called a box and whisker plot.

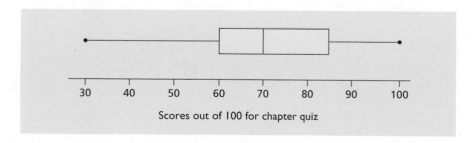

Scores out of 100 for chapter quiz

Appropriate Use of Data Display Formats

One of the important things students need to learn is which graph is most appropriate in a given circumstance. There is often more than one good choice, but there can be inappropriate choices as well, for example, a histogram to display discrete data or a circle graph to display a set of data that does not represent a whole.

When to Use Each Type of Data Display

PICTOGRAPHS AND BAR GRAPHS

Pictographs and bar graphs are appropriate for quickly and visually comparing frequencies of data in different categories, no matter how great or small those frequencies are. The data categories can be either non-numerical (as in the pictograph shown here), or numerical (as in the interval bar graph).

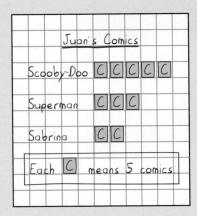

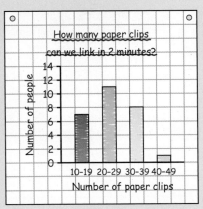

HISTOGRAMS

Histograms are suitable when the data are continuous, that is, when the data categories are number intervals with no gaps between them and the bars show the frequency for each category. Graphs like these are often used to show measurement data. Histograms are not generally introduced until later grades.

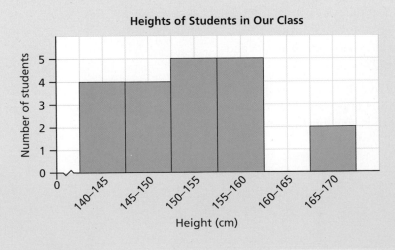

(continued)

When to Use Each Type of Data Display (Continued)

STEM-AND-LEAF PLOTS

Stem-and-leaf plots are used when numerical data are best organized by place value, in intervals or stems of 10 or 100 or some other power of 10. They show the frequency of data in each interval, as well as each individual piece of data (the leaves), making the stem-and-leaf plot a source of raw data and a data display. Seeing individual pieces of data displayed in order is useful for determining the range, mode, and median.

Test Scores

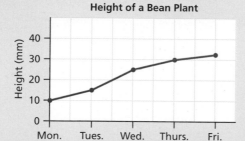

7	1 2 2 7 8 9
8	0 3 4 4 5 8 9 9 9
9	0 0 0 0 1 1 2 2 3 3 3 5 5 8

BROKEN-LINE GRAPHS

Broken-line graphs are used to display a trend or relationship. A broken-line graph can show how something changes, usually over time. When a solid line is used between plotted points, the data can be discrete or continuous (as shown in the graph below). If the line is dashed, it indicates that the data are discrete. For example, suppose money was collected every Monday for several months and the data was displayed in a broken line graph to show the cumulative amount over time. A dashed line could be used to indicate that no money was collected between the Mondays. Note that the use of a dashed line is optional.

Height of a Bean Plant

SCATTER PLOTS

Scatter plots are used to look for trends and determine if there is a relationship between two variables. For example, a scatter plot might help students determine if there is a relationship between test scores and hours of study.

Are Study Hours Related to Test Scores?

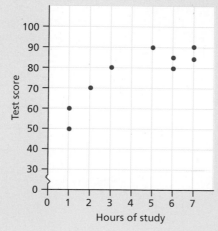

(continued)

ACTIVITY 21.18

Ask students to think first of a situation where both a bar graph and a circle graph might be useful, and then of another where only one of those graphs would actually be useful.

_____

Critical Thinking

CIRCLE GRAPHS

Circle graphs show how a whole set of data can be subdivided into categories. They allow the viewer to compare the frequencies of categories, but do not usually show the actual values of those frequencies. Circle graphs should not be used if there is no meaning to the total set of data. For example, a circle graph showing how many children have a sibling is not meaningful unless all the children surveyed represent a group, such as all the children in a classroom.

Do You Have a Brother?

BOX PLOTS

Box plots are used to show how data in a set of data are spread or distributed. Using a box plot, it is easy to see where most of the data lie. The plot below shows that the scores ranged from 60 to 80 and 50% of the students scored between 70 and 78 on the test, 25% scored between 60 and 70, and 25% scored between 78 and 80.

Test Scores

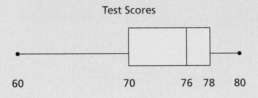

Common Errors and Misconceptions

Data Display: Common Errors, Misconceptions, and Strategies

COMMON ERROR OR MISCONCEPTION	SUGGESTED STRATEGY
Aligning Categories When making concrete and picture graphs, students do not ensure a consistent baseline for each category line and do not ensure that the items in the lines are equally spaced.	Use a large grid so that items are automatically placed to align with items in the other categories. For larger items or people graphs, a graphing floor mat can be used. 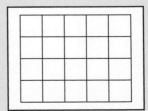 Large grid for aligning objects or pictures

(continued)

Data Display: Common Errors, Misconceptions, and Strategies (Continued)

COMMON ERROR OR MISCONCEPTION	SUGGESTED STRATEGY
Aligning Pictures on Graphs When students create picture graphs or pictographs, they do not ensure that the pictures are lined up, one right below or beside the other.  Misaligned pictures	Provide large grid paper on which students can create their graphs. If the cells are large enough, students can draw their pictures inside each cell. 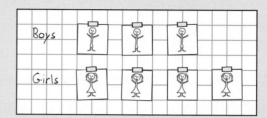
Different Pictograph Symbols When students create pictographs, the symbols might be different sizes and the spacing might be irregular. For example, they might use a different-sized ball for each sport as shown below. 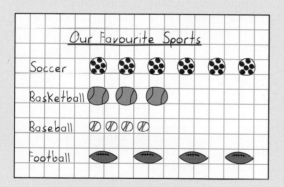 Symbols of different sizes with uneven spacing	There is some debate as to whether using different symbols is actually incorrect. Early pictographs often use a different symbol for each category. These early pictographs introduce students to the notion of using a consistent symbol. They serve as a transition from picture graphs that use a different picture for each object or person to later pictographs that use one symbol throughout. To show why it is a good idea to use a consistent symbol, show a pictograph that uses symbols of different sizes and irregular spacing, and talk about how using the same-size symbol and equal spacing might make the graph easier to read and be less misleading. For example, using the pictograph to the left, you might ask, "Can you tell, without counting symbols, which sport was chosen by the fewest students?"
Irregular Scales When students create bar graphs, they use an irregular scale based on the actual data values instead of an evenly spaced number line. For example, suppose 6 students (A to F) are asked how many times they have used the Internet in the last month. The data values for the number of times they logged on are as follows: 35, 60, 6, 8, 22, and 16. A student might graph the data as shown below.	Students should look at the greatest value first. They estimate how many squares high they want their graph to be, and then decide how much each square has to represent. They then skip count and record the axis scale before they actually begin making their bars. For example, for the use-of-Internet data, students need to go to at least 60, so they might decide to have each square height represent either 5 or 10, depending on how large they want the graph to be. They should create the bars only after the scale is recorded. *(continued)*

Data Display: Common Errors, Misconceptions, and Strategies (Continued)

COMMON ERROR OR MISCONCEPTION	SUGGESTED STRATEGY

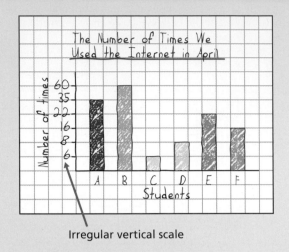

Irregular vertical scale

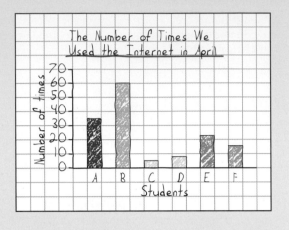

Omitting Repeated Values

When creating stem-and-leaf plots, students omit repeated data values.

Ask students to create a stem-and-leaf plot for each set of data shown below:

Set 1: 21, 21, 21, 21, 21, 21, 21, 22, 31, 32

Set 2: 21, 31, 32

If students create the same stem-and-leaf plot, have them look back at the data. Ask what they notice about the first set (there are a lot of 21s), and ask whether the stem-and-leaf plot reflects this.

Omitting Categories

Students omit a bar on a histogram or a stem row on a stem-and-leaf plot if there are no pieces of data within that interval.

Students always need to check that the numbers are continuous as they read down the list of stems for a stem-and-leaf plot or across the intervals for a histogram. (This is not the case with other graphs that show discrete data, such as bar graphs or pictographs.)

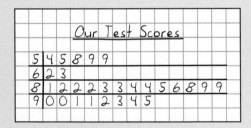

Missing stem row for 7

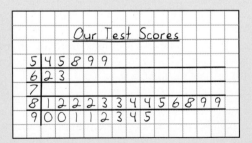

(continued)

Data Display: Common Errors, Misconceptions, and Strategies (Continued)

COMMON ERROR OR MISCONCEPTION	SUGGESTED STRATEGY

Leaves Out of Order

When creating stem-and-leaf plots, students do not put the leaves in order within each stem.

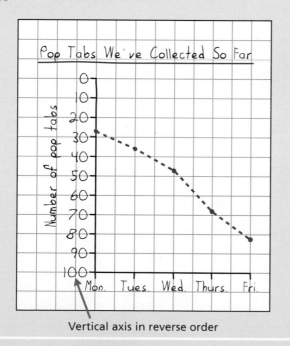

Leaves are not in order

Remind students to double-check their values in each stem for order. Some students prefer to create a working stem-and-leaf plot by recording all the data values within each stem in the order that the data appear or occur; they then create a final stem-and-leaf plot by putting the leaves in order.

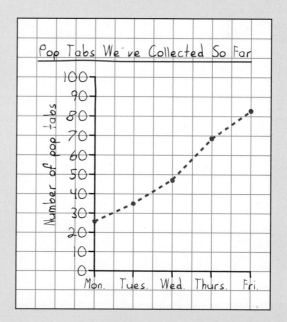

Students can also order the data in a list before constructing the stem-and-leaf plot. Making an ordered list can also be helpful for determining the range in order to establish appropriate stems.

Axes in Reverse Order

When students are making bar graphs or line graphs, they number the vertical axis from top to bottom, rather than from bottom to top. If a student numbers the vertical axis from top to bottom, then the data appear in inverted form.

In the graph to the left, there appears to be a decline in the number of pop tabs, when the collection is actually increasing. Discuss with students why this happened, and remind them that both the vertical and the horizontal axes on a grid should be labelled from the bottom-left corner.

Vertical axis in reverse order

Not Including "0" on Axes

Students do not include the "0" along numbered axes.

The "0" is considered optional. Many mathematicians create graphs without the "0," as it is assumed. However, encourage students to make their graphs as complete as possible and model the inclusion of "0" when creating graphs.

(continued)

Data Display: Common Errors, Misconceptions, and Strategies (Continued)

COMMON ERROR OR MISCONCEPTION	SUGGESTED STRATEGY

Numbering the Wrong Axis

When students are making line graphs or stem-and-leaf plots, they plot the independent variable along the vertical axis instead of the horizontal axis. A student who has plotted the variables in the reverse positions may have difficulty interpreting the graph. In the example below, the slope of the line makes it appear that the number of pop tabs rose quickly on Monday and Tuesday, and the increase tapered off on Wednesday and Thursday. In actual fact, the greatest increase occurred from Wednesday to Thursday. See the corrected graph in the right column.

At the elementary level, it is not necessary for students to understand independent and dependent variables, although it is a good idea for teachers to model a correct approach. Invite students to predict what the graph to the left would look like if the number of pop tabs were graphed on the other axis. Talk about how this would make it easier to see the "shape" of the data.

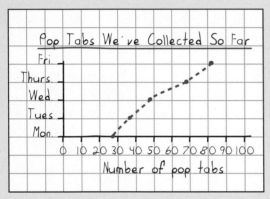

The days of the week should be along the horizontal axis.

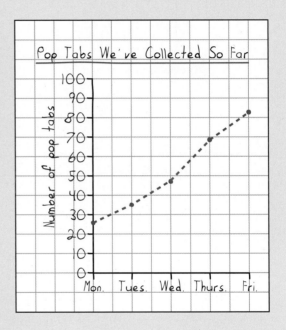

Percents Do Not Add to 100%

If the percents shown in a circle graph do not add to 100%, there may be an error somewhere in their calculations or it may be due to rounding.

Encourage students to check their work by adding the final percents in the circle graph. If students are rounding percents to make the graph, then the rounding process can sometimes result in a sum that is very close to, but not exactly, 100%. Students who are using the percents to determine angle measures may need to adjust some measures by rounding differently so the angles will total 360°.

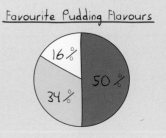

Appropriate Manipulatives

Data Display: Examples of Manipulatives

GRAPHING MATS

A graphing mat is a large sheet of vinyl divided into cells by equally spaced horizontal and vertical lines. Ideally, each grid space should be large enough for a person to stand on. A graphing grid can also be created on the floor using masking tape.

EXAMPLE

A graphing mat ensures that students align themselves or objects when working with concrete graphs.

A graphing floor mat helps keep people and large objects aligned when making concrete graphs.

CONCRETE GRAPH MATERIALS

Materials that can be used to create concrete graphs include

• linking cubes
• counters
• clothes pins
• square tiles
• square blocks
• paper clips
• links made from paper, plastic, etc.

Using square counters or blocks to create concrete graphs is a helpful transition from concrete graphs to bar graphs.

EXAMPLES

Linking materials provide a quick way to create concrete graphs that are accurate and easy to read.

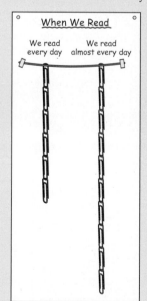

(continued)

Data Display: Examples of Manipulatives (Continued)

GRID PAPER AND FRACTION CIRCLES	EXAMPLES
Grid paper in various sizes is used to create graphs. Fraction circles (including percent circles) can be used to create circle graphs.	• Using grid paper to create bar graphs helps students keep bars the same size and evenly spaced, and provides a guide for a consistent scale.

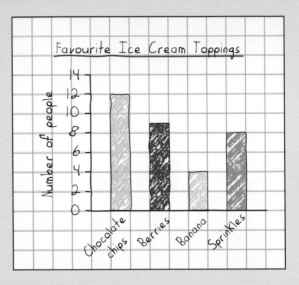

• A piece of grid paper that measures 10 × 10 can be used as a hundredths grid. See page 605 for an example of a circle graph alternative made with a hundredths grid.

• Fraction circles divided according to the data group size make it easy to make circle graphs. See page 604 for an example of a circle graph created using a fraction circle in tenths to graph data about a group of 10 students.

PICTURE AND PICTOGRAPH MATERIALS	EXAMPLE
Students can use stickers, photos, magazine cutouts, stencils, or stamps to create interesting picture graphs and pictographs.	Stickers make interesting pictographs and are often appropriate for scales of 2 to 1 because they can usually be cut in half.

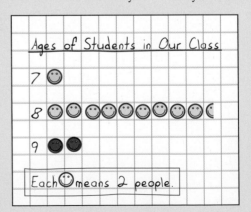

Data Analysis
Reading Graphs

When students interpret graphs constructed by others, they learn to appreciate the features that can help them make sense of a visual display of data. A good graph should communicate some overall impressions of the data to the reader "at a glance." This goal is facilitated by the choice of a graph type that suits the data, clear labelling and titling, and accuracy in representing the data.

The following sample graphs represent different levels of complexity. Each is constructed to make it easy to read the information.

Interpreting Different Types of Graphs

CONCRETE GRAPHS

This concrete graph allows the reader to quickly see that there are more green cubes than red or black ones because it

- uses cubes of the same size in all categories
- starts each row of cubes on a common baseline
- is clearly labelled

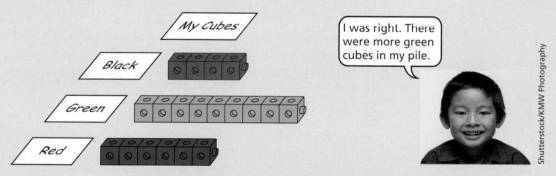

A well-constructed concrete graph makes it easy to compare categories.

PICTURE GRAPHS

This picture graph allows the reader to easily extract all the data because it
- uses a grid to make sure the pictures in each category are equally spaced
- starts each column of pictures on a common baseline
- is clearly labelled
- includes a title that clearly explains what the graph shows

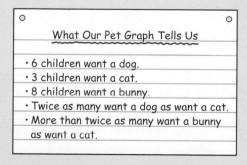

What Our Pet Graph Tells Us

- 6 children want a dog.
- 3 children want a cat.
- 8 children want a bunny.
- Twice as many want a dog as want a cat.
- More than twice as many want a bunny as want a cat.

A well-constructed picture graph makes it easy to extract information.

(continued)

PICTOGRAPHS

This pictograph allows the reader to interpret the symbols because it

- uses the same symbol throughout
- includes a scale statement
- starts the symbols in each row on a common baseline
- uses a symbol that is easily divided in half to represent 1 movie
- is clearly labelled
- includes a title that clearly explains what the graph shows

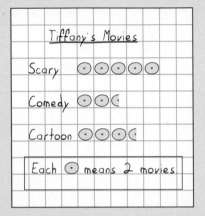

A well-constructed pictograph makes it easy to interpret partial symbols.

LINE GRAPHS

This line graph allows the reader to quickly determine any trends in rainfall over the year because it

- uses dashed lines to indicate to the reader that the data between the plotted points has no meaning
- includes labels on both axes that allow the reader to easily estimate the amount of precipitation in each of the 12 months
- includes a title that clearly explains what the graph shows

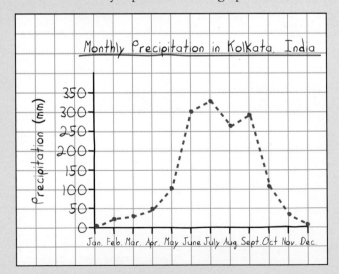

A well-constructed broken-line graph makes it easy to interpret the data and see trends.

Drawing Inferences from Graphs

One of the reasons teachers use visual displays of data is to "paint a picture" of the data in such a way that the display tells more about the data than numbers alone. You want students to be able to read specific pieces of information or facts from a graph and also work with multiple facts, for example, to make comparisons. Eventually, you want them to make inferences about what they see on the graph with appropriate justification.

Below are some examples that show what sort of information can be gleaned from graphs, including possible inferences.

The *Which pet do you want?* graph (page 615)

- A young student would report one or two facts from this graph; for example, 8 students want a bunny and 3 want a cat.
- A slightly older student might also conclude that more children want a bunny than either a dog or a cat.
- A student in Grades 5 to 8 might also infer that more people want a bunny because dogs and cats are more typical pets, and many of those students picking a bunny may already have a dog or cat. Note that making inferences often involves personal knowledge and experience.

The *Tiffany's Movies* graph (page 616)

- A student in Grades 2 to 4, even without knowing how to interpret the scale, would be able to conclude from this graph that Tiffany has more scary movies than either of the other two types.
- A possible inference for a student in Grades 5 to 8 might be that, assuming Tiffany bought all the movies herself, she prefers scary movies.

The *Monthly Precipitation* graph (page 616)

A student in Grades 4 to 8 would likely use this graph to

- report that, in the year this set of data was collected, the heavy rain months were from June to September, with a peak in July, and that there was very little rain from November to April, with a low point in December and January.
- infer that, assuming this is a typical precipitation pattern, the rainy season in Kolkata is usually from June to September.

Inference Activities

Even young students have the capacity to interpret graphical information and make inferences (see **Activity 21.20** below).

ACTIVITY 21.20

Show students two bar graphs without titles or labels:

- Graph A has two bars: one bar is 24 squares high, and the other bar is 1 square high.
- Graph B also has two bars, but one bar is 10 squares high, and the other bar is 14 squares high.

Explain that

- one graph shows the number of children compared to adults in a Grade 2 classroom
- one graph shows the number of 7-year-olds compared to 6-year-olds in a Grade 2 classroom

Ask students to decide which graph is which and why.

Critical Thinking

ACTIVITY 21.19

Provide an untitled and unlabelled graph, and ask students to come up with different sets of data that might realistically be represented by the graph. For example:

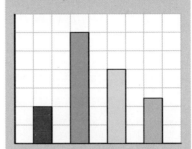

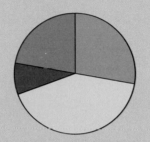

The bar graph might represent

- the number of students in a class with each hair colour: red, brown, black, and blond (using a scale of 2)

- the number of books read by four family members over the summer

The circle graph might represent

- the amount of time spent in a day sleeping (green), being at school (blue), eating and snacking (red), enjoying leisure time (yellow)

- the favourite leisure activities of students in a class: watching TV (green), doing sports (yellow), reading (blue), listening to music (red)

Critical Thinking

Inferring Relationships

Line graphs are particularly well suited for inferring a relationship between variables. For example, the graph below shows running times for Olympic winners for the 100-m women's race from 1948 to 2004.

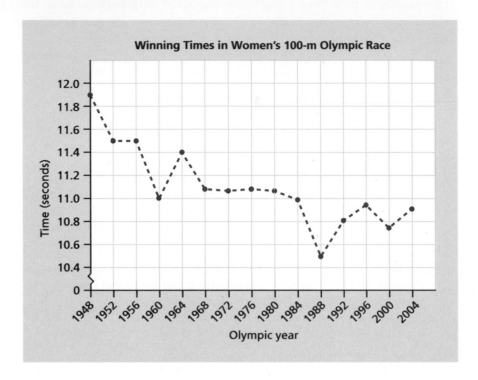

You can infer from this graph that there is a relationship between time and speed; that is, the times to complete the race have been improving over time. However, this improvement has not been continuous, since there is a slight backslide starting in 1992. As well, you can also predict that, as the times get closer to 10 s, the rate of decrease will get less and less.

Interpolation and Extrapolation

One specific way to make inferences from a graph is *interpolation*. Interpolation happens when the reader makes a judgment about values between two given or known values on a graph or in a table.

The broken-line graph in the margin shows that the size of the ozone hole has been increasing since 1980, with the sharpest increase from 1980 to 1985. No data were plotted for 1995, but students might estimate that the size of the hole in 1995 was between 18 million km^2 and 26 million km^2— perhaps about 22 million km^2. As with other inferences, it is important to give students a chance to justify their interpolations.

Sometimes students also *extrapolate*—they predict what would happen next. For example, a student might notice that the ozone hole increased in size by roughly 4 million km^2 every 5 years until 2000, and predict that this increase would continue. The student would then predict that the size of the hole would be 30 million km^2 in 2005, and 34 million km^2 by 2010. Again, justification should accompany any extrapolation.

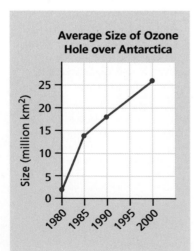

Generally, students are less comfortable with extrapolation than with interpolation and this is reasonable. It is important to emphasize that when line graphs display discrete data, interpolation is inappropriate because there are no data between the known data points. Many line graphs do not use dashed lines even if the data are discrete, so students should be cautioned to analyze line graphs carefully before making any assumptions about interpolating.

Misleading Graphs

One of the main points students need to understand is that it is important to be careful when they are creating and interpreting visual displays. Graphs can be misleading, sometimes deliberately, but more often accidentally.

The following types of errors can lead to misleading graphs.

Misuse of Pictures or Symbols

A typical misleading graph involves the use of pictures or symbols that are not of a consistent shape or size. For example, a student has created the graph on the next page to show the shoe sizes of students. In an attempt to convey the idea that the size 13 shoes are bigger than the size 11 and 12 shoes, the student has used different-sized pictures to represent each shoe size, which has inadvertently misled the reader. It appears that the same number of students wear size 13 as size 11 because the lengths of both lines are the same. It also appears that more students are wearing size 12 than size 11 because the length of the line representing size 12 is longer.

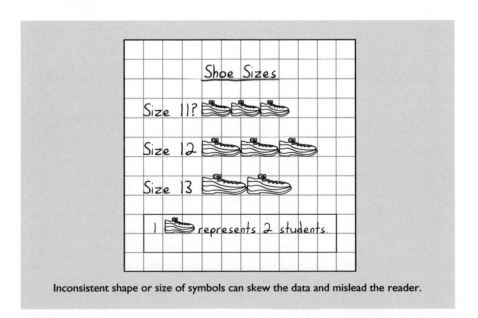

Inconsistent shape or size of symbols can skew the data and mislead the reader.

Misuse of Intervals

Interval bar graphs are supposed to use intervals of equal size. If unequal intervals are used, the graph can be misleading. For example, perhaps in an attempt to determine which interval to use to display his or her data, a student has created the two graphs below. The graphs show the same data, but tell very different stories.

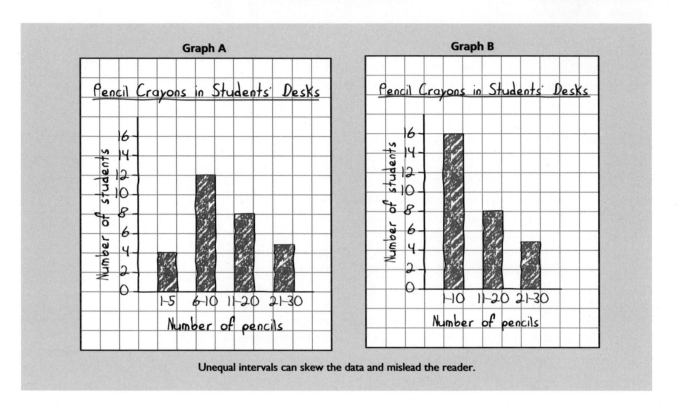

Unequal intervals can skew the data and mislead the reader.

Graph B is accurate, indicating that the group of students who have 1 to 10 pencil crayons is double the size of the group with 11 to 20, and more than triple the size of the group with 21 to 30. Graph A minimizes these differences because the data from the first interval on Graph B is graphed as two intervals on Graph A.

Misuse of Scale

Inappropriate Scale The importance of choosing an appropriate scale is exemplified by the two graphs below. In Graph A, a scale of 100 is used, necessitating the use of an axis break, shown with a wiggly line, indicating that data values have been omitted. In Graph B, the same data are shown using a scale of 1000. The impressions left by the graphs showing the same data are quite different.

In Graph C, cheddar appears to be the most popular cheese by far because the height of the cheddar bar relative to the other two bars appears so much greater. In fact, this is only because of the axis break in the vertical scale

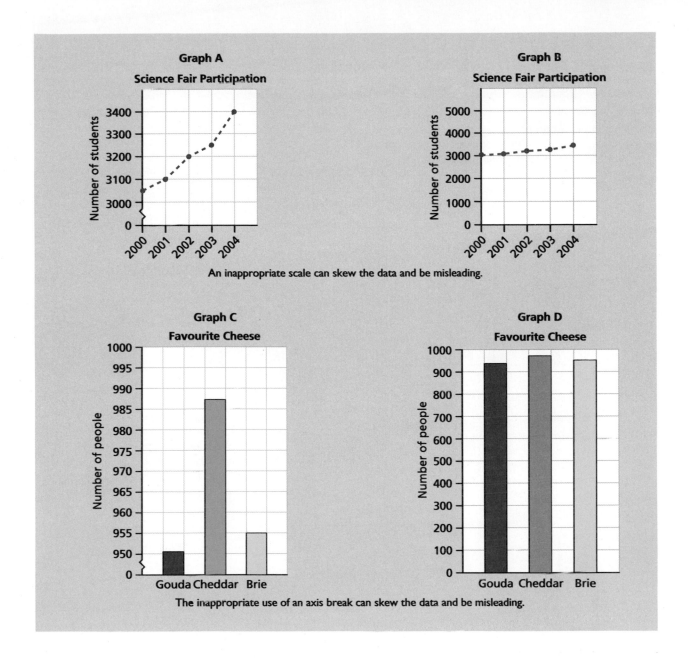

An inappropriate scale can skew the data and be misleading.

The inappropriate use of an axis break can skew the data and be misleading.

between 0 and 950 people. As a result, the first square in each bar on Graph C actually represents 950 people, while the other squares only represent 5 people. In Graph D, every square represents 100 people. Graph D leaves a more accurate impression of people's cheese preferences, indicating that about the same number of people chose each type of cheese.

Common Errors and Misconceptions

Data Analysis: Common Errors, Misconceptions, and Strategies

COMMON ERROR OR MISCONCEPTION	SUGGESTED STRATEGY
Misleading Graphs Students interpret graphs at face value and can be misled. For example, a student might look at this graph and conclude that Town A has twice as many people as Town C. 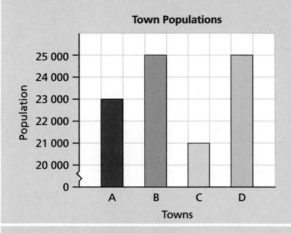	Alert students to aspects of graphs that can be potentially misleading, such as the axis break on this graph. (See *Misleading Graphs* on page 619.) Here, it might help to ask students to write the number of people who live in each town, and then make comparisons. Students might also benefit from creating their own misleading graphs using different techniques.
Unrealistic Inferences Students make unrealistic assumptions when drawing inferences. For example, a student might conclude from this graph that, since the temperature has risen 2° every hour, it will continue this pattern and reach 27° by 4 p.m. 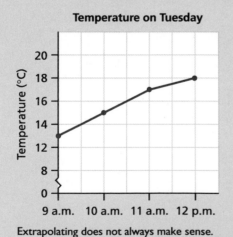 Extrapolating does not always make sense.	It is important for students to be able to justify any inferences they make. (See *Drawing Inferences from Graphs* on page 617.) In this case, you might ask students whether the temperature is likely to keep rising throughout the day, and what this would indicate about the temperature at midnight.
Inappropriate Interpolation Students interpolate between discrete data points on broken-line graphs. For example, suppose the data were based on science fairs held in April (see Graph B on page 621). It would not make sense to say that, in October 2001, participation in the science fair was a little more than 3000, because the science fair is held only once a year.	Make sure students know that when a line graph uses a dashed line it indicates the data is discrete (and interpolating does not make sense). When a graph uses a solid line, it can indicate that the data values are discrete or continuous. (See *Line Graphs* on page 601.) Remind students to think about the meaning of the data and whether it would make sense to interpolate between the plotted points.

Appropriate Children's Books

The Great Graph Contest (Leedy, 2005).
This book for primary students instructs them on how to create different types of graphs. The characters are a toad and a lizard who are competing to create the best graph. Instructional suggestions are provided at the end of the story.

Tiger Math: Learning to Graph from a Baby Tiger (Nagda and Bickel, 2002).
This book charts the growth of an orphaned tiger in a zoo using picture, circle, bar, and line graphs. The book is most appropriate for Grades 4 to 8.

More or Less a Mess (Keenan, 2001).
A girl who is asked to clean her room organizes and reorganizes the mess in different ways—this is an opportunity for students to see a real-life example of sorting and resorting. Some classroom sorting activities are suggested at the back of the book.

Appropriate Digital Resources

See the MindTap site for a selection of appropriate digital resources.

Assessing Student Understanding

- Link sorting activities to mathematics in other strands. For example, you might ask students to sort sets of numbers based on a variety of characteristics, or they might even sort graphs or patterns.

- It is important to assess not only students' ability to calculate statistics, but also their understanding of what those statistics really tell you about the data. For example, instead of providing a set of data and asking students to calculate the mean and median, you might pose a question such as, "The mean of a set of data is much lower than the median. What do you know about the set of data?"

- Make sure that you separately assess students' ability to read a graph, draw inferences or conclusions from it, and create it. These are separate skills and you probably want to know which skills are problematic for students and which are not.

- Ask questions that encourage students to consider which graph to use in a particular situation and to explain their reasoning. Often, teachers tell students what graph to use instead of leaving the choice to them.

- Provide students with the opportunity to translate data from one type of display to another. In this way, students will interpret one graph and create another. They will also have the chance to show you whether they recognize when the translation is inappropriate.

Applying What You've Learned

1. What strategy did you use to solve the chapter problem? Why was that strategy appropriate?

2. A student in your Grade 3 class is preparing to do a survey to find out how fellow students get to school. The student's question is: How do you get to school?

   a) What are some potential problems with this question?

b) How might you get the student to think of those possible problems?

c) How might you help the student consider what the nature of the sample should be?

3. Examine the Statistics Canada website. In particular, look at the Census at School section. Create a lesson plan in which data from the website can form the basis for exploring data collection or statistics.

4. One topic that was not included in the chapter is the topic of "outliers." Find out what they are, if you are not already familiar with the term. Discuss whether and why you think outliers should be a topic for students prior to secondary school.

5. How would you help students better understand when each different measure of central tendency is most appropriate?

6. For what purpose is each type of graph that you learned about in this chapter most appropriate? least appropriate?

7. How could a teacher who is teaching students about stem-and-leaf plots or histograms use students' knowledge about bar graphs to support the instruction?

8. Create an activity you would use to introduce the notion of using a scale on a pictograph. Explain why the selected activity is appropriate.

9. Read an article about graphicacy (e.g., Friel and Bright, 1996). Explain what graphicacy actually is and make an argument for the importance of developing graphicacy at the K–8 level.

10. How can you use work with graphing and data display to support students' number sense development?

Interact with a K–8 Student:

11. Tell students that you want to create a graph to compare the number of cans of food brought in by different classes for a food drive for the needy. Ask for their advice on how they would do this.

Discuss with a K–8 Teacher:

12. Many teachers spend time teaching students how to read, interpret, and create graphs, but less time on data collection. Talk to a teacher about how important he or she feels it is to teach data collection and why. Do you agree with his or her perspective? Explain.

Selected References

Aldrich, F., and Sheppard, L. (2000). Graphicacy: The fourth 'r'? *Primary Science Review, 64,* 8–11.

Ash, C. (2012). *The top 10 of everything Canadian edition.* Toronto, ON: Dorling Kindersley.

Ash, R. (1996). *Incredible comparisons.* Toronto, ON: Dorling Kindersley.

Bremigan, E.G. (2003). Developing a meaningful understanding of the mean. *Mathematics Teaching in the Middle School, 9,* 22–27.

Bright, G.W., Brewer, W., McClain, K., and Mooney, E.S. (2003). *Navigating through data analysis in grades 6–8.* Reston, VA: National Council of Teachers of Mathematics.

Chapin, S., Koziol, A., MacPherson, J., and Rezba, C. (2003). *Navigating through data analysis and probability in grades 3–5.* Reston, VA: National Council of Teachers of Mathematics.

Copley, J.V. (2000). *The young child and mathematics.* Washington, DC: National Association for the Education of Young Children and National Council of Teachers of Mathematics.

Curcio, F.R. (2010). *Developing data-graph comprehension in grades K–8* (3rd ed.). Reston, VA: National Council of Teachers of Mathematics.

English, L.D. (2014). Statistics at play. *Teaching Children Mathematics, 21,* 37–44.

Friel, S.N., and Bright, G.W. (1996). Building a theory of graphicacy: How do students read graphs? *Paper presented at the Annual Meeting of the American Educational Research Association*, New York: American Educational Research Association. (ERIC Document Reproduction Service No. ED 395 277).

Friel, S.N., Curcio, F.R., and Bright, G.W. (2001). Making sense of graphs: Critical factors influencing comprehension and instructional implications. *Journal for Research in Mathematics Education, 32*, 124–158.

Garcia-Mila, M., Marti, E., Gilabert, S., and Castells, M. (2014). Fifth through eighth grade students' difficulties in constructing bar graphs: Data organization, data aggregation, and integration of a second variable. *Mathematical Thinking and Learning, 16*: 201–233.

Grummer, D. (1995). Plotting Margo's party. *Teaching Children Mathematics, 2*, 176–179.

Harper, S.R. (2004). Students' interpretation of misleading graphs. *Mathematics Teaching in the Middle School, 9*, 340–343.

Hudson, R.A. (2012). Balance at the elusive mean. *Mathematics Teaching in the Middle School, 18*, 301–306.

Kajander, A. (2013). MB4T … Mathematics by and 4 teachers: How close can we get? Discrete and continuous data. *The Ontario Mathematics Gazette, 51*, 22–23.

Keenan, S. (2002). *More or less a mess*. New York: Scholastic.

Konold, C., Higgins, T., Russell, S.J., and Khalil, K. (2015). Data seen through different lenses. *Educational Studies in Math, 88*, 305–325.

Lacefield, W.O. (2009). The power of representation: Graphs and glyphs in data analysis lessons for young learners. *Teaching Children Mathematics, 15*, 324–327.

Lappan, G., Fey, J., Fitzgerald, W.M., Friel, S.N., and Phillips, E.D. (1998). *Data about us*. (Connected Mathematics). White Plains, NY: Dale Seymour Publications.

Leavy, A.M., Friel, S.N., and Mamer, J.D. (2009). It's a Fird! Can you compute a median of categorical data? *Mathematics Teaching in the Middle School, 14*, 344–351.

Leedy, L. (2005). *The great graph contest*. New York: Holiday House.

McMillen, S., and McMillen, B. (2010). My bar graph tells a story. *Teaching Children Mathematics, 16*, 430–442.

Mittag, K.C., Taylor, S.E. and Fies, D. (2010). Mean, median or model: Which one is my pencil? *Mathematics Teaching in the Middle School, 15*, 548–554.

Mokros, J., and Wright, T. (2009). Zoos, aquariums, and expanding students' data literacy. *Teaching Children Mathematics, 15*, 524–530.

Nagda, A.W., and Bickel, C. (2002). *Tiger Math: Learning to graph from a baby tiger*. New York: Owlet Paperbacks.

Niezgoda, D.A., and Moyer-Packenham, S. (2005). Hickory dickory dock: Navigating through data analysis. *Teaching Children Mathematics, 11*, 292–300.

Sakshaug, L. (2000). Which graph is which? *Teaching Children Mathematics, 6*, 454–455.

Sheffield, L.J., Cavanagh, M., Dacey, L., Findell, C., Greenes, C., and Small, M. (2002). *Navigating through data analysis and probability, prekindergarten–grade 2*. Reston, VA: National Council of Teachers of Mathematics.

Simmt, E. (2010). Pencils and crayons. *Teaching Children Mathematics, 16*, 64–67.

Small, M. (2006). *PRIME: Data management and probability: Background and strategies*. Toronto, ON: Thomson Nelson.

Stewart, M. (2007). *Giraffe graphs*. New York: Scholastic Children's Press.

Torres-Velasquez, D., and Lobo, G. (2005). Culturally responsive mathematics teaching and English language learners. *Teaching Children Mathematics, 11*, 249–255.

Wall, J.J., and Benson, C.C. (2009). So many graphs, so little time. *Mathematics Teaching in the Middle School, 15*, 82–92.

Michael Newman/PhotoEdit

Chapter 22

Probability

IN A NUTSHELL

The main ideas in this chapter are listed below:

1. Probability is a measure of likelihood. It can be expressed qualitatively or quantitatively as a fraction or decimal between 0 and 1 or an equivalent percent.

2. Unless an event is either impossible or certain, you can never be sure how often it will occur.

3. To determine an experimental probability, a large representative sample provides more consistent results.

4. To determine a theoretical probability, an analysis of possible equally likely outcomes is required.

CHAPTER PROBLEM

What is the probability that at least one person in your class was born on the 11th day of a month?

Fundamental Notions about Probability

Probability is the study of measures of likelihood for various events or situations. How likely it is to rain tomorrow, how likely it is that a contestant will spin a particular number on a game show, or how likely it is that a particular candidate will win an election are all examples of probability situations. Probabilities are sometimes calculated theoretically. For example, the probability of tossing a head on a coin is $\frac{1}{2}$ since there are two equally likely possible outcomes, and only one is a head. Experimental probability is calculated by actually performing an experiment.

To determine a probability experimentally, you need many samples, or a very large sample, before you can confidently draw a conclusion about the probability of an event. The greater the sample size, the more confident you can be about the probability. For example, suppose students want to know the probability of a Grade 6 student being 11 years old when he or she starts school in September. They could survey their own classmates and find that 7 students out of 28, or $\frac{1}{4}$ of the students, were 11 when they began school this year. They cannot conclude that this is the probability in the greater population from that small sample. They could expand their survey to include the other Grade 6 classes in the school, where they may or may not get similar results. As the sample size increases, so should their confidence in the probability.

You can never be sure what will happen on a particular occasion, unless the event is either impossible or certain. For example, many students will predict that, if they flip a coin, say, 10 times, it will land heads up 5 times. However, it is quite possible to flip the coin 10 times and have it land heads up anywhere from 0 to 10 times. This is because of the randomness of flipping a coin. If you repeat the 10-flip experiment many times, the average number of heads is likely to get closer and closer to 5.

Probability Misconceptions

Young students and even some adults often have misconceptions about probability. For example, many students (and adults) mistakenly think that if a coin is flipped and lands heads up 5 times in a row, it is likely to land heads up again. Others think just the opposite—that it is unlikely to land heads up next time. It takes experience to understand that the chance that the coin will land heads up each time is no different from the time before. Each time, the probability of landing heads up is $\frac{1}{2}$.

Early Work with Probability

Initially, students think about familiar everyday events in their lives and assign very rough probability measures to describe them. This is in keeping with the idea of working at a "concrete" level. "Concrete," in this sense, means familiar contexts that have relevance to students. Events might include the following:

• the sun will rise tomorrow
• a parent will be home when you get home from school
• you will have spaghetti for dinner
• an elephant will come to school on Friday
• you will watch TV tonight

Young students are often asked to describe events such as these by using probability language. Teachers introduce the words *always* and *never* as well as *likely* and *unlikely*.

Using a Probability Line

A *probability line* is a pictorial model that shows relative probabilities, making it a useful tool for helping students describe and compare the likelihoods of events. The arrows describing the parts of the lines sometimes say *less likely* and *more likely*, and sometimes *less probable* and *more probable*. The labels at the ends of the line sometimes say *impossible* and *certain*, and sometimes *never* and *always*. An event at the midpoint of the line is one that is *equally as likely* to happen or not happen.

Event A below could be any event that is fairly probable, or likely. You can place several letters at different points along the probability line and ask students to describe a possible event for each.

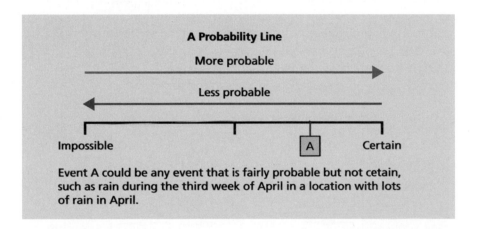

Event A could be any event that is fairly probable but not cetain, such as rain during the third week of April in a location with lots of rain in April.

Students often find a probability line useful when they are working with multiple events since the line allows them to compare the events' probabilities. One event is more likely than another if its position is farther to the right on the line. An event is less likely than another if its position is farther to the left.

As students are ready, additional terms can be used to describe parts of the probability line.

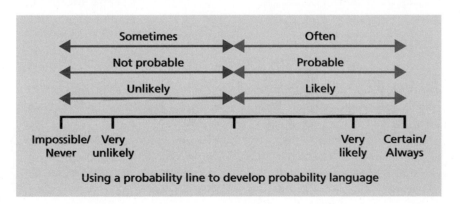

Using a probability line to develop probability language

ACTIVITY 22.2

Students could be asked to suggest activities that might be represented by the boxes A, B, and C, below.

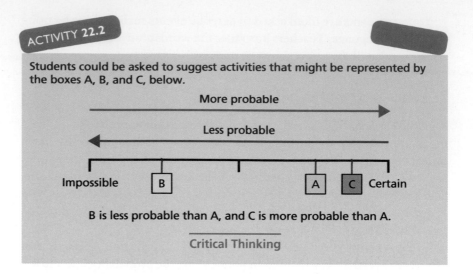

B is less probable than A, and C is more probable than A.

Critical Thinking

ACTIVITY 22.3

Ask students to think about situations in their own lives that are

- very likely
- very unlikely
- something in between

You might start them off by making suggestions such as snow in July or having Jello for dinner.

They can also keep track of how they use and describe probability over a given period of time.

Creative Thinking

One difficulty that students encounter is the incongruity between the way certain terms are used in everyday language and the way these same terms are used in mathematics. An event might be defined as *likely* if it had any probability greater than $\frac{1}{2}$. Whereas, some students reserve the term *likely* for events that are very likely, or closer to a probability of 1.

New vocabulary might be put on separate cards on a word wall. The cards can be taken down and students can sort and order them.

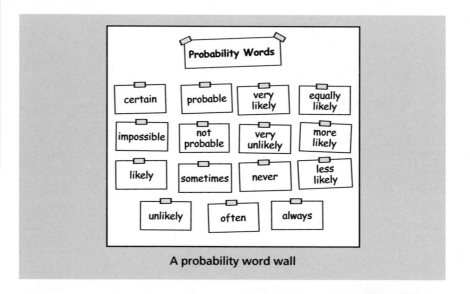

A probability word wall

Outcomes, Events, and Sample Space

The possible results of a probability experiment are called *outcomes*. For example, the *possible outcomes* of flipping a coin are heads and tails. If you roll a standard die, the possible outcomes are 1, 2, 3, 4, 5, and 6. You could be interested in the probability of any one of those outcomes, such as the probability of rolling a 5, or you could be interested in the probability of a combination of outcomes, such as the probability of rolling an even number (which includes the outcomes 2, 4, and 6). The term *event* is used to describe the outcome or combination of outcomes that one is interested in, for example, rolling a 5 or rolling an even number.

In secondary school, students encounter the term *sample space* to describe the set of all possible outcomes. They also learn the term *favourable outcome* to describe the outcome or combination of outcomes that they are "looking for." For example, if students are conducting an experiment to calculate the probability of the event: rolling a number greater than 3, the sample space is any roll from 1 to 6, and any roll of 4, 5, or 6 is considered a favourable outcome.

Simple and Compound Events

SIMPLE EVENT	COMPOUND EVENT
A *simple event* is simply one event, such as the probability of drawing a heart from a deck of cards.	A *compound event* is an event that involves two or more simple events, such as the probability of drawing a heart and then another heart from a deck of cards.
To determine the experimental probability, a card can be drawn from a deck of cards numerous times (with the card returned to the deck each time and the deck shuffled), and the number of favourable outcomes can be compared to the total number of trials.	To determine the experimental probability, two cards can be drawn from a deck of cards (returning the first card and shuffling the deck before drawing the second card each time), and the number of favourable outcomes can be compared to the total number of trials.
Thus, if hearts are drawn 12 times in 50 draws, the experimental probability can be labelled as *unlikely* or, once quantitative descriptions are introduced, as 12 out of 50 or $\frac{12}{50}$.	If two hearts are drawn in a row 5 times in 50 trials, the experimental probability can be labelled as *very unlikely* or, once quantitative descriptions are introduced, as 5 out of 50 or $\frac{5}{50}$.

Hearts	⫫⫫ ⫫⫫ //
Not hearts	⫫⫫ ⫫⫫ ⫫⫫ ⫫⫫ ⫫⫫ ⫫⫫ ⫫⫫ ///

The probability of drawing a heart is $\frac{12}{50}$.

Two hearts in a row	⫫⫫
Not two hearts in a row	⫫⫫ ⫫⫫ ⫫⫫ ⫫⫫ ⫫⫫ ⫫⫫ ⫫⫫ ⫫⫫ ⫫⫫

The probability of drawing 2 hearts in a row is $\frac{5}{50}$.

Independent and Dependent Compound Events

In the card-draw experiments described above, the first card you draw has no bearing on the second. When one event does not influence the other, the two events are said to be *independent events*. If, on the other hand, the first card had not been returned to the deck before the second draw, then the two events would be *dependent events*, meaning that the second event would be influenced in some way by the first. For example, if the first draw is a heart, then there is less chance of drawing a heart on the second draw because one heart has already been removed from the deck. Although at the elementary level it is certainly not necessary to use the language of independent and dependent events, the concept will come up and can be dealt with informally at the middle school or junior high level.

Probabilities as Ratios and Fractions

Although initially students use words like *very likely*, *certain*, or *unlikely* to describe probabilities, they eventually need to move to more quantitative descriptions. Initially, descriptions might be given as ratios, for example, "In a bag with 10 blue and 2 red cubes, I drew a blue 9 times out of 10, so the probability is 9 out of 10." Later, students use fractions, in this case, $\frac{9}{10}$, to describe that probability. Note that some students are ready to move to fraction descriptions earlier than others. The least possible value of a probability is 0, which indicates that the event could never occur; the greatest is 1, which indicates that the event must always occur.

The probability is defined as the fraction or ratio that relates all favourable outcomes to all possible outcomes. For example, an experimental probability of $\frac{3}{10}$ means that, out of 10 trials, a favourable outcome occurred 3 times.

Students can continue to use probability lines, but the labelling is now numerical. The label *equally likely*, in the middle of the line, is replaced with $\frac{1}{2}$; the label *certain*, at the far right of the line, is replaced with 1; and the label *impossible*, at the far left, is replaced with 0. Once students become comfortable with percents, they might use 0% and 100%, instead of 0 and 1, as the endpoints of the probability line.

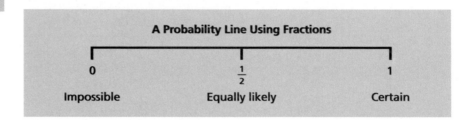

A Probability Line Using Fractions

0	$\frac{1}{2}$	1
Impossible	Equally likely	Certain

The benchmark fraction of $\frac{1}{2}$ is an important one in the study of probability. The words *equally likely* describe a situation where there are two possible outcomes and the probability of each is $\frac{1}{2}$. It is important to note that the words *equally likely* can also apply to other situations. For example, the probability of rolling each of the numbers 1 to 6 on a standard die is $\frac{1}{6}$, and these six probabilities are all *equally likely*. You generally attach the word *likely* to events with probabilities greater than $\frac{1}{2}$, and *unlikely* to events with probabilities less than $\frac{1}{2}$.

As students learn to add fractions, they will notice that the probabilities of all the possible outcomes in a situation must add to 1. This makes it possible to calculate the probability that an event will *not* occur. For example, to calculate the probability that a standard die will not roll 3, they might determine the probability of rolling a 3 and subtract this number from 1.

Experimental Probability

Most of the probability studied at the elementary level involves experiments. This is in keeping with the notion that students should begin their work with concrete activities. The transition to theoretical probability will come later when students are better able to deal with more abstract notions.

In an experiment, students find out what happens when they try things. For example, when they roll a die, does each number come up equally often?

When they roll two dice, does each sum come up equally often? When they spin the spinner, which colour is likely? Even at the earliest grades, students can conduct simple experiments. For young students, however, the teacher will need to carefully define exactly what must be done.

Typical experiments require random probability devices that produce two or more randomly occurring outcomes—those that cannot be predicted with any certainty. Random devices include coins, two-sided tiles, dice, spinners, and draw bags containing small items. Typical experiments might involve the following:

- flipping a coin repeatedly and counting the number of times each side comes up
- drawing coloured cubes from an opaque bag repeatedly and keeping track of the colours drawn
- rolling a die repeatedly and observing the numbers rolled
- spinning spinners with coloured or numbered sectors repeatedly and keeping track of the results

Sample Size

Students need to make sure that an experiment has many trials and/or repeat an experiment a number of times to ensure that the sample size is large enough to allow them to generalize from their results. In an elementary classroom environment, however, it is important to keep in mind that the number of trials and/or repetitions of the experiment should be reasonable.

One way to increase sample size is to use technology (e.g., applets) to perform multiple simulations of flips, rolls, and spins very quickly.

Our Class Coin Flipping Results	
Possible results	Number of students who got this result
0 heads and 10 tails	0
1 head and 9 tails	0
2 heads and 8 tails	0
3 heads and 7 tails	3
4 heads and 6 tails	5
5 heads and 5 tails	5
6 heads and 4 tails	3
7 heads and 3 tails	3
8 heads and 2 tails	1
9 heads and 1 tail	0
10 heads and 0 tails	0

Consolidating results to increase sample size

An alternative to multiple trials is to have each student conduct just a few trials, and then consolidate everyone's results. In a coin-flip experiment, one student may flip a coin 10 times and flip 8 heads and 2 tails. From just 10 trials, it is not reasonable to conclude that heads is more likely than tails. However, if everyone in the class did the same experiment and the teacher consolidated the results in a chart, then the class could make a reasonable conclusion about the probability of flipping heads or tails. From the chart above, you could reasonably conclude that it is very likely to get equal or nearly equal numbers of heads and tails, and very unlikely to get all heads or all tails.

Students can flip two-coloured counters, red on one side and yellow on the other, repeatedly to see how many times each colour comes up.

If young students flip 10 counters, they practise the sums for 10 at the same time as they think about probability.

Building Number Sense

Prepare 3 opaque bags

- one with 2 blue and 8 yellow cubes
- one with 5 blue and 5 yellow cubes
- one with 8 blue and 2 yellow cubes

Tell students the contents of the 3 bags, but not which bag is which.

Pull a cube from one of the bags, allow students to see the colour, and then return the cube to the bag.

Repeat the draw 10 times.

Ask students how many yellow cubes they think are in the bag—2, 5, or 8.

Proportional Reasoning

Show students how they can use a spinner as a tool to help them make a decision. For example, present a scenario like this:

Mike cannot decide whether to build his science project around the topic of lions or tigers. How could he use this spinner to help him decide?

Critical Thinking

Making Predictions Based on Experimental Results

Making predictions is an important part of any experiment. You want students to use prior experiences to help them predict what will happen next. Students need to learn that it is all right if their predictions do not come true; in fact, it is critical to their understanding of the concept of probability that they recognize that they can never be certain of what will happen. Still, students should be able to explain or justify the predictions they make.

For example, after a die-rolling experiment like the one below, a teacher might ask the class to predict how many 6s they expect to see in another 10 rolls of the die. Many students will say 2, basing their prediction on the prior results, but other students may think that since 3 did not come up in the last set of rolls, there will be more 3s next time and, therefore, fewer 6s. As students develop their understanding of probability, they will begin to use theoretical probability to make their predictions. (See *Theoretical Probability* on page 635.) Once they understand that the theoretical probability of rolling a 6 is $\frac{1}{6}$, because there are 6 possible and equal outcomes, they might reason that there will be about two 6s in the next 10 rolls.

	My Rolls
I rolled	This many times
1	2
2	1
3	0
4	3
5	2
6	2
Total rolls	10

Probability of rolling a 6: $\frac{2}{10}$ or $\frac{1}{5}$

ACTIVITY 22.8

One way to find out what students know about making predictions is to ask them to create a situation that will reflect a given probability. For example, you might ask them to make a spinner where the experimental probability of spinning green might be 6 in 10 spins. Or you might give them three spinners and ask which one is most likely to result in green 6 times out of 10, as shown below. For younger students, you might use qualitative descriptions, for example, you might ask them to make a spinner that is more likely to spin green than red.

Which spinner will result in green 6 times out of 10?

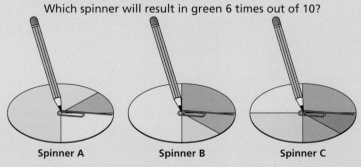

| Spinner A | Spinner B | Spinner C |

Spinner A is the most likely to spin 6 greens in 10 spins.

Critical Thinking

Theoretical Probability

Students usually start to think about *theoretical* or *expected probability* more formally somewhere around Grade 5 or 6 after students have had ample opportunity to work with experimental probability. However, informal work with theoretical probability begins much earlier. For example, when students look at a spinner that is $\frac{1}{2}$ red and predict they will spin red half the time, or when they predict that about half of their coin flips will land heads up, they are using theoretical probability, albeit informally.

Using Logic and Analysis to Make Predictions

Experimental probability is determined by the results of an experiment that has already occurred. In contrast, theoretical probability involves analyzing possible outcomes in advance, and using logic and reason to predict what is likely to happen. For example, when you roll a die, you expect that, if the die is random and fair, each outcome is just as likely as any other. Since there are 6 possible outcomes for rolling a die, the probability of rolling a particular number is $\frac{1}{6}$.

Students might also think about theoretical probability using, for example, a bag containing 6 red and 3 blue cubes. Students know what is in the bag and might be asked to predict how likely they think it will be that a red cube will be drawn from the bag.

We want students to reason that since there are 9 cubes and 6 are red, it makes sense that $\frac{6}{9}$ of the time, a red cube will be pulled.

Like experimental probability, theoretical probability can also be used to determine the likelihood of an event that involves more than 1 outcome. For example, for the spinner shown below, a student could expect to spin a number less than 3 about half the time, since the sectors for numbers less than 3 cover $\frac{2}{4}$ or $\frac{1}{2}$ of the spinner's area.

Ask students to choose a ratio or fraction and create a spinner that they think will result in a probability of spinning blue that ratio or fraction of the time.

After their first response, ask them to create a spinner using a different number of sections.

They should always test their predictions.

Proportional Reasoning

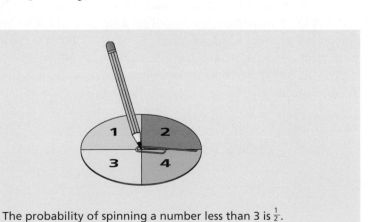

The probability of spinning a number less than 3 is $\frac{1}{2}$.

The Transition from Experimental to Theoretical for Compound Events

Coin-flipping experiments can serve as a lead-in to theoretical probability involving compound events. For example, students are asked to predict what will happen if they flip two coins 100 times. In an initial discussion of the possible outcomes, they might decide that there are three possible outcomes: 2 heads, 2 tails, or 1 head and 1 tail. Since a coin is a fair device, it might appear as if each of the 3 possible outcomes will occur about the same number of times. When students conduct the experiment with a large enough sample size, they will discover the 3 outcomes are not equally likely, as shown below.

Results of Flipping Two Coins 100 Times	
Outcome	Number of times
2 heads	ЖЖ ЖЖ ЖЖ ЖЖ II
2 tails	ЖЖ ЖЖ ЖЖ ЖЖ ЖЖ II
1 head and 1 tail	ЖЖ ЖЖ ЖЖ ЖЖ ЖЖ ЖЖ ЖЖ ЖЖ ЖЖ ЖЖ I

Flipping a head and a tail appears to be most likely.

Students can then be asked to explain why the "1 head and 1 tail" outcome occurred more often than predicted. They might conclude that the sample size was too small and, if they add more trials, the results for the 3 outcomes will even out. If they continue flipping, however, they will soon discover this is not the case. At this point, students need to begin looking at theoretical probability and how they can analyze the situation differently.

There are different models students can use to do this. A tree diagram, for example, can be used to systematically display the possible results for flipping two coins. (See *Models for Determining Theoretical Probability Involving Compound Events* on page 638.) They will discover that there are, in fact, 4 possible outcomes because there are 2 outcomes "hidden" in the 1 head and 1 tail outcome. A new experiment with all 4 outcomes listed might show a more equal distribution of results, as shown below.

Results of Flipping Two Coins 100 Times	
Outcome	Number of times
2 heads	ЖЖ ЖЖ ЖЖ ЖЖ I
2 tails	ЖЖ ЖЖ ЖЖ ЖЖ ЖЖ I
1 head and then 1 tail	ЖЖ ЖЖ ЖЖ ЖЖ ЖЖ ЖЖ II
1 tail and then 1 head	ЖЖ ЖЖ ЖЖ ЖЖ I

There are 4 possible outcomes when flipping two coins.

Reconciling Theoretical and Experimental Probability

It is important for students to understand that, while theoretical probabilities can tell them what is likely to happen, they cannot be used to predict what will certainly happen in a particular situation. Many students feel that something must be wrong if they know intuitively that the probability of flipping heads is $\frac{1}{2}$, but they have just flipped 10 times and ended up with 7 heads, or even more.

Some of the results that surprise students might not be those that teachers expect. For example, some students think that it is harder to roll a 6, or sometimes a 1 or 6, on a die than the "middle numbers." It is only through many experiences that they overcome these misconceptions.

This is where it is important to emphasize the importance of a reasonably large sample size. The results of a small number of trials or just one experiment can be misleading, but when multiple trials are used and/or an experiment is repeated many more times, the experimental probability will gradually approach the theoretical probability. This seeming incongruity between experimental and theoretical probability can sometimes be confusing for students.

Determining Theoretical Probability

When all the possible outcomes of an event are equally likely, the theoretical probability of the event can be expressed as a fraction as shown below:

$$\text{theoretical probability} = \frac{\text{number of favourable equally likely outcomes}}{\text{number of equally likely outcomes}}$$

For example, the probability of rolling an even number with a single roll of a fair die is $\frac{3}{6}$ because there are 3 equally likely favourable outcomes (2, 4, and 6), and 6 equally likely possible outcomes (1, 2, 3, 4, 5, and 6).

Determining theoretical probability becomes more challenging when the outcomes are not equally likely. For example, the spinner on the left below has 4 sectors, 3 of which are red, but the probability of spinning red on this spinner is not $\frac{3}{4}$. The sectors are different sizes, and so they are not equally likely to be spun. To determine the probability, the sectors need to be partitioned into equal parts as shown below on the right.

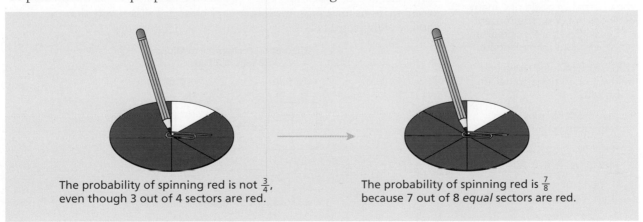

The probability of spinning red is not $\frac{3}{4}$, even though 3 out of 4 sectors are red.

The probability of spinning red is $\frac{7}{8}$ because 7 out of 8 *equal* sectors are red.

ACTIVITY 22.10

You can combine probability work with number work by posing probability problems related to number.

For example, you can have students use a multiplication chart to calculate various probabilities:

- the probability that the product of two single-digit numbers is less than 20

- the probability that the product of two single-digit numbers is in the 20s

- the probability that the product of two single-digit numbers is even

Building Number Sense

ACTIVITY 22.11

Ask students to use a certain number of coins to represent a certain amount, for example, 3 coins to represent 45¢. They then imagine the coins are in a paper bag, and one coin is to be drawn.

- Ask if it is more likely that a quarter or a nickel would be drawn.

- Ask how their answer might change if the 45¢ was represented using 5 coins.

Proportional Reasoning

ACTIVITY 22.12

Searching through journals and the Internet, you can find many activities involving the concept of fair games. Here is one example students could investigate:

Have students play the game below 5 or 10 times to decide if it is fair.

- Two students play. They take turns rolling two dice.

- If the total roll is an even number, player A gets a point.

- If the total roll is greater than 7, player B gets a point.

Critical Thinking

Models for Determining Theoretical Probability Involving Compound Events

There are several models that students can use to determine theoretical probability involving compound events.

TREE DIAGRAMS

A tree diagram is a graphic organizer that can help students determine all the possible outcomes for a compound event. It is important for the student to make sure that any outcomes represented in the diagram are equally likely, or the results will be misleading.

This tree diagram shows the possible results of 2 coin flips. The outcomes for each coin (heads/tails) are equally likely.

By looking at the tree diagram, you can draw conclusions about the theoretical probability. For example, this diagram not only shows that there are 4 possible outcomes, but also that the probability of flipping 2 heads in a row (HH) is 1 out of 4, or $\frac{1}{4}$, and that the probability of flipping 1 head and 1 tail (HT or TH) is 2 out of 4 or $\frac{2}{4}$.

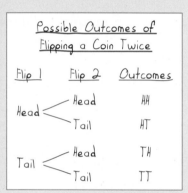

AREA MODELS

Another model for displaying and/or determining the theoretical probability of a compound event is an area model. Again, this pictorial model relies on students' abilities to represent the situation with equal parts.

Suppose you want to show the possible results of flipping a coin twice. The first diagram clearly shows that the first coin will land on heads half the time, and tails the other half. The second diagram shows the possible combinations for 2 flips, making it very clear in a visual way that the probability of flipping 2 tails is $\frac{1}{4}$.

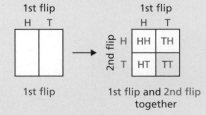

The probability of flipping 2 tails is $\frac{1}{4}$.

Common Errors and Misconceptions

Probability: Common Errors, Misconceptions, and Strategies

COMMON ERROR OR MISCONCEPTION	SUGGESTED STRATEGY
Understanding Independent Events Students think that previous events affect future ones even though the events are independent. For example, they might think that, if you roll a die 5 times and the results are 1, 2, 3, 6, 4, the next result will likely be a 5 because it has not been rolled yet.	This is the kind of misconception that can be remedied through experience. By performing this experiment many times, students come to see that the next roll could be any number. (Note that, when compound events are dependent, previous events *do* influence future events. See *Independent and Dependent Compound Events* on page 631.)
Influencing Experimental Results Students think that the purpose of a probability experiment is to get a desired outcome most often, rather than to see what will happen in a fair and random situation. For example, they might be tempted to peek inside a draw bag to make sure they will choose the counter that is their favourite colour.	Help students to understand that there is no purpose for doing an experiment if you already know for certain what the result will be. On the other hand, if the experiment is conducted fairly, students are likely to learn something interesting that can help them in other situations. Most students will outgrow this sort of behaviour as they mature.
Probability Language Students believe that the word *likely* means *almost always*.	This is not a misconception so much as a vocabulary issue. Words such as *likely* and *unlikely* need to be discussed. Placing a variety of events along a probability line can also help.
"Hidden" Outcomes Students do not identify all of the possible equally likely outcomes. For example, they identify only 3 possible outcomes for a double coin flip: 2 heads, 2 tails, or 1 head and 1 tail.  2 heads 2 tails 1 head and 1 tail	Encourage students to conduct an experiment with multiple trials. (See *The Transition from Experimental to Theoretical for Compound Events* on page 635.) As the results accumulate, students will begin to look for an error in their thinking. For example, in the double coin-flip experiment, they will come to realize that there are actually 4 possible outcomes: • heads / heads • tails / tails • heads / tails • tails / heads A tree diagram or area model (see page 638) can also help students discover "hidden" outcomes.
Equivalent Probability Situations Many students do not recognize the equivalence of different probability situations. For example, students do not realize that flipping 10 coins once each is equivalent to flipping one coin 10 times. Either could be used to determine the experimental probability of flipping heads or tails. Or they may not recognize that drawing a red cube out of a bag of 5 red and 5 blue cubes is equivalent to flipping heads. Either could be used in a situation that calls for a device with a probability of $\frac{1}{2}$.	Working with different probability models can be helpful in establishing this equivalence. The probability of rolling an even number is $\frac{1}{2}$. The probability of flipping a head is also $\frac{1}{2}$.

(continued)

Probability: Common Errors, Misconceptions, and Strategies (Continued)

COMMON ERROR OR MISCONCEPTION	SUGGESTED STRATEGY
Looking for Patterns So much of students' mathematical education has been based on patterns that the topic of probability is jarring. Here events are random. Just because you get HHT in the first 3 tosses of a coin, doesn't mean that it will happen again. Some students keep expecting a pattern.	Students need many early experiences with experimental probability to fully appreciate randomness. They need to see that even the most reasonable prediction can be incorrect because of randomness.
Unequal Outcomes Students fail to recognize when possible outcomes are not equally likely. For example, when spinning a spinner with 4 unequal outcomes, such as that shown below, students think the probability of spinning blue is $\frac{1}{4}$ because there are 4 outcomes. 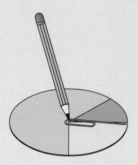	Provide several different four-sector spinners with the sectors labelled 1, 2, 3, and 4. On one spinner, the sectors should be equal. On the rest, they should be unequal. Ask students to spin each spinner 20 times to see how many times they spin a 4. This experiment should illustrate that the relative size of each sector labelled "4" affects the likelihood that 4 will be spun. 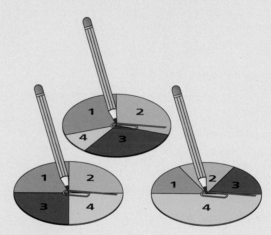 Even though there are 4 sectors on each spinner, the probabilities will differ.

Student Response

This student has incorrectly described the probability of rolling 3 as $\frac{3}{6}$ instead of $\frac{1}{6}$. This is not surprising since the numbers he or she is thinking of are 3, the value of the roll, and 6, the number of outcomes.

What is the probability of rolling a 3 when you roll a die?

The probalbility of rolling a 3 IS $\frac{3}{6}$ it can be possible but it is un likely.

Appropriate Manipulatives

Probability: Examples of Manipulatives

COINS	EXAMPLE
Real or play coins can be used to conduct coin-flip experiments.	Students can conduct an experiment to decide if you are more likely to get 3 heads and 3 tails or 2 of one and 4 of the other when flipping a coin 6 times.

SPINNERS

Students can use many types of spinners for probability experiments. Spinners can be adapted by changing the number of sectors, and/or by mixing equal and unequal sectors. Sectors can be numbered or named to represent categories of interest.

To create a spinner, use a fraction circle along with a pencil and a paper clip. The paper clip is spun as the pencil holds it in place.

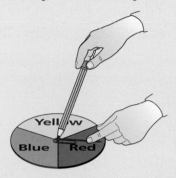

EXAMPLE

Students can determine the probability of spinning a particular number, colour, season, or food item, as well as the probability of various combinations.

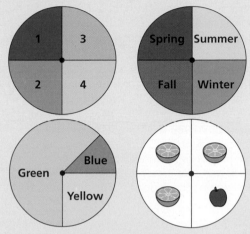

Spinners are versatile because they can be adapted to any context, or number of sectors, and the sectors can be equal or unequal.

TWO-SIDED COUNTERS

Counters with a different colour on each side can be flipped or spilled. Students can use these to conduct various probability experiments. Counters provide an alternative to using coins.

EXAMPLE

Students can flip 2 counters repeatedly to estimate the probability that both flips will result in the same colour.

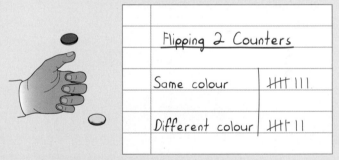

The experimental probability of both counters landing the same colour up is $\frac{8}{15}$.

DRAW BAGS

Students can conduct probability experiments by putting tiles, counters, or cubes of different colours in opaque bags and drawing them from the bag. Draw bags are versatile probability devices because the contents can be adapted to reflect any proportion.

EXAMPLE

Students can predict the probability that they will draw 2 tiles of the same colour from a bag containing 5 red tiles and 5 blue tiles. In a draw-bag experiment, each draw should be returned to the bag after being recorded so that the events are independent.

	Drawing Coloured Tiles
Different colours	✓ ✓ ✓ ✓ ✓
Same colours	✓ ✓ ✓ ✓

The experimental probability of drawing 2 tiles of the same colour is $\frac{4}{10}$ or $\frac{2}{5}$.

(continued)

Probability: Examples of Manipulatives (Continued)

DICE OR NUMBER CUBES	EXAMPLE

Dice or number cubes are versatile tools for probability experiments. They come with different numbers of faces, with different symbols on the faces (blank cubes are also available), and in different colours.

Using two different-coloured dice helps students uncover "hidden" outcomes. For example, it makes it easier for them to see that rolling a blue 5 and a red 6 is different from rolling a red 5 and a blue 6.

You can make dice even more versatile by labelling the faces with different words, numbers, or pictures. Because they are so easy to obtain and adapt, dice are useful random devices for simulations.

Students can roll 2 dice to determine the probability that the sum of the numbers rolled is 6 or more.

Rolling Sums	
Sum is 5 or less	⊞⊞ I
Sum is 6 or more	⊞⊞ ⊞⊞ IIII

The experimental probability of rolling a sum of 5 or less with these dice is $\frac{6}{20}$ or $\frac{3}{10}$.

PLAYING CARDS	EXAMPLE

Playing cards are useful in probability experiments because of their richness:

• 52 different cards
• 4 different suits
• 2 different colours
• 13 different card types

Students can use a shuffled deck of cards to investigate probabilities such as the following:

• the probability of drawing a red card ($\frac{1}{2}$)
• the probability of drawing a diamond ($\frac{1}{4}$)
• the probability of drawing a 3 ($\frac{1}{13}$)
• the probability of drawing a 3 of diamonds ($\frac{1}{52}$)

Students can also investigate compound independent events, such as the probability of drawing four 3s.

Appropriate Children's Books

No Fair! (Holtzman, 1997).
Two children play games trying to decide which ones are fair. This book is suitable for primary children. It is written to support the mathematics curriculum, rather than as a story on its own merits, so the plot is not as engaging as some of the other plots; however, it is an attractive way to raise the idea of fairness.

Pigs at Odds (Axelrod, 2003).
Pigs are playing games at a fair. Mr. Pig struggles to win; he believes that the odds are against him. This book is suitable for students in Kindergarten through Grade 4.

Probably Pistachio (Murphy, 2001).
A variety of probability words are introduced as the character in the story experiences a very bad day. This book is suitable for young elementary students.

Charlie and the Chocolate Factory (Dahl, 1998).
This Roald Dahl classic has as its main premise the winning of tickets in a draw. You can make a connection to probability by holding similar "mock" draws in the school. Many children will know the story from having seen the film.

Do You Wanna Bet? Your Chance to Find Out about Probability (Cushman, 1991).
Two boys recognize the role probability plays in their everyday lives. This book is probably more suitable for students in Grade 4 or higher.

Socrates and the Three Pigs (Mori, 1986).
A wolf tries to figure out the likelihood of finding one of three little pigs in five possible houses. This book is suitable for students in Grades 6 to 8.

Appropriate Digital Resources

See the MindTap site for a selection of appropriate digital resources.

Assessing Student Understanding

- Be clear with students as to whether you intend them to calculate a probability experimentally or theoretically.
- Although some students should be using a provided tool to record experimental results, once they are ready, students should have opportunities to create their own recording schemes for organizing their data.
- Students should not only perform experiments, but also interpret provided results.
- Questions might be asked where students interpret the reasonableness of a probability statement. For example, you might ask, *Which of these statements is most likely? Why?*
  – I flipped a coin 10 times and I got 2 heads.
  – I flipped a coin 100 times and I got 20 heads.
  – I flipped a coin 1000 times and I got 200 heads.
- Make sure to ask students in Grades 6 to 8 questions that help them deal with the notion of randomness. For example, what feedback would you give this student?

Applying What You've Learned

1. What was your solution to the chapter problem? How did you solve it? Is it reasonable for different students in different classes (or the same class) to get a different solution?

2. What do you see as the most important probability ideas for students to learn in each grade grouping: K–2, 3–5, 6–8? Be aware that in Canada, different provinces take different positions on this.

Student Response

This student recognizes the variability of experimental results, but assumes that they will be close to theoretical results.

> Paul and Chris each flipped a coin **100** times.
> Paul got heads **55** times.
> Chris got heads **48** times.
>
> **a)** How many heads would you have predicted? ___53___ heads
>
> Explain your prediction.
> I predicted this because most of the time you will not get half right on, but it is usualy extremely close.
>
> **b)** Why did they get different results?
> It was possible for them to get the same but with it being near so it could be over or under.

3. Make sure you are comfortable with these vocabulary terms. How might you ensure that students are comfortable with the terms they need at their grade level?

Probability Vocabulary

Experimental probability	Outcome	Dependent event
Theoretical probability	Event	Sample size
Random	Sample space	Equally likely
Sample	Simple event	Favourable outcome
Representative	Compound event	Tree diagram
Probability line	Independent event	Simulation

4. Use one of the children's literature suggestions listed above. Develop the outline of a lesson plan for probability that uses the book as a basis.

5. Find a journal article on the learning of probability ideas at the K–8 level. You might use the references listed at the end of this chapter to choose from, or you might find an article on the Internet. List three new things you learned reading that article.

6. There is plenty of literature on what are called "fair games." How valuable do you think an introduction to the topic of fair games is for the learning of probability concepts? Why?

7. List three ways to use a TV game show or an Internet game to enrich a probability unit for students in Grades 6 to 8.

8. Use both a tree diagram and an area model to calculate the probability of spinning two 3s on the spinner shown below. What are the advantages of each model?

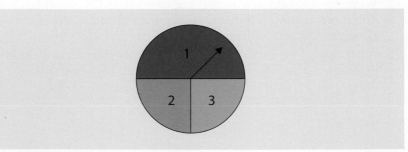

9. Some people argue that probability is too abstract for young students to deal with. In fact, it used to be a high school topic. Argue both sides of the debate. Where do you stand?

10. At some point, we introduce the notion of recording a probability as a fraction. How might a teacher integrate the exploration of fraction concepts with an exploration of probability concepts?

Interact with a K–8 Student:

11. Play the game below with a student in Grade 4 or higher. Adapt the game for a younger student using a single die and single-digit numbers for a total of 6.

> **Sixty-Six**
>
> Take turns with the student.
>
> On each turn, the player rolls two dice to create a two-digit number.
>
> Predict whether the sum of this number and the next one will be greater than 66.
>
> Roll again to make the second number. Add to your first number.
>
> Win a point for a correct prediction.
>
> Win the game with 10 points.

a) Ask them what they liked best about the game.

b) Once you have completed the game, analyze its value for practising number skills.

Discuss with a K–8 Teacher:

12. How much time do you usually spend teaching probability? Do you wish you had more time for it, or do you think that the amount of time is adequate? Could you elaborate?

Selected References

Amir, G.S., and Williams, J.S. (1999). Cultural influences on children's probabilistic thinking. *Journal of Mathematical Behavior, 18,* 85–107.

Axelrod, A. (2003). *Pigs at odds.* New York: Aladdin Picture Books.

Black, S.A., and Huse, V.E. (2007). A virtual spin on the teaching of probability. *Teaching children mathematics, 13,* 482–486.

Bright, G.W., Frierson, D.F., Jr., Tarr, J.E., and Thomas, C. (2003). *Navigating through probability in grades 6–8.* Reston, VA: National Council of Teachers of Mathematics.

Burns, M. (1994). *Math by all means: Probability, grades 3–4.* Sausalito, CA: Math Solutions Publications.

Chapin, S., Koziol, A., MacPherson, J., and Rezba, C. (2003). *Navigating through data analysis and probability in grades 3–5.* Reston, VA: National Council of Teachers of Mathematics.

Cochran, J. (2014). Gone fishing: Science, proportions and probability. *Mathematics Teaching in the Middle School, 20,* 17–23.

Dahl, R. (1998). *Charlie and the chocolate factory.* New York: Puffin USA.

Dowd, D.S. (2013). A circle model for multiplying probabilities. *Mathematics Teaching in the Middle School, 18,* 464–466.

Fischbein, E., and Schnarch, D. (1997). The evolution with age of probabilistic, intuitively based misconceptions. *Journal for Research in Mathematics Education, 28,* 96–105.

Frykholm, J.A. (2001). Eenie, meenie, minie, moe … building on intuitive notions of chance. *Teaching Children Mathematics, 8,* 112–118.

Hoiberg, K.B., Sharpt, J., Hodgson, T., and Colbert, J. (2005). Geometric probability and the areas of leaves. *Mathematics Teaching in the Middle School, 10,* 326–332.

Holtzman, C. (1997). *No fair!* New York: Cartwheel Books.

Jones, G.A., Langrall, C.W., Thornton, C.A., and Mogill, A.T. (1999). Students' probabilistic thinking in instruction. *Journal for Research in Mathematics Education, 30,* 487–519.

Jones, G.A., Thornton, C.A., Langrall, C.W., and Tarr, J.E. (1999). Understanding students' probabilistic reasoning. In Stiff, L.V., and Curcio, F.R. (Eds.). *Developing mathematical reasoning in grades K–12.* Reston, VA: National Council of Teachers of Mathematics, 146–155.

Lamphere, P. (1995). Fair or unfair—that is the question! *Teaching Children Mathematics, 1,* 500–503.

McCoy, L., Buckner, S., and Munley, J. (2007). Probability games from diverse cultures. *Mathematics Teaching in the Middle School, 12,* 394–402.

Mori, T. (1986). *Socrates and the three pigs.* New York: Philomel.

Murphy, S. (2001). *Probably pistachio.* New York: Harper-Trophy.

Nicholson, C.P. (2005). Is chance fair? One student's thoughts on probability. *Teaching Children Mathematics, 12,* 83–89.

Sheffield, L.J., Cavanagh, M., Dacey, L., Findell, C., Greenes, C., and Small, M. (2002). *Navigating through data analysis and probability, pre-kindergarten–grade 2.* Reston, VA: National Council of Teachers of Mathematics.

Speer, W.R. (1997). Exploring random numbers. *Teaching Children Mathematics, 3,* 242–246.

Usnick, V., McCarthy, J., and Alexander, S. (2001). Mrs. Whatsit "socks" it to probability. *Teaching Children Mathematics, 8,* 246–249.

Way, J. (2000). *The development of young children's notions of probability.* CERME 3: Third Conference of the European Society for Research in Mathematics Education.

Young, E. (2010). Probability: A whale of a tale. *Teaching Children Mathematics, 17,* 106–113.

Index

Numbers

2-D shapes
  area, 501
  components, 402–406
  congruence, 425–426
  construction, 428
  drawing, 417–418
  errors/misconceptions, 431–433
  identification, 397–398
  manipulatives, usage, 433–435
  models, 459
  properties, 402–406
  reflective symmetry, 408–410
  rotational symmetry, 410–411
  similarity, 427–429
  tile functions, 454–455
  virtual 2-D shapes, drawing, 418
  vocabulary, 430
3-D shapes
  components, 402, 430
  congruence, 427
  drawing, 416–417
  errors/misconceptions, 430
  identification, 397–398
  manipulatives, usage, 433–435
  orthographic drawings, 416–417
  planes, relationship, 406
  reflective symmetry, 408–410
  rotational symmetry, 411
  types, 401–402
  vocabulary, 430
24-hour clock, interpretation, 552
24-hour time, 547
100 Chart (pattern), 364

A

Addend meaning, usage, 340
Addition, 158–164, 220–232
  algorithms, 224–228, 232–234, 299
  approaches, 222–231
  communication, 231–232
  dart addition, example, 110
  errors/misconceptions, 164, 232–233
  facts, 187–190
  joining, 158
  manipulatives, usage, 165–166, 234
  meanings, 158–159
  number line, usage, 278
  numbers, 110, 161, 164
  order, 163
  part-part-whole, 158
  principles, 162–164, 187 189
  relating, 161–162
  repetition, 167, 169
  situations, understanding, 160–161
  subtraction, inverse operations, 162

Algebra, 369–381
  children's books, 388–389
  digital resources, 389
  errors/misconceptions, 386–387
  manipulatives, usage, 387–388
  student understanding, assessment, 389
  tiles, 388
Algebraic expressions, 21, 49
Algebraic manipulation, 381–385
Algebraic notation, 372–376
Algebraic reasoning, 22–25
Algebra, proportional reasoning (usage), 323
Algorithms, 239–247
  alternative algorithms, 223–231, 239–247, 300–301
  invented algorithms, 223, 239–247
Alternative algorithms, 223–231, 239–247, 300–301
Analog clocks, 546, 554
Analysis, usage, 635
Anecdotal comments, 42
Anecdotal grades/percents, letter grades/percents
  (contrast), 56–57
Angles
  calculation, dissecting (usage), 423–424
  children's books, 567
  classification, 561
  concepts, 557–563
  definition/comparison stage, 558
  digital resources, 567 568
  errors/misconceptions, 563–565
  full turn, nonstandard unit, usage, 560
  manipulatives, usage, 565–567
  measurement, 426, 429, 555–557, 561–563
  nonstandard unit protractor, 559
  nonstandard unit stage, 558–560
  rulers, 567
  standard units, 560–563
  student understanding, assessment, 567–568
  usage, 450–451, 604
Answers (elimination), logical reasoning (usage), 62
Ante meridiem (A.M.), 547, 552
Anticipation guides, 122
Area
  calculation formulas, 496–503
  children's books, 510–511
  concepts, 488
  definition/comparison stage, 488–489
  digital resources, 511–512
  errors/misconceptions, 505–507
  estimation, nonstandard units, 494
  iteration, relationship, 492
  length, confusion, 505
  manipulatives, usage, 508–510
  measurement, 488–504
  measures (recording), standard units (usage), 496
  models, 638
  nonstandard units, 489–494

perimeter, 502, 507
    Pythagorean theorem, 504
Area (*continued*)
    standard units, 494–496
    student understanding, assessment, 511–512
Arrays, 167, 169
    model, usage, 497
Assessment, 36
    change, 37
    characteristics, 38–42
    communication assessment, 52–54
    data, 43–50, 58
    discrete tasks, 40
    exit passes, 49
    formats, inclusion, 48
    grading, 56–58
    group assessment, 55
    growth measurement, 39
    homework, 50
    interviews, 48–49
    large-scale assessment, 58–62
    learning, relationship, 37
    NCTM principle, 8
    observation, 46–48
    performance tasks, 40, 45–46
    plan, 38–40
    portfolios, 43–44
    problem-solving assessment, 51–52
    process assessment, 51–54
    purpose, appropriateness, 38
    quizzes, 49–50
    reporting, 56–58
    results, interpretation, 56
    sample task, 51–53
    self-assessment, 54–55
    student preparation, 41–42
    student problem solving, assessment, 104
    summative data, 39
    surface area/volume rubric, 47
    tasks, 39–41
    technology, usage, 55–56
    tests, 49–50
    tracking, 51
Associative property, 177
Attribute blocks, 368, 577
Attributes
    properties, contrast, 431
    recognition, 572–573
Axes, problems, 611–612

B

Bansho (lesson strategy), 71
Bar graphs, 594–601, 606
Base plans, 417
Base ten
    blocks, 207, 487, 510, 539
    materials, 234
    place value system, 199, 292

Beaded number line, 146, 152, 165, 166
Benchmark numbers, 205
    fractions, comparison, 267
Big ideas
    application, 18–22
    approaches, 16–18
    number/geometry, 17
    strand-based big ideas, examples, 21–22
    sub-ideas, 17
    variation, 16
Blocks, 433
Box plots, 605, 608
Broken-line graphs, 601, 607

C

Calculators, usage, 232
Capacity
    concepts, 516–521
    definition/comparison stage, 517
    digital resources, 567–568
    errors/misconceptions, 535–537
    estimation, nonstandard units (usage), 518
    judgment, 535
    manipulatives, usage, 538–540
    measurement, 516, 520–521, 535
    nonstandard measuring tools, making, 519
    nonstandard units, 518–519
    standard units, 520–521
    student understanding, assessment, 567–568
    volume, relationship, 528–529
Cardinal numbers, errors/misconceptions, 150
Categories
    alignment, 608
    omission, 610
Centicubes, 539
Centimetres, 477–478
    cubes/squares, 486
    grids, usage, 496
    rulers, introduction, 477
    square centimetre, defining/introducing, 495
Central tendency
    mean, 582–584
    measures, 582–585
    median, 584–585
    mode, 585
Change (description), percent (usage), 326–327
Children, numbers (usage), 138
Circle graphs, 603–605, 608
    creation, 603
    variation, 605
Circles, 402
    area, 501
    perimeter (circumference), 482
Classifying, 572
Clock face
    minutes, misinterpretation, 551
    usage, 548
Coins, usage, 640

Colour, reflective symmetry (relationship), 432
Common denominators, usage, 283
Common factors, 211
Communication
  assessment, 52–54
  forms, 118–129
  graphical communication, 129–130
  mathematical communication, importance, 118
  NCTM standard, 118
  oral communication, 118–124
  patterns, 119
  physical communication, 130
  sample rubric, 54
  student engagement, 134–135
  symbolic communication, 129–130
  written communication, 124–129
Comparing (subtraction), 159
  situations, 161
  taking away, comparison, 159–160
Comparison
  language, 143
  spatial comparison, 143
Complex fractions, decimals (relationships), 206
Composite numbers, 213–214
Compound events, 631
  experimental/theoretical transition, 635–636
  involvement, 638
Computational patterns, 365
Computational relationships (exploration), patterns (usage), 365
Computational strategies, 31
Concepts
  explanation, 128
  hierarchy, 6
  maps, 83, 133
Conceptual understanding, importance, 2–3
Concrete circle graph, creation, 603
Concrete graphs, 589–590, 613
  interpretation, 615
Concrete models, 78–79, 413
Concrete thinking, shift, 78–80
Cones, 401, 528
Confidence (building), problem solving (impact), 95
Congruence, 424–427
Congruent edges, 431
Congruent shapes, construction methods, 426
Conjectures, making/testing, 28–29
Connections, 29–30
Constructions, 455–456
Content
  mathematical learning, 5–10
  organization, 16–22
Continuous whole, part, 256
Cooperative grouping, 72–73
Coordinate grids, 442–444
  games/activities, 444
  transformations, 445–446
Coordinates, inversion, 458

Counters
  two-sided counters, 641
  usage, 150, 165–166, 270, 276–277, 285, 352, 387
Counting
  comparison language, 143
  counting back, 141
  counting on, 140–141
  errors/misconceptions, 149–150
  one, usage, 139
  place value, basis, 204
  principles, 138
  sequence, position, 143
  skip counting, 141–142
  strategies, 139–142
  zero, usage, 139
Creative writing, 126
Cubic centimetres, 525, 536
Cubic decimetres, 525
Cubic metres, 525, 536
Cuisenaire rods, 271, 487
Curriculum
  NCTM principle, 8
  public involvement/expectations, 9–10
Customary units, 471
Cylinders, 401
  volume formulas, 527

D

Dance/song/play, usage, 440
Dart addition, example, 110
Data
  children's books, 623
  digital resources, 623
  primary data (firsthand data), 580
  proportional reasoning, usage, 322
  secondary data (secondhand data), 480
  student understanding, assessment, 623
Data analysis, 614–621
  errors/misconceptions, 622–623
Data collection, 578–580
  errors/misconceptions, 581
  factors, 580–581
  manipulatives, usage, 582
  reasons, 578
  topics, selection, 579
Data display, 587–608
  bar graphs, 594–601, 606
  box plots, 605, 608
  circle graphs, 603–605, 608
  concrete graphs, 589–590
  errors/misconceptions, 608–612
  formats, 587–608
  frequency tables, 588
  histograms, 597–599, 606
  line graphs, 601
  manipulatives, usage, 613–614
  pictographs, 591–594, 606

picture graphs, 590–591
scatter plots, 601–602, 607
tally charts, 588
type, usage (timing), 606–608
Data organization, 572–576
errors/misconceptions, 576–577
manipulatives, usage, 577
Data spread
measures, 585–586
range, 585–586
Decimals
addition/subtraction, 299–301
children's books, 308
comparison, 297–298, 304
complex fractions, relationships, 296
contexts, 291
digital resources, 308–309
digits, interpretation, 305
equivalence, 295
equivalent decimals, 294
errors/misconceptions, 304–305
fractions, 268, 297
grids, models (usage), 295, 306
ignoring, 302–303
in-between decimals, creation, 298
manipulatives, 305–308
mental math algorithms, 303
multiplication/division, 301–303
multiplication, modelling, 302
operations, 299–303
principles, 291–294
reading, 297, 304
remainder, usage, 246
renaming, 293–294, 305
representation, 290–298
rounding/estimation, 296–297
strips, 306
student understanding, assessment, 308–309
understanding, 304
usage, 292
writing, 297, 329
Decimetres, 478
Definition/comparison (measurement instruction stage),
468, 469, 473, 488–489
Degree referents, 561
Denominators
addition, 284
common denominators, usage, 283
Dependent compound events, 631
Dependent variables, 602
Descriptive writing, 126
Diagram, implicit information, 485
Diamond graphic organizer, example, 96
Dice/cubes, usage, 642
Differences, estimation, 220–222
Differentiation, 78–88
Digital clocks, 554
Digits
alignment, 305
switching, example, 112

Dilatations, 452–454
Direct instruction (lesson style), 70–71
Discrete tasks, 40
Dissecting problems, sample, 423
Distracters, 61
Distributive property, 176, 177–178, 345
Dividend, 179, 238
Divisibility tests, 212–213
Division, 166–179, 235–248
algorithms, 239–249, 303
children's books, 181, 251
communication, 247–248
digital resources, 181–182, 251–252
errors/misconceptions, 179, 248–249
facts, 190–193
interpretation, 305
inverse operations, 174
manipulatives, usage, 180, 249–250
meanings, 169–171
multiplication, relationship, 173
patterns, usage, 237
place value concepts, usage, 236–237
powers of ten, usage, 235–237
principles, 173–179, 191–192
region fraction, comparison, 258
situations, understanding, 171–173
student understanding, assessment, 181–182,
251–252
written division algorithms, 303
Dominoes/dice, usage, 151
Double-bar graphs, 597
Doubles, 188, 191
multiplication, example, 111
Double-scale protractor, usage, 562
Draw bags, usage, 641

E

Early number sense, 149–150
manipulatives, examples, 150–153
Elapsed time, measurement/calculation, 548, 552
Elementary school math, strands, 17–18
End time, usage, 550
English as a Second Language (ESL) immersion,
83–86
English language learning (ELL)
assessment, 85–86
immersion, strategies, 85–86
students, considerations, 84
Equal groups/sets, 167, 172
Equality/inequality, 374–376
Equal sharing/grouping, 170
Equation (solving)
balance, maintenance, 383–385
guessing/checking, usage, 382
manipulatives, usage, 382
opposite operations, usage, 382
Equity (NCTM principle), 8
Equivalent decimals, 294
Equivalent fractions, 262–263, 294–296
Equivalent ratios, 313–315

Estimation, 31, 296–297
   factors, 220–222
   nonstandard units, usage, 494
   overestimation/underestimation, 238
   rounding, contrast, 220
   strategies, 221–222, 237
   usage, student reluctance, 222
Euclidean transformations, 445
Evaluation, 36
   anecdotal comments, 42
   group evaluations, inclusion, 58
   rubric, 42
   scoring guide, 42
   success criteria, 42
   tools, 42
Even numbers, 208
Events, 630–631
   independent/dependent compound events, 631
   simple/compound events, 631
Exemplars, provision, 128
Exit passes, 49
Experimental probability, 632–634
   theoretical probability, reconciliation, 637
Experimental results
   impact, 639
   usage, 634
Explanatory writing, 126
Exploration (lesson style), 70
Exponents, 347–349
   children's books, 353
   digital resources, 353–354
   errors/misconceptions, 351
   manipulatives, usage, 352–353
   student understanding, assessment, 353–354
Extrapolation, 618–619

F

Face maps, 416
Factors, 209–213
   common factors, 211
   determination, 210–211
   divisibility, relationship, 211
   division, 175
Facts, 186–187
   acquisition sequence, 189–190, 193
   addition/subtraction facts, learning, 187–190
   assessment process, 193–194
   children's books, 195
   digital resources, 195
   errors/misconceptions, 194
   fluency, meaning, 186–187
   learning, importance, 186
   manipulatives, usage, 194–195
   multiplication/division facts, learning, 190–193
   practice, 193
   strategies (development), multiplication/division
      principles (usage), 191–192
   student learning, assessment, 195
   total, 190

Fermi problems, 320–321
Financial literacy, proportional reasoning (usage), 323
Five, benchmarks, 145–146
Five-frame, 145, 151
Flip lines, 448, 450
Flips, 445, 448–450, 457
   confusion, 458
   properties, 449–450
Four-quadrant grids, 443
Fractions, 632
   addition/subtraction, 272–278
   adjacency, requirement (absence), 261
   attribute, consideration, 259
   benchmark numbers, relationship, 267
   children's books, 286
   circles, 566, 604, 614
   comparison, principles, 264–268
   decimals, 268, 297
   definitions, 258
   digital resources, 286–287
   equivalence, 295
   equivalent fractions, 262–263
   errors/misconceptions, 268–269, 284–285
   grids/counters, 276–277
   improper fractions, 263–264
   inversion, 284
   manipulatives, usage, 270–272, 285
   meanings, 256–262
   modelling, manipulatives (usage), 272
   multiplication/division, 278–284, 285
   names, 262
   numerators/denominators, values, 262, 266–267
   operations, 272–284
   pieces, 269
   principles, 258–262
   proper fractions, 262–263
   remainder, usage, 246
   renaming, 267–268
   representation/comparison, 256–268
   set/region fractions comparison, 257–258
   strips, 275, 285
   student understanding, assessment, 286–287
   usage, 450
   visualization, usage, 264
   whole number division, 282
   whole number multiplication, 279
Frayer model map, 133
Frequency tables, 588
Full turn, nonstandard unit, usage, 560
Functions, description, 376

G

Gallery walk (lesson strategy), 71
Game materials, usage, 152, 165, 166, 180
Geoboards, 271, 285, 435, 459, 508, 566
   usage, 493–494
Geometric attributes/properties, 398–401
Geometric shapes, 577
Geometric solids, 539

Geometric thinking, development, 395–397
Geometric thought, Van Hiele's taxonomy, 395–396
Geometry, 394–395
  big ideas, 17
  proportional reasoning, usage, 322
Geostrips, 434, 565
Gifted learners, strategies, 88
Glossary, 132
Grade bands, big ideas (variation), 16
Grades, 56–57
Grading, 56–58
  group evaluations, inclusion, 58
  weighting schemes, 58
Grams, 534
Graphical communication, 129–130
Graphs
  alignment, 609
  inferences, 617–619
  interpretation, 615–616
  misuse, 619–621, 622
  reading, 615
Grids, 276–277, 285
  coordinate grids, transformations, 445–446
  four-quadrant grids, 443
  paper, 460, 510
  points, location, 458
  simple grids, transformations, 445
  usage, 443–444
Group assessment, 55
Grouping, 119
  cooperative grouping, 72–73
  equal grouping, 170
  heterogeneous/homogeneous grouping, 72
  limitations, 73
  planning grouping, 71–74
Group size, 72
Group work, tasks, 73
Growing patterns, 360–361
Growth measurement, 39
Growth mindset, 5
Guess and test, 101
Guided activity (lesson style), 70
Guided groups, 81–82

H

Half/double, 191
Heterogeneous grouping, 72
Hidden outcomes, 639
Histograms, 597–599, 606
Home-school connections, 88–89
Homework, 50, 88–89
Homogeneous grouping, 72
Hour hand, location, 551
Hours (time), 544
Hundredths circles, 307

I

Ideas, 16–22
  representation, 26–27

Immersion
  English as a Second Language (ESL), 83–86
  English language learning (ELL) strategies, 85–86
Improper fractions, 263–264, 269
In-between decimals, creation, 298
Independent compound events, 631
Independent events, understanding, 639
Independent variables, 602
Individual instruction, balancing, 73–74
Inferences
  activities, 617
  creation, 617–619
  problems, 622
Instruction
  adaptations, 82
  balancing, 73–74
  centres/stations, 81
  differentiation, 78–88
  English as a Second Language (ESL), 83–86
  guided groups, 81–82
  mathematically gifted, enrichment, 87–88
  open tasks, 80
  organizational tools/strategies, 82–83
  parallel tasks, 80–81
Integers, 336
  addition, 338–339, 345
  children's books, 353
  comparison, 337
  contexts, 336
  digital resources, 353–354
  division, 345–346
  equation, modelling, 79
  errors/misconceptions, 351
  manipulatives, usage, 352–353
  modelling, 79
  multiplication, 342–345
  reading/writing, 336–337
  student understanding, assessment, 353–354
  subtraction, 340–342
  tiles, 352
Internal zeros, 248, 249
Interpolation, 618–619
  problems, 622
Intervals, 595–597
  misuse, 620
  selection, 596–597
Interviews, 48–49
  management, 48–49
  performance evaluation criteria, 49
  questions, usage, 49
  sample summary sheet, 48
Invented algorithms, 223, 239–247
Irrational numbers
  children's books, 353
  digital resources, 353–354
  errors/misconceptions, 351
  manipulatives, usage, 352–353
  rational numbers, contrast, 349–350
  student understanding, assessment, 353–354

Irregular shapes, area, 501–502
Isometric drawings, 416
Iteration
  area, relationship, 492
  learning, 475
  problems, 484

J

Joining, 158
  situations, 160

K

Kilograms, 534
Kilometres, 478
Kitchen timers, usage, 554

L

Language
  arts, mathematics (integration), 133
  comparison language, 143
  English as a Second Language (ESL), 83–86
  English language learning (ELL), 85–86
  usage, 131
Large numbers, 198
Large-scale assessment, 58–62
Learning
  assessment, 36–37
  disabilities (students), 82–83
  English language learning (ELL) students,
    considerations, 84
  NCTM principle, 8
  problem-centred learning, 87
  student self-assessment, 38–39
Learning clocks, 554
Length
  area, confusion, 505
  comparison, 483
  concepts, introduction, 472
  definition/comparison stage, 473
  direct/indirect comparison, 473
  errors/misconceptions, 483–485
  estimation, nonstandard units (usage), 475–476
  manipulatives, usage, 486–487
  measurement, 472–482, 483
  metric units, learning, 477–478
  nonstandard unit stage, 473–476
  Pythagorean theorem, 504
  standard units, 477–480
Lesson
  planning, 67–69
  three-part lessons, 73–74
Lesson strategies, 71
  bansho, 71
  gallery walk, 71
  math congress, 71
Lesson style, 69–71
  differences, 70–71
  direct instruction, 70–71

exploration, 70
  guided activity, 70
  mini-lessons, 71
  varied lesson style, importance, 69–70
Letter grades/percents, anecdotal grades/percents
  (contrast), 56–57
Linear measure, 472
Line graphs, 601
  interpretation, 616
Lines, 407
  symmetry, 408–409
Listening, encouragement, 121–122
Litres, 520
Location/movement, 440
  children's books, 460
  digital resources, 460–461
  errors/misconceptions, 456–458
  manipulatives, usage, 459–460
  student understanding, assessment, 460–461
Logical reasoning, usage, 62, 106
Logic, usage, 635

M

Manipulatives, 4–5, 150–153
  examples, 150–153, 165, 166
Many-to-one correspondence, 592–593
Maps, 442–444
  drawing/interpretation, 442
Mass
  comparison, pan balances (usage), 531
  concepts, 530–535
  conservation, learning, 537
  definition/comparison stage, 530–531
  digital resources, 567–568
  errors/misconceptions, 535–537
  estimation, nonstandard units (usage), 533–534
  manipulatives, usage, 538–540
  measurement, 516, 533, 535
  metric units, 534
  misinterpretation, 537
  nonstandard units, 532–533
  student understanding, assessment, 567–568
Mathematical communication, importance, 118
Mathematical concepts (development), patterns (usage),
  365–366
Mathematical learning
  conceptual understanding, importance, 2–3
  constructivist approach, 3–4
  content, 5–10
  manipulatives, usage, 4–5
  mindset, 5
  research, 2–5
Mathematically gifted
  enrichment, 87–88
  motivated/gifted learners, strategies, 88
Mathematical objects/relationships
  comparison, 18
  information, limitation, 18–19
Mathematical performance, observation, 46, 48

Mathematics
   anxicty, 66–67
   computational strategies, 31
   concepts/skills, hierarchy, 6
   congress (lesson strategy), 71
   connections, 29–30
   content/processes, measurement (balance), 38
Mathematics (*continued*)
   curriculum, public involvement/expectations, 9–10
   defining, perspectives, 6–7
   developmental teaching, 10
   estimation, 31
   language, 131, 133
   mental math, 31
   NCTM process standards, 26
   pattern, study, 6–7
   procedures, set, 6
   processes, 26–32, 48
   provincial curricula, 7–8
   reasoning, 27–29
   reflecting, usage, 32
   representation, 26–27
   sense, improvement, 95
   strands, 16–18
   student understanding, assessment, 32
   symbols, 131–133
   tasks, personal engagement, 134
   teaching, 10–11, 66–67
   terminology, 131
   textbooks, reading strategies, 76
   thinking process, 7
   tools, selection, 31
   value, perspectives, 7–10
Mathematics vocabulary, 131–133
   concept maps, 133
   glossary, 132
   mnemonics, 133
   reinforcement strategies, 131–133
   sentence completion/creation, 133
   word wall, 131–132
Mean, 582–584
   meaningfulness, 583
   notion, establishment, 583
   properties, 584
Meanings, limitations/equivalence, 169, 171
Measurement, 466–468
   geometry patterns, relationship, 366
   instruction, stages, 468–470
   metric system, 470–472
   nonstandard units, usage, 491
   precision, increase, 480
   principles, 466–468
   proportional reasoning, usage, 321
   renaming, 479–480
   units, usage, 490
Measures, absence (example), 111
Median, 584–585
   calculation, problems, 586
Mental math, 31, 303

Metres, 477
Metric measurement, powers
   (relating), 348
Metric prefixes, 471–472
Middle school math, strands, 17–18
Millilitres, 520
Millimetres, 478
Mindset, 5
Mini-lessons, 71
Minutes (time), 544, 551
Miras, 459
Mirrors, 435, 448–450, 459
Mirror symmetry, 408
Missing addend (subtraction), 159
Mixed numbers, 263–264
   addition/subtraction, 277–278, 284
   decimals, representation, 292
   division, 284
   multiplication, 281–282
Mode, 585
Modifying tasks, 86
Motivated learners, strategies, 88
Multi-attribute patterns, 359–361, 367
Multi-directional pattern, 401
Multiple-choice distracters, understanding, 61
Multiple-choice question formats, 61–62
Multiple representations, importance, 146–147
Multiples, 208–209
Multiples-of-9 patterns, 365
Multiplication, 166–179, 235–248
   algorithms, 238–249, 302–303
   children's books, 181, 251
   communication, 247–248
   digital resources, 181–182, 251–252
   division, relationship, 173
   doubles, example, 111
   errors/misconceptions, 179, 248–249
   facts, 190–193
   inverse operations, 174
   manipulatives, usage, 180, 249–250
   meanings, 166–169
   patterns, usage, 236
   percent, relationship, 330
   place value concepts, usage, 235
   powers of ten, usage, 235–237
   principles, 173–179, 191–192, 249
   situations, understanding, 171–173
   student understanding, 181–182, 251–252

N

Name patterns, example, 45
National Council of Teachers of Mathematics
   (NCTM)
   communication standard, 118
   principles/standards, 8–9, 26
   process standards, 26
Negative temperatures
   interpretation, 550
   misreading, 553

Nets, 414–415
Non-Euclidean transformations (dilatations), 452–454
Non-rectangle, length/width multiplication, 507
Nonstandard units (measurement instruction stage),
    468–470, 473–476, 486, 489–494, 518–519
  rulers, 476
  scale drawings, relationship, 476
Numbers
  addition, 110, 163–164
  beaded number line, 146, 152
  benchmark numbers, 205
  big ideas, 17
  children's books, 153
  comparison, 203–204
  comparison language, 143
  composite numbers, 213–214
  coordinates, 443–444
  counting sequence, position, 143
  digital resources, 153–154
  division, 174–175, 176
  early number sense, 149–150
  errors/misconceptions, 149–150
  estimation, 204–205
  even/odd numbers, 208
  exploration, 144–145
  factors, 209–213
  first number, example, 113
  five-frame, 145
  five/ten, benchmarks, 145–146
  forms, 202–203
  involvement, 220
  large numbers, 198
  lines, 278, 285, 306, 352
    example, 266, 271, 274–275
  manipulatives, 150–153
  multiples, 208–209
  multiplication, order, 174–175
  numbers to ten, 144–146
  numerals, reading/writing, 147–149
  one-to-one correspondence, 142–143
  one, usage, 139
  pan balance, 153
  prime numbers, 213–214
  rational numbers, 347
  representation, 50, 199–200
  rounding, 205
  sense, 142–146
  size, powers of ten (usage), 348
  spatial comparison, 143
  standard/symbolic form, 203–204
  strategies, 149–150
  student understanding, assessment, 153–154
  subitizing, 144
  subtraction, 163–164
  teen numbers, 146
  ten-frame, 145–146
  usage, 21, 138
  walk-on number line, usage, 152
  zero, usage, 139

Number theory, 208–214
  children's books, 216
  digital resources, 216–217
  errors/misconceptions, 215
  manipulatives, usage, 215
  student understanding, assessment, 216–217
Numerals
  reading/writing, 147–149
  writing, student experience, 148
Numeration
  errors/misconceptions, 206, 215
  manipulatives, usage, 206–207
  principles, 198–204
  system, patterns, 200–202

O

Observation, 46–48
  assessment data, evaluation basis, 58
  mathematical performance, 46, 48
Odd numbers, 208
One-to-one correspondence (numbers), 142–143
One, usage, 139
Open sentence, 102, 164
Open tasks, 80
Operations, 158, 220
Optical illusions, 426
Oral communication, 118–124
  anticipation guides, 122
  cultural considerations, 124
  fostering, 119
  listening, encouragement, 121–122
  opportunities, 123–124
  opposite sides, 122–123
  peer discussion, importance, 119
  response, alternatives (allowance), 120
  students, 119–122
  wait time, 120
  written communication, contrast, 118
Order of operations, 348–349
Ordinal numbers, errors/misconceptions, 150
Orientation, changes, 431
Original shape, learning, 21
Orthographic drawings, 416–417
Outcomes, 630–631, 639, 640
Overestimation/underestimation, 238

P

Pan balance, usage, 153, 531, 540
Parallelograms, 432, 498–499
Parallel tasks, 80–81
Parents, contact, 89
Partial grid squares, usage, 506
Partial product digits, alignment, 248
Partial symbols, 593–594
Part-part-whole, 158, 161, 316
Parts, addition, 192
Pattern blocks, 270, 368, 434, 509, 565
  usage, 420–421
Pattern(s), 358–366

computational patterns, 365
concept maps, 83
creation, 364
description/extension, 361–363
errors/misconceptions, 366–367
examination, 102
Pattern(s) (*continued*)
  geometry patterns, 366
  growing/shrinking patterns, 360–361
  incomplete pattern rules, 366
  manipulatives, usage, 367–369
  mathematical situations, 364–365
  multi-attribute patterns, 359–361
  multiples-of-9 patterns, 365
  repeating patterns, 358–360
  search, 640
  shift, 369–372
  study, 6–7
  3-by-3 grids, 364
  translating, 363
  usage, 236, 237, 365–366
  work, assessment tasks, 41
Peer discussion, importance, 119
Peer talk, 119
Pentominoes, 435
Percent, 323–329
  addition problems, 612
  change, description, 329
  children's books, 331
  circles, 331
  digital resources, 331–332
  errors/misconceptions, 329–330
  manipulatives, usage, 330–331
  principles, 323–329
  ratio, comparison, 323–325
  student understanding, assessment, 332
  usage, 326–327
Percent grades, pitfalls, 57
Performance evaluation criteria, 49
Performance tasks, 40, 45–46
  evaluation, 46
  sample, 46
Perimeter
  area, 502, 507
  errors/misconceptions, 483–485
  manipulatives, usage, 486–487
  measurement, 481–482
  pairs, example, 112
Perpendicular lines, orientation, 432
Perseverance (building), problem solving (impact), 95
Personal writing, 125
Physical communication, 130
Pictographs, 591–594, 606, 614
  interpretation, 616
  symbols, differences, 609
Pictorial models, examples, 78–79
Picture graphs, 590–591
  interpretation, 615

Pictures
  alignment, 609
  drawing, 101
  misuse, 619
Placeholder, 203
Place value
  basis, 204
  concepts, usage, 235, 236
  mats, 234, 250, 307
  system, 203, 292, 364
Planes, 406–407
  symmetry, understanding/determining, 410
Plan, making/execution, 95
  example, 97
Planning
  grouping, 71–74
  lesson planning, 67–69
  opportunities, 76–78
  support, 69, 74–76
  unit planning, 67, 68–69
  year planning, 67–68
Playing cards, usage, 642
Polydrons, 435
Polygons, 402
  naming, 403
  types, 403
  vertices/sides, relationship, 403–404
Polyhedrons, 401
Portfolios, 43–44
  evaluation, 43
  items, sample, 43
  product rubric, 44
Positional vocabulary, development, 440–442
Positive/negative, product, 342–344
Post meridiem (P.M.), 547
  confusion, 552
Powers of ten, usage, 235–237, 348
Practice
  appearance, 77–78
  content, 77
  importance, 76–77
  planning opportunities, 76–78
  provision, problems (impact), 95
  time, amount (requirement), 77
Predicting, usage, 123
Predictions
  experimental results, usage, 634
  logic/analysis, usage, 635
Primary data (firsthand data), 580
Prime numbers, 213–214
Prisms
  base, identification, 430
  rectangle-based prism, 503
  surface areas, 503
  triangle-based prism, 503
  volume formulas, 527

Probability
  children's books, 642–643
  digital resources, 643
  equivalent situations, 639
  errors/misconceptions, 638–639
  experimental probability, 632–634
  language, 639
  line, usage, 629–630
  manipulatives, usage, 639–640
  misconceptions, 628
  notions, 628
  proportional reasoning, usage, 322
  ratio/fraction function, 632
  student understanding, assessment, 643
  theoretical probability, 635–638
  usage, 628–629
Problem(s)
  characteristics, 98
  creation, techniques, 98
  defining, 94
  K–8 content basis, 108–113
  modelling, 78
  motivation, increase, 95
  problem-centred learning, 87
  simplification, solution, 104
  solution, example, 97
  sources, 113–114
  student-created problems, 114
  suitability, 108–114
  understanding, 95
    example, 97
  word problems, creation, 126
Problem solving
  advice, 114–115
  approach, 95
  assessment, 51–52, 104
  chart/table/graph, making, 103
  extreme cases, consideration, 105–106
  guess and test, 101
  impact, 95
  logical reasoning, usage, 106
  open sentence, usage, 102
  pattern, examination, 102
  picture, drawing, 101
  possibilities, consideration, 105
  practice, importance, 95
  process, 95–97
  sample rubric, 52
  strategies, 98–107, 327–329
  usage, 94–97
  value, reasons, 94
  working backward, 107
  written communication, 127
Procedures
  explanation, 127
  set, 6
Processes, assessment, 51–54
Process writing, 126

Products
  estimation, 237–238
  generalization, 179
Proper fractions, 262–263
Proportional reasoning, 22–23, 312
  instruction, focusing, 22–25
  usage, 321–323
Protractors, 459, 566
  misalignment, 564
  scale, problem, 432
Provincial mathematics curricula, 7–8
Pyramid, volume, 528
Pythagorean theorem, 504

Q

Quadrilaterals, classification, 405–406
Questions
  interview questions, 49
  multiple-choice question formats,
    61–62
  parts, reading, 76
  refocusing, 121
  stems, 75
Quizzes, 49–50
  creation, 50
  sample items, 50
Quotients
  estimation, 237–238, 283
  signs, assignation (rules), 346

R

Range, 585–586
  reporting, problems, 587
Rates, 319–323
  children's books, 331
  digital resources, 331–332
  errors/misconceptions, 329–330
  Fermi problems, 320–321
  manipulatives, usage, 330–331
  student understanding, assessment, 332
  unit rates, usage, 320
Rational numbers, 347
  irrational numbers, contrast, 349–350
Ratios, 312–319, 632
  children's books, 331
  digital resources, 331–332
  equivalent ratios, 313–315
  errors/misconceptions, 329–330
  manipulatives, usage, 330–331
  part-part-whole, 317
  percent, comparison, 323–325
  problems, 316–320
  stretchers/shrinkers, 317
  student understanding, assessment, 332
  well-chunked measures, 316
Rays, 407
Real-world situation (description), algebraic expression
    (usage), 21

Reasoning, 27–29
  algebraic reasoning, 23–24
  logical reasoning, usage, 62, 106
  proportional reasoning, 22–23, 312
  spatial reasoning, 24–25
Rectangles
  area, 167, 497–498
  congruence/similarity, 427
  rectangle-based prism, 503
  testing, diagonals (usage), 428
  width/length, 170
Reflecting, usage, 32
Reflective symmetry (reflectional symmetry), 408–410
  colour, relationship, 432
  parallelograms, relationship, 432
  rotational symmetry, contrast, 433
Region fraction
  division, comparison, 258
  example, 260
Regrouped values, inclusion, 249
Rekenreks, 152, 166
Relationships
  description, 373–374, 377–381
  inference, 618
  perception/discussion, 124
  showing, 376, 377
  usage, 497–498
Remainders, 179
  ignoring/rounding, 247
  interpretation, 246–247
  treatment, 246
  whole number/fraction/decimal, 246
Repeating patterns, 358–360
  core, 358–359
  representation, 359
Reporting, 56–58
  discretion, usage, 57
  percent grades, pitfalls, 57
  weighting schemes, 58
Representation, 26–27
  interview questions, 49
  multiple representations, importance, 146–147
  sample quiz items, 50
Right angles, misinterpretation, 564
Rolling products, example, 113
Rotational symmetry (turn symmetry), 408, 410–411, 452
  reflective symmetry, contrast, 433
Rounding, 205, 220, 296–297
Rubric, 42, 54
Ruler placement, 484

S

Sample size, 633
Sample space, 630–631
Sand time, misuse, 551
Scaffolding, 86, 128
Scale, 594–595
  correspondence, 592–593
  drawings, nonstandard units
    (relationship), 476
  irregularity, 609
  misuse, 620–621
  symbols, 593–594
Scatter plots, 601–602, 607
Scoring guide, 42
Secondary data (secondhand data), 580
Seconds (time), 544, 552
Segments, 407
Self-assessment, 54–55
Self-talk, 119
Sentences, 102, 164
  completion/creation, 133
Separating situations, 161
Shapes
  area calculation formulas, 496–503
  children's books, 436
  combination, 420–422
  combining, 419–424
  comparison, 398–399
  congruent shapes, construction
    methods, 426
  construction, 409
  creation, dissecting (usage), 422
  digital resources, 436
  dissecting, 419, 422–424
  hunt, example, 109
  identification/classification,
    397–398
  irregular shapes, area, 501–502
  modelling, 412–415
  patterns, 401
  representation, 412–418
  sorting/patterning, 399–401
  student understanding, assessment, 436
  technology, usage, 429
  volume, 523–524, 527
Shrinking patterns, 360–361
SI base units, 471
Side lengths, measurement, 428
SI derived/customary units, 471
Sides, measurement, 426, 429
Similarity, 424–428
Simple events, 631
Simple grids, transformations, 445
Skeletons, 413–414
Skills, hierarchy, 6
Skip counting, 141–142
Slides, 445, 446–447
Small group instruction, balancing,
  73–74
Small units, usage, 484
Sorting, 572
  one attribute, usage, 573–574
  rule, description, 573–574
Spatial comparison, 143
Spatial reasoning, 24–25
  instruction, focusing, 22–25
Spheres, 401, 528
Spinners, 641
Square area, 498

Square centimetre
  conversion, 507
  defining/introducing, 495
  referents, 495
  shape, 506
Square grids, usage, 429
Square kilometres, 495
Square metres, 495, 506, 507
Square roots, 350
Square side length/perimeter,
  relationship, 377
Square tiles, 353, 508
Standard units (measurement instruction stage), 468, 470,
  494–496
  estimation, referents (usage), 479
  measuring tools, 487
  usage, 477–480, 520–521
Statistics, 582–586
  errors/misconceptions, 586–587
  manipulatives, usage, 587
Stem-and-leaf plots, 599–601, 607
  leaves, order (absence), 611
Stopwatches, 554
Straight line, usage, 584
Strands
  big ideas, application, 18–22
  elementary school math, strands, 17–18
  mathematics, 16–18
  middle school math, strands, 17–18
  proportional reasoning, role, 321–323
  strand-based big ideas, examples, 21–22
Stretch (shrink) ratio, 257
Students
  communication, engagement, 134–135
  differences, support (instruction differentiation), 78–88
  English language learning (ELL) students,
    considerations, 84
  expectations, setting, 39
  fairness, 38
  grouping, 119
  interviews, 48–49
  large-scale assessment preparation, 60–62
  learning disabilities, 82–83
  math anxiety, reduction, 67
  mathematical learning content, 5–10
  mathematical thinking, insight, 95
  multiplication/division understanding, 181–182
  needs/expectations, assessment (alignment), 38
  problem solving, 95, 114
  prompting (oral communication), 122
  responses, oral communication evaluation/response,
    120–121
  student-created problems, 114
  student-made thermometers, 555
  summative assessment data, 39
  understanding, assessment, 32
Sub-ideas, 17
Subitizing, 144

Subtraction, 158–164, 220–232
  addition, inverse operations, 162
  algorithms, 228–231, 232–234, 300
  approaches, 222–231
  communication, 231–232
  comparing, 159
  errors/misconceptions, 164, 232–233
  facts, 187–190
  manipulatives, usage, 165–166, 234
  meanings, 159–160
  missing addend, 159
  number stories, solving, 161
  order, importance, 163
  principles, 162–164, 187–189
  problems, modelling, 78
  relating, 161–162
  repetition, 170
  situations, understanding, 160–161
  taking away, 159
Success criteria, 42
Sums, estimation, 220–222
Superimposing, usage, 426
Surface area, 47, 503, 528
Survey questions
  asking, 578–579
  audience, identification, 578–579
  clarity, absence, 581
  non-discrete categories,
    problems, 581
Symbolic communication, 129–130
Symbolic models, examples, 78–79
Symbolic thinking, shift, 78–80
Symbols, 131–133
  misuse, 619
  partial symbols, 593–594
  scale symbols, 593–594
  selection, 592
Symmetry, 408–411
  line symmetry, understanding/determining,
    408–409
  plane symmetry, understanding/determining, 410
  reflective symmetry, 408–410

T

Tables, simplification, 192
Take away meaning, usage, 340
Taking away (subtraction), 159–160
Tally charts, 588
Tangrams, usage, 421–422, 435, 509
Tasks, 39–41
  discrete tasks, 40
  modifying tasks, 86
  open tasks, 80
  parallel tasks, 80–81
  performance tasks, 40,
    45–46
  scaffolding tasks, 86
  sharing, 123

Teachers
    communication, 118
    math anxiety, reduction, 67
    pedagogical content knowledge, importance, 10–11
Teaching
    NCTM principle, 8
    problem solving, usage, 94–97
Technology
    NCTM principle, 8
    usage, 55–56
Teen numbers, 146
Temperature
    change, measurement/calculation, 550
    concepts, 549–550
    errors/misconceptions, 550–553
Temperature (continued)
    estimation, 550
    manipulatives, usage, 555
    measurement, 540
    negative temperatures, 550, 553
    reading, 553
Ten, benchmarks, 145–146
Ten-frame, 145–146, 151, 165–166
Tens, 188–189, 199–200
Tessellations, 454–456
Tests, 49–50
Textbook
    order, following, 75
    reading, 75–76
    usage process, 75–76
Theoretical probability, 635–638
    determination, 637–638
        models, compound events (involvement), 638
    experimental probability, reconciliation, 637
Thermometers, 555
Thinking, 7
    mathematical thinking, insight, 95
    shift, 78–80
Time
    A.M./P.M., 547
    concepts, 541–548
    definition/comparison stage, 543
    elapsed time, measurement/calculation, 548, 552
    end time, usage, 550
    errors/misconceptions, 550–553
    estimation, nonstandard units (usage), 544
    manipulatives, usage, 553–554
    measurement, 540, 545
    misinterpretation, 552
    nonstandard units, 543–544
    standard units, 544–547
    24-hour time, 547
Timeline, usage, 548
Transformations, 444–456
Transparent grid, usage, 493, 510
Transparent mirrors, 448–450
Trapezoid, area, 501
Tree diagrams, 638

Triangles, 108
    area, 500–501
    triangle-based prism, 503, 527
Turns, 445, 450–452
    centre, 451
    confusion, 458
    description, 450–451
    full turn, nonstandard unit, usage, 560
    properties, 452
Two-attribute pattern, repetition, 401
Two-dimensional pattern, 401
Two-sided counters, 641

U

Understanding, potential (maximization), 95
Unequal outcomes, 640
Units
    distinction, 485
    planning, 67, 68–69
    rates, usage, 320
    renaming, 484
    volume, relationship, 526
Unknown, concept (modelling), 79–80

V

Value
    placement, 200–202
    repetition, omission, 610
Varied lesson styles, importance, 69–70
Venn diagrams, 574–576
    one-attribute setting, 575
    two-attribute setting, 575–576
    usage, 577
Virtual 2-D shapes, drawing, 418
Visualization, 30–31, 264
Vocabulary, 131–133
    concept maps, 133
    glossary, 132
    importance, 131
    reinforcement strategies, 131–133
    sentence completion/creation, 133
    word wall, 131–132
Volume
    calculations, inconsistent units (usage), 536
    capacity, relationship, 528–529
    concepts, 521–529
    conservation, 536
    definition/comparison stage, 522
    digital resources, 567–568
    errors/misconceptions, 535–537
    estimation, nonstandard units (usage), 524
    formulas, 528
    manipulatives, usage, 538–540
    measurement, 516, 526–528
    nonstandard units, 523–524
    shape, relationship, 523–524
    standard units, 525–529
    student understanding, assessment, 567–568

surface area, relationship, 528
units, relationship, 526

W

Wait time, 120
Walk-on number line, 164
  usage, 152, 165, 166
Weighting schemes, 58
Well-chunked measures, 316
Whole class instruction, balancing, 73–74
Whole numbers
  decimal powers, multiplication, 301
  decimals, representation, 292
  errors/misconceptions, 215
  fraction division, 282
  manipulatives, usage, 206–207, 233–234
  remainder, usage, 246
Whole set, part, 257
Word
  problems, creation, 126
  walls, 131–132, 440–442
Writing
  creative writing, 126
  descriptive writing, 125
  explanatory writing, 126

opportunities, finding, 126
personal writing, 125
process writing, 126
Written communication, 124–129
  concepts, explanation, 128
  criteria, 126
  exemplars, provision, 128
  fostering, 128–129
  importance, 124–125
  problem solving, 127
  procedure, explanation, 127
  scaffolding, provision, 128
  types, 125–126
Written communication, oral communication
  (contrast), 118

Y

Year planning, 67–68

Z

Zero
  internal zeros, 248, 249
  property, 337–338, 340–341
  usage, 139

Credits

This page constitutes an extension of the copyright page. We have made every effort to trace the ownership of all copyrighted material and to secure permissions from copyright holders. In the event of any question arising as to the use of any material, we will be pleased to make the necessary corrections in future printings. Thanks are due to the authors, publishers, and agents for permission to use the material indicated.

Text

Pages 20, 51, 81, 103, 105, 117, 121, 132, 571, 572, 573, 574, 575, 577, 579, 582, 583, 584, 588, 589, 590, 591, 592, 593, 594, 595, 597, 598, 600, 602, 603, 604, 605, 606, 610, 611, 612, 613, 614, 615, 616, 617, 618, 619, 620, 621, 622, 629, 630, 631, 632, 633, 634, 635, 636, 637, 638, 639, 640, 641, 642: From Small et al. *Nelson Math Prof Learn Prog K–6 Data Mgmt/Prob Tchr Resource,* 1E. © 2005 Nelson Education Ltd. Reproduced by permission. www.cengage.com/permissions

Pages 21, 399, 402, 403, 404, 405, 406, 407, 409, 412, 413, 414, 415, 416, 421, 422, 423, 426, 430, 431, 432, 433, 434, 435, 443, 446, 448, 451, 453, 454, 455: From Small et al. *Nelson Math Prof Learn Prog K–6 Geometry Tchr Resource,* 1E. © 2007 Nelson Education Ltd. Reproduced by permission. www.cengage.com/permissions

Pages 35, 40, 77, 78, 99, 114, 127, 130, 133, 134, 140, 142, 148, 149, 150, 151, 152, 153, 159, 160, 162, 163, 164, 165, 167, 168, 169, 170, 171, 173, 175, 176, 177, 178, 179, 180, 198, 201, 203, 205, 206, 208, 210, 214, 222, 223, 224, 225, 226, 227, 228, 229, 230, 232, 233, 235, 237, 240, 241, 242, 243, 247, 250, 256, 257, 258, 260, 261, 263, 264, 268, 270, 272, 290, 292, 293, 295, 296, 300, 302, 304, 305, 306, 307, 308, 324, 330, 331, 336, 337, 352: From Small et al. *Nelson Math Prof Learn Prog K–6 Nums/Operations Tchr Resource,* 1E. © 2004 Nelson Education Ltd. Reproduced by permission. www.cengage.com/permissions

Pages 62, 79, 85, 108, 109, 128, 129, 362, 363, 367, 377, 382, 383, 384, 387: From Small et al. *Nelson Math Prof Learn Prog K–6 Patterns/Algebra Tchr Res,* 1E. © 2005 Nelson Education Ltd. Reproduced by permission. www.cengage.com/permissions

Page 132: From Small, Simmons et al. *Nelson Math Focus 1,* 1E. © 2008 Nelson Education Ltd. Reproduced by permission. www.cengage.com/permissions

Page 339: From Small, Hope et al. *Nelson Math Focus 7,* 1E. © 2008 Nelson Education Ltd. Reproduced by permission. www.cengage.com/permissions

Page 441: From Currie/Bever. *InfoRead Math 1,* 1E. © 2004 Nelson Education Ltd. Reproduced by permission. www.cengage.com/permissions